W9-CBH-377

# 39 STEPS TO BIOLOGY

READINGS FROM
# SCIENTIFIC AMERICAN

# 39 STEPS TO BIOLOGY

WITH INTRODUCTIONS BY
## GARRETT HARDIN
UNIVERSITY OF CALIFORNIA, SANTA BARBARA

## W. H. FREEMAN AND COMPANY
SAN FRANCISCO AND LONDON

Each of the SCIENTIFIC AMERICAN articles in *39 Steps to Biology* is available as a separate Offprint at twenty cents each. For a complete listing of more than 600 articles now available as Offprints, write to W. H. Freeman and Company, 660 Market Street, San Francisco, California 94104.

# Preface

Antaeus, son of Poseidon and Mother Earth, defeated all his wrestling opponents (until the wily Hercules took him on) because every time he was thrown to the earth, contact with his mother gave him new strength. Almost a quarter of a century ago the physiologist Lawrence Blinks used this myth to point up a moral for biologists: that no matter how clever we may be in forcing nature to give us answers by restricting our questions to narrowly selected organisms and experimental procedures, we should, from time to time, return to the more direct experience of observing nature in all her uncensored exuberance in less structured settings. We must never lose sight of the incredible variety of natural adaptations.

The advice (which has been repeated by many biologists) is as sound now as it was when it was first given. In the past decade "molecular biology" has come to the fore and has done a magnificent job of revealing important unities in biology. But a great advance, like a great man, may have "the defects of its qualities": an advance that intoxicates us with its logical beauty may tend to make us selectively blind to the equal beauty of the diversity of the living world, and to the unities that spring from work carried out at other levels of organization. It is hoped that this collection of offprints from *Scientific American* will be useful in redressing the balance of topics treated in general biology courses.

Limitation of space (always at a premium) has necessitated the omission of molecular biology from this collection. The omission should do no harm, because this book can be supplemented with the excellent assemblage of offprints selected by Donald Kennedy under the title *The Living Cell*, or with any of the numerous textbooks that provide clear discussions of molecular biology. Many other fascinating topics have also been omitted. This cannot be helped. The world of biology, with its $10^6$ different species and nearly as many different ecological niches, is too diverse to be adequately sampled in a mere 39 articles!

It is impossible to be "fair" to all fields, so I have not attempted the impossible. Instead, I have selected those articles from the past twenty years of *Scientific American* that seem to me to be most noteworthy for intrinsic interest and good writing. I have given priority to articles on important topics often omitted in conventional biology courses. The resultant sample, which can hardly be called random, shows some surprising and puzzling facets of the world of biology. I am not unaware of the fragmentary nature of this collection, but I think the embryologist Hans Spemann has given a powerful justification for pondering over such fragments:

> I should like to work like the archeologist who pieces together the fragments of a lovely thing which are left alone to him. As he proceeds, fragment by fragment, he is guided by the conviction that these fragments are part of a whole which, however, he does not yet know. He must be enough of an artist to recreate, as it were, the work of the master, but he dare not build according to his own ideas. Above all, he must keep holy the broken edges of the fragments; in that way only may he hope to fit new fragments into their proper place . . .

GARRETT HARDIN

April, 1968

# Contents

## IV: ECOLOGICAL APPROACHES TO POPULATION PROBLEMS

## V: MAN-CREATED PROBLEMS

NOTE ON CROSS-REFERENCES

Cross-references within the articles are of three kinds. A reference to an article included in this book is noted by the title of the article and the page on which it begins; a reference to an article that is available as an offprint but is not included here is noted by the article's title and offprint number; a reference to a SCIENTIFIC AMERICAN article that is not available as an offprint is noted by the title of the article and the month and year of its publication.

# Adaptation: "Fearfully and Wonderfully Made"

# Adaptation: "Fearfully and Wonderfully Made"

## INTRODUCTION

I

George Wald's essay "Innovation in Biology" serves as an introduction not only to this section but to the entire volume. The beginner in any field cannot help but wonder how it is possible to discover anything new. The contradictions of the moment are always presented in such a way that they seem irresolvable (which is why we persist in seeing them as contradictions). It is only when someone notices that the contradictions are in part a creation of the imperfect way in which we verbalized them that the trouble dissolves and we all say, "Why, of course!" How can we learn to doubt the indubitable? There are no programmatic answers to this question: but it helps to see how others before us have wrestled with riddles. Wald sensitizes us to the problem of creativity: the rest is up to us.

When the Psalmist said, "I will praise thee: for I am fearfully and wonderfully made," he expressed an emotion the modern biologist can share. But in the biologist the emotion springs from an intellectual ground that differs from that of the Psalmist in two significant ways. The Psalms, like all the Old Testament, are man-centered; but the modern biologist looks at all living things and finds every one of the millions of species "fearfully and wonderfully made." *Made?* No: *evolved*—and this (the second difference) is even more wonderful. The articles in this section show how wonderfully non-human creatures have been fashioned by natural selection.

Miriam Rothschild takes what many would regard as a very humble class of beings, "Fleas," and shows what surprising adaptations they exhibit. Even the reproductive cycle of these parasites has been modified so that they may take advantage of the host's hormonal fluctuations.

In their discussion of "Butterflies and Plants," Paul R. Ehrlich and Peter H. Raven emphasize that evolution never involves merely a single kind of animal or plant, but is always some sort of coevolution of two or more organisms which are linked to each other by ecological bonds. Once one sees the strong ecological connection between insects and the plants they feed on, the significance of many structures in both becomes readily apparent. The evolution of poisonous alkaloids becomes understandable in terms of the needs of the plants (and not the needs of a Borgia or a Timothy Leary!).

In an animal-dominated world we take for granted the eating of plants by animals; the reverse surprises us. Though not as spectacular as the man-eating plants of science fiction, the nematode-catching fungi are remarkable enough: Joseph J. Maio describes these little known "Predatory Fungi."

H. N. Southern's "Nocturnal Animals" introduces a world that is all around us, and yet is completely unknown to most people. Even professional biologists may spend an entire lifetime productively working in sun-illumined field work without becoming aware of the other world that comes to life when the sun goes down. The first night spent in a mature forest with only occasional and carefully guarded light is something of an emotional experience for the biologist who has previously made only diurnal sorties. A particular way in which some of the nocturnal organisms play the predator-prey game is described in Kenneth D. Roeder's article "Moths and Ultrasound," which shows how the most sophisticated physical apparatus can help reveal what would otherwise be very mysterious biological phenomena. Even after the mystery is dispelled (though not wholly!) the wonder of the adaptations persists in our minds.

It is humbling to try to imagine what the mental world might be like in an animal with strikingly different sensory abilities. How does the world "look" to a dog, whose eyesight is much worse than ours, but whose olfactory sense is much better? Where we see a landscape, does the dog perceive a "smellscape"? And what mental construct is made of the environment by a sonar-using moth or bat? Can we really imagine it? Even more difficult to imagine is the mental map of reality made by one of the fishes described by H. W. Lissmann in "Electric Location by Fishes." Science fiction writers sometimes dwell on the difficulty of picturing how a mythical Martian sees things. They need not go so far to titillate our imaginations; the living world right here on earth is, as J. B. S. Haldane said, stranger than we could ever imagine.

Closer to the human situation is that of the diving mammals (particularly now that skin-diving has become common). What happens when a mammal leaves the aquatic-terrestrial world to enter the aquatic? Some of the physiological adaptations (evolved over millions of years) are described in P. F. Scholander's "The Master Switch of Life."

Physiological adaptations to the extremes of hot and cold are described in Knut Schmidt-Nielsen's "The Physiology of the Camel," and Laurence Irving's "Adaptations to Cold." Schmidt-Nielsen's article destroys some myths about the adaptation of the "ship of the desert" to its environment, revealing truths that are even more remarkable. When the student has read the facts here revealed, he should ask himself this question: what difference would it make in the life of the camel if the day-night cycle were 36 hours long instead of 24?

The word "adaptation" is a tricky one for biologists: it refers both to the sort of adjustment that an individual can make to his environment from moment to moment, and to the species-characteristic adaptations that have been produced by long evolution. The two meet in a phenomenon called the "Baldwin effect," which is discussed in "Habitat Selection," by Stanley C. Wecker. The Baldwin effect is seldom included in elementary biology texts. After learning what it is, the student should ask himself if this omission is justifiable. Also: does it seem likely that the Baldwin effect has been significantly involved in recent human evolution? And what of the future?

However wonderful evolutionary adaptation may be, in the long run— in the *very* long run—adaptation fails. Extinction is a fact of evolution as death is a fact of physiology. Both invite cogitation. In "Crises in the History of Life," Norman D. Newell has given us a broad history of extinctions with some suggestions of their "causes."

# 1 Innovation in Biology

GEORGE WALD · September 1958

No great idea is ever lost. Like Antaeus, it is overthrown only to rise again with renewed vigor. It is dismissed only to return, yet never quite the same. Its rejection is only a step in its further development.

One could say better that all great ideas come in pairs, the one the negation of the other, and both containing elements of truth. Each generation has the satisfaction of overthrowing the idea in one of its forms, each succeeding generation the triumph of rediscovering it. The onlooker, watching this vacillation, has the illusion that no progress is made. Yet this is the very mechanism of progress. It is the progress of a screw, which advances as it rotates. Science turns the idea about and about, now accepting it, now rejecting it, giving it always fuller, more detailed and exact meaning.

The great idea emerges originally in the consciousness of the race as a vague intuition; and this is the form it keeps, rude and imposing, in myth, tradition and poetry. This is its core, its enduring aspect. In this form science finds it, clothes it with fact, analyzes its content, develops its detail, rejects it, and finds it ever again. In achieving the scientific view, we do not ever wholly lose the intuitive, the mythological. Both have meaning for us, and neither is complete without the other. The Book of Genesis contains still our poem of the Creation; and when God questions Job out of the whirlwind, He questions us.

Let me cite an example. Throughout our history we have entertained two kinds of views of the origin of life: one that life was created supernaturally, the other that it arose "spontaneously" from nonliving material. In the 17th to 19th centuries these opinions provided the ground of a great and bitter controversy. There came a curious point, toward the

end of the 18th century, when each side of this controversy was represented by a Roman Catholic priest. The principal opponent of the theory of spontaneous generation was then the Abbé Lazzaro Spallanzani, an Italian priest; and its principal champion was John Turberville Needham, an English Jesuit.

Since the only alternative to some form of spontaneous generation is a belief in supernatural creation, and since the latter view seems firmly implanted in the Judaeo-Christian theology, I wondered for a time how a priest could support the theory of spontaneous generation. Needham tells one plainly. The opening paragraphs of the Book of Genesis can in fact be reconciled with either view. In its first account of the Creation, it says not quite that God made living things, but that He commanded the earth and waters to produce them. The language used is: "Let the waters bring forth abundantly the moving creature that hath life. . . . Let the earth bring forth the living creature after his kind." In the second version of the Creation, the language is different and suggests a direct creative act: "And out of the ground the Lord God formed every beast of the field, and every fowl of the air. . . ." In both accounts man himself—and woman—are made by God's direct intervention. The myth itself therefore offers justification for either view. Needham took the position that the earth and waters, having once been ordered to bring forth life, remained ever after free to do so; and this is what we mean by spontaneous generation.

This great controversy ended in the mid-19th century with the experiments of Louis Pasteur, which seemed to dispose finally of the possibility of spontaneous generation. For almost a century afterward biologists proudly taught

their students this history and the firm conclusion that spontaneous generation had been scientifically refuted and could not possibly occur. Does this mean that they accepted the alternative view, a supernatural creation of life? Not at all. They had no theory of the origin of life, and if pressed were likely to explain that questions involving such unique events as origins and endings have no place in science.

A few years ago, however, this question re-emerged in a new form. Conceding that spontaneous generation does not occur on the earth under present circumstances, it asks how, under circumstances that prevailed earlier upon this planet, spontaneous generation did occur and was the source of the earliest living organisms. Within the past 10 years this has gone from a remote and patchwork argument spun by a few venturesome persons—A. I. Oparin in Russia, J. B. S. Haldane in England—to a favored position, proclaimed with enthusiasm by many biologists.

Have I cited here a good instance of my thesis? I had said that in these great questions one finds two opposed views, each of which is periodically espoused by science. In my example I seem to have presented a supernatural and a naturalistic view, which were indeed opposed to each other, but only one of which was ever defended scientifically. In this case it would seem that science has vacillated, not between two theories, but between one theory and no theory.

That, however, is not the end of the matter. Our present concept of the origin of life leads to the position that, in a universe composed as ours is, life inevitably arises wherever conditions permit. We look upon life as part of the order of nature. It does not emerge immediately with the establishment of that order; long ages must pass before it appears. Yet given enough time, it is an inevitable consequence of that order.

When speaking for myself, I do not tend to make sentences containing the word God; but what do those persons mean who make such sentences? They mean a great many different things; indeed I would be happy to know what they mean much better than I have yet been able to discover. I have asked as opportunity offered, and intend to go on asking. What I have learned is that many educated persons now tend to equate their concept of God with their concept of the order of nature. This is not a new idea; I think it is firmly grounded

in the philosophy of Spinoza. When we as scientists say then that life originated inevitably as part of the order of our universe, we are using different words but do not necessarily mean a different thing from what some others mean who say that God created life. It is not only in science that great ideas come to encompass their own negation. That is true in religion also; and man's concept of God changes as he changes.

Let me go to another example. There are two great views of the animal kingdom: that of Darwin, and that of Goethe. The first view treats of evolu-

tion and its ways, the second of contemporary organisms. Darwin tells us how animals became as they are; Goethe how they are.

(Many biologists will regard this coupling of names as a species of sacrilege. Darwin represented well-nigh the perfection, Goethe the frustration, of biology as we conceive it. In Goethe's biology the poetic insight prevailed: observation entered only to stimulate and then to bolster intuition. All fruitful science contains both these ingredients; it is the proportion in which Goethe mixed them that we now reject. Goethe esteemed some of his scientific writings

THE CREATION is depicted in this woodcut from the Lübeck Bible, published in 1494. In the center God creates Eve out of Adam's rib. In the circle around this scene are the waters; in the next circle, the heavens. In the outermost circle are the angels.

SIX HISTORIC FIGURES mentioned by Wald are depicted. At left is Johann Wolfgang von Goethe. Second from left is Louis Pasteur; third, Charles Darwin; fourth, Georg Wilhelm Friedrich Hegel; fifth, Benedict Spinoza. At right is Lazzaro Spallanzani.

more than his poetry; we vastly prefer his poetry. All this conceded, Goethe stressed an idea that states a genuine biological problem. In his theory of archetypes he attempted to define the ideal forms which fit animals for the various ways in which they live upon the earth—the ideal swimming animal, the ideal flying animal, the ideal insect, the ideal mammal.)

Students of biology tend frequently to confuse the problem of origins with that of contemporary organisms. They speak at times as though a modern protozoon were the ancestor of a modern fish, and that in turn of a salamander, and that of a bird or man. But of course no contemporary animal is the ancestor of any other; each is the end-product of its own evolution. Each has been tempered in the fire of natural selection, each selected over the ages as the choicest representative of its kind. A present-day protozoon expresses whatever has best been achieved in the fashioning of protozoa; just as modern man is as much as evolution has yet been able to do with men. In this sense each contemporary animal is an approach to one of

Goethe's archetypes, a creature fitted meticulously by natural selection for one possible mode of earthly existence.

Generations of biologists have rejected Goethe's position with scorn; indeed, Goethe stated it badly, and with nonsensical accretions. Nevertheless, here are two views, both true, and both necessary to understand living organisms. Now that the Darwinian position is firm, biologists are finding an awakened interest in the way in which contemporary organisms fill all the niches open to them. Wherever and however on our planet organisms can live, one finds them; and whatever peculiarities of structure and function their environment demands of them they fulfill. Virtually every chemical process that can yield free energy on the surface of the earth has associated with it living organisms particularly adapted to take advantage of that process, and to use that energy to live by. We believe that organisms achieved this diversity and their present capacities by the Darwinian mechanisms of evolution; but the end result, the design of the present product relative to its way of life—the contem-

porary as opposed to the historical problem—these come close to the essential ideas with which Goethe struggled and which he tried to express.

This opposition of ideas within an essential, eventual unity is not peculiar to biology. Much of the recent history of physics has involved such resolutions of conflicting viewpoints. In a recent discussion by Niels Bohr of the fundamental implications of the indeterminacy principle, on which Einstein and he held opposed views, Bohr said:

"Surely, in a situation like this, where it has been difficult to reach mutual understanding not only between philosophers and physicists but even between physicists of different schools, the difficulties have their root not seldom in the preference for a certain use of language suggesting itself from the different lines of approach. In the Institute in Copenhagen, where through those years a number of young physicists from various countries came together for discussions, we used, when in trouble, often to comfort ourselves with jokes, among them the old saying of the two kinds of truth. To the one kind belong statements so

simple and clear that the opposite assertion obviously could not be defended.
The other kind, the so-called 'deep
truths,' are statements in which the opposite also contains deep truth. Now,
the development in a new field will usually pass through stages in which chaos
becomes gradually replaced by order;
but it is not least in the intermediate
stage where deep truth prevails that the
work is really exciting and inspires the
imagination to search for a firmer hold."

What I have been trying to say is
that biology is filled with such
"deep truths." In this it is by no means
unique among the sciences; nor, as I
have already indicated, in other realms
of thought. Indeed the further one departs from the natural sciences, with
their special effort to achieve rigorous-
ness of thinking, the more deep truths
abound. It is amusing in this regard to
see how difficult it is to make genuinely
meaningless sentences involving large
general concepts. One might think, for
example, to achieve the ultimate in
meaninglessness by stating something to
be its exact opposite. George Orwell
tried this in constructing the corrupt
slogans of his book 1984: War is Peace;
Freedom is Slavery; Ignorance is
Strength. There is a point at which all
such paradoxes fail; for these words involve the deep truths, and one must
concede with sorrow that however bit-
terly one repudiates such sentences, one
can find meaning in them.

Indeed, such aphorisms have at times
been uttered solemnly, and received
with veneration. One has only to recall
Hegel's famous dictum, "Freedom is the
recognition of necessity," which holds
a high place in the Marxian lexicon.
(What does it mean? Is that society
freest that forces the most complete
recognition of the most wide-ranging
necessity? How judge what is necessary
without testing it by denial? Yet one can
impart meaning to this as to all such
sentences.) Much of the force of the
Sermon on the Mount derives from the
shock of paradox conveyed in such statements as "Blessed are the poor in spirit.
. . . Blessed are they that mourn. . . ."

To return to science: From what has
been said one might draw the conclusion that an alert biologist should deal
habitually in antitheses; should recognize beforehand that not only his general
statements but their opposite are good
biology; and so turn what has heretofore
been mere historical vacillation into a
positive technique. The technique does
not need to be invented; it is the dialectical method formulated by Hegel and

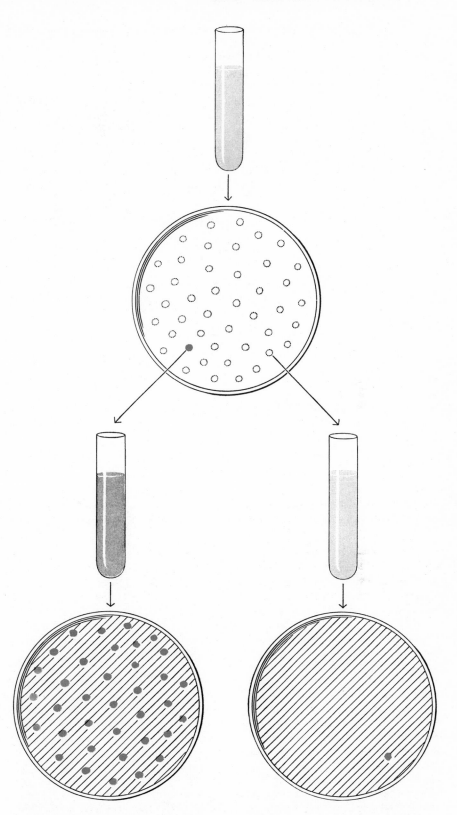

**PROBLEM OF BIOLOGICAL "FITNESS"** is suggested by the microbiological experiment
outlined in this chart. The test tube at the top contains highly diluted bacteria. When the
bacteria are poured over a nutrient medium at the bottom of a dish (*second row from top*),
individual bacteria divide and ultimately form small round colonies. One of the bacteria is
a mutant which can survive on a medium containing streptomycin, which kills the normal
bacteria. This bacterium gives rise to a colony of mutants (*color*). Bacteria of this strain are
again diluted (*test tube at left in third row*), and poured over a medium containing streptomycin (*dish at left in bottom row*). The mutant bacteria form colonies. When normal
bacteria (*test tube at right*) are poured over a medium containing streptomycin, they fail
to multiply (*dish at right*). One of them, however, may be a new mutant which gives rise to
a colony. Thus the relative "fitness" of the two strains depends upon their environment.

**TWO EXTINCT MAMMALS** also illustrate the problem of "fitness." At top is the "Irish elk," a huge member of the deer family which flourished in western Europe contemporaneously with early man. At bottom is the hairy mammoth, which lived in Europe, Asia and North America in the same period. Both animals were presumably "fit" in their original environment, and, since they are extinct, it is assumed that a change in their environment made them "unfit." But no biologist would have been able to predict this result.

summarized in the triad: thesis, antithesis, synthesis. Marx and Engels, appreciating the method but disapproving Hegel's content, "corrected" this to construct what they called the materialist—*i.e.,* "scientific"—dialectic, which formulated much that we have discussed above in such phrases as "negation of the negation," "the unity of opposites," and a third phrase that raises an issue we have not discussed, "the transformation of quantity into quality."

In the 1920s a book appeared called *Science at the Crossroads,* containing a series of papers given by Russian scientists in commemoration of Isaac Newton, which laid claim to revolutionizing the technique of science by deliberate application of the principles of dialectical materialism. The claim is still urged by scientists within the Soviet orbit, and by certain others outside, though of recent years fewer of the latter than formerly, and with much less assurance.

I did what I could to examine this view as a young student, for I thought that if this was to be the new way of science, I had better know about it. It was an interesting but on the whole disappointing venture. For one thing, modern expositions of this point of view seem to me to have an obsessive quality that I think derives in part from inverting the true order of the argument. Science *is* dialectical, and of course materialist. Marx and Engels, recognizing this, attempted to formulate these qualities in the natural sciences so as to impress them upon philosophers, economists, sociologists and historians. To preach dialectical materialism to scientists is carrying coals to Newcastle.

It might be urged, however, that the dialectic of science is mainly unconscious, and would be more effective if made explicit. It seems to me that there is some point in this for the history and philosophy of science, and very little for the scientific enterprise, for science as an activity. In the latter regard I think the materialist dialectic has fatal weaknesses. It provides an interesting way to look backward but no guide for going ahead. It is easy, for example, to pick striking instances of the unity of opposites out of the past—I have already cited several—but to assert such unity as a working hypothesis seems to me a discouraging kind of exercise. It tends to lead into sterile intellectual constructions rather than to stimulate one to act—to do the experiments that need doing, to state the unifying hypothesis, fragmentary, usually biased, but thereby sharp and provocative, that needs to be

defended or attacked. The dialectical approach has too much of strategy and too little of tactics. It neglects too greatly the scientist's own motivations, which are greatly stimulated by stating and working out one point of view, while neglecting and even appearing to demolish opposed attitudes. What is St. George without his dragon? This may be a weakness, but it is a powerful one. In a sense the scientist is willing to plunge blindly, the better to plunge. His primary goal—in Francis Bacon's phrase—is "to command nature in action." The logic is left to be repaired later.

Nevertheless I think that the rubrics of the materialist dialectic are useful aids to thought, and helpful formulations of the dynamics of development, in and out of science. They are not alone in their retrospective quality. This is shared by certain great scientific hypotheses and is a weakness in them as it is in dialectical materialism. I think particularly of the hypothesis that Marx and Engels hailed as the monumental expression of all that the materialist dialectic attempts to convey: the hypothesis of evolution by natural selection.

The theory of natural selection rests upon three phenomena: the continuous production in animals and plants of heritable variations ("mutations"); the struggle for existence, owing to the fact that over long periods of time animals always overreach their means of subsistence, a concept Darwin borrowed from Malthus; and, as a result of the latter working upon the former, the survival of the fittest. The first two of these are matters of direct observation and experiment; the third is a concept circular in construction and entirely retrospective in outlook.

What do we mean by biological "fitness"? Biologists use this term frequently, and even analyze it to a degree in terms of heritable characters to which they assign positive or negative survival value, *i.e.,* characters which promote or hinder survival. How do we judge fitness, and estimate survival value? Only in retrospect, by observing what has survived; and so long as there are survivors at all, the final issue remains in doubt. Faced with a new mutation in an organism, or a fundamental change in its living conditions, the biologist is frequently in no position whatever to predict its future prospects. He has to wait and see. The species may seem to prosper; it may begin to decline, eventually to extinction; it may decline for a time, and then, perhaps through a change in conditions or by the realiza-

tion of possibilities implicit in the first mutation by the addition of others which develop its potentialities, may rise to a position of dominance. The point at which a forelimb began to be modified into a wing may have represented a considerable temporary embarrassment, yet an ultimate advantage, for it opened the way to achieving through further mutations a wing. The hairy mammoth seems to have been an admirable animal, intelligent and well-accoutered. Now that it is extinct, we try to understand why it failed. I doubt that any biologist thinks he could have predicted that failure. Fitness and survival are by nature estimates of past performance. The interrelationships within a living organism, among diverse organisms, and between organisms and their physical environments are much too complex to offer firm ground for prediction.

For this reason our evolutionary constructions are formulations of past history and have little to say about the future. This is an important consideration, because in our technological culture one is tempted frequently to try to supplant processes of organic development by deliberate design, to substitute technological plan for natural selection. Societies and governments, as Darwin recognized, are subject to much the same laws of adaptation, competition and survival as are living organisms; and they are perhaps even more complex in their interrelationships. How is one to know whether a change in social institutions or ethics will in the long run prove advantageous or catastrophic? Only by watching and waiting; and again one cannot be sure so long as anything is left. As with living species, a human society might adopt some course that almost extinguishes it yet, on further development, leads to its ultimate dominance. We cannot predict better here than in organic evolution; probably not as well. The concept of a planned society rests on much shakier foundations than would the concept of a planned organism; but biologists are much too wary to attempt to plan organisms.

This is only one of the essential complexities of biology. The biologist who does not accept complexity as being at the very heart of his enterprise is a poor biologist. The biologist who does not occasionally assert simplicity as an analytical tactic is also a poor biologist.

Yet one kind of complication permeates the whole structure of biology. Niels Bohr has proposed a point of view that he calls "complementarity," worked out primarily in association with problems raised in physics by the indeterminacy principle, but which Bohr suggests should find much wider application, perhaps particularly in biology. There is of course a kind of complementarity in biology that biologists have long recognized and accepted. Confronting any phenomenon in living organisms, the biologist has always to ask three kinds of questions, each independent of the others: the question of mechanism (how does it work?), the question of adaptation (what does it do for the organism?), the twin questions of embryogeny and evolution (how did it come about?). These things must be worked out one by one, for they are quite separate questions, and one goes about answering them in very different ways. Yet one really understands only when all three have been answered.

It is interesting to realize that of these fundamental questions, only the first has a substantial place in physics or chemistry. It is only the biologist who habitually asks whence and wherefore. These questions are for the most part meaningless, except when asked of living organisms.

A curious thing about biology is that it flourishes as the science of life without attempting to define life. We are often told that the beginning step in any science is to define its terms, indeed to give them *operational* definitions, by which one usually means, to describe the operations by which they can be measured. It is a gross overstatement.

Once years ago I was asked to attend a conference entitled "Fatigue in the Reading of Microfilm." For the first two days we all gave papers; they were about everything to do with vision except fatigue. A round-table conference on the third day was opened by a psychologist with a paper on fatigue. He began by defining fatigue as a deterioration in performance. He then described giving experimental subjects a battery of about a dozen different tests of performance, then keeping them awake for two or three days and retesting them. None showed any demonstrable deterioration in performance. The psychologist kept assuring us that nevertheless he was certain that these persons were fatigued.

I learned then that this familiar concept, fatigue, cannot be adequately defined. The most rigorous operation for determining fatigue seems to be to ask a person whether he feels tired. For a long period there was a Fatigue Laboratory in operation at Harvard University. At one time its director, reviewing the subject of industrial fatigue, concluded that it is largely boredom. And how does one define boredom?

Biologists long ago became convinced that it is not useful to define life. The trouble with any such definition is that one can always construct a model that satisfies the definition, yet clearly is not alive. And of course we do not ever measure life. We can measure many of its manifestations accurately; and we combine those with others that we observe, but perhaps cannot measure, to make up our concept of what it means to be alive. The life itself is neither observed nor measured. It is a summary of and judgment upon our measurements and observations.

What biologists do about life is to *recognize* it. If that seems a slipshod procedure, I beg the reader, try to define your wife. You have no trouble recognizing her; I think you will grant the operation to be accurate and unequivocal. But define her? Well, that's the way it is with biologists and life.

I should like to speak of a last peculiarity of biology among the sciences. The fundamental task of science is to state the minimum number of general laws needed to encompass all verifiable observations. The biologist regularly observes classes of phenomena that are unique to living organisms, and cannot be observed elsewhere. Matter exists in a hierarchy of states of organization: ultimate particles, atoms, molecules, formed molecular aggregates, living organisms, plant and animal societies. Each step in this ascending scale of complexity introduces new phenomena, not to be observed at lower levels; and ordinarily such new phenomena demand the formulation of new laws.

Yet biologists have been content to accept the laws of chemistry and physics, and have exercised great restraint about stating new laws. Indeed many of them hold that the task of biology is to "reduce" its phenomena to the level of chemistry and physics. Some of the most fundamental and stubborn problems of biology could be disposed of, at least semantically, if biologists only permitted themselves a few new laws. They prefer, however, to let their problems stand as problems. I think this is not diffidence, but wisdom. We can afford to wait; though I am sure that no amount of waiting will "reduce" the most characteristic problems of biology to present-day chemistry and physics. If biology ever is "reduced" to chemistry and physics, it will be only because the latter have grown up to biology. At that point it will be hard to say which is which.

# 2 Fleas

MIRIAM ROTHSCHILD · December 1965

Mammals have been available as possible hosts for parasitic insects for some 180 million years. There is little doubt that fleas became parasites of mammals comparatively early in the history of their hosts; a fossil flea, scarcely different from living species and displaying all the specialized features associated with them, has been found in Baltic amber dating from 50 million years ago.

It is not known how one animal first becomes parasitic on another, but it is fairly certain that all the principal groups of parasitic insects arose as free-living organisms. The genesis of parasitism is opportunity. The future parasite and its host must be brought together by circumstances intimately and frequently, and then sooner or later the smaller of the two exploits the situation. As an Edwardian wag said, familiarity breeds contempt, but you cannot breed without familiarity! This is not quite correct; certain starfish and more highly evolved animals consign their eggs and sperm to the water and as adults can dispense with even fleeting intimacy. It nonetheless applies in parasitic relationships.

Fleas probably arose as winged scavenging flies, feeding as larvae on the excrement in the homes of burrowing mammals. Almost countless generations of such pre-fleas may have eked out a sheltered life in prehistoric burrows before the first pioneer crept into the fur of a passing ratlike occupant. Possibly there is an even shorter step between piercing the dried outer layer of excrement to reach the semifluid matter below it and piercing a mammal's skin and imbibing the first drink of blood. Blood as food may confer such advantages that the insect is immediately started along the risky road to overdependence and overspecialization. Once fleas became parasites their fate was linked to the fate of their hosts; moreover, the 100-million-year running battle between host and parasite was joined, never to end unless one or the other should perish.

Although parasitic animals may well be more numerous than other animals, fleas do not constitute a notably successful group of organisms. Some 300,000 kinds of beetles have been described and named, but only 1,500 species of fleas are known. There are many more types of bird lice than there are types of birds, but mammalian species greatly outnumber the species of fleas, and one may deduce that many kinds of fleas have been exterminated in the past. This fact is advantageous for the investigator who studies fleas: he (or she) has to cope with only a relatively small literature and consequently can spend more time at the microscope and in the field and less in the library. A mere 1,000 works on fleas have been published during the past five years; a quarter of them are written in Russian.

## The Hazards of Parasitism

The problems that beset parasites differ from those confronting nonparasitic animals. The rat flea, once it is on the rat, has at its disposal a virtually limitless supply of food. Provided that the flea can avoid the extremely efficient extermination tactics of the host—an end to which the flea's whole external anatomy has become highly modified—its difficulties as an individual are over. The nonparasitic animal must strive endlessly for its daily food and has highly developed sense organs to assist it. The flea's breakfast is permanently at its feet, but on the other hand the future of the species is always in jeopardy. Sometimes the interest of the individual parasite may even run counter to the interests of subsequent generations. For example, if too many fleas live on one rat, they may weaken their host and eventually kill it. Parasites must be modest in their demands and unobtrusive in their ways; they must attract the minimum of attention and yet somehow ensure that their offspring are always in a position to find a similar opportunity and continue their long and now essential intimacy with the host.

Occasionally some unforeseen circumstance arises that turns the well-adapted flea, in whose interest it is never to seriously harm the host on which it depends, into an instrument of self-destruction. Thus the rat flea, carrying the plague bacillus from one sick rat to its neighbor and then moving on to the next available host, was responsible for initiating pandemics that in the Middle Ages exterminated a quarter of the human population of Europe. The rat flea must therefore rank as one of the greatest killers of all time. Yet for every rat or man that died 10 times as many fleas must have perished.

Such hazards engendered by the intimate relation between parasite and host are even more dramatic if specialization has gone one step further and the parasite can feed on only one species of host. This situation has been studied recently in Britain as a result of the introduction of myxomatosis, a lethal virus disease of rabbits. In South America both the indigenous rabbits and their fleas have become reasonably adapted to the myxoma virus and recover from infections. In Britain the rabbit population was not immune and an ideal vector existed in the host-specific rabbit flea *Spilopsyllus cuniculi* Dale, one of the most successful of all known fleas. An epizootic swept the British rabbit population; perhaps as many as 100 million rabbits died during the first outbreak. It is estimated that each rabbit in Britain carried some 75 fleas; few, if any, of these parasites infesting rabbits dying of myxomatosis can have survived, since this particular species of flea is confined to a single host. (There is some evidence, however, that it is becoming adapted to the hare.) At a conservative estimate the epizootic must have killed off a billion fleas in Britain alone.

Thus added to the dangers of the parasite's own existence are the dangers to which the host is subjected. The successful parasite must adapt itself closely to the life of the host, and yet such adaptation inevitably involves dependence and a loss of potential versatility. When a cataclysm such as the advent of myxomatosis occurs, there are no alternative possibilities for a species such as the rabbit flea. The rat flea, which is not quite so highly specialized, can leave the dying host for a man or a mouse; without the rabbit the rabbit flea dies. Perhaps nowhere in the animal kingdom are the danger and cost of success more clearly illustrated. Blessed are the meek—that is, the not too successful—for they shall inherit the earth. One of the unpalatable truths about natural selection is that it imposes a certain mediocrity.

Easily the most interesting features of fleas are their adaptations, which they have been perfecting for perhaps 100 million years. They have adapted firstly to the general parasitic mode of life on a hairy or feathered warm-blooded host; secondly, they have achieved the extremely subtle specializations that enable them to survive on a particular type of mammal or bird. The European rabbit flea is an outstanding example of specialization: it has even surrendered to the host the control of its own breeding cycle! Of this I shall have more to say later.

## Adaptations of the Flea

The early stages of a flea's life cycle are passed in the nest of the host or in refuse on the floors of caves or lairs. The larvae feed on debris, but the majority also require iron in order to form their hard external cuticle. This they obtain from blood that is squirted out of the anus of the adult flea and that frequently falls into the host's nest or cracks and crevices or onto the ground where the host sleeps.

Flea larvae are very susceptible to dryness and thrive best in a humid atmosphere, which is of course characteristic of burrows. They can be remarkably indifferent to cold. For example, it has recently been discovered that a bird flea parasitizes an Antarctic petrel; these fleas are found in the nest of the petrel, which is presumably buried for nine months of the year under several meters of ice and snow.

Even the adult rabbit flea is well adapted to survive cold spells, probably because it lives in a cool climate on a host that does not hibernate. Specimens can be kept in a refrigerator for nine months at about −1 degree centigrade (but not below −10 degrees C.), rattling about like pebbles in their glass container, and yet they appear quite unharmed and able to feed and jump only a few minutes after defrosting. Adaptations, particularly those of a physiological nature, that enable a living insect to cope with extreme cold have recently excited considerable attention. The storage of live animals (as well as live sperm) in a state of suspended animation for comparatively long periods of time has become a reality, and therefore such natural adaptations as those exhibited by the Antarctic flea and the rabbit flea are of general as well as scientific interest.

Other examples of refined adaptations in the flea have to do with finding the host and staying on it. Wings are clearly disadvantageous when the flea is living in fur: they impede progress. The permanent parasite must be elusive on

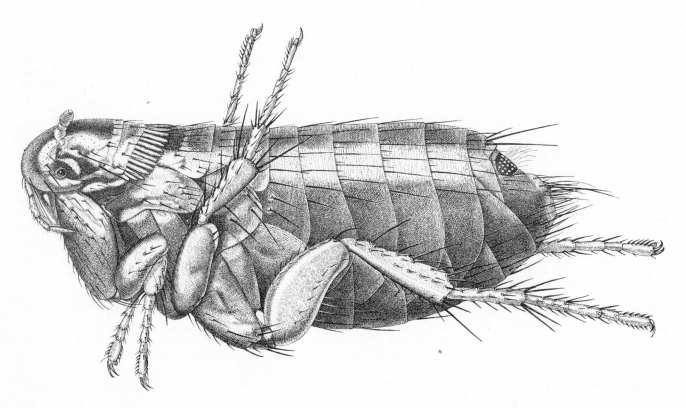

JUMPING FLEA, the common "rat flea (*Nosopsyllus fasciatus*), is depicted on the basis of a rare photograph made during a jump and the results of an experimental procedure in which fleas were made to jump into a fixative. The flea frequently turns end over end several times during a jump, holding one or two pairs of legs aloft for use as grappling hooks when it lands on the fur of its host.

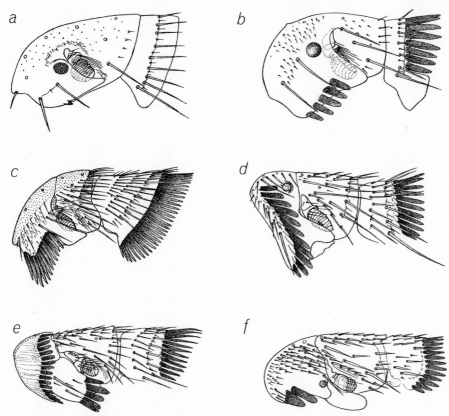

FLEA HEADS, which are among the means of distinguishing one type of flea from another, are depicted for several kinds of flea: (*a*) the human flea, (*b*) the European rabbit flea, (*c*) a mole flea, (*d*) a South African flea, which is found on small rodents, (*e*) a helmet flea, appearing on marsupials in Ecuador, and (*f*) a bat flea. The heads are not drawn to scale.

the host's body, and the loss of a more general mobility is the lesser of two evils. Only a few genuinely parasitic flies have wings, and these are often shed or bitten off when the flies have found a host. It is generally assumed that the majority of insects parasitic on mammals or birds had winged ancestors but lost their organs of flight during the course of evolution.

Fleas are presumably no exception (traces of wing rudiments have been reported in their pupal stage), but they have secondarily evolved powerful jumping legs to assist them in reaching a host. Such legs are unquestionably the most important of all their adaptations. Some species of fleas are better jumpers than others; it has been noted that there are differences in leaping ability even in various strains of the human flea. The jump is too rapid to follow with the human eye, but it has been supposed that the powerful thrust of the flea's leg is the result of the simultaneous extension of its two middle segments—the femur and the tibia.

A flea such as the rat flea that carries plague weighs between .15 and .40 milligram. Its average jump is about 18 centimeters—the record distance is 31 centimeters. It is not necessary to postu-

late some mysterious mechanism to account for these performances; the flea's powerful muscles are adequate for the job. There are, however, certain curious features in the flea's jump. First, the flea frequently lands facing in the direction from which it came, which suggests that the insect turns over in midair. Second, by making fleas jump into a fixative that "froze" them in their jumping attitudes it was found that during their leap they often hold one of their three pairs of legs (sometimes the second pair and sometimes the third) aloft, rotated upward at the trochanter and femoral joints through an angle of about 160 degrees.

This originally gave me the idea that possibly the large air sacs in the legs of fleas, first described by Sir Vincent Wigglesworth of the University of Cambridge, fulfilled some special function in jumping and did not merely provide buoyancy. It also occurred to me that perhaps the flea obtained some special advantage by turning cartwheels rather than somersaults, but after I had watched fleas jump onto rabbits a much simpler explanation presented itself. Such a standing jump for a flea is rather like a leap onto the side of a hairy, windswept cliff. It becomes obvious at

once that the legs held aloft, with their powerful claws directed forward, act as grappling irons. Under these circumstances all six legs provide a highly specialized and quite effective type of landing gear. In order to be sure that fleas do normally hold a pair of legs aloft while jumping, a camera was constructed by which the animal could take a photograph of itself in midair. The photograph showed that at that moment it was traveling through the air upside down with its second pair of legs held well and truly aloft [*see illustration on preceding page*].

It is in their host-finding abilities that fleas show their most impressive adaptability and versatility. One species of bird flea—the sand-martin flea—depends for its survival on a sensitive response to temperature and air currents and also possibly to shadows. These fleas, which spend the winter in the temporarily abandoned underground nests of sand martins, are so sensitive to the gradual onset of warmer spring weather in Britain that they may hatch from their cocoons on the very day the migrating sand martins return from Africa and arrive at their nesting sites. If an artificial sand martin with wings that are mechanically flapped is dangled on a string in front of the burrow nest, the expectant sand-martin fleas will jump onto it.

The cat flea, on the other hand, responds to the warm emanations of carbon dioxide exhaled by the cat, and the rat flea is attracted by the pungent odor of the rat. Fleas that are parasites of the large jird, a rodent that lives in the sandy soil along the Ili River of central Asia, congregate in the first bend of their host's burrow; it was observed that they became aware of the tread of a man within half a meter of the burrow and would emerge and pursue him for quite a distance. They can apparently distinguish the direction from which vibrations come and can also orient themselves to the direction of an air current. It seems that in their efforts to reach the right host, fleas are able to gain assistance from gravity, light, vibrations, noise, temperature gradients, atmospheric pressure, air currents, odors and other chemical stimuli.

Antony R. Mead-Briggs of the British Ministry of Agriculture has demonstrated the rabbit flea's talents in this regard. He liberated 270 marked specimens at intervals in an enclosed meadow with an area of 2,000 square yards. Into this enclosure he introduced three rabbits. Within a few days 45 percent of the marked fleas were recovered from them. The host-finding ability of the rabbit flea is therefore prodigious. It must be realized that a flea on the ground in a meadow is in the situation of a man in a forest where the trees are 600 feet high. (To be sure, the flea is much more mobile.)

### The Rabbit Flea

The rabbit flea merits detailed discussion because it provides an example of a unique type of adaptation: dependence on the sex-hormone cycle of the vertebrate host. Once on the rabbit the fleas make their way to the ears, where they attach themselves to the skin with their serrated mouth parts. Being a semisedentary species, they usually remain with their piercing mandibles more or less continuously embedded in the rabbit's flesh for long periods of their lives.

The fleas that settle on the rabbit's ears can never breed unless their host becomes pregnant or they can transfer to a rabbit already expecting young or to newborn nestlings. In this way the breeding cycle of the flea has become geared to the sex hormones secreted by the host and concentrated in its blood. Ten days before the young rabbits are born the eggs of the female fleas begin to develop, and by the last day of the host's pregnancy they are ripe. A few hours after the rabbits are born the fleas detach themselves from the mother's ears and move to her face. While the mother is tending her young and eating

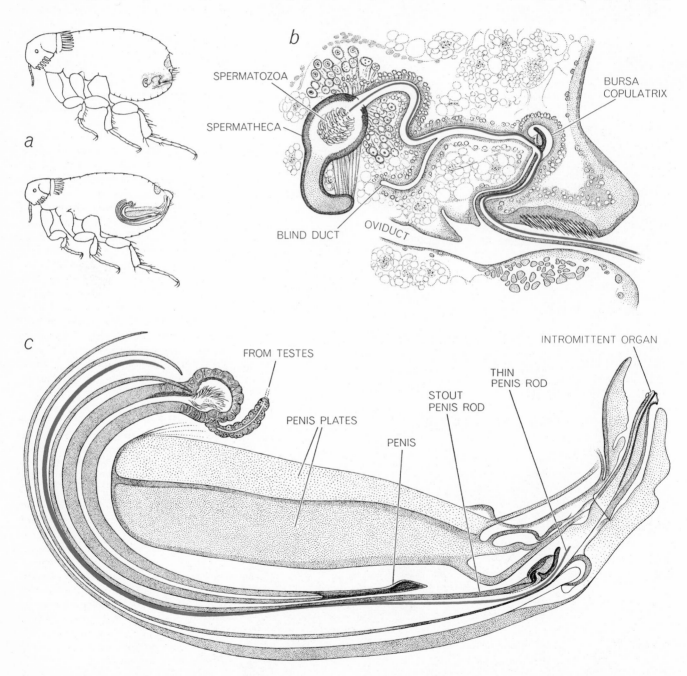

**EUROPEAN RABBIT FLEA reproduces with the aid of an unusually complicated genital apparatus. At *a* the female (*top*) and male are depicted with their copulatory organs outlined, at *b* the female's organs are shown in detail and at *c* details of the male organ are depicted in part. The thin penis rod (*color*) runs through a slot in the** spoonlike end of the stout penis rod, picking up sperm. The thick rod enters the female's *bursa copulatrix* and guides the thinner rod into the threadlike duct leading to the spermatheca, or sperm-storage organ of the female, as shown in *b*. The precise method by which the thin penis rod deposits the sperm is not known.

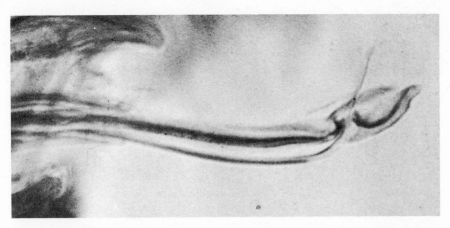

PENIS RODS of a flea appear in a photograph made by freezing two fleas during copulation and then gently separating them. These structures are shown in the illustration on the preceding page as they appear before protraction. The thinner rod is visible passing through the slot in the thicker rod like a rope over a pulley and then projecting upward. The faint fuzz at the end of the thinner rod is sperm, which is wound around the tip of the rod.

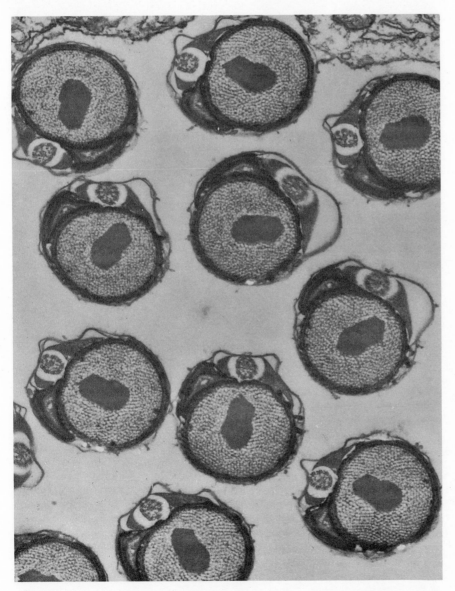

SPERM TAILS of the rat flea are shown in cross section at an enlargement of 58,000 diameters in this electron micrograph made by A. V. Grimstone of the University of Cambridge. The cross section is through the tails of a bundle of rat-flea sperm. A different view of such a bundle of sperm is shown in the illustration at top left on the next page.

the placenta, the fleas pass on to the nestlings, on which they feed voraciously. There they mate and lay eggs. After about 12 days of egg-laying in the nest the fleas suddenly abandon the young rabbits and return to the mother. If she becomes pregnant again, they can begin a new breeding cycle.

The fleas come under the influence of physiological changes in the rabbit the moment the buck rabbit sets eyes on the doe. The temperature of pairing rabbits' ears rises precipitately—sometimes by as much as seven degrees centigrade —and the fleas as well as their hosts become excited and can be seen hopping about and moving from the buck to the doe and back again. In female rabbits ovulation follows coitus; within a few hours, perhaps sooner, the anterior lobe of the pituitary gland—the master gland controlling the sexual cycle of the rabbit—releases sex hormones into the blood. The sex hormones in turn stimulate target organs such as the ovaries and the adrenal glands to secrete other hormones.

One of the first noticeable effects on the fleas is to induce them to attach themselves more firmly to the skin of the doe. In spite of their semisedentary inclinations there is a considerable exchange of fleas between rabbits that come into contact with each other, but once a flea has moved onto a pregnant doe under the influence of the sex hormones it remains there. The future mother thus tends to amass a heavier load of fleas than her virgin companions or the bucks—to the great advantage of the fleas.

Ten days before the rabbit gives birth there is a rise of the level in its blood of another hormone from the anterior lobe of the pituitary: the adrenocorticotrophic hormone, which stimulates the adrenal glands to release corticosteroids. These are the principal hormones controlling maturation and egg-laying in the rabbit flea, although thyroxine and estradiol also play a significant role in these processes. The hormones known as progestins are responsible for checking the growth of the flea's ovaries and for initiating the regression and resorption of the yolk and developing eggs. It is worth mentioning that man-made progestins are used as human contraceptives—this is "the pill" that has recently attracted so much notice.

Apart from the development of the female reproductive organs both male and female fleas undergo profound changes under the influence of the maturation hormones. The salivary glands develop and more than double in size;

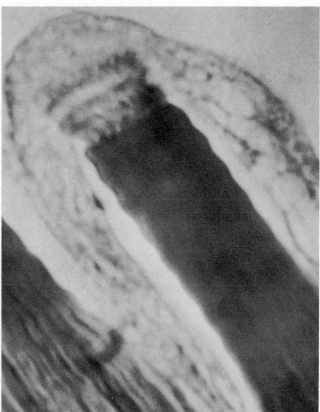

**RAT-FLEA SPERM** is shown enlarged 250 diameters. The partially developed heads (*center*) are held together in a gelatinous pointed cap. The tails of these sperm have short wave frequencies.

**RABBIT-FLEA SPERM**, enlarged 325 diameters, has a membranous envelope along the sides reminiscent of a bridal veil. The wave frequencies in the tails are longer than those in the rat-flea sperm.

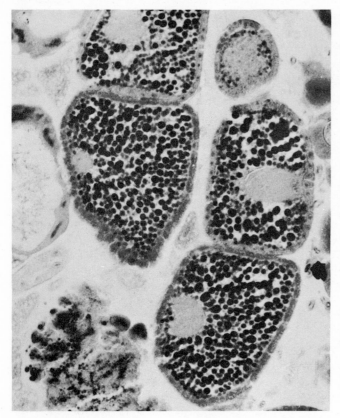

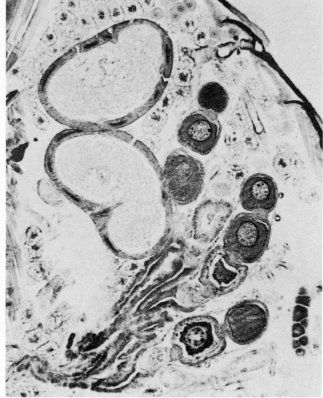

**INFLUENCE OF HORMONES** of the host on the eggs of a rabbit flea is depicted. At left the eggs are developing after the rabbit has been injected with hydrocortisone. At right the eggs, which are

the dark circular structures to the right of the pale, dark-rimmed structures, are regressing after injections of a progestin hormone into the rabbit. The enlargement is approximately 40 diameters.

SPECIAL CAMERA constructed at a Royal Air Force experimental station to photograph the jump of a flea consisted of a bank of one-inch lenses with overlapping fields that covered all of a glass cell in which the flea jumped. The flea itself triggered the camera by interrupting a narrow beam of light as it jumped. The glass cell was nine inches long, seven inches in height and one inch thick.

there is an overall increase in the size of the gut, together with great enlargement and proliferation of the epithelial cells lining its middle portion, and the rate at which the fleas defecate increases steadily as the levels of corticosteroids rise. Normally a flea defecates about once every 20 minutes; immediately before the rabbit gives birth the female flea is squirting blood out of its anus once every one to four minutes and the male flea about once every four to six minutes. This blood, as I have previously noted, subsequently provides the flea larvae with an essential factor in their diet.

Whereas a slight increase in the level of hormones in the blood of the rabbit induces the fleas to attach themselves more firmly to the host—a fact easily demonstrated experimentally—a big rise reverses this effect: the fleas detach themselves and run onto the doe's face. A change in hormone levels is almost certainly the cause of their detachment immediately before they pass on to the young. By this extraordinary adaptation the fleas are assured of a suitable place in which to breed. The female rabbit generally builds her nest some distance from the main warren, in a "stop," or short tunnel. By gearing their own reproduction to that of the host the fleas are guided to the nest at precisely the right moment, and the eggs are ready for fertilization the very day the young rabbits are born. Moreover, the larvae are assured of enough dried blood on which to feed.

It has been possible to sort out which of the various pituitary hormones are involved in these processes by injecting the rabbits with each in turn, and in different combinations and at different levels; it has been particularly useful to employ castrated buck rabbits as the experimental hosts, since they have a minimum of their own sex hormones. It has also been found that the fleas react to steroid hormones sprayed on them, and that they respond differently to the different corticosteroid hormones. Thus the rabbit flea, used as a kind of biological indicator, suggested that the corticosteroids cortisol and corticosterone were both present in the pregnant female rabbit during the last 10 days of pregnancy and in the rabbit from one to seven days old, but that when the young were three to four weeks old the levels in their blood had fallen precipitately. These indications were subsequently confirmed by D. Exley of the University of Oxford, who examined the rabbit's blood by means of thin-layer chromatography and with the aid of radioactive tracers and fluorescent techniques.

Many bird fleas, if they are slightly warmed, copulate on emerging from their pupae, without a blood meal and before their ovaries mature. In the large majority of species, however, the female has to take a blood meal before she will mate. It has been noted that at least one species of male flea lacks the sexual drive if it is reared on an unusual host but recovers its keenness after a meal of blood from its normal host. The rabbit flea is quite an exceptional case; in nature it will mate only after the female has fed on rabbits one to seven days old. The two flea sexes can remain side by side for weeks or months on an adult rabbit, the females either immature or full of ripe eggs, and no attempt at mating is made. After a period of feeding on the young rabbits a transformation occurs in the female; she suddenly attracts the male and is herself willing to mate.

In this species neither maturation of the eggs nor maturation of the sperm is concerned with copulation. After feeding on a young rabbit a female flea with unripe eggs will mate with a male that lacks fully ripe sperm in its testes. What is the signal the female gives when she has imbibed the necessary copulation factor? Does she release a pheromone—a hormone secreted externally—that stimulates the male? The characteristic zigzag approach made by the male on these occasions suggests that it is following some airborne trail of scent.

In spite of the fact that the fleas do not mate on the pregnant doe there was considerable evidence to suggest that the factor was present in her blood but in weak concentrations. This clue was followed up; it was found during preliminary experiments that still another hormone secreted by the anterior lobe of the pituitary—somatotropin, the growth hormone—is one of the factors that can control the copulation of fleas. This hormone, unlike the corticosteroids, tends to be specific in its action. That is, the growth hormone of cattle or the human growth hormone can be expected to work effectively only if it is injected into the animal that normally secretes it. No rabbit growth hormone, which would be expected to activate the rabbit flea more effectively than any other growth hormone, is yet available for experiments. Nevertheless, injections of human growth hormone into the rabbit can sometimes stimulate the rabbit flea to copulate on the adult host and more frequently on young rabbits more than eight days old. (It is of interest that somatotropin is one of the hormones that have been used to increase fertility in women and that have attracted considerable attention following several multiple births to women so treated.) Other factors not fully understood also play a part in controlling the copulation of the European rabbit flea.

### The Reproductive Process

Even though the male flea freshly emerged from its pupa already has a full complement of sperm in its testes, the sperm are by no means fully developed. They are gathered together in bundles; their heads, which are barely distinguishable at this stage, are held firmly in a pointed gelatinous capsule with a giant nucleus at its apex. Seen through the microscope, the bundles of sperm are enveloped in membranes that resemble gracefully flowing bridal veils [*see illustration at top right on page 16*]. Sometimes the individual sperm heads are already developed (their development may depend on the food supply of the larvae), but even so there is always plenty of space between the bundles of sperm in the testes. When the heads of the sperm are well developed, the tails are sufficiently free within their capsules to produce wonderfully synchronized wavelike undulations in the available space. After the male flea begins to feed on a host these spaces are gradually obliterated by the fact that the sperm increase in size, but it is only after the male flea has been feeding on the pregnant rabbit and her newborn young for a certain period that both the flea and its sperm reach their maximum size.

At this stage sections of the fleas' testes reveal a solid tangled mass; possibly the sperm are not capable of fertilizing the eggs until this stage of development is reached. It would require rather a long period of study with the aid of the electron microscope to clarify and work out the effect of the rabbit's sex hormones, on the development of the sperm. The picture at the bottom of page 15 was made with such a microscope by A. V. Grimstone of the University of Cambridge. It is a transverse section, enlarged 58,000 diameters, through partly developed sperm from the testes of a flea feeding on a nonpregnant host. Each tail seen in the section has two fibers surrounded by a circular array of nine other fibers; this arrangement is characteristic of all cilia and flagella and is the basis for the swimming abilities of the sperm.

Even with the relatively low magnification of the light microscope it is pos-sible to note differences between the sperm of different species of fleas. If the reader compares the micrographs of rat-flea and rabbit-flea sperm at the top of page 16, he will see that the wave frequency of the tails of the former is very much shorter than that of the latter; each tail of the rat-flea sperm at this stage of development has a kinky appearance. Rat-flea sperm are also much larger than rabbit-flea sperm. There appears to be a correlation between the size of the spermatheca, or sperm-storage organ of the female, and the size of the sperm. The mole flea (*Hystrichopsylla talpae*) belongs to a group of the largest fleas (between five and seven millimeters in length), but its sperm cell is relatively small and is stored in two correspondingly small spermatheca.

It would be interesting if an electron microscope study of the sperm confirmed the evolutionary relation of the order of fleas that was worked out by the late Karl Jordan of the Tring Museum in England. This classification is partly based on the organs that assist in conveying the sperm into the female. The copulatory apparatus of the male flea is the most elaborate genital organ in the animal kingdom. Recently the German entomologist Kurt Günther has described it for the mole flea and has clarified many obscure features. A glance at the illustration on page 14 will convey some idea of its complexity. Any engineer looking objectively at such a fantastically impractical apparatus would bet heavily against its operational success. The astonishing fact is that it works. Twenty-four hours after the rabbit fleas leave the doe for her young all the female fleas have been fertilized.

The various complicated steps in fertilization have not been observed in detail. The only part of the male flea's genitalia capable of extrusion are the two penis rods; these slide forward and uncurl like watch springs. Only in the rabbit flea has the conveyance of sperm actually been observed. The sperm is wound around the terminal portion of the thinner of the two penis rods rather like spaghetti on the end of a fork. This rod runs through a slot in the spoonlike end of the thicker penis rod like a rope running over a pulley. The thick rod enters the female's *bursa copulatrix*, into which it fits very snugly, and guides the thinner rod into the threadlike duct leading to the sperm-storage organ of the female. The photograph at the top of page 15 shows the end of the stouter rod with the thin rod running through the slot. The faint fuzz surrounding the tip is the mass of sperm. In order to

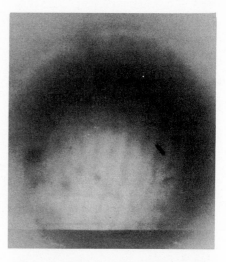

FLEA DURING JUMP was photographed with the apparatus shown on the preceding page. Base of cell is dark area at bottom.

take this photograph it was necessary to freeze two fleas during copulation, so that the penis rods remained erect when male and female were separated. Unfortunately the duct leading to the spermatheca is covered with heavy cuticle and therefore is not transparent. This makes direct observation by transmitted light impossible, and as a consequence the method by which the rod packs sperm into the spermatheca through this duct is not known.

George P. Holland, a Canadian entomologist who has greatly enlarged our understanding of copulation in various fleas, has described an odd membranous organ somewhat resembling a willow catkin with which the male strokes the female sensillum during the act of coitus. An analogous structure probably exists in many fleas but escapes attention because it is so transparent and diaphanous that it disappears entirely when specimens are prepared for permanent preservation. This is the case with the organ in the rabbit flea, which resembles a feather duster and is erected only during mating. Apparently it is also used for stroking the female, but on the lower surface. This is quite an astonishing fact; the clasping organs of the male flea are so elaborate and so encumbered with spines, struts and hooks that it would appear that only brute force is used to subdue the female. Furthermore, serious injuries are frequently inflicted on the female during impregnation, and it seems curious that she could notice the effect of this feather-like stimulator during the violent treatment she appears to be receiving simultaneously. Perhaps our interpretation of this organ is quite incorrect. Is it conceivable that it is the male who receives stimulation and with his feather duster sweeps up a pheromone released by the female?

Two particularly interesting questions are posed by the unraveling of the life cycle of the rabbit flea. First, how do these hormones act? Do they work by way of substances secreted by specialized cells in the flea's brain, which in turn act on the appropriate organ that releases the flea's own hormones, or do the corticosteroids, estrogens and progestins act directly on the various tissues of the flea? Second, what role do the host's hormones play in the lives of parasites in general? Is the hormonal dependence of the European rabbit flea unique?

Obviously the most promising species to investigate in this respect are the American rabbit fleas, which are fairly closely related to the European species. Unfortunately the cottontail rabbit is a difficult host to keep in captivity. It is quite certain, however, that the breeding of the plague-carrying Oriental rat flea (*Xenopsylla cheopis*) is not dependent on the hormones of the rat. This flea copulates and lays eggs even on a rat that has been castrated and in addition has had both its adrenal glands and its pituitary gland removed surgically, so that it is virtually deprived of all sex hormones. The fleas are probably less fertile than those laying eggs on a normal rat, and it is not yet known if their eggs produce offspring. It has been noted, however that the number of fleas on female bats increases noticeably in the spring just before the bats migrate to their summer breeding roosts. This suggests that in the case of bat fleas, as in that of the European rabbit flea, the hormones of the host may play an active role in the fleas' reproductive cycle.

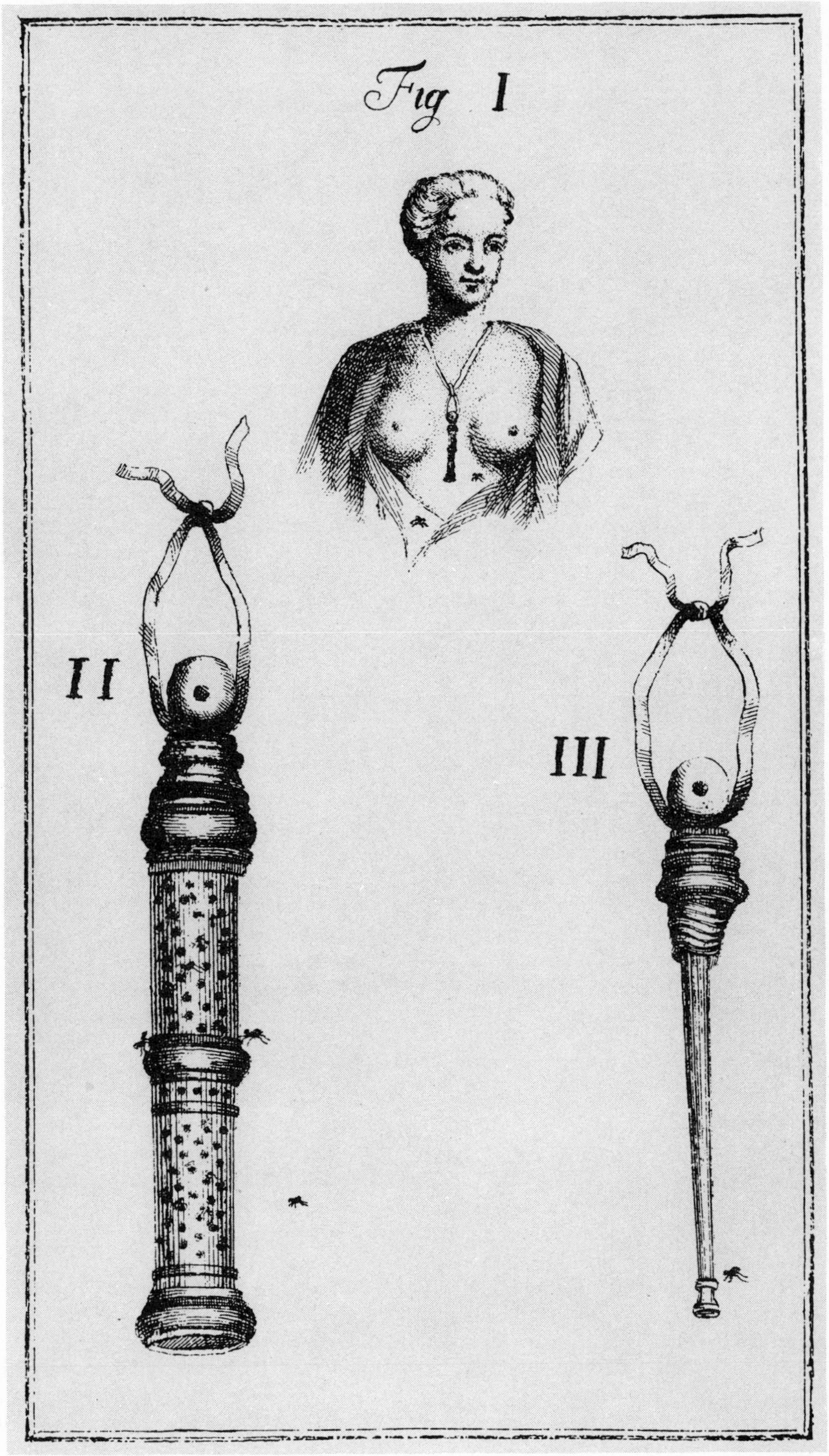

## Open Questions

It is characteristic of nature that some apparently unique feature displayed by a particular animal is only unique in degree. A careful examination of related species shows that the same tendencies are present but to a very modest extent and have consequently escaped notice. It seems reasonable to suppose that in the future many instances will be discovered in which the hormones of vertebrate animals play some unobtrusive but definite role in the development of their parasites, particularly those such as the parasitic worms that live in such naked intimacy with their hosts.

In the old literature it was repeatedly stated that women are attacked more frequently by fleas than men are. This has been generally attributed to the more delicate skin and more sensitive nature of the fair sex. In old books it is always women who are pictured wearing the latest flea trap [see *illustration at left*.] Perhaps this is faulty reasoning and the truth of the matter is that the human flea (*Pulex irritans*) also responds to the attraction of the ovarian hormones. This is food for reflection. Here we have a simple and fascinating line of research on which any one of us can embark tomorrow.

FLEA TRAP was depicted in a German book of 1739. Old books often show such traps being worn by women; it was often said that women were attacked by fleas more often than men were. The cause may conceivably have been a response by fleas to ovarian hormones.

BUTTERFLY EGGS (*top*) stand upright on a leaf of clover, the egg-laying site selected by the gravid female. Clover is the food plant preferred by this species: *Colias philodice*, the clouded sulphur. After hatching (*bottom*), growing clouded sulphur larvae feed on the plant preselected for them by the parent. When they metamorphose, they too will seek out clover as an egg-laying site.

# 3 Butterflies and Plants

PAUL R. EHRLICH and PETER H. RAVEN · June 1967

Anyone who has been close to nature or has wandered about in the nonurban areas of the earth is aware that animal life sometimes raises havoc with plant life. Familiar examples are the sudden defoliation of forests by hordes of caterpillars or swarms of locusts and the less abrupt but nonetheless thorough denudation of large areas by grazing animals. A visitor to the Wankie National Park of Rhodesia can see a particularly spectacular scene of herbivore devastation. There herds of elephants have thinned the forest over hundreds of square miles and left a litter of fallen trees as if a hurricane had passed through.

Raids such as these are rare, and the fertile regions of the earth manage to remain rather green. This leads most people, including many biologists, to underestimate the importance of the perennial onslaught of animals on plants. Detailed studies of the matter in recent years have shown that herbivores are a major factor in determining the evolution and distribution of plants, and the plants in turn play an important part in shaping the behavior and evolution of herbivores.

The influence of herbivores on plants is usually far from obvious, even when it is most profound. In Australia huge areas in Queensland used to be infested with the spiny prickly-pear cactus, which covered thousands of square miles of the area and made it unusable for grazing herds. Today the plant is rare in these areas. It was all but wiped out by the introduction of a cactus moth from South America, which interestingly enough is now hardly in evidence. When one searches scattered remaining clumps of the cactus, one usually fails to find any sign of the insect. The plant survives only as a fugitive species; as soon as a clump of the cactus is discovered by the moth it is devoured, and the population of moths that has flourished on it then dies away. A similar situation is found in the Fiji Islands. There a plant pest of the genus *Clidemia* was largely destroyed by a species of thrips brought in from tropical America, and the parasitic insect, as well as the plant, has now become rare in Fiji.

The interplay of plant and animal populations takes many forms—some direct, some indirect, some obvious, some obscure. In California the live oak is disappearing from many areas because cattle graze on the young seedlings. In Australia a native pine that was decimated by rabbits has made a dramatic comeback since the rabbit population was brought under control by the myxomatosis virus. Australia also furnishes a striking example of how the evolution of a plant can be influenced by the presence or absence of certain animals. The plant involved is the well-known acacia. In Africa and tropical America, where grazing mammals abound, the acacia species are protected by thorns that are often fearsomely developed. Until recently there were comparatively few grazing mammals in Australia, and most of the acacia plants there are thornless, apparently having lost these weapons of their relatives on other continents.

By far the most important terrestrial herbivores are, of course, the insects. They have evolved remarkably efficient organs for eating plants: a great variety of mouthparts with which to pierce, suck or chew plant material. They eat leaves from the outside and the inside, bore through stems and roots and devour flowers, fruits and seeds. In view of the abundance, variety and appetites of the insects, one may well wonder how it is that any plants are left on the earth. The answer, of course, is that the plants have not taken the onslaught of the herbivores lying down. Some of their defenses are quite obvious: the sharp spines of the cactus, the sharp-toothed leaves of the holly plant, the toxins of poison ivy and the oleander leaf, the odors and pungent tastes of spices. The effectiveness of these weapons against animal predators has been demonstrated by laboratory experiments. For example, it has been shown that certain leaf-edge-eating caterpillars normally do not feed on holly leaves but will devour the leaves when the sharp points are cut away.

The plant world's main line of defense consists in chemical weapons. Very widespread among the plants are certain chemicals that apparently perform no physiological function for the plants themselves but do act as potent insecticides or insect repellents. Among these are alkaloids, quinones, essential oils, glycosides, flavonoids and raphides (crystals of calcium oxalate). Long before man learned to synthesize insecticides he found that an extract from chrysanthemums, pyrethrin, which is harmless to mammals, is a powerful killer of insects.

Particularly interesting are the alkaloids, a heterogeneous group of nitrogenous compounds found mainly in flowering plants. They include nicotine, caffeine, quinine, marijuana, opium and peyote. Considering the hallucinogenic properties of the last three drugs, it is amusing to speculate that the plants bearing them may practice "chemopsychological warfare" against their enemies! Does an insect that has fed on a fungus containing lysergic acid diethylamide (LSD) mistake a spider for its mate? Does a zebra that has eaten a

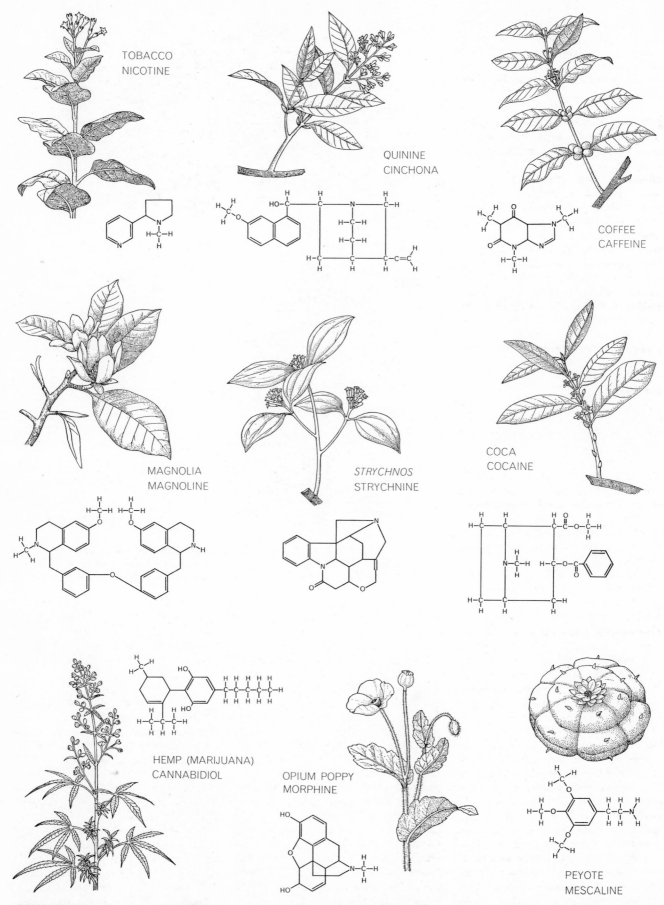

TOBACCO
NICOTINE

QUININE
CINCHONA

COFFEE
CAFFEINE

MAGNOLIA
MAGNOLINE

*STRYCHNOS*
STRYCHNINE

COCA
COCAINE

HEMP (MARIJUANA)
CANNABIDIOL

OPIUM POPPY
MORPHINE

PEYOTE
MESCALINE

**ALKALOIDS** give the plants that contain them protection from predators; nine such plants are illustrated. The authors note that plant alkaloids can disturb a herbivore's physiology and that hallucinogenic alkaloids may be "chemopsychological" weapons.

plant rich in alkaloids become so intoxicated that it loses its fear of lions? At all events, there is good reason to believe eating plant alkaloids produces a profound disturbance of animals' physiology.

Of all the herbivores, the group whose eating habits have been studied most intensively is the butterflies—that is to say, butterflies in the larval, or caterpillar, stage, which constitutes the major part of a butterfly's lifetime. Around the world upward of 15,000 species of butterflies, divided taxonomically into five families, have been identified. The five families are the Nymphalidae (four-footed butterflies), the Lycaenidae (blues, metalmarks and others), the Pieridae (whites and yellows), the Papilionidae (including the swallowtails, the huge bird-wings of the Tropics and their relatives) and the Libytheidae (a tiny family of snout butterflies). The Nymphalidae and Lycaenidae account for most (three-fourths) of the known genera and species.

A caterpillar is a formidable eating machine: by the time it metamorphoses into a butterfly it has consumed up to 20 times its dry weight in plant material. The numerous species vary greatly in their choice of food. Some are highly selective, feeding only on a single plant family; others are much more catholic in their tastes, but none feeds on all plants indiscriminately. Let us examine the food preferences of various groups and then consider the evolutionary consequences.

One group that is far-ranging in its taste for plants is the Nymphalinae, a subfamily of the Nymphalidae that comprises at least 2,500 species and is widespread around the world. The plants that members of this group feed on include one or more genera of the figwort, sunflower, maple, pigweed, barberry, beech, borage, honeysuckle, stonecrop, oak, heather, mallow, melastome, myrtle, olive, buttercup, rose, willow and saxifrage families. Another group that eats a wide variety of plants is the Lycaeninae, a subfamily of the Lycaenidae that consists of thousands of species of usually tiny but often beautifully colored butterflies. The Lycaeninae in general are catholic in their tastes, and among their many food plants are members of the pineapple, borage, pea, buckwheat, rose, heather, mistletoe, mint, buckthorn, chickweed, goosefoot, morning glory, gentian, oxalis, pittosporum and zygophyllum families.

What determines the caterpillars'

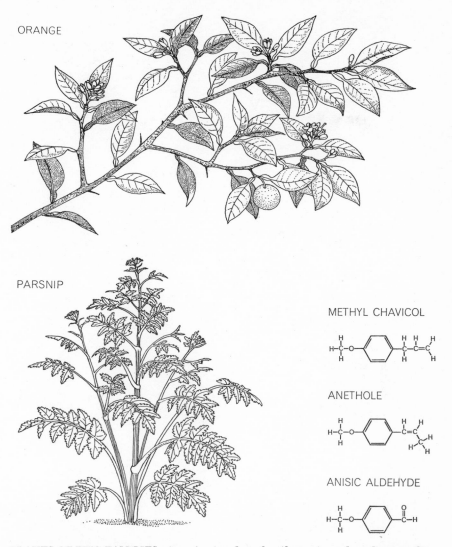

ORANGE

PARSNIP

METHYL CHAVICOL

ANETHOLE

ANISIC ALDEHYDE

**PLANTS OF TWO FAMILIES,** citrus (*top*) and parsley (*bottom*), produce the same three essential oils attractive to the larvae of black swallowtail butterflies. The chemical kinship between these plant families suggests a closer ancestral tie than had been suspected.

food preferences? We learn a great deal about this subject by examining the diets of those butterfly species that are particularly selective in their choice of plants. One large group of swallowtails, for example, confines its diet mainly to plants of the Dutchman's-pipe family. Another feeds only on the "woody Ranales," a group of primitive angiosperms that includes the magnolias, the laurels and many tropical and subtropical plants. A third group of swallowtails is partial to plants of the citrus and parsley families; the striped caterpillars of these butterflies, which extrude two bright orange scent horns when they are disturbed, are familiar to gardeners, who often see them feeding on parsley, dill, fennel and celery plants. The caterpillars of the white butterfly group (a subfamily of the Pieridae) feed primarily on caper plants in the Tropics and on plants of the mustard family in temperate regions. Similarly, the monarch butterfly and its relatives (a subfamily of the Nymphalidae) confine their diet primarily to plants of the milkweed and dogbane families.

Analysis of the plant selections by the butterfly groups has made it clear that their choices have a chemical basis, just as parasitic fungi choose hosts that meet their chemical needs. Vincent G. Dethier, then at Johns Hopkins University, noted some years ago that plants of the citrus and parsley families, although apparently unrelated, have in common certain essential oils (such as methyl chavicol, anethole and anisic aldehyde) that presumably account for their attractiveness to the group of swallowtails that feeds on them. Dethier found that caterpillars of the black swallowtail would even attempt to feed on filter paper soaked in these substances. The

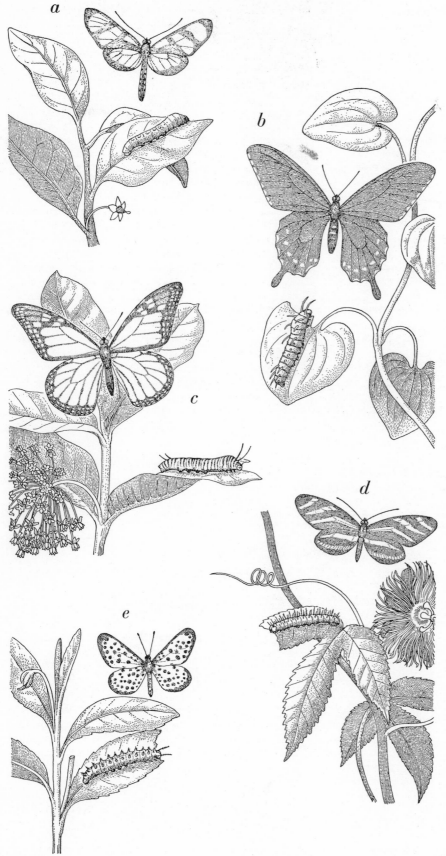

**FIVE BUTTERFLIES** protected by their unpalatability are illustrated with their preferred plants. They are *Thyridia themisto* and one of the nightshades (*a*), *Battus philenor* and Dutchman's-pipe (*b*), *Danaus plexippus* and milkweed (*c*), *Heliconius charitonius* and passion flower (*d*) and *Pardopsis punctatissima* and a representative of the violet family (*e*).

same caterpillars could also be induced to feed on plants of the sunflower family (for example goldenrod and cosmos), which contain these oils but are not normally eaten by the caterpillars in nature.

The chemical finding, incidentally, raises an interesting question about the evolutionary relationship of plants. The sunflower, citrus and parsley families have been considered to be very different from one another, but their common possession of the same group of substances suggests that there may be a chemical kinship after all, at least between the citrus and the parsley family. Chemistry may therefore become a basis for reconsideration of the present classification system for plants.

In the case of the cabbage white butterfly larva the attractive chemical has been shown to be mustard oil. The pungent mustard oils are characteristic of plants of the caper and mustard families (the latter family includes many familiar food plants, such as cabbages, Brussels sprouts, horseradish, radishes and watercress). The whites' larvae also feed occasionally on plants of other families that contain mustard oils, including the garden nasturtium. The Dutch botanist E. Verschaeffelt found early in this century that these larvae would eat flour, starch or even filter paper if it was smeared with juice from mustard plants. More recently the Canadian biologist A. J. Thorsteinson showed that the larvae would eat the leaves of plants on which they normally do not feed when the plants were treated with mustard oil glucosides.

In contrast to the attractive plants, there are plant families on which butterfly larvae do not feed (although other insects may). One of these is the coffee family. Although this family, with some 10,000 species, is probably the fourth largest family of flowering plants in the world and is found mainly in the Tropics, as the butterflies themselves are, butterfly larvae rarely, if ever, feed on these plants. A plausible explanation is that plants of the coffee family are rich in alkaloids. Quinine is one example. Other plant families that butterflies generally avoid eating are the cucurbits (rich in bitter terpenes), the grape family (containing raphides) and the spiny cactus family.

One of the most interesting findings is that butterflies that are distasteful to predators (and that are identified by conspicuous coloring) are generally narrow specialists in their choice of food. They tend to select plants on which other butterfly groups do not feed, notably plants that are rich in alkaloids. It seems highly probable that their use of these plants for food has a double basis: it provides them with a feeding niche in which they have relatively little competition, and it may supply them with the substances, or precursors of substances, that make them unpalatable to predators. The distasteful groups of butterflies apparently have evolved changes in physiology that render them immune to the toxic or repellent plant substances and thus enable them to turn the plants' chemical defenses to their own advantage. Curiously, the butterfly species that mimic the coloring of the distasteful ones are in general more catholic in their feeding habits; evidently their warning coloration alone is sufficient to protect them.

The fact that some butterflies' diets are indeed responsible for their unpalatability has been demonstrated recently by Lincoln P. Brower of Amherst College and his co-workers. They worked with the monarch butterfly, whose larvae normally feed on plants of the milkweed family. Such plants are rich in cardiac glycosides, powerful poisons that are used in minute quantities to treat heart disease in man. When adult butterflies of this species are offered to hand-reared birds (with no previous experience with butterflies), the butterflies are tasted and then promptly rejected, as are further offerings of either the monarch or its close mimic, the viceroy. Recently Brower succeeded in spite of great difficulties in rearing a generation of monarch butterflies on cabbage and found that the resulting adults were perfectly acceptable to the birds, although they were refused by birds that had had previous experience with milkweed-fed monarchs.

The concept of warfare between the plants and the butterflies leads to much enlightenment on the details of evolutionary development on both sides. On the plants' side, we can liken their problem to that of the farmer, who is obliged to defend his crops from attack by a variety of organisms. The plants must deploy their limited resources to protect themselves as best they can. They may confine their growing season to part of the year (limiting their availability to predators); they may be equipped with certain mechanical or chemical defenses; some develop a nutrient-poor sap or nutritional imbalances that make them an inefficient or inadequate source of food. The herbivorous insects, for their part, reply with specializations to cope with the special defenses, as a hunter uses a high-powered rifle to hit deer or bear, a shotgun to hit birds or a hook to catch fish. No butterfly larva (or other herbivore) possesses the varieties of physical equipment that would allow it to feed on all plants; in order to feed at all it must specialize to some degree. Some of the specializations are extremely narrow; certain sap-sucking insects, for example, have developed filtering mechanisms that trap the food elements in nutrient-poor sap, and some of the caterpillars possess detoxifying systems that enable them to feed on plants containing toxic substances.

By such devices herbivores of one kind or another have managed to breach the chemical defenses of nearly every group of plants. We have already noted several examples. The mustard oils of the mustard and caper plant families,

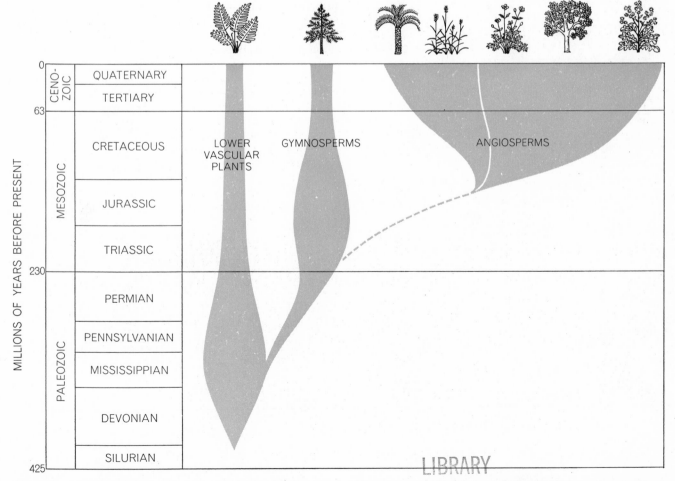

**RECORD OF EVOLUTION** within the plant kingdom shows that among the vascular plants the gymnosperms (*center*) declined as the angiosperms (*right*) became abundant. The authors attribute this to the acquisition of chemical defenses by the angiosperms.

for instance, serve to make these plants unpalatable to most herbivores, but the white butterflies and certain other insects have become so adapted to this defense mechanism that the mustard oils actually are a feeding stimulus for them. O. L. Chambliss and C. M. Jones, then at Purdue University, showed that a bitter, toxic substance in fruits of the squash family that repels honeybees and yellow jackets is attractive to the spotted cucumber beetle. Incidentally, this substance has been bred out of the cultivated watermelon, as any picnicker who has had to wave yellow jackets away from the watermelon can testify. By selecting against this bitter taste man has destroyed one of the natural protective mechanisms of the plant and must contend with a much wider variety of predators on it than the watermelon had to in the wild.

An important aspect of the insects'

chemical adaptability is the recent finding that insects that feed on toxic plants are often immune to man-made insecticides. They evidently possess a generalized detoxifying mechanism. H. T. Gordon of the University of California at Berkeley has pointed out that this is commonly true of insects that are in the habit of feeding on a wide variety of plants. He suggests that through evolutionary selection such insects have evolved a high tolerance to biochemical stresses.

What can we deduce, in the light of the present mutual interrelations of butterflies and plants, about the evolutionary history of the insects and flowering plants? We have little information about their ancient history to guide us, but a few general points seem reasonably clear.

First, we can surmise that the great success of the angiosperm plants (plants

with enclosed seeds), which now dominate the plant world since most of the more primitive gymnosperm lines have disappeared, is probably due in large measure to the angiosperms' early acquisition of chemical defenses. One important group of protective secondary plant substances, the alkaloids, is found almost exclusively in this class of plants and is well represented in those groups of angiosperms that are considered most primitive. Whereas other plants were poorly equipped for chemical warfare, the angiosperms were able to diversify behind a biochemical shield that gave them considerable protection from herbivores.

As the flowering plants diversified, the insect world also underwent a tremendous diversification with them. The intimate present relation between butterflies and plants leaves no doubt that the two groups evolved together, each

MODEL                MIMETIC FORM                NONMIMETIC FORM

UNPALATABLE BUTTERFLIES, whose disagreeable taste originates with the plants they ate as larvae, are often boldly marked and predators soon learn to avoid them. The three "models," so called because unrelated species mimic them, are the monarch, *Danaus* (*a*), another Danaine, *D. chrysippus* (*d*) and a third Danaine, *Amauris* (*f*). Their imitators are the viceroy, *Limenitis* (*b*), one form of *Papilio dardanus* (*e*) and another form of *P. dardanus* (*g*). Mimicry is not a genus-wide phenomenon: *L. astyanax* (*c*), a relative of the viceroy, is nonmimetic. So is a third form of *P. dardanus* (*h*), whose cousins (*e*, *g*) mimic two of the Danaine models.

influencing the development of the other. In all probability the butterflies, which doubtless descended from the primarily nocturnal moths, owe their success largely to the decisive step of taking to daytime feeding. By virtue of their choice of food plants all butterflies are somewhat distasteful, and Charles L. Remington of Yale University has suggested that this is primarily what enabled them to establish themselves and flourish in the world of daylight. The butterflies and their larvae did not, of course, overwhelm the plant world; on the contrary, in company with the other herbivores they helped to accelerate the evolution of the plants into a great variety of new and more resistant forms.

From what little we know about the relationships between other herbivore groups and their associated plants, we can assume that the butterfly-plant association is typical of most herbivore-plant pairings. This information gives us an excellent starting point for understanding the phenomenon that we might call "communal evolution," or coevolution. It can help, for example, to account for the great diversity of plant and insect species in the Tropics compared with the much smaller number of species in the temperate zones. The abundance of plant-eating insects in the Tropics, interacting with the plants, unquestionably has been an important factor, perhaps the most important one, in promoting the species diversity of both plants and animals in those regions. Indeed, the interaction of plants and herbivores may be the primary mechanism responsible for generating the diversity of living forms in most of the earth's environ-

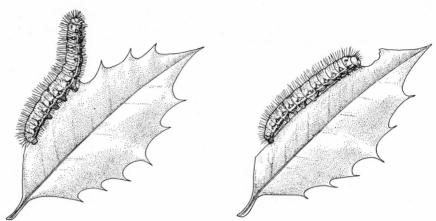

**TOOTHED EDGE** of the holly (*left*) normally protects it from leaf-edge eaters, such as the tent caterpillar. After the leaf's teeth are trimmed (*right*) the insect readily devours it.

ments.

Since the welfare, and even the survival, of mankind depend so heavily on the food supply and on finding ways to deal with insects without dangerous contamination of the environment with insecticides, great benefits might be derived from more intensive study of plant-herbivore associations. With detailed knowledge of these associations, plants can be bred for resistance to insects. Crop plants might be endowed with bred-in repellents, and strains of plants containing strong attractants for pests might be planted next to the crops to divert the insects and facilitate their destruction. New methods of eliminating insects without danger to man might be developed. Carroll M. Williams of Harvard University and his co-workers have discovered, for example, that substances analogous to the juvenile hormone of some insects are present in tissues of the American balsam fir. Since the juvenile

hormone acts to delay metamorphosis in insects, plants bred for such substances might be used to interfere with insect development. It is even possible that insects could be fought with tumor-inducing substances: at least one plant alkaloid, nicotine, is known to be a powerful carcinogen in vertebrates.

Such methods, together with techniques of biological control of insects already in use and under development, could greatly reduce the present reliance on hazardous insecticides. The insects have shown that they cannot be conquered permanently by the brand of chemical warfare we have been using up to now. After all, they had become battle-hardened from fighting the insecticide warfare of the plants for more than 100 million years. By learning from the plants and sharpening their natural weapons we should be able to find effective ways of poisoning our insect competitors without poisoning ourselves.

# 4 Predatory Fungi

JOSEPH J. MAIO · July 1958

Unless man succeeds in duplicating the process of photosynthesis, it appears that animals will always have to feed upon plants. But the plant world exacts its retribution. A number of plants have turned the tables on the animal kingdom, reversing the roles of predator and prey. These are the plant carnivores—plants that trap and consume living animals. Most famous are the pitcher plant, with its reservoir of digestive fluid in which to drown hapless insects; the sundew, with its fly-paper-like leaves; and Venus's-flytrap, with its snapping jaws. But there are other carnivorous plants of larger significance in the balance of nature. We ought to know them better because they are to be found in great profusion and variety in any pinch of forest soil or garden compost. They are microscopic in size, but just as deadly to their animal prey as the sundew or Venus's-flytrap.

These tiny predators are members of the large group of fungi we call molds. They grow in richly branching networks of filaments visible to the naked eye as hairy or velvety mats. Molds do not engage in photosynthesis. Like most bacteria, they lack chlorophyll and so must

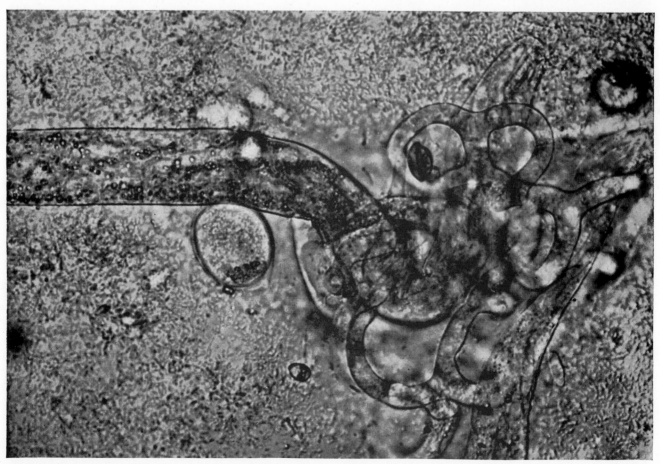

NEMATODE WORM IS TRAPPED by the adhesive fungus *Trichothecium cystosporium* in this photomicrograph by the British biologist C. L. Duddington. The entangling network of the fungus is at right; the body of the worm extends to the left. The oval object below the body of the worm is one of the spores by which the fungus reproduces. At lower right are the remains of another worm.

derive their food from other plants and from animals. Molds have long been familiar as scavengers of dead organisms, promoters of the process of decay. It was not until 1888 that a German mycologist, named Friedrich Wilhelm Zopf, beheld molds in the act of trapping and killing live animals—in this case the larvae of a tiny worm, the wheat-cockle nematode.

The nematodes (eelworms, hookworms and their like) are not the only prey of these animal-eating plants. Their victims run the gamut from the comparatively formidable nematodes down to small crustaceans, rotifers and the lowly amoeba. Charles Drechsler of the U. S. Department of Agriculture, a student of the subject for some 25 years, has identified a large number of carnivorous molds and matched them to their prey. Many are adapted to killing only

one species of animal, and some are equipped with traps and snares which are marvels of genetic resourcefulness. How they evolved their predatory habits and organs remains an evolutionary mystery. These molds belong to quite different species and have in common only their behavior and some similarities of trapping technique. They present a challenging subject for investigation which may throw light on some fundamental questions in biology and may lead also to new methods for control of a number of crop-killing nematodes.

The simplest of the molds have no special organs with which to ensnare their victims. Their filaments, however, secrete a sticky substance which holds fast any small creature that has the misfortune to come in contact with

it. The mold then injects daughter filaments into the body cavity of the victim and digests its contents. Most of the animals caught in this way are rhizopods—sluggish amoebae encased in minute hard shells. Sometimes, however, the big, vigorous soil nematodes are trapped by this elementary means.

More specialized is an unusual water mold, of the genus *Sommerstorffia*, which catches rotifers, its actively swimming prey, with little sticky pegs that branch from its filaments. When a rotifer, browsing among the algae on which this mold grows, takes one of these pegs in its ciliated mouth, it finds itself impaled like a fish on a hook.

Some molds do their trapping in the spore stage. The parent mold produces staggering numbers of sticky spores. When a spore is swallowed by or sticks

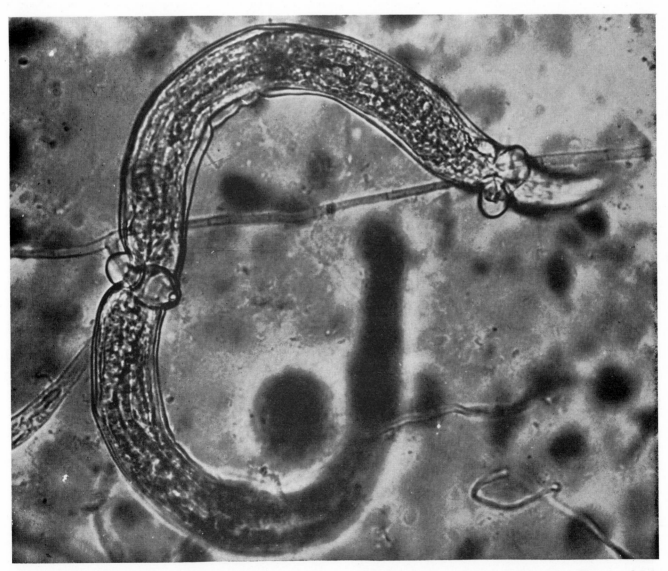

**TWO CONSTRICTING RINGS** of the fungus *Dactylaria gracilis* grasp another nematode in this photomicrograph by Duddington. The nematode was first caught by the head (*upper right*), and then flicked its body into another ring (*left center*). The rings deeply constrict the body of the worm. The horizontal line above the middle of the picture is a filament to which the rings are attached.

to a passing amoeba or nematode, it germinates in the body of its luckless host and sends forth from the shriveled corpse new filaments and new spores to intercept other victims.

The most remarkable of all killer molds are found among the so-called *Fungi Imperfecti*, or completely asexual fungi. The advanced specialization of these molds is particularly interesting because they are not killers by obligation but can live quite well on decaying organic matter when nematodes, their animal victims, are not available. If nematodes are present, these molds immediately develop highly specialized structures which re-adapt them to a carnivorous way of life. They will do so even if they are merely wetted with water in which nematodes have lived.

One of these molds is *Arthrobotrys oligospora*, the nematode-catching fungus that was first studied by Zopf. When nematodes are available, it develops networks of loops, fused together to form an elaborate nematode trap. An extremely sticky fluid secreted by the mold seems to play an important role in capturing the nematode, which need not even enter the network in order to be held fast. The fluid is so sticky that one-point contact with the network frequently is enough to doom the nematode. In its frenzied struggles to escape, the worm only becomes further entangled in the loops, and finally, after a few hours of exertion, weakens and dies. The destruction these molds can cause in a laboratory culture of nematodes is appalling, particularly from the point of view of the nematode!

Two French biologists, Jean Comandon and Pierre de Fonbrune, have made motion pictures which show that the fungus's secretion of this adhesive substance is accompanied by intense activity in its cells. Material in the cytoplasm of the cell streams toward the point of contact with the worm. The mold may be bringing up reserves of adhesive and digestive enzymes to subdue the nematode; it may also secrete a narcotic or an intoxicant to speed the process.

Even more artfully contrived are the "rabbit snares" employed by some molds. First fully described by Charles Drechsler, these are rings of filament which are attached by short branches to the main filaments, hundreds of them growing on one mold plant. The rings are always formed by three cells and have an inside diameter just about equal to the thickness of a nematode. When a nematode, in its blind wanderings

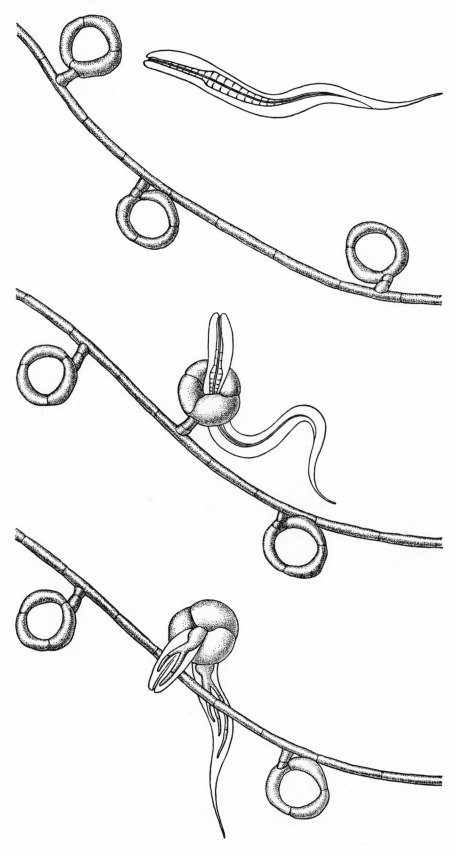

**CAPTURE AND CONSUMPTION** of a nematode worm by a fungus of the constricting-ring type is depicted in this series of three drawings. At the top the worm approaches a ring attached to a filament of the fungus. In middle the three cells of one ring have expanded to trap the worm. At bottom filaments have branched out of the fungus to digest the worm.

through the soil, has the ill luck to stick its head into one of these rings, the three cells suddenly inflate like a pneumatic tire, gripping it in a stranglehold from which there is no escape.

The rings respond almost instantaneously to the presence of a nematode; in less than one tenth of a second the three cells expand to two or three times their former volume, obliterating the opening of the ring. It is difficult to understand how the delicate filaments can hold the powerfully thrashing worm in so unyielding a grip. Occasionally a muscular worm does escape by breaking the ring off its stalk. But this victory only postpones the inevitable. The ring hangs on like a deadly collar and ultimately generates filaments which invade the worm, kill it and consume it.

We are not yet sure what cellular mechanisms activate these deadly nooses. We know that in the case of the constricting ring of one mold the activating stimulus is the sliding touch of the nematode as it enters the ring. A nematode that touches the outer surface of the ring will not trigger the mechanism. But if the worm passes inside the ring, its doom is certain. This mold, then, exhibits a sharply localized "paratonic" or touch response like that of the Venus's-flytrap.

Perhaps the inflation of the cells is caused by a change in osmotic pressure, resulting in an intake of water either from the environment or from neighboring cells. Or perhaps it results from changes in the colloidal structure of the cell protoplasm. There is a recent report from England that the constricting rings of one species react to acetylcholine—the substance associated with the transmission of impulses across synapses in the animal nervous system!

Some species of molds prey upon root eelworms that infest cereal crops, potatoes and pineapples. This has inspired experiments to use these fungi to control the pests. In one early experiment, conducted in Hawaii by M. B. Linford of the University of Illinois and his associates, a mulch of chopped pineapple tops was added to soil known to harbor the pineapple root-knot eelworm. This mulch produced an increase in the numbers of harmless, free-wandering nematodes which thrive in rich soil. The presence of these decay nematodes stimulated molds in the soil to develop nematode traps, which caught the eelworms as well as the harmless species. A recent experiment in England gives similar promise that the molds may be effective against the cereal root eelworm. Plants protected by stimulated molds showed slight damage compared to the eelworm-ravaged control plants.

Investigators in France have reported an experiment which suggests that molds may be used to control nematode parasites of animals as well as those of plants. Two sheep pens were heavily infested with larvae of a hookworm, closely related to the hookworms of man, which causes severe pulmonary and intestinal damage to sheep. One of the pens was sprinkled with the spores of three molds that employ snares or sticky nets to trap nematodes. Healthy lambs were placed in both pens. After 35 days of exposure the lambs in the pen inoculated with the molds were found free of infection, while those in the control pen showed signs of infestation with the worm.

The carnivorous molds offer many possibilities for future investigation. One subject that needs to be explored is their role in the complex biology of the soil. We would also like to know more about the physiological mechanism that underlies the extraordinary behavior of the nematode "snares." The results of experiments on mold control of nematodes are already encouraging. They suggest that one day these peculiar little plants may perform an even more important role in agriculture than they played in nature, silently and unobtrusively, throughout the millennia before their discovery.

**NEMATODE IS INVADED** by filaments of a fungus which has trapped it. This photomicrograph was made by David E. Pramer of the New Jersey Agricultural Experiment Station.

# 5 Nocturnal Animals

H. N. SOUTHERN · October 1955

Animals avoid competing with one another by evolving more or less specialized ways of life. Such specialization may take the form of being bigger or smaller than other animals, of eating different foods, of living in different habitats or different niches of the same habitat, of foraging at different times of day. It is not surprising, therefore, that many animals concentrate their vital activity in the nighttime.

The study of night animals has always been a challenging one for the naturalist. Their dark world is as unknown and difficult to probe as life in the depths of the sea. Its investigation demands unusual methods, much labor and patience and a carefully governed imagination.

My own interest in nocturnal animals arose in a severely logical way. I wished to make a quantitative study of the predator-prey relationships among birds and mammals. Because both the predator and the prey populations would have to be laboriously censused, it was necessary to select a predator which did not range over too large a territory or prey on too many different kinds of animals. After considering various possibilities, I decided that the most promising was the tawny owl (*Strix aluco*). This species, slightly larger than the barn owl, feeds primarily upon small mice and voles. Although I was led to the choice of an owl by logic, it would be idle to pretend that the fascination of night work counted for nothing. I was soon absorbed in the problem of finding ways to learn the natural history of animals hidden by darkness.

First of all I had to examine closely the night animals' sensory equipment,

**TAWNY OWL SWOOPS down on a wood mouse. The owl's flight is quite silent.**

both to determine how they get about and to discover methods of observing them without detection. Obviously some nocturnal animals must have unusually acute vision and hearing. The wood mouse (*Apodemus sylvaticus*), a night-worker which is one of the chief foods of the tawny owl, has ultrasensitive eyes and greatly enlarged ear lobes. It responds quickly to the faintest sound, especially in the higher registers. But it is not itself a silent creature. On a still night about an hour after dark, the woodland floor can be heard rustling all over with the excursions of mice. It is the predator rather than the prey which must move in silence. The owl, flying softly on wings with frayed edges, is the most soundless of all night animals. One of the most unnerving hazards of field work in the woodland at night is the sudden, silent onslaught of the tawny owl, which may fiercely attack anyone approaching its chicks. The tawny owl apparently hunts both by sight and by ear, watching and pouncing from a perch. Most owls hunt mainly by ear, locating their prey with asymmetrical ears.

Many animals active by night have no obvious adaptations of sight or hearing to help them move in the darkness. We have learned in recent years that there is another sense which guides animals, including man, in moving about in a familiar territory. For want of a better term we call it the "kinesthetic" sense. It boils down to a conditioned, and therefore swift, repetition of set sequences of muscular movements. The trained muscles of a pianist's fingers produce almost miraculous sequences of movements. A person in his own home can walk down a flight of stairs in the dark and grasp a doorknob with uncanny precision. In night animals the kines-

thetic sense is all-important as a guide to movement and territory.

Let me cite two illustrations. If we put a house mouse into an unfamiliar cage, it will quickly explore its new home, traversing and retraversing it in every possible way. For ease of handling wild mice, I usually keep a refuge box in each cage, into which one can drive the mouse or mice to free the cage for cleaning and so forth. If a mouse is disturbed before it has made its preliminary explorations, it will panic and perhaps leap out of the cage. But if it has first had an opportunity to explore the cage, it will react to a disturbance by darting, swift as lightning, into the refuge box. It has achieved in a short time a familiarity with the environment which enables it to take the right path without "thinking," indeed almost without looking.

The second illustration is furnished by young owls. The chicks of the tawny owl are dependent upon their parents for an extremely long time—up to three months. This extended adolescence is devoted not to lessons in hunting but to learning the territory. A fortnight after learning to fly, the young owls have thoroughly explored a limited area. If one chases them with a flashing torch, they will fly only as far as the boundary of that area and then fly back to the middle of the territory. A week later this boundary has rippled outwards for 100 yards or so. Thus the young birds gradually extend their territory to the final range, which for an adult pair of tawny owls is some 25 to 80 acres of woodland. A territory is a thing which has to be known with an almost indecent intimacy. This appears to me the reason why animals find so little difficulty in maintaining their territorial rights.

Whether or not an animal is equipped with acute sight or hearing, it is likely to rely largely upon the kinesthetic sense in moving about its territory. We need only watch a wood mouse running through a dense tangle of undergrowth with truly fantastic speed and certitude to realize that it is not "seeing" its way. Kinesthetic sense is clearly the answer. As for shrews and moles, animals which have to forage both by day and by night because their appetites need perpetual appeasement, their journeyings are governed so completely by kinesthetic sense that they are equally efficient in the light and the dark. They have little need of eyes, and their eyes can hardly function at all. Indeed, it appears that certain animals have developed nocturnal vision almost, as it were, by chance. They are a sort of random sample of night creatures—a small percentage that has taken this line of specializa-

tion as an "extra." Among rodents the wood mouse is an outstanding example of adaptation to the faintest illumination; another, less outstanding, is the rabbit. Among predators, of course, the owls are pre-eminent.

All of these animals have eyes with similar characteristics: *viz.*, the eye is greatly enlarged and has many rods, which respond to dim light. Some owls can be trained to find even dead, motionless prey in the dark. But the owl's eye is especially fitted to detect movement across the field of view, because rods are sensitive principally to changes of light intensity; cones, which perceive patterns and colors, are absent, or nearly so, from the owl's retina. Less than a millionth of one candle power, about the amount of light that falls on the forest floor on a cloudy summer night, is suffi-

cient to reveal a mouse to the tawny owl. The bird, whose eyes are immobile, has a peculiar way of moving its head constantly up and down and from side to side when it concentrates on some object, presumably to make the object move across its field of view, even if it is motionless.

Having learned something about our subjects' adaptations to darkness, we could proceed to consider ways of outwitting them. To begin with, owls are noisy in communicating over their large territories. Their rather melancholy hooting, so characteristic of English woodlands at night, is a proclamation of territory. Vocal combats between neighboring tawny owls are not infrequent and can be recognized a quarter of a mile away by the hasty and excited way

HIDDEN IN BLIND in Wytham woods, the author spent many nights watching tawny owls. At first he tried to use an infrared Sniperscope, with indifferent success. Later he found he could flood the forest in rather strong red light without disturbing the birds.

in which the hooting rises to a screech or a wail. Furthermore, some males can be identified by a consistent aberration of their hooting, and thus their range of movements can be traced.

From intensive listening throughout the night, and especially in the few hours after dusk when activity is at a peak, a plan can be pieced together of the territories over quite a large area. I found it relatively easy, once I had learned the tricks, to census the tawny owls living on 1,000 acres of woodland.

This map of tawny owl territories was confirmed in an unexpected way. To take censuses of the populations of mice, I trapped large numbers of them, marked them with numbered metal leg-rings, and then released them. Simultaneously I was analyzing each month castings from the tawny owls. These contained the bones and fur of the prey they had eaten, and in the pellets I recovered many of the leg-rings with which I had marked the mice. From a single owl nest I might recover 20 to 30 rings. I knew, of course, at what points in the forest the mice marked with these rings had been released, and so I could test whether the area covered by the predations of the owls in question corresponded with the territory I had sketched in from listening. This correspondence was, in fact, almost perfect, so no room was left for doubting either the territoriality of the owls or the validity of the territory measurements.

When I turned to the task of finding a way to watch the animals directly, I first tried a wartime German invention: the infrared telescope popularly called the Sniperscope or, more flippantly, the Snooperscope. It converts an image formed from invisible, infrared rays into a visible, fluorescent image. I had beaten this sword into a plowshare by using it to watch the feeding behavior of wild Norway rats in the dark. My colleague, Dennis Chitty, had become interested in the problem of determining how it was that any alteration in the setting of bait, even so slight a change as placing it in a tin lid instead of on the bare floor, would cause rats to avoid an accustomed food. With the help of the Sniperscope we were able to watch the suspicious behavior of the rat in all its details.

Nevertheless, the Sniperscope had certain disadvantages. Among other things, the resolution of the image was coarse and the transformer supplying the current to the image-converter tube made a high-pitched whine. This last feature alone was enough to scare tawny owls. I therefore turned to another method of illumination: an automobile

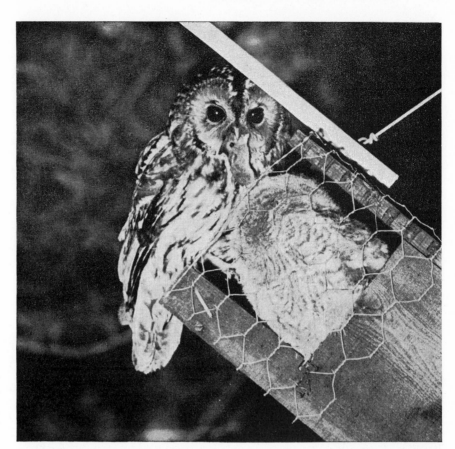

OWL FEEDS WOOD MOUSE to its owlet. Owl breeding closely follows the mouse population. In seasons when mice are abundant, tawny owls may attempt to rear two broods.

head lamp screened, like a darkroom lamp, to give visible red rays. At that time I had some 30 nest boxes for tawny owls distributed through the woodland, all fitted with electrical recording apparatus to show the number and frequency of visits by the parents throughout the night. It was urgent to evolve some method of overnight watching to check how many of the visits actually produced prey and what these prey were. The red light gave the perfect answer. It was invisible to the owls. Ensconced in a blind where I could watch an owl's nest through a large pair of 10 x 80 binoculars mounted on a tripod, I was able to see every detail of the owls' movements and the game brought home from their hunting, even the beetles which they occasionally brought to their young. Of some dozen families of owls that I watched intensively over two breeding seasons, no bird ever betrayed the slightest sign of nervousness of the red flood which illuminated its activities.

At one nest I managed to watch throughout eight complete nights. During this time the male brought home 20 prey, most of which were bank voles, then particularly abundant. This continuous watching was very fatiguing

even though the night was divided between two observers, because it was essential never to take one's eyes away from the binoculars.

During these watches much valuable information was gained on calls and the general behavior of the owls. It was most interesting to see the chicks, as they grew stronger, climbing up to the lip of the box to be fed. I remember one which made a somewhat premature attempt. It was so unsteady that it nearly fell from the box. Thereupon it fairly bolted back into the nest and refused to reappear until several more nights had passed.

The red-light watches disclosed that during the summer tawny owls eat large numbers of earthworms. For some time I had noticed that their castings often contained no fur or bones but had a matrix of vegetable fibers. Under the direct watch it developed that some tawny owl parents organized a regular ferry service of earthworms to their chicks. When the vegetable castings were examined under the microscope, they proved to be full of earthworm chaetae (bristles). Few of the large owls eat earthworms; the tawny owl's habit of doing so may well contribute to its success as a species.

When I applied the red light to watch-

**WOOD MICE NIBBLE BAIT** near a live-trap. Dominant members of the mouse social hierarchy staked out a territorial claim to the trap and were caught in it repeatedly.

foraging animals at night. I have so far tried this only on the badger, which is a fairly noisy animal. By creeping up when the badger is stamping about and freezing when it is still, it is relatively easy to see closely what the badger is up to.

I believe that this method has great promise. If it can be used so successfully on the relatively few nocturnal animals of temperate latitudes, it should be of even greater value in exploring the richer faunas of the tropics. Its great merit is its simplicity. My apparatus has sometimes been cumbersome and costly, but a good flashlight with a concentrated spot and a red celluloid cap will serve for many purposes. To this one needs to add, however, plenty of perseverence.

The specific project which originally prompted me to test these various methods of night observation has been carried on now for eight years. The analysis and publication of the full results will take a long time. Nevertheless, we are able already to tell a number of things about the interaction between tawny owl and wood mouse populations.

In the first place, a continuous study of the contents of owl castings from all over the 1,000-acre woodland through eight years has shown very interesting seasonal variations in the diet. The owls' predations on wood mice and bank voles are greatest when ground cover is at its scantiest—from the fall of the leaves in late November until the beginning of May. During this period 70 to 80 per cent of the tawny owls' diet may consist of small mammals. Since the mouse population falls to its lowest ebb in early spring (just before the breeding season), it is clear that the preying of the owls must bear heavily on that population. During late spring, summer and early autumn, when the vegetation is thick, the owls turn to young moles and rabbits and to invertebrates such as cockchafers, ground beetles and earthworms.

The making of censuses and plotting of territories, achieved by the listening methods described earlier, revealed an astonishingly high density of owls. In 1947, after an exceptionally long and snowy winter, the breeding population on the 1,000 acres studied was 15 pairs. The following year it had increased to 20 pairs, and at the present this number has expanded further to 26 pairs, which means that each couple lives, feeds and sometimes rears young on only about 40 acres of woodland. It is unlikely that any other bird of prey which feeds principally on vertebrates can exhibit a steady density of this order.

ing the behavior of wood mice, I was especially interested in determining the answer to a perplexing question. Live-traps set out in the woodland catch mice already marked more frequently than they do unmarked mice. Obviously this must throw all askew any attempt to estimate the total mouse population. I therefore watched a trap for several nights, pinning up the door so that it would not close when mice visited the trap for food. I discovered that of half a dozen mice which came to the trap on those nights, one pair completely dominated the scene. The others were all younger ones and only came to feed when the dominant pair had had their fill. Thus I learned that a social hierarchy existed among these wild mice, and that a trap would merely go on catching the same mouse over and over again.

I became interested to learn what other English mammals were red-blind. So far I have tested only badgers and foxes. Both of these animals appear to be quite unconscious of red illumination. Probably most carnivores that hunt at night have the same limitation. Their world is known to them more in terms of scent and kinesthetic conditioning than of vision; their nocturnal habit may be due partly to daytime persecution.

The red light can be useful not only for watching nests but also for tracking

**NOISY BADGER** at the entrance to its den pays no attention to red illumination. Southern crept up on the animal while it was stamping about and got close without being heard.

The population figures for the mice and voles are still very approximate. But the trends of the populations from year to year are quite clear. There is a very obvious link between the abundance of mice and the success of the owls in rearing young. In some years a tawny owl pair may raise two or three chicks; in others they make no attempt to breed at all. When the mice are neither abundant nor very scarce, the owls may lay eggs and allow them to chill (presumably because the hen must leave the nest to feed herself, if the male cannot bring her enough prey) or may lose chicks through starvation. If a clutch of eggs is lost, it is unusual for a second clutch to be laid. Second clutches were found on a widespread scale during only one of the years of the investigation—a year in which the populations of mice and voles reached the highest recorded peak.

The tawny owl's reluctance to replace lost clutches, as well as its early start in breeding (usually between March 18 and April 1), probably is due to the long period of the chicks' dependence on their parents. It is curious that, although the young hatchling in the nest is in great hazard of its life, once it has begun to fly it is extremely unlikely to be lost during the remainder of the dependence period.

August in woodland is a month of silence and inscrutability as far as tawny owls are concerned. The young have begun to fend for themselves, and their loud food cries cease. I have yet to evolve a method of studying the owls directly at that time. This is unfortunate, because an important part of the annual mortality falls just then. Indirect evidence suggests that the newly independent chicks suffer very high losses. For one thing, when the owls become territorially vociferous—in late September and October—their numbers have declined sharply. Returns from banded chicks show that the young owls rarely go outside the estate to establish new territories. The most important evidence, finally, is that a number of chicks have been found in a semistarved state during the latter part of August and early September.

With the exception of this period the life cycle of the tawny owl has been pieced together fairly coherently by now, and the history of this particular population is in a fair way to being depicted in quantitative terms. With certain reservations the same is true of the prey populations. In the time available very little information would have been obtainable without the methods of observation described above.

# 6 Moths and Ultrasound

KENNETH D. ROEDER · April 1965

If an animal is to survive, it must be able to perceive and react to predators or prey. What nerve mechanisms are used when one animal reacts to the presence of another? Those animals that have a central nervous system perceive the outer world through an array of sense organs connected with the brain by many thousands of nerve fibers. Their reactions are expressed as critically timed sequences of nerve impulses traveling along motor nerve fibers to specific muscles. Exactly how the nervous system converts a particular pattern of sensory input into a specific pattern of motor output remains a subject of investigation in many branches of zoology, physiology and psychology.

Even with the best available techniques one can simultaneously follow the traffic of nerve impulses in only five or perhaps 10 of the many thousands of separate nerve fibers connecting a mammalian sense organ with the brain. Trying to learn how information is encoded and reported among all the fibers by following the activity of so few is akin to basing a public opinion poll on one or two interviews. (Following the activity of all the fibers would of course be like sampling public opinion by having the members of the population give their different answers in chorus.) Advances in technique may eventually make it possible to follow the traffic in thousands of fibers; in the meantime much can be learned by studying animals with less profusely innervated sense organs.

With several colleagues and students at Tufts University I have for some time been trying to decode the sensory patterns connecting the ear and central nervous system of certain nocturnal moths that have only two sense cells in each ear. Much of the behavior of these simple invertebrates is built in, not learned, and therefore is quite stereo-typed and stable under experimental conditions. Working with these moths offers another advantage: because they depend on their ears to detect their principal predators, insect-eating bats, we are able to discern in a few cells the nervous mechanisms on which the moth's survival depends.

Insectivorous bats are able to find their prey while flying in complete darkness by emitting a series of ultrasonic cries and locating the direction and distance of sources of echoes. So highly sophisticated is this sonar that it enables the bats to find and capture flying insects smaller than mosquitoes. Some night-flying moths—notably members of the families Noctuidae, Geometridae and Arctiidae—have ears that can detect the bats' ultrasonic cries. When they hear the approach of a bat, these moths take evasive action, abandoning their usual cruising flight to go into sharp dives or erratic loops or to fly at top speed directly away from the source of ultrasound. Asher E. Treat of the College of the City of New York has demonstrated that moths taking evasive action on a bat's approach have a significantly higher chance of survival than those that continue on course.

A moth's ears are located on the sides of the rear part of its thorax and are directed outward and backward into the constriction that separates the thorax and the abdomen [see top illustration on page 40]. Each ear is externally visible as a small cavity, and within the cavity is a transparent eardrum. Behind the eardrum is the tympanic air sac; a fine strand of tissue containing the sensory apparatus extends across the air sac from the center of the eardrum to a skeletal support. Two acoustic cells, known as A cells, are located within this strand. Each A cell sends a fine sensory strand outward to the eardrum and a nerve fiber inward to the skeletal support. The two A fibers pass close to a large nonacoustic cell, the B cell, and are joined by its nerve fiber. The three fibers continue as the tympanic nerve into the central nervous system of the moth. From the two A fibers, then, it is possible—and well within our technical means—to obtain all the information about ultrasound that is transmitted from the moth's ear to its central nervous system.

Nerve impulses in single nerve fibers can be detected as "action potentials," or self-propagating electrical transients, that have a magnitude of a few millivolts and at any one point on the fiber last less than a millisecond. In the moth's A fibers action potentials travel from the sense cells to the central nervous system in less than two milliseconds. Action potentials are normally an all-or-nothing phenomenon; once initiated by the sense cell, they travel to the end of the nerve fiber. They can be detected on the outside of the fiber by means of fine electrodes, and they are displayed as "spikes" on the screen of an oscilloscope.

Tympanic-nerve signals are demonstrated in the following way. A moth, for example the adult insect of one of the common cutworms or armyworms, is immobilized on the stage of a microscope. Some of its muscles are dissected away to expose the tympanic nerves at a point outside the central nervous system. Fine silver hooks are placed under one or both nerves, and the pattern of passing action potentials is observed on the oscilloscope. With moths thus prepared we have spent much time in impromptu outdoor laboratories, where the cries of passing bats provided the necessary stimuli.

In order to make precise measurements we needed a controllable source of ultrasonic pulses for purposes of comparison. Such pulses can be generated by electronic gear to approximate natural bat cries in frequency and duration. The natural cries are frequency-modulated: their frequency drops from about 70 kilocycles per second at the beginning of each cry to some 35 kilocycles at the end. Their duration ranges from one to 10 milliseconds, and they are repeated from 10 to 100 times a second. Our artificial stimulus is a facsimile of an average series of bat cries; it is not frequency-modulated, but such modulation is not detected by the moth's ear. Our sound pulses can be accurately graded in intensity by decibel steps; in the sonic range a decibel is roughly equivalent to the barely noticeable difference to human ears in the intensity of two sounds.

By using electronic apparatus to elicit and follow the responses of the A cells we have been able to define the amount of acoustic information avail-

MOTH EVADED BAT by soaring upward just as the bat closed in to capture it. The bat entered the field at right; the path of its flight is the broad white streak across the photograph. The smaller white streak shows the flight of the moth. A tree is in background. The shutter of the camera was left open as contest began. Illumination came from continuous light source below field.

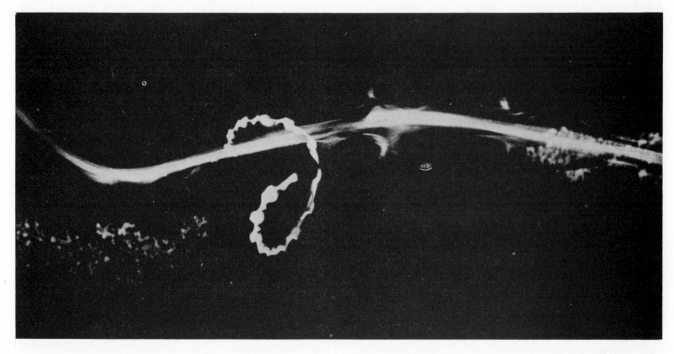

BAT CAPTURED MOTH at point where two white streaks intersect. Small streak shows the flight pattern of the moth. Broad streak shows the flight path of the bat. Both streak photographs were made by Frederic Webster of the Sensory Systems Laboratories.

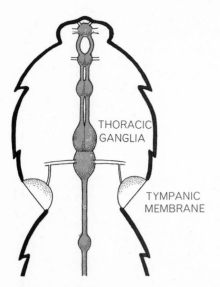

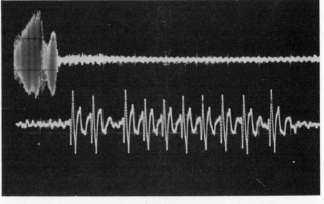

THORACIC GANGLIA

TYMPANIC MEMBRANE

AIR SAC

B FIBER

$A_2$ FIBER

$A_1$ FIBER

TYMPANIC MEMBRANE

**NERVES FROM EAR** to central nervous system of moth are shown at two magnifications. Drawing at left indicates position of the tympanic organs on each side of the moth and the tympanic nerves connecting them with the thoracic ganglia. Central nervous system is colored. Drawing at right shows two nerve fibers of the acoustic cells joined by a nonacoustic fiber to form the tympanic nerve.

able to the moth by way of its tympanic nerve. It appears that the tympanic organ is not particularly sensitive; to elicit any response from the A cell requires ultrasound roughly 100 times more intense than sound that can just be heard by human ears. The ear of a moth can nonetheless pick up at distances of more than 100 feet ultrasonic bat cries we cannot hear at all. The reason it cannot detect frequency modulation is simply that it cannot discriminate one frequency from another; it is tone-deaf. It can, however, detect frequencies from 10 kilocycles to well over 100 kilocycles per second, which covers the range of bat cries. Its greatest talents are the detection of pulsed sound—short bursts of sound with intervening silence—and the discrimination of differences in the loudness of sound pulses.

When the ear of a moth is stimulated by the cry of a bat, real or artificial, spikes indicating the activity of the A cell appear on the oscilloscope in various configurations. As the stimulus increases in intensity several changes are apparent. First, the number of A spikes increases. Second, the time interval between the spikes decreases. Third, the spikes that had first appeared only on the record of one A fiber (the "$A_1$" fiber, which is about 20 decibels more sensitive than the $A_2$ fiber) now appear on the records of both fibers. Fourth, the greater the intensity of the stimulus, the sooner the A cell generates a spike in response.

The moth's ears transmit to the oscilloscope the same configuration of spikes they transmit normally to the central nervous system, and therein lies our interest. Which of the changes in auditory response to an increasingly in-tense stimulus actually serve the moth as criteria for determining its behavior under natural conditions? Before we face up to this question let us speculate on the possible significance of these criteria from the viewpoint of the moth. For the moth to rely on the first kind of information—the number of A spikes—might lead it into a fatal error: the long, faint cry of a bat at a distance could be confused with the short, intense cry of a bat closing for the kill. This error could be avoided if the moth used the second kind of information—the interval between spikes—for estimating the loud-ness of the bat's cry. The third kind of information—the activity of the $A_2$ fiber—might serve to change an "early warn-ing" message to a "take cover" message. The fourth kind of information—the length of time it takes for a spike to be generated—might provide the moth with

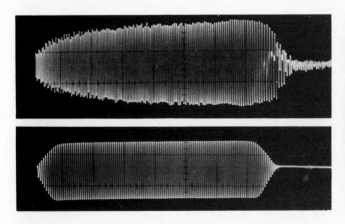

**OSCILLOSCOPE TRACES** of a real bat cry (*top*) and a pulse of sound generated electronically (*bottom*) are compared. The two ultrasonic pulses are of equal duration (length), 2.5 milliseconds, but differ in that the artificial pulse has a uniform frequency.

**BAT CRY AND MOTH RESPONSE** were traced on same oscillo-scope from tape recording by Webster. The bat cry, detected by microphone, yielded the pattern at left in top trace. Reaction of the moth's acoustic cells produced the row of spikes at bottom.

the means for locating a cruising bat; for example, if the sound was louder in the moth's left ear than in its right, then *A* spikes would reach the left side of the central nervous system a fraction of a millisecond sooner than the right side.

Speculations of this sort are profitable only if they suggest experiments to prove or disprove them. Our tympanic-nerve studies led to field experiments designed to find out what moths do when they are exposed to batlike sounds from a loudspeaker. In the first such study moths were tracked by streak photography, a technique in which the shutter of a camera is left open as the subject passes by. As free-flying moths approached the area on which our camera was trained they were exposed to a series of ultrasonic pulses.

More than 1,000 tracks were recorded in this way. The moths were of many species; since they were free and going about their natural affairs most of them could not be captured and identified. This was an unavoidable disadvantage; earlier observations of moths captured, identified and then released in an enclosure revealed nothing. The moths were apparently "flying scared" from the beginning, and the ultrasound did not affect their behavior. Hence all comers were tracked in the field.

Because moths of some families lack ears, a certain percentage of the moths failed to react to the loudspeaker. The variety of maneuvers among the moths that did react was quite unpredictable and bewildering [*see illustrations at top of next page*]. Since the evasive behavior presumably evolved for the purpose of bewildering bats, it is hardly surprising that another mammal should find it confusing! The moths that flew close to the loudspeaker and encountered high-intensity ultrasound would maneuver toward the ground either by dropping passively with their wings closed, by power dives, by vertical and horizontal turns and loops or by various combinations of these evasive movements.

One important finding of this field work was that moths cruising at some distance from the loudspeaker would turn and fly at high speed directly away from it. This happened only if the sound the moths encountered was of low intensity. Moths closer to the loudspeaker could be induced to flee only if the signal was made weaker. Moths at about the height of the loudspeaker flew away in the horizontal plane; those above the loudspeaker were observed to turn directly upward

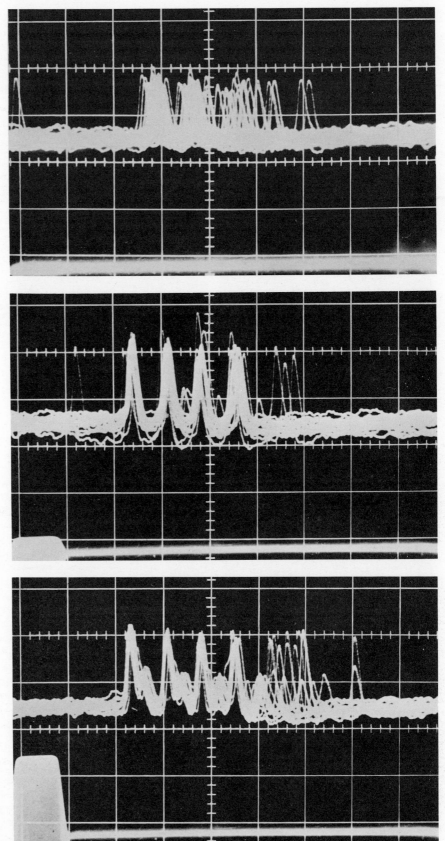

**CHANGES ARE REPORTED** by moth's tympanic nerve to the oscilloscope as pulses used to simulate bat cries gain intensity. Pulses (*lower trace in each frame*) were at five decibels (*top frame*), 20 (*middle*) and 35 (*bottom*). An increased number of tall spikes appear as intensity of stimulus rises. The time interval between spikes decreases slightly. Smaller spikes from the less sensitive nerve fiber appear at the higher intensities, and the higher the intensity of the stimulus, the sooner (*left on horizontal axis*) the first spike appears.

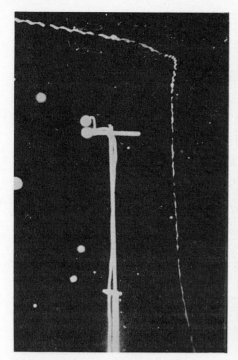

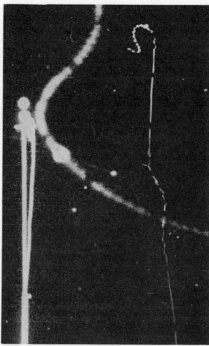

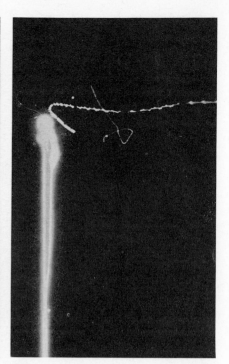

POWER DIVE is taken by moth on hearing simulated bat cry from loudspeaker mounted on thin tower (*left of moth's flight path*).

PASSIVE DROP was executed by another moth, which simply folded its wings. Blur at left and dots were made by other insects.

TURNING AWAY, an evasive action involving directional change, is illustrated. These streak photographs were made by author.

or at other sharp angles. To make such directional responses with only four sensory cells is quite a feat. A horizontal response could be explained on the basis that one ear of the moth detected the sound a bit earlier than the other. It is harder to account for a vertical response, although experiments I shall describe provide a hint.

Our second series of field experiments was conducted in another outdoor laboratory—my backyard. They were designed to determine which of the criteria of intensity encoded in the pattern of A-fiber spikes play an important part in determining evasive behavior. The percentage of moths showing "no re-

action," "diving," "looping" and "turning away" was noted when a 50-kilocycle signal was pulsed at different rates and when it was produced as a continuous tone. The continuous tone delivers more A impulses in a given fraction of a second and therefore should be a more effective stimulus if the number of A impulses is important. On the other hand, because the A cells, like many other sensory cells, become progressively less sensitive with continued stimulation, the interspike interval lengthens rapidly as continuous-tone stimulation proceeds. When the sound is pulsed, the interspike interval remains short because the A cells have had time to regain their sensitivity during the

brief "off" periods. If the spike-generation time—which is associated with difference in the time at which the A spike arrives at the nerve centers for each ear—plays an important part in evasive behavior, then continuous tones should be less effective. The difference in arrival time would be detected only once at the beginning of the stimulus; with pulsed sound it would be reiterated with each pulse.

The second series of experiments occupied many lovely but mosquito-ridden summer nights in my garden and provided many thousands of observations. Tabulation of the figures showed that continuous ultrasonic tones were much less effective in producing evasive

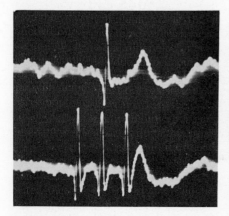

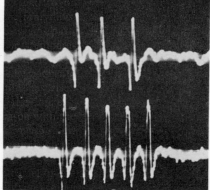

RESPONSE BY BOTH EARS of a moth to an approaching bat was recorded on the oscilloscope and photographed by the author. In trace at left the tympanic nerve from one ear transmits only one spike (*upper curve*) while the nerve from the other ear sends three. As the bat advances, the ratio becomes three to five (*middle*), then 10 to 10 (*right*), suggesting that the bat has flown overhead.

behavior than pulses. The number of nonreacting moths increased threefold, diving occurred only at higher sound intensities and turning away was essentially absent. Only looping seemed to increase slightly.

Ultrasound pulsed between 10 and 30 times a second proved to be more effective than ultrasound pulsed at higher or lower rates. This suggests that diving, and possibly other forms of nondirectional evasive behavior, are triggered in the moth's central nervous system not so much by the number of $A$ impulses delivered over a given period as by short intervals (less than 2.5 milliseconds) between consecutive $A$ impulses. Turning away from the sound source when it is operating at low intensity levels seems to be set off by the reiterated difference in arrival time of the first $A$ impulse in the right and left tympanic nerves.

These conclusions were broad but left unanswered the question: How can a moth equipped only with four $A$ cells orient itself with respect to a sound source in planes that are both vertical and horizontal to its body axis? The search for an answer was undertaken by Roger Payne of Tufts University, assisted by Joshua Wallman, a Harvard undergraduate. They set out to plot the directional capacities of the tympanic organ by moving a loudspeaker at various angles with respect to a captive moth's body axis and registering (through the $A_1$ fiber) the organ's relative sensitivity to ultrasonic pulses coming from various directions. They took precautions to control acoustic shadows and reflections by mounting the moth and the recording electrodes on a thin steel tower in the center of an echo-free chamber; the effect of the moth's wings on the reception of sound was tested by systematically changing their position during the course of many experiments. A small loudspeaker emitted ultrasonic pulses 10 times a second at a distance of one meter. These sounds were presented to the moths from 36 latitude lines 10 degrees apart.

The response of the $A$ fibers to the ultrasonic pulses was continuously recorded as the loudspeaker was moved. At the same time the intensity of ultrasound emitted by the loudspeaker was regulated so that at any angle it gave rise to the same response. Thus the intensity of the sound pulses was a measure of the moth's acoustic sensitivity. A pen recorder continuously graphed the changing intensity of the ultrasonic pulses against the angle from which

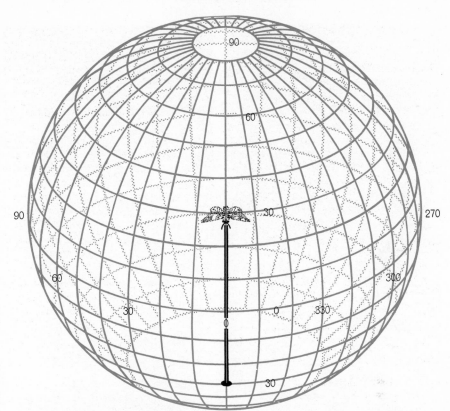

**SPHERE OF SENSITIVITY,** the range in which a moth with wings in a given position can hear ultrasound coming from various angles, was the subject of a study by Roger Payne of Tufts University and Joshua Wallman, a Harvard undergraduate. Moths with wings in given positions were mounted on a tower in an echo-free chamber. Data were compiled on the moths' sensitivity to ultrasound presented from 36 latitude lines 10 degrees apart.

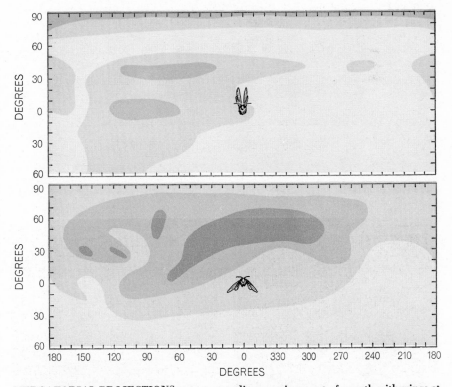

**MERCATORIAL PROJECTIONS** represent auditory environment of a moth with wings at end of upstroke (*top*) and near end of downstroke (*bottom*). Vertical scale shows rotation of loudspeaker around moth's body in vertical plane; horizontal scale shows rotation in horizontal plane. At top the loudspeaker is above moth; at far right and left, behind it. In Mercatorial projections, distortions are greatest at poles. The lighter the shading at a given angle of incidence, the more sensitive the moth to sound from that angle.

they were presented to the moth. Each chart provided a profile of sensitivity in a certain plane, and the data from it were assembled with those from others to provide a "sphere of sensitivity" for the moth at a given wing position.

This ingenious method made it possible to assemble a large amount of data in a short time. In the case of one moth it was possible to obtain the data for nine spheres of sensitivity (about 5,000 readings), each at a different wing position, before the tympanic nerve of the moth finally stopped transmitting impulses. Two of these spheres, taken from one moth at different wing positions, are presented as Mercatorial projections in the bottom illustration on the preceding page.

It is likely that much of the information contained in the fine detail of such projections is disregarded by a moth flapping its way through the night. Certain general patterns do seem related, however, to the moth's ability to escape a marauding bat. For instance, when the moth's wings are in the upper half of their beat, its acoustic sensitivity is 100 times less at a given point on its side facing away from the source of the sound than at the corresponding point on the side facing toward the source. When flight movements bring the wings below the horizontal plane, sound coming from each side above the moth is in acoustic shadow, and the left-right acoustic asymmetry largely disappears. Moths commonly flap their wings from 30 to 40 times a second. Therefore left-right acoustic asymmetry must alternate with up-down asymmetry at this frequency. A left-right difference in the A-fiber discharge when the wings are up might give the moth a rough horizontal bearing on the position of a bat with respect to its own line of flight. The absence of a left-right difference and the presence of a similar fluctuation in both left and right tympanic nerves at wingbeat frequency might inform the moth that the bat was above it. If neither variation occurred at the regular wingbeat frequency, it would mean that the bat was below or behind the moth.

This analysis uses terms of precise directionality that idealize the natural situation. A moth certainly does not zoom along on an even keel and a straight course like an airliner. Its flapping progress—even when no threat is imminent—is marked by minor yawing and pitching; its overall course is rare-

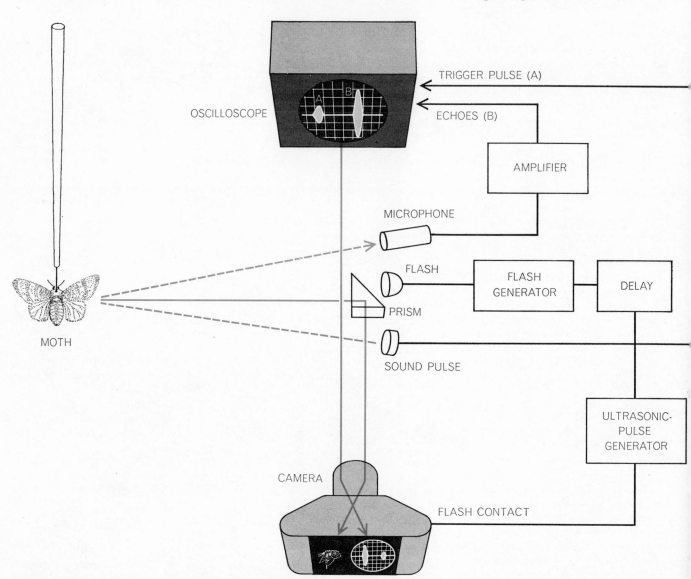

ARTIFICIAL BAT, the electronic device depicted schematically at right, was built by the author to determine at what position with respect to a bat a moth casts its greatest echo. As a moth supported by a wire flapped its wings in stationary flight, a film was made by means of a prism of its motions and of an oscilloscope that showed the pulse generated by the loudspeaker and the echo picked up by the microphone. Each frame of film thus resembled the composite picture of moth and two pulses shown inverted at bottom.

ly straight and commonly consists of large loops and figure eights. Even so, the localization experiments of Payne and Wallman suggest the ways in which a moth receives information that enables it to orient itself in three dimensions with respect to the source of an ultrasonic pulse.

The ability of a moth to perceive and react to a bat is not greatly superior or inferior to the ability of a bat to perceive and react to a moth. Proof of this lies in the evolutionary equality of their natural contest and in the observation of a number of bat-moth confrontations. Donald R. Griffin of Harvard University and Frederic Webster of the Sensory Systems Laboratories have studied in detail the almost unbelievable ability of bats to locate, track and intercept

small flying targets, all on the basis of a string of echoes thrown back from ultrasonic cries. Speaking acoustically, what does a moth "look like" to a bat? Does the prey cast different echoes under different circumstances?

To answer this question I set up a crude artificial bat to pick up echoes from a live moth. The moth was attached to a wire support and induced to flap its wings in stationary flight. A movie camera was pointed at a prism so that half of each frame of film showed an image of the moth and the other half the screen of an oscilloscope. Mounted closely around the prism and directed at the moth from one meter away were a stroboscopic-flash lamp, an ultrasonic loudspeaker and a microphone. Each time the camera shutter opened and exposed a frame of film a

short ultrasonic pulse was sent out by the loudspeaker and the oscilloscope began its sweep. The flash lamp was controlled through a delay circuit to go off the instant the ultrasonic pulse hit the moth, whose visible attitude was thereby frozen on the film. Meanwhile the echo thrown back by the moth while it was in this attitude was picked up by the microphone and finally displayed as a pulse of a certain height on the oscilloscope. All this took place before the camera shutter closed and the film moved on to the next frame. Thus each frame shows the optical and acoustic profiles of the moth from approximately the same angle and at the same instant of its flight. The camera was run at speeds close to the wingbeat frequency of the moth, so that the resulting film presents a regular series of wing positions and the echoes cast by them.

Films made of the same moth flying at different angles to the camera and the sound source show that by far the strongest echo is returned when the moth's wings are at right angles to the recording array [see illustrations at left]. The echo from a moth with its wings in this position is perhaps 100 times stronger than one from a moth with its wings at other angles. Apparently if a bat and a moth were flying horizontal courses at the same altitude, the moth would be in greatest danger of detection if it crossed the path of the approaching bat at right angles. From the bat's viewpoint at this instant the moth must appear to flicker acoustically at its wingbeat frequency. Since the rate at which the bat emits its ultrasonic cries is independent of the moth's wingbeat frequency, the actual sequence of echoes the bat receives must be complicated by the interaction of the two frequencies. Perhaps this enables the bat to discriminate a flapping target, likely to be prey, from inert objects floating in its acoustic field.

The moth has one advantage over the bat: it can detect the bat at a greater range than the bat can detect it. The bat, however, has the advantage of greater speed. This creates a nice problem for a moth that has picked up a bat's cries. If a moth immediately turns and flies directly away from a source of ultrasound, it has a good chance of disappearing from the sonar system of a still-distant bat. If the bat has also detected the moth, and is near enough to receive a continuous signal from its target, turning away on a straight course is a bad tactic because the moth is not likely to outdistance its pursuer. It is then to the moth's advantage to

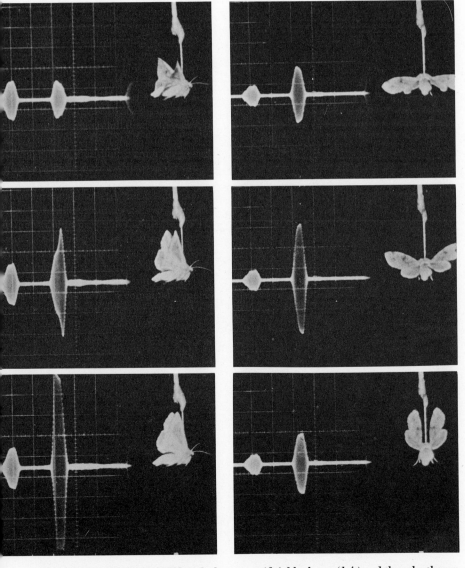

COMPOSITE PHOTOGRAPHS each show an artificial bat's cry (*left*) and the echo thrown back (*middle*) by a moth (*right*). The series of photographs at left is of a moth in stationary flight at right angles to the artificial bat. Those at right are of a moth oriented in flight parallel to the bat. The echo produced in the series of photographs at left is much the larger.

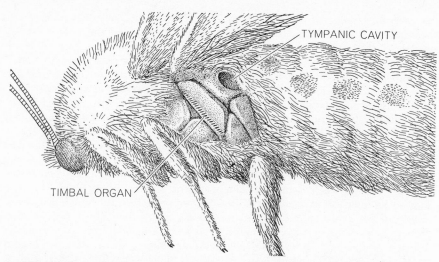

TYMPANIC CAVITY

TIMBAL ORGAN

**NOISEMAKING ORGAN** possessed by many moths of the family Arctiidae and of other families is a row of fine parallel ridges of cuticle that bend and unbend when a leg muscle contracts and relaxes. This produces a rapid sequence of high-pitched clicks.

go into tight turns, loops and dives, some of which may even take it toward the bat.

In this contest of hide-and-seek it seems much to a moth's advantage to remain as quiet as possible. The sensitive ears of a bat would soon locate a noisy target. It is therefore surprising to find that many members of the moth family Arctiidae (which includes the moths whose caterpillars are known as woolly bears) are capable of generating trains of ultrasonic clicks. David Blest and David Pye of University College London have demonstrated the working of the organ that arctiids use for this purpose.

In noisemaking arctiids the basal joint of the third pair of legs (which roughly corresponds to the hip) bulges outward and overlies an air-filled cavi-

ty. The stiff cuticle of this region has a series of fine parallel ridges [see illustration above]. Each ridge serves as a timbal that works rather like the familiar toy incorporating a thin strip of spring steel that clicks when it is pressed by the thumb. When one of the moth's leg muscles contracts and relaxes in rapid sequence, it bends and unbends the overlying cuticle, causing the row of timbals to produce rapid sequences of high-pitched clicks. Blest and Pye found that such moths would click when they were handled or poked, that the clicks occurred in short bursts of 1,000 or more per second and that each click contained ultrasonic frequencies within the range of hearing of bats.

My colleagues and I found that certain arctiids common in New England could also be induced to click if they were exposed to a string of ultrasonic

pulses while they were suspended in stationary flight. In free flight these moths showed the evasive tactics I have already described. The clicking seems almost equivalent to telling the bat, "Here I am, come and get me." Since such altruism is not characteristic of the relation between predators and prey, there must be another answer.

Dorothy C. Dunning, a graduate student at Tufts, is at present trying to find it. She has already shown that partly tamed bats, trained to catch mealworms that are tossed into the air by a mechanical device, will commonly swerve away from their target if they hear tape-recorded arctiid clicks just before the moment of contact. Other ultrasounds, such as tape-recorded bat cries and "white" noise (noise of all frequencies), have relatively little effect on the bats' feeding behavior; the tossed mealworms are caught in midair and eaten. Thus the clicks made by arctiids seem to be heeded by bats as a warning rather than as an invitation. But a warning against what?

One of the pleasant things about scientific investigation is that the last logbook entry always ends with a question. In fact, the questions proliferate more rapidly than the answers and often carry one along unexpected paths. I suggested at the beginning of this article that it is my intention to trace the nervous mechanisms involved in the evasive behavior of moths. By defining the information conveyed by the acoustic cells I have only solved the least complex half of that broad problem. As I embark on the second half of the investigation, I hope it will lead up as many diverting side alleys as the study of the moth's acoustic system has.

# 7 Electric Location by Fishes

H. W. LISSMANN · March 1963

Study of the ingenious adaptations displayed in the anatomy, physiology and behavior of animals leads to the familiar conclusion that each has evolved to suit life in its particular corner of the world. It is well to bear in mind, however, that each animal also inhabits a private subjective world that is not accessible to direct observation. This world is made up of information communicated to the creature from the outside in the form of messages picked up by its sense organs. No adaptation is more crucial to survival; the environment changes from place to place and from moment to moment, and the animal must respond appropriately in every place and at every moment. The sense organs transform energy of various kinds—heat and light, mechanical energy and chemical energy—into nerve impulses. Because the human organism is sensitive to the same kinds of energy, man can to some extent visualize the world as it appears to other living things. It helps in considering the behavior of a dog, for example, to realize that it can see less well than a man but can hear and smell better. There are limits to this procedure; ultimately the dog's sensory messages are projected onto its brain and are there evaluated differently.

Some animals present more serious obstacles to understanding. As I sit writing at my desk I face a large aquarium that contains an elegant fish about 20 inches long. It has no popular name but is known to science as *Gymnarchus niloticus*. This same fish has been facing me for the past 12 years, ever since I brought it from Africa. By observation and experiment I have tried to understand its behavior in response to stimuli from its environment. I am now convinced that *Gymnarchus* lives in a world totally alien to man: its most important

sense is an electric one, different from any we possess.

From time to time over the past century investigators have examined and dissected this curious animal. The literature describes its locomotive apparatus, central nervous system, skin and electric organs, its habitat and its family relation to the "elephant-trunk fishes," or mormyrids, of Africa. But the parts have not been fitted together into a functional pattern, comprehending the design of the animal as a whole and the history of its development. In this line of biological research one must resist the temptation to be deflected by details, to follow the fashion of putting the pieces too early under the electron microscope. The magnitude of a scientific revelation is not always paralleled by the degree of magnification employed. It is easier to select the points on which attention should be concentrated once the plan is understood. In the case of *Gymnarchus,* I think, this can now be attempted.

A casual observer is at once impressed by the grace with which *Gymnarchus* swims. It does not lash its tail from side to side, as most other fishes do, but keeps its spine straight. A beautiful undulating fin along its back propels its body through the water—forward or backward with equal ease. *Gymnarchus* can maintain its rigid posture even when turning, with complex wave forms running hither and thither over different regions of the dorsal fin at one and the same time.

Closer observation leaves no doubt that the movements are executed with great precision. When *Gymnarchus* darts after the small fish on which it feeds, it never bumps into the walls of its tank, and it clearly takes evasive action at some distance from obstacles placed in

its aquarium. Such maneuvers are not surprising in a fish swimming forward, but *Gymnarchus* performs them equally well swimming backward. As a matter of fact it should be handicapped even when it is moving forward: its rather degenerate eyes seem to react only to excessively bright light.

Still another unusual aspect of this fish and, it turns out, the key to all the puzzles it poses, is its tail, a slender, pointed process bare of any fin ("gymnarchus" means "naked tail"). The tail was first dissected by Michael Pius Erdl of the University of Munich in 1847. He found tissue resembling a small electric organ, consisting of four thin spindles running up each side to somewhere beyond the middle of the body. Electric organs constructed rather differently, once thought to be "pseudoelectric," are also found at the hind end of the related mormyrids.

Such small electric organs have been an enigma for a long time. Like the powerful electric organs of electric eels and some other fishes, they are derived from muscle tissue. Apparently in the course of evolution the tissue lost its power to contract and became specialized in various ways to produce electric discharges [see "Electric Fishes," by Harry Grundfest; SCIENTIFIC AMERICAN, October, 1960]. In the strongly electric fishes this adaptation serves to deter predators and to paralyze prey. But the powerful electric organs must have evolved from weak ones. The original swimming muscles would therefore seem to have possessed or have acquired at some stage a subsidiary electric function that had survival value. Until recently no one had found a function for weak electric organs. This was one of the questions on my mind when I began to study *Gymnarchus*.

I noticed quite early, when I placed a

ELECTRIC FISH *Gymnarchus niloticus,* from Africa, generates weak discharges that enable it to detect objects. In this sequence the fish catches a smaller fish. *Gymnarchus* takes its name, which means "naked tail," from the fact that its pointed tail has no fin.

new object in the aquarium of a well-established *Gymnarchus*, that the fish would approach it with some caution, making what appeared to be exploratory movements with the tip of its tail. It occurred to me that the supposed electric organ in the tail might be a detecting mechanism. Accordingly I put into the water a pair of electrodes, connected to an amplifier and an oscilloscope. The result was a surprise. I had expected to find sporadic discharges co-ordinated with the swimming or exploratory motions of the animal. Instead the apparatus recorded a continuous stream of electric discharges at a constant frequency of about 300 per second, waxing and waning in amplitude as the fish changed position in relation to the stationary electrodes. Even when the fish was completely motionless, the electric activity remained unchanged.

This was the first electric fish found to behave in such a manner. After a brief search I discovered two other kinds that emit an uninterrupted stream of weak discharges. One is a mormyrid relative of *Gymnarchus;* the other is a gymnotid, a small, fresh-water South American relative of the electric eel, belonging to a group of fish rather far removed from *Gymnarchus* and the mormyrids.

It had been known for some time that the electric eel generates not only strong discharges but also irregular series of weaker discharges. Various functions had been ascribed to these weak discharges of the eel. Christopher W. Coates, director of the New York Aquarium, had suggested that they might serve in navigation, postulating that the eel somehow measured the time delay between the output of a pulse and its reflection from an object. This idea was untenable on physical as well as physiological grounds. The eel does not, in the first place, produce electromagnetic waves; if it did, they would travel too fast to be timed at the close range at which such a mechanism might be useful, and in any case they would hardly penetrate water. Electric current, which the eel does produce, is not reflected from objects in the surrounding environment.

Observation of *Gymnarchus* suggested another mechanism. During each discharge the tip of its tail becomes momentarily negative with respect to the head. The electric current may thus be pictured as spreading out into the surrounding water in the pattern of lines that describes a dipole field [*see illustration on the next page*]. The exact configuration of this electric field depends on the conductivity of the water and on the distortions introduced in the field by objects with electrical conductivity different from that of the water. In a large volume of water containing no objects the field is symmetrical. When objects are present, the lines of current will converge on those that have better conductivity and diverge from the poor conductors [*see top illustration on page 51*]. Such objects alter the distribution of electric potential over the surface of the fish. If the fish could register these changes, it would have a means of detecting the objects.

Calculations showed that *Gymnarchus* would have to be much more sensitive electrically than any fish was known to be if this mechanism were to work. I had observed, however, that *Gymnarchus* was sensitive to extremely small external electrical disturbances. It responded violently when a small magnet or an electrified insulator (such as a comb that had just been drawn through a person's hair) was moved near the aquarium. The electric fields produced in the water by such objects must be very small indeed, in the range of fractions of a millionth of one volt per centimeter. This crude observation was enough to justify a series of experiments under more stringent conditions.

In the most significant of these experiments Kenneth E. Machin and I trained the fish to distinguish between objects that could be recognized only by an electric sense. These were enclosed in porous ceramic pots or tubes with thick walls. When they were soaked in water, the ceramic material alone had little effect on the shape of the electric field. The pots excluded the possibility of discrimination by vision or, because each test lasted only a short time, by a chemical sense such as taste or smell.

The fish quickly learned to choose between two pots when one contained aquarium water or tap water and the other paraffin wax (a nonconductor). After training, the fish came regularly to pick a piece of food from a thread suspended behind a pot filled with aquarium or tap water and ignored the pot filled with wax [*see bottom illustration on page 51*]. Without further conditioning it also avoided pots filled with air, with distilled water, with a close-fitting glass tube or with another nonconductor. On the other hand, when the electrical conductivity of the distilled water was matched to that of tap or aquarium water by the addition of salts or acids, the fish would go to the pot for food.

A more prolonged series of trials showed that *Gymnarchus* could distinguish mixtures in different proportions of tap water and distilled water and perform other remarkable feats of discrimination. The limits of this performance can best be illustrated by the fact that the fish could detect the presence of a glass rod two millimeters in diameter and would fail to respond to a glass rod .8 millimeter in diameter, each hidden in a

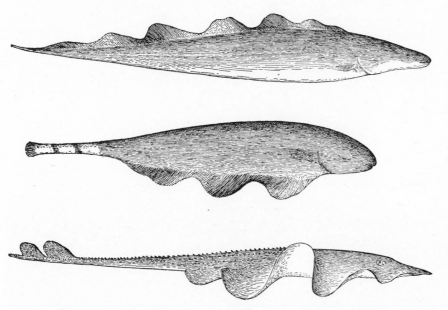

UNUSUAL FINS characterize *Gymnarchus* (*top*), a gymnotid from South America (*middle*) and sea-dwelling skate (*bottom*). All swim with spine rigid, probably in order to keep electric generating and detecting organs aligned. *Gymnarchus* is propelled by undulating dorsal fin, gymnotid by similar fin underneath and skate by lateral fins resembling wings.

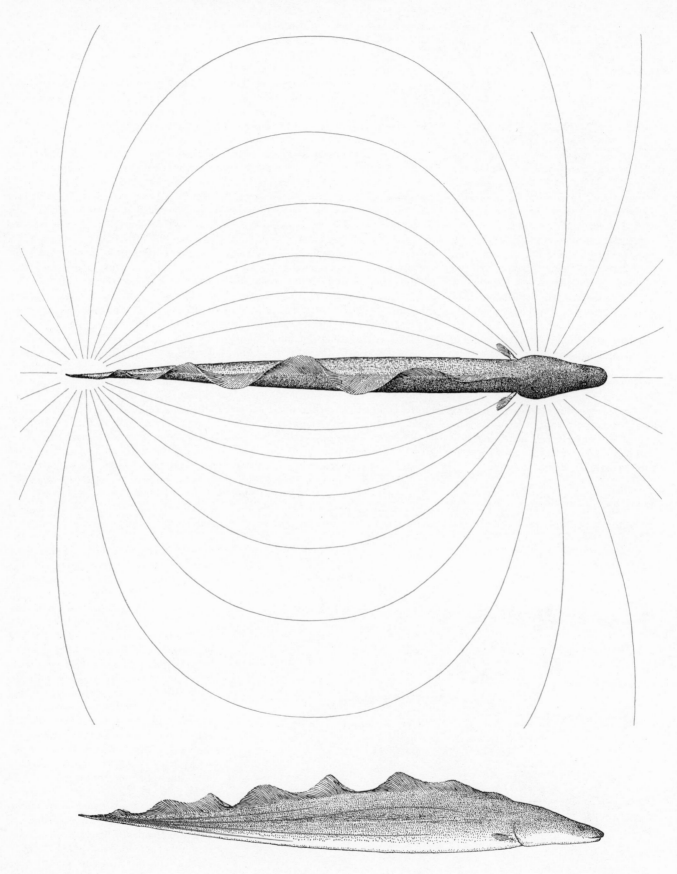

**ELECTRIC FIELD** of *Gymnarchus* and location of electric generating organs are diagramed. Each electric discharge from organs in rear portion of body (*color in side view*) makes tail negative with respect to head. Most of the electric sensory pores or organs are in head region. Undisturbed electric field resembles a dipole field, as shown, but is more complex. The fish responds to changes in the distribution of electric potential over the surface of its body. The conductivity of objects affects distribution of potential.

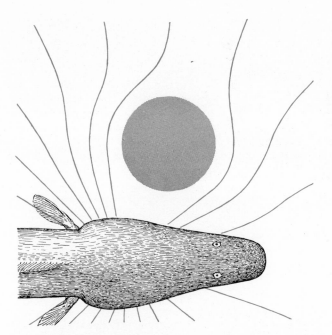
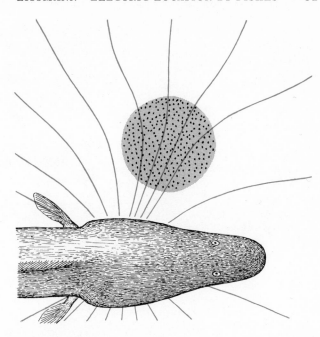

OBJECTS IN ELECTRIC FIELD of *Gymnarchus* distort the lines of current flow. The lines diverge from a poor conductor (*left*) and converge toward a good conductor (*right*). Sensory pores in the head region detect the effect and inform the fish about the object.

pot of the same dimensions. The threshold of its electric sense must lie somewhere between these two values.

These experiments seemed to establish beyond reasonable doubt that *Gymnarchus* detects objects by an electrical mechanism. The next step was to seek the possible channels through which the electrical information may reach the brain. It is generally accepted that the tissues and fluids of a fresh-water fish are relatively good electrical conductors enclosed in a skin that conducts poorly. The skin of *Gymnarchus* and of many mormyrids is exceptionally thick, with layers of platelike cells sometimes arrayed in a remarkable hexagonal pattern [*see top illustration on page 54*]. It can therefore be assumed that natural selection has provided these fishes with better-than-average exterior insulation.

In some places, particularly on and around the head, the skin is closely perforated. The pores lead into tubes often filled with a jelly-like substance or a loose aggregation of cells. If this jelly is a good electrical conductor, the arrangement would suggest that the lines of electric current from the water into the body of the fish are made to converge at these pores, as if focused by a lens. Each jelly-filled tube widens at the base into

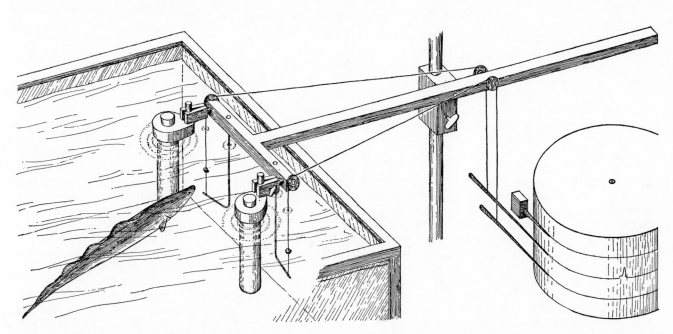

EXPERIMENTAL ARRANGEMENT for conditioned-reflex training of *Gymnarchus* includes two porous pots or tubes and recording mechanism. The fish learns to discriminate between objects of different electrical conductivity placed in the pots and to seek bait tied to string behind the pot holding the object that conducts best. *Gymnarchus* displays a remarkable ability to discriminate.

a small round capsule that contains a group of cells long known to histologists by such names as "multicellular glands," "mormyromasts" and "snout organs." These, I believe, are the electric sense organs.

The supporting evidence appears fairly strong: The structures in the capsule at the base of a tube receive sensory nerve fibers that unite to form the stoutest of all the nerves leading into the brain. Electrical recording of the impulse traffic in such nerves has shown that they lead away from organs highly sensitive to electric stimuli. The brain centers into which these nerves run are remarkably large and complex in *Gymnarchus*, and in some mormyrids they completely cover the remaining portions of the brain [*see illustration on next page*].

If this evidence for the plan as well as the existence of an electric sense does not seem sufficiently persuasive, corroboration is supplied by other weakly electric fishes. Except for the electric eel, all species of gymnotids investigated so far emit continuous electric pulses. They are also highly sensitive to electric fields. Dissection of these fishes reveals the expected histological counterparts of the structures found in the mormyrids: similar sense organs embedded in a similar skin, and the corresponding regions of the brain much enlarged.

Skates also have a weak electric organ in the tail. They are cartilaginous fishes, not bony fishes, or teleosts, as are the mormyrids and gymnotids. This means that they are far removed on the family line. Moreover, they live in the sea, which conducts electricity much better than fresh water does. It is almost too much to expect structural resemblances to the fresh-water bony fishes, or an electrical mechanism operating along similar lines. Yet skates possess sense organs, known as the ampullae of Lorenzini, that consist of long jelly-filled tubes opening to the water at one end and terminating in a sensory vesicle at the other. Recently Richard W. Murray of the University of Birmingham has found that these organs respond to very delicate electrical stimulation. Unfortunately, either skates are rather uncooperative animals or we have not mastered the trick of training them; we have been unable to repeat with them the experiments in discrimination in which *Gymnarchus* performs so well.

*Gymnarchus*, the gymnotids and skates all share one obvious feature: they swim in an unusual way. *Gymnarchus* swims with the aid of a fin on its back; the gymnotids have a similar fin on their

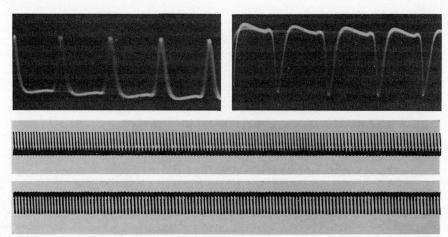

ELECTRIC DISCHARGES of *Gymnarchus* show reversal of polarity when detecting electrodes are rotated 180 degrees (*enlarged records at top*). The discharges, at rate of 300 per second, are remarkably regular even when fish is resting, as seen in lower records.

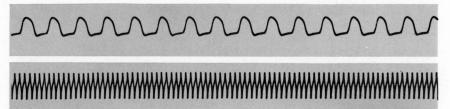

DISCHARGE RATES DIFFER in different species of gymnotids. *Sternopygus macrurus* (*upper record*) has rate of 55 per second; *Eigenmannia virescens* (*lower*), 300 per second.

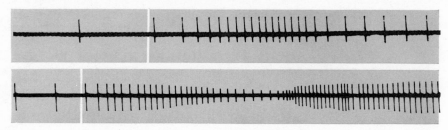

VARIABLE DISCHARGE RATE is seen in some species. Tap on tank (*white line in upper record*) caused mormyrid to increase rate. Tap on fish (*lower record*) had greater effect.

underside; skates swim with pectoral fins stuck out sideways like wings [*see illustration on page 49*]. They all keep the spine rigid as they move. It would be rash to suggest that such deviations from the basic fish plan could be attributed to an accident of nature. In biology it always seems safer to assume that any redesign has arisen for some reason, even if the reason obstinately eludes the investigator. Since few fishes swim in this way or have electric organs, and since the fishes that combine these features are not related, a mere coincidence would appear most unlikely.

A good reason for the rigid swimming posture emerged when we built a model to simulate the discharge mecha-

nism and the sensory-perception system. We placed a pair of electrodes in a large tank of water; to represent the electric organ they were made to emit repetitive electric pulses. A second pair of electrodes, representing the electric sense organ, was placed some distance away to pick up the pulses. We rotated the second pair of electrodes until they were on a line of equipotential, where they ceased to record signals from the sending electrodes. With all the electrodes clamped in this position, we showed that the introduction of either a conductor or a nonconductor into the electric field could cause sufficient distortion of the field for the signals to reappear in the detectors.

In a prolonged series of readings the

slightest displacement of either pair of electrodes would produce great variations in the received signal. These could be smoothed to some extent by recording not the change of potential but the change in the potential gradient over the "surface" of our model fish. It is probable that the real fish uses this principle, but to make it work the electrode system must be kept more or less constantly aligned. Even though a few cubic centimeters of fish brain may in some respects put many electronic computers in the shade, the fish brain might be unable to obtain any sensible information if the fish's electrodes were to be misaligned by the tail-thrashing that propels an ordinary fish. A mode of swimming that keeps the electric field symmetrical with respect to the body most of the time would therefore offer obvious advantages. It seems logical to assume that *Gymnarchus*, or its ancestors, acquired the rigid mode of swimming along with the electric sensory apparatus and subsequently lost the broad, oarlike tail fin.

Our experiments with models also showed that objects could be detected only at a relatively short distance, in spite of high amplification in the receiving system. As an object was moved farther and farther away, a point was soon reached where the signals arriving at the oscilloscope became submerged in the general "noise" inherent in every detector system. Now, it is known that minute amounts of energy can stimulate a sense organ: one quantum of light registers on a visual sense cell; vibrations of subatomic dimensions excite the ear; a single molecule in a chemical sense organ can produce a sensation, and so on. Just how such small external signals can be picked out from the general noise in and around a metabolizing cell represents one of the central questions of sensory physiology. Considered in connection with the electric sense of fishes, this question is complicated further by the high frequency of the discharges from the electric organ that excite the sensory apparatus.

In general, a stimulus from the environment acting on a sense organ produces a sequence of repetitive impulses in the sensory nerve. A decrease in the strength of the stimulus causes a lower frequency of impulses in the nerve. Conversely, as the stimulus grows stronger, the frequency of impulses rises, up to a certain limit. This limit may vary from one sense organ to another, but 500 impulses per second is a common upper limit, although 1,000 per second have been recorded over brief intervals.

In the case of the electric sense organ of a fish the stimulus energy is provided by the discharges of the animal's electric organ. *Gymnarchus* discharges at the rate of 300 pulses per second. A change in the amplitude—not the rate—of these pulses, caused by the presence of an object in the field, constitutes the effective stimulus at the sense organ. Assuming that the reception of a single discharge of small amplitude excites one impulse in a sensory nerve, a discharge of larger amplitude that excited two impulses would probably reach and exceed the upper limit at which the nerve can generate impulses, since the nerve would now be firing 600 times a second (twice the rate of discharge of the electric organ). This would leave no room

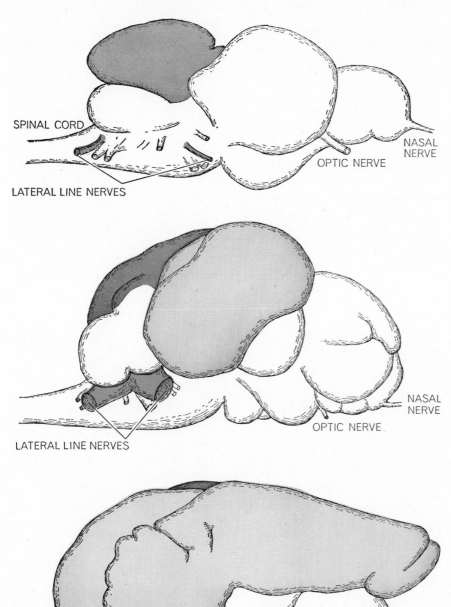

**BRAIN AND NERVE ADAPTATIONS** of electric fish are readily apparent. Brain of typical nonelectric fish (*top*) has prominent cerebellum (*gray*). Regions associated with electric sense (*color*) are quite large in *Gymnarchus* (*middle*) and even larger in the mormyrid (*bottom*). Lateral-line nerves of electric fishes are larger, nerves of nose and eyes smaller.

SPINAL CORD

LATERAL LINE NERVES

OPTIC NERVE

NASAL NERVE

LATERAL LINE NERVES

OPTIC NERVE

NASAL NERVE

LATERAL LINE NERVES

OPTIC NERVE

NASAL NERVE

to convey information about gradual changes in the amplitude of incoming stimuli. Moreover, the electric organs of some gymnotids discharge at a much higher rate; 1,600 impulses per second have been recorded. It therefore appears unlikely that each individual discharge is communicated to the sense organs as a discrete stimulus.

We also hit on the alternative idea that the frequency of impulses from the sensory nerve might be determined by the mean value of electric current transmitted to the sense organ over a unit of time; in other words, that the significant messages from the environment are averaged out and so discriminated from the background of noise. We tested this idea on *Gymnarchus* by applying trains of rectangular electric pulses of varying voltage, duration and frequency across the aquarium. Again using the conditioned-reflex technique, we determined the threshold of perception for the different pulse trains. We found that the fish is in fact as sensitive to high-frequency pulses of short duration as it is to low-frequency pulses of identical voltage but correspondingly longer duration. For any given pulse train, reduction in voltage could be compensated either by an increase in frequency of stimulus or an increase in the duration of the pulse. Conversely, reduction in the frequency required an increase in the voltage or in the duration of the pulse to reach the threshold. The threshold would therefore appear to be determined by the product of voltage times duration times frequency.

Since the frequency and the duration of discharges are fixed by the output of the electric organ, the critical variable at the sensory organ is voltage. Threshold determinations of the fish's response to single pulses, compared with quantitative data on its response to trains of pulses, made it possible to calculate the time over which the fish averages out the necessarily blurred information carried within a single discharge of its own. This time proved to be 25 milliseconds, sufficient for the electric organ to emit seven or eight discharges.

The averaging out of information in this manner is a familiar technique for improving the signal-to-noise ratio; it has been found useful in various branches of technology for dealing with barely perceptible signals. In view of the very low signal energy that *Gymnarchus* can detect, such refinements in information processing, including the ability to average out information picked up by a large number of separate sense organs,

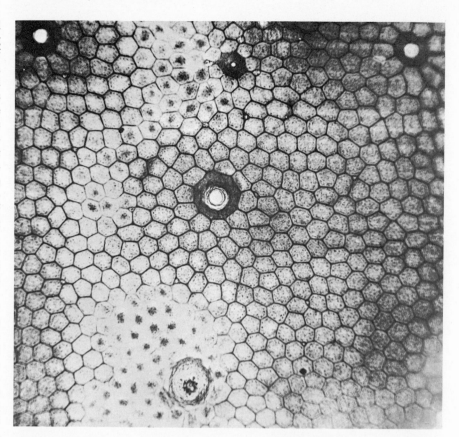

SKIN OF MORMYRID is made up of many layers of platelike cells having remarkable hexagonal structure. The pores contain tubes leading to electric sense organs. This photomicrograph by the author shows a horizontal section through the skin, enlarged 100 diameters.

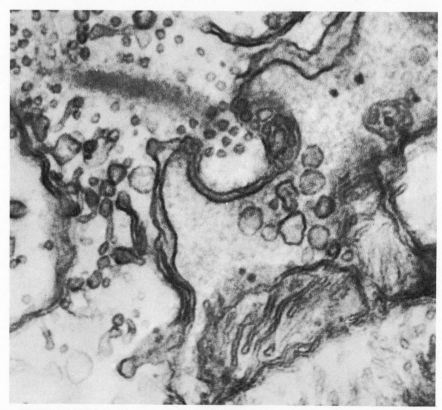

MEETING POINT of electric sensory cell (*left*) and its nerve (*right*) is enlarged 120,000 diameters in this electron micrograph by the author and Ann M. Mullinger. Bulge of sensory cell into nerve ending displays the characteristic dense streak surrounded by vesicles.

appear to be essential. We have found that *Gymnarchus* can respond to a continuous direct-current electric stimulus of about .15 microvolt per centimeter, a value that agrees reasonably well with the calculated sensitivity required to recognize a glass rod two millimeters in diameter. This means that an individual sense organ should be able to convey information about a current change as small as .003 micromicroampere. Extended over the integration time of 25 milliseconds, this tiny current corresponds to a movement of some 1,000 univalent, or singly charged, ions.

The intimate mechanism of the single sensory cell of these organs is still a complete mystery. In structure the sense organs differ somewhat from species to species and different types are also found

in an individual fish. The fine structure of the sensory cells, their nerves and associated elements, which Ann M. Mullinger and I have studied with both the light microscope and the electron microscope, shows many interesting details. Along specialized areas of the boundary between the sensory cell and the nerve fiber there are sites of intimate contact where the sensory cell bulges into the fiber. A dense streak extends from the cell into this bulge, and the vesicles alongside it seem to penetrate the intercellular space. The integrating system of the sensory cell may be here.

These findings, however, apply only to *Gymnarchus* and to about half of the species of gymnotids investigated to date. The electric organs of these fishes emit pulses of constant frequency. In the other gymnotids and all the mormyrids the discharge frequency changes with the state of excitation of the fish. There is therefore no constant mean value of current transmitted in a unit of time; the integration of information in these species may perhaps be carried out in the brain. Nevertheless, it is interesting that both types of sensory system should have evolved independently in the two different families, one in Africa and one in South America.

The experiments with *Gymnarchus*, which indicate that no information is carried by the pulse nature of the discharges, leave us with a still unsolved problem. If the pulses are "smoothed out," it is difficult to see how any one fish can receive information in its own frequency range without interference from its neighbors. In this connection Akira Watanabe and Kimihisa Takeda at the University of Tokyo have made the potentially significant finding that the gymnotids respond to electric oscillations close in frequency to their own by shifting their frequency away from the applied frequency. Two fish might thus react to each other's presence.

For reasons that are perhaps associated with the evolutionary origin of their electric sense, the electric fishes are elusive subjects for study in the field. I have visited Africa and South America in order to observe them in their natural habitat. Although some respectable specimens were caught, it was only on rare occasions that I actually saw a *Gymnarchus*, a mormyrid or a gymnotid in the turbid waters in which they live. While such waters must have favored the evolution of an electric sense, it could not have been the only factor. The same waters contain a large number of

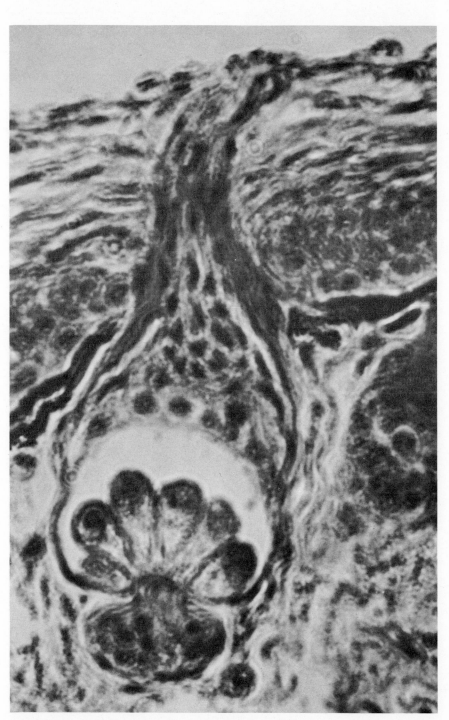

**VERTICAL SECTION** through skin and electric sense organ of a gymnotid shows tube containing jelly-like substance widening at base into a capsule, known as multicellular gland, that holds a group of special cells. Enlargement of this photomicrograph is 1,000 diameters.

other fishes that apparently have no electric organs.

Although electric fishes cannot be seen in their natural habitat, it is still possible to detect and follow them by picking up their discharges from the water. In South America I have found that the gymnotids are all active during the night. Darkness and the turbidity of the water offer good protection to these fishes, which rely on their eyes only for the knowledge that it is day or night. At night most of the predatory fishes, which have well-developed eyes, sleep on the bottom of rivers, ponds and lakes. Early in the morning, before the predators wake up, the gymnotids return from their nightly excursions and occupy inaccessible hiding places, where they often collect in vast numbers. In the rocks and vegetation along the shore the ticking, rattling, humming and whistling can be heard in bewildering profusion when the electrodes are connected to a loudspeaker. With a little practice one can begin to distinguish the various species by these sounds.

When one observes life in this highly competitive environment, it becomes clear what advantages the electric sense confers on these fishes and why they have evolved their curiously specialized sense organs, skin, brain, electric organs and peculiar mode of swimming. Such well-established specialists must have originated, however, from ordinary fishes in which the characteristics of the specialists are found in their primitive state: the electric organs as locomotive muscles and the sense organs as mechanoreceptors along the lateral line of the body that signal displacement of water. Somewhere there must be intermediate forms in which the contraction of a muscle, with its accompanying change in electric potential, interacts with these sense organs. For survival it may be important to be able to distinguish water movements caused by animate or inanimate objects. This may have started the evolutionary trend toward an electric sense.

Already we know some supposedly nonelectric fishes from which, nevertheless, we can pick up signals having many characteristics of the discharges of electric fishes. We know of sense organs that appear to be structurally intermediate between ordinary lateral-line receptors and electroreceptors. Furthermore, fishes that have both of these characteristics are also electrically very sensitive. We may hope one day to piece the whole evolutionary line together and express, at least in physical terms, what it is like to live in an electric world.

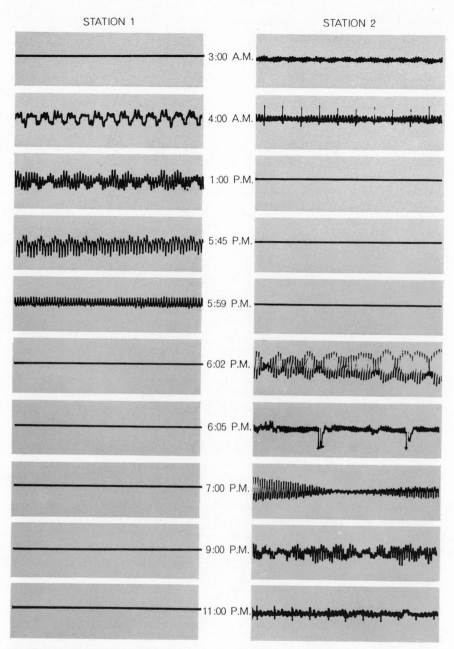

STATION 1    STATION 2

3:00 A.M.

4:00 A.M.

1:00 P.M.

5:45 P.M.

5:59 P.M.

6:02 P.M.

6:05 P.M.

7:00 P.M.

9:00 P.M.

11:00 P.M.

TRACKING ELECTRIC FISH in nature involves placing electrodes in water they inhabit. Records at left were made in South American stream near daytime hiding place of gymnotids, those at right out in main channel of stream, where they seek food at night.

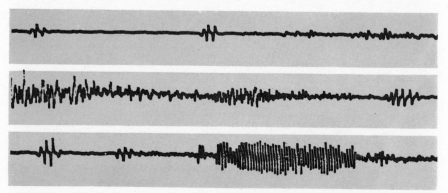

AFRICAN CATFISH, supposedly nonelectric, produced the discharges shown here. Normal action potentials of muscles are seen, along with odd regular blips and still other oscillations of higher frequency. Such fish may be evolving an electric sense or may already have one.

# 8  The Master Switch of Life

P. F. SCHOLANDER · December 1963

In the higher animals breathing and the beating of the heart seem synonymous with life. They implement the central process of animal metabolism: the respiratory gas exchange that brings oxygen to the tissues and removes carbon dioxide. Few events are more dangerous to life than an interruption of breathing or circulation that interferes with this exchange. It is not that all the tissues of an animal need to be continuously supplied with fresh oxygen; most parts of the human body display a considerable tolerance for asphyxia. The tissues of an arm or a leg can be isolated by a tight tourniquet for more than an hour without damage; the kidney can survive without circulation for a similar period and a corneal transplant for many hours. The heart and the brain, however, are exquisitely sensitive to asphyxia. Suffocation or heart failure kills a human being within a few minutes, and the brain suffers irreversible damage if its circulation ceases for more than five minutes.

One might expect that the body would respond with heroic measures to the threat of asphyxia. It does indeed. The defense is a striking circulatory adaptation: a gross redistribution of the blood supply to concentrate the available oxygen in the tissues that need it most. The identification of this defense mechanism has resulted from studies, extending over a number of years, of animals that are specialized to go for an unusual length of time without breathing: the diving mammals and diving birds. Only recently has it become clear that this "master switch" of life is the generalized response of vertebrate animals to the threat of asphyxia from any one of a number of quite different circumstances.

A cat or a dog or a rabbit—or a human being—dies by drowning in a few minutes. A duck, however, can endure submersion for 10 to 20 minutes, a seal for 20 minutes or more and some species of whales for an hour or even two hours. How do they do it? The simplest explanation would be that diving animals have a capacity for oxygen storage that is sufficient for them to remain on normal aerobic, or oxygen-consuming, metabolism throughout their dives. As long ago as the turn of the century the physiologists Charles R. Richet and Christian Bohr realized that this could not be the full story. Many diving species do have a large blood volume and a good supply of oxygen-binding pigments: hemoglobin in the blood and myoglobin in the muscles. Their lungs, however, are not unusually large. Their total store of oxygen is seldom even twice that of comparable nondiving animals and could not, it was clear, account for their much greater ability to remain submerged.

At the University of Oslo during the 1930's I undertook a series of experiments to find out just what goes on when an animal dives. For this purpose it was necessary to bring diving animals into the laboratory, where they could be connected to the proper instruments for recording in detail the physiological events that take place before, during and after submergence. Over the years my colleagues—Laurence Irving in particular—and I have worked with many mammals and birds. We have found seals to be ideal experimental animals: they tame easily and submit readily to a number of diving exercises. At first we confined them to a board that could be lowered and raised in a bathtub full of water. Lately my colleague Robert W. Elsner at the Scripps Institution of Oceanography has trained seals to "dive" voluntarily, keeping their noses under water for as long as seven minutes.

Our first experiments at Oslo confirmed the earlier discovery, by Richet and others, of diving bradycardia, or slowing of the heart action. When the nose of a seal submerges, the animal's heartbeat usually falls to a tenth or so of the normal rate. This happens quickly, indicating that it occurs by reflex action before it can be triggered by any metabolic change. The initiation of bradycardia is affected by psychological factors. It can be induced by many stimuli other than diving, such as a sharp handclap or a threatening movement on the part of the investigator when the seal is completely out of the water. Conversely, bradycardia sometimes fails to develop in a submerged seal if the animal knows it is free to raise its head and breathe whenever it likes. In long dives, however, the slowing down is always pronounced. It is significant that the impulse is so strong it ordinarily continues for the duration of the dive, even when the animal works hard—a situation that would normally cause a rise in the heart rate.

Bradycardia occurs in every diving animal that has been studied. It has been reported in such diverse species as the seal, porpoise, hippopotamus, dugong, beaver, duck, penguin, auk, crocodile and turtle. The same thing happens in fishes when they are taken out of the water. And when such nondivers as cats, dogs and men submerge, bradycardia develops too, although it is often less pronounced than in the specialized divers.

When the heart of a seal beats only five or six times a minute, what happens to the blood pressure? We found that the central blood pressure—in the main artery of a hind flipper, for instance—stays at a normal level. The shape of the pressure trace, however, reveals that

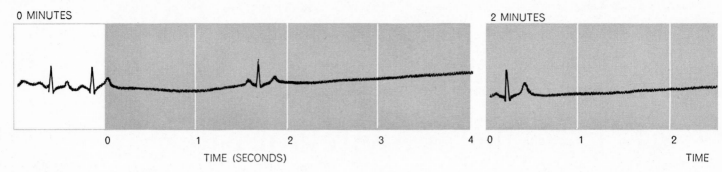

DIVING BRADYCARDIA, the slowing of the heart rate that occurs in vertebrates when they submerge, is quite apparent in this electrocardiogram of a diving seal. Three segments of the record are shown, made at the beginning of, during and at the end of an

whereas the pressure rise with each beat is normal, the subsequent drop in pressure is gradual and prolonged. This indicates that, although the systolic phase of the heartbeat is almost normal, the diastolic phase, during which the blood is forced through the aorta, encounters resistance: the peripheral blood vessels are constricted. Measurements in a small toe artery in the seal's flipper show that the pressure there drops when the dive begins, falling rapidly to the much lower level maintained in the veins. In other words, we found that the circulation in the flippers shuts down to practically nothing during a dive [see bottom illustration on opposite page].

For another clue to circulation we measured the level of lactic acid in the muscles and blood of a diving seal. Lactic acid is the end product of the anaerobic metabolic process from which muscles derive energy in the absence of oxygen. The concentration of this metabolite in muscle tissue rises sharply during a dive but the concentration in the blood does not; then, when the seal begins to breathe again, lactic acid floods into the bloodstream. The same sequence of

events has been found to occur in most other animals, showing that the muscle circulation remains closed down as long as the dive continues. Similarly, oxygen disappears from muscle tissue a few minutes after a seal submerges, whereas the arterial blood still contains plenty of oxygen—enough to keep the myoglobin saturated if the muscles are being supplied with blood [see illustrations on page 61]. Other experiments revealed that in the seal both the mesenteric and the renal arteries, supplying the intestines and kidneys respectively, close down during diving. All these findings made it apparent that a major portion of the peripheral circulation shuts off promptly on submergence. This was evidently the reason the heart slows down.

At this point our results tied in nicely with some conclusions reached by Irving, who was then at Swarthmore College. His efforts had been stimulated by pioneering studies of circulatory control conducted in the 1920's by Detlev W. Bronk, then at Swarthmore, and the late Robert Gesell of the University of

Michigan. Bronk and Gesell had discovered in 1927 that in a dog rendered asphyxic by an excess of carbon dioxide and a lack of oxygen the muscle circulation slowed down as the blood pressure remained normal and the brain circulation increased. Irving noted in 1934 that this phenomenon might explain a diving animal's resistance to asphyxia, and he proceeded to measure blood flow in a variety of animals by introducing heated wire probes into various tissues and recording the rate at which their heat was dissipated. His data indicated that during a dive the flow in muscle tissue is reduced but the brain blood flow remains constant or even increases. He decided that the essence of the defense against asphyxia in animals would prove to be some mechanism for the selective redistribution of the circulation, with preferential delivery of the decreasing oxygen store to those organs that can least endure anoxia: the brain and the heart.

When the blood flow closes down in most tissues during a dive, what happens to energy metabolism? This is best studied during a quiet dive, with a seal or

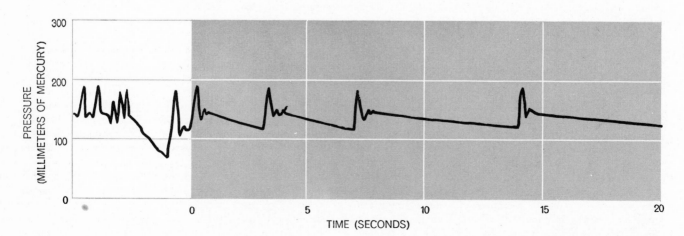

CENTRAL BLOOD PRESSURE stays at about a normal level during a seal's dive (color); the rate of increase in pressure during a contraction is also normal. The slow pressure drop between contractions, however, suggests constriction of peripheral blood vessels.

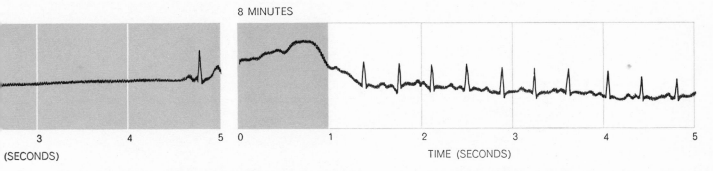

8 MINUTES

3        4        5    0        1        2        3        4        5

(SECONDS)                                    TIME (SECONDS)

eight-minute dive, the duration of which is shown in color. The heart slows down at the start of the dive. The rate remains as low as seven or eight per minute during the dive and then returns to a normal 80 or so per minute as soon as the seal breathes again.

duck trained to remain inactive while under water. The oxygen stores are large enough to provide only a quarter of the energy expended in a predive resting period of the same length. The next question was: Do anaerobic processes, including lactic acid production, substitute fully for the lack of oxygen? Muscle on anaerobic metabolism incurs an "oxygen debt" that must be paid off when oxygen becomes available. The excess oxygen intake on recovery from a dive is a measure of that debt. If an animal consumed energy at the same rate during a dive as before it, this excess intake would be enough to equal a normal oxygen-consumption rate during the dive. We found that it was characteristic in quiet dives, however, for the seal or duck to exhibit an oxygen debt much smaller than this. In the case of the sloth, a tree-living animal that is curiously tolerant of submersion, there was no apparent oxygen debt at all [see *illustration on page 62*]. The implication was that metabolism must slow down.

We could not settle this definitely by studying the oxygen debt alone; it was conceivable that the debt was being paid off so slowly it eluded us. Temperature measurements, however, confirmed the impression of decreased metabolism. We often noticed that after long dives (20 minutes or so) the seal would be shivering during the recovery period. We found that the animal lost body temperature at a rapid rate while submerged. Now, this could not be because of increased heat loss, since there was no substantial change in the thermal contact between the seal and the water; only the nostrils were submerged for the dive. Moreover, the reduction of circulation meant that heat conductivity was lessened, not increased. The loss in body temperature therefore meant an actual decrease in heat production—a slowing down of metabolism. Apparently the lack of blood in the tissues simply jams the normal metabolic processes by mass action; the flame of metabolism is damped and burns lower. It is quite logical that submergence should bring about a progressive reduction in energy metabolism, considering that the suspension of breathing ultimately terminates in death, or zero metabolic activity.

In most dives under natural conditions, of course, this general metabolic slowing down is masked. The animal is actively gathering food, and its muscles probably expend energy at several times the resting rate for the total animal. After a few minutes the muscles have used up the private store of oxygen in their myoglobin, and then they depend on anaerobic processes resulting in lactic acid formation. After such dives there is a substantial oxygen debt reflecting the amount of exercise; it is therefore impossible to detect the subtle lowering of metabolism that must still occur in the nonactive tissues deprived of circulation.

It has been fascinating, and of particular interest from the point of view of evolution, to discover the very same asphyxial defense in fishes taken out of the water—diving in reverse, as it were. The response is found in a variety of fishes, including many that would never leave the water under normal conditions. It is most striking in the aquatic versions of diving mammals and diving birds: the fishes that routinely make excursions out of the water, such as the fly-

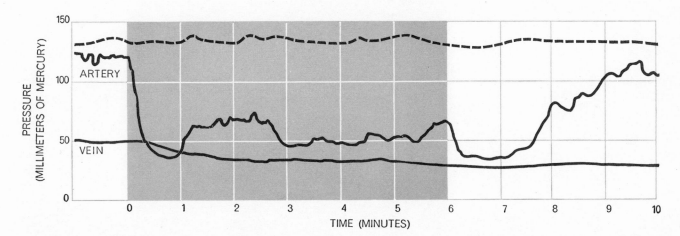

PERIPHERAL PRESSURE, taken in a small toe artery, drops appreciably during a seal's dive (*colored area*). From near the central blood-pressure level (*broken line*) it falls almost to the venous level, which indicates a closing down of circulation in the flipper.

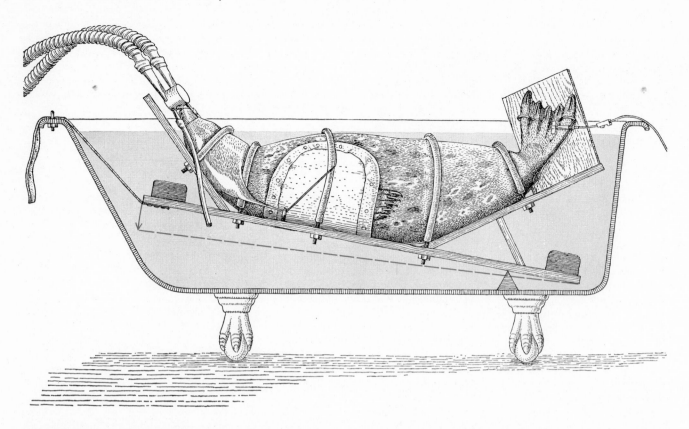

**SEAL DIVES IN LABORATORY** by being ducked in a bathtub full of water. The animal is strapped loosely to a weighted board. Its head is covered by a mask connected to a device for recording respiration. When the board is tilted down (*broken line*), the mask fills with water and the seal's nose is submerged. An artery in a hind flipper is shown cannulated for removal of blood samples.

**VOLUNTARY DIVING** eliminates any possibility that restraint affects the seal's responses. This harbor seal (*Phoca vitulina*) is being trained to keep its nose under water until the experimenter lowers his warning finger and instead displays the reward, a fish.

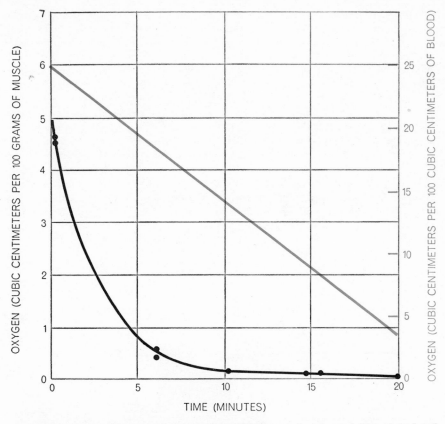

**OXYGEN** concentration is traced in the muscle (*black curve*) and arterial blood (*colored curve*) of a harbor seal during a dive. The sharp drop in muscle oxygen while the blood is still more than half-saturated suggests that there is no appreciable blood flow in muscle.

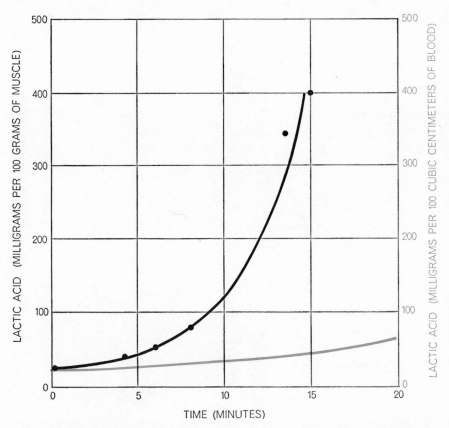

**LACTIC ACID** concentration confirms lack of blood flow in muscle. Lactic acid builds up in the muscle as the oxygen there is used up, but little enters the blood. The blood lactic acid level rises sharply only after the muscle circulation is restored when breathing resumes.

ing fish. It would be interesting to obtain an electrocardiogram of a flying fish taking off on a natural flight, but this would call for a rather tricky technique. When the leap is simulated, however, by lifting a flying fish out of the water, a profound bradycardia develops immediately.

Another fish that survives on land for some time is the grunion, an amazing little member of the herring family that frequents the coast of California. These fish spawn only on a few nights with maximum tides during the spring. They ride up the beach on a long wave at high tide. As the water recedes the female digs into the sand tail first and deposits her eggs; the male curves around her and fertilizes them. When they have finished, the fish ride out to sea again on another high wave. The spawning procedure can last five or 10 minutes or even longer and is accompanied by much thrashing about; in spite of this activity there is a profound bradycardia during the entire period. Walter F. Garey and Edda D. Bradstreet of the Scripps Institution have studied the lactic acid sequence in grunions caught on the beach and kept overnight in a laboratory tank. The fish are placed in a dish and prodded to keep them wriggling; blood and muscle are sampled during this period and after return to the water. Garey and Miss Bradstreet found that during the anaerobic period lactic acid increases rapidly in the muscles; practically none appears in the circulation until the fish is back in the water. Then, as the peripheral circulation opens up again, lactic acid is flushed out of the muscles and suddenly appears in the blood [see the upper illustration on page 64].

Whereas fishes such as the grunion dive in reverse, the mudskipper (*Periophthalmus*) performs a double reverse. It spends most of its time out of the water in mangrove swamps at the edge of tropical seas, perching on a mangrove root and slithering, if it is frightened, into a burrow in the mud. These mudholes are frequently devoid of oxygen. By dint of heroic and slippery investigations in northern Australian mangrove swamps, Garey has determined that the heart of a mudskipper in its mudhole develops a pronounced bradycardia. It would seem, then, that the creature has turned evolution around: it is more at home as an air-breathing animal than as a proper fish!

In view of the strikingly similar responses to asphyxia in so many quite different vertebrate animals, it would be strange if human beings did not conform to the common scheme. Indeed, a number of recent studies of human divers, of birth anoxia in babies and of several pathological conditions have turned up exactly the same pattern.

My associates and I obtained valuable information by examining the native pearl divers of northern Australia, who are trained from boyhood to make deep dives. (We found, incidentally, that these experts seldom stay down for longer than a minute; many individual divers can remain submerged for twice as long, but this is evidently too strenuous as a regular practice.) A diver develops bradycardia within 20 to 30 seconds whether he remains quiet or swims about. The arterial blood pressure is normal or even elevated; just as in the seal, the diastolic pressure drop is slowed down, apparently by constriction of the peripheral blood vessels. As we expect-

ed, there is little or no rise in the lactic acid level in the blood during the dive, but there is an acute rise in the recovery period. In all these respects human divers respond like other vertebrates. In one respect, however, human beings may be unique: Pathological arrhythmias, or irregularities of the heartbeat, are alarmingly common in man after only half a minute's dive and such arrhythmias have so far not been observed in animals.

In our laboratory at the Scripps Institution, Elsner has been able to demonstrate ischemia, or lack of blood flow, in the muscles of an extremity simply by having a volunteer submerge his face in a basin of water. An electrocardiograph measures the heart rate, and the flow of blood into the calf is measured by plethysmography. In this technique a cuff placed around the thigh

is inflated just enough to occlude the return of blood through the veins while leaving the arteries open to supply blood to the lower part of the leg. As the calf fills with blood its circumference is measured and traced by a recording device. As soon as the subject immerses his face his heart slows down. At the same time there is a sharp decrease in the extent to which the calf expands when the venous return is obstructed; the constriction of the small arteries diminishes and may virtually stop blood flow into the calf. As soon as the subject lifts his face out of the water and breathes, the arterioles open up again and the calf expands [see illustrations on page 65]. If a subject is merely told to hold his breath without submerging his face, all these effects are less pronounced. As in the case of the seal that is free to breathe at will, psychological

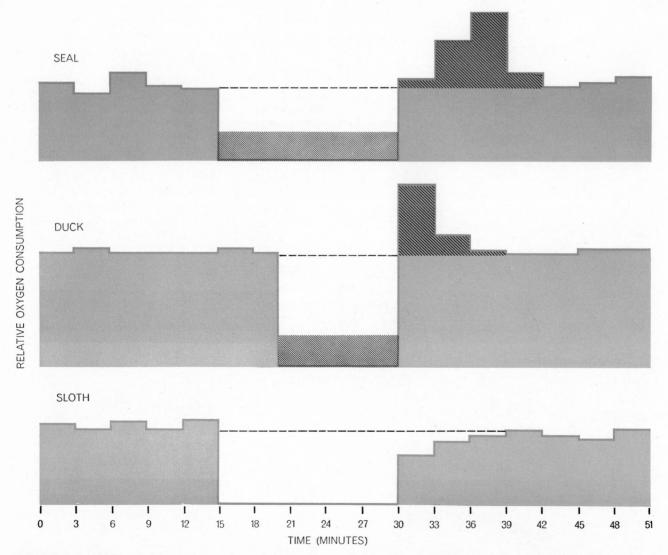

METABOLIC SLOWING DOWN during a dive is demonstrated in three animals by the record of oxygen consumption in successive three-minute periods. In the seal and duck the amount of excess oxygen intake after the dive (hatching on color) represents the oxygen debt incurred by anaerobic metabolism during the dive. This debt (hatching on white) is clearly not enough to have sustained an energy expenditure at a normal rate (broken lines) during the dive. The sloth seems to incur no oxygen debt while diving.

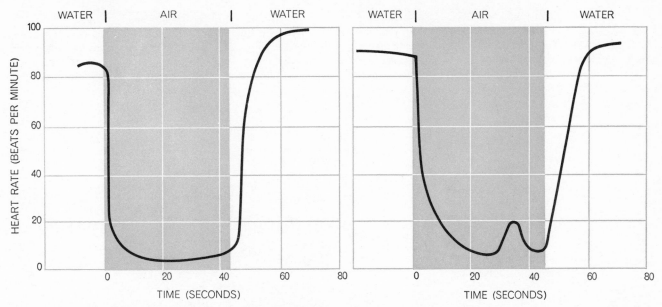

FISH OUT OF WATER develops bradycardia just as a diving animal does when it submerges. These two graphs show the sharp decrease in heart rate that occurs in the grunion (*left*) and the flying fish (*right*) when they are temporarily taken out of water.

factors seem to influence the physiological response to asphyxia.

Physicians have been aware that bradycardia sometimes occurs in babies before, during and immediately after birth and that this can be a sign of asphyxia induced by obstruction or final interruption of the placental blood flow. This concept has been strengthened by lactic acid measurements in newborn infants by Stanley James of the Columbia University College of Physicians and Surgeons. Judging by his data, a normal birth is always followed by a sharp rise in the blood lactic acid. This rise is sharper and higher in babies that have survived a difficult delivery and show clinical symptoms of birth distress; in other words, the longer the period of anoxia, the greater the lactic acid build-up [*see lower illustration on page 64*]. Newborn animals in general have a short period of increased resistance to asphyxia. The sequence of events in babies suggests that selective ischemia is an important asphyxial defense even in newborn infants.

Various pathological conditions that decrease cardiac output, such as arrhythmias and coronary occlusions, are sometimes followed by such apparently unrelated complications as damage to the kidneys or even gangrenous sores in the intestine. Donald D. Van Slyke and his collaborators at the Rockefeller Institute for Medical Research found in 1944 that severe shock in dogs resulted in decreased kidney function and tissue damage—and that the same symptoms appeared if they simply clamped the renal artery of a healthy dog. Pointing out the analogy to the peripheral vasoconstriction we had reported in diving animals, Van Slyke concluded that under stress the blood supply to the brain is maintained, if necessary, at the cost of restriction of circulation to other areas: the organism, as he said recently, is reduced to "a heart-lung-brain preparation."

More recently Eliot Corday and his

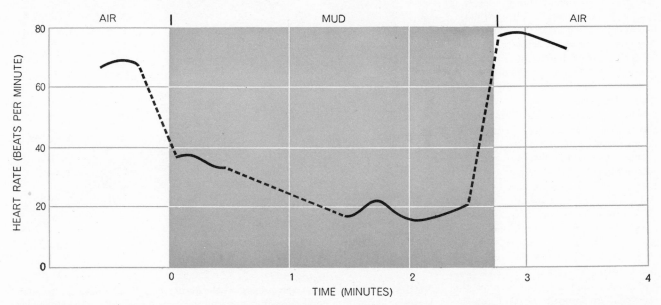

MUDSKIPPER is a curious fish that has become acclimated to breathing air. While it is out of water, its heart rate is normal; when it enters its mud-filled burrow, it develops bradycardia. Broken lines join the various segments of this fragmentary record.

colleagues at the University of California at Los Angeles have found that the same events account for certain gangrenous lesions of the intestine. They impaired the circulation of dogs in various ways, inflicting cardiac arrhythmias by electrical stimulation or decreasing the blood pressure by bleeding the animals. With modern blood-flow-metering techniques and blood-pressure measurements they were able to demonstrate a widespread vasoconstriction that tends to sustain the blood pressure near a normal level but leaves the kidney, the gastrointestinal tract, the muscles and the skin with greatly reduced circulation. These workers again recognized the sequence as a mechanism for maintaining an adequate blood supply to the most sensitive organs.

A quite different physiological event that seems to depend on the same circulatory switch as the prime control is hibernation. In all the relatively few species of mammals and birds that hibernate the body temperature is lowered in the presence of an unfavorable thermal environment. In most animals hibernation is seasonal but in others the temperature drops in a daily cycle. The dormant state is characterized, in any case, by a body temperature only a degree or so warmer than the surroundings; along with this there is a correspondingly low metabolic rate, perhaps a tenth or less of the resting rate in the waking condition. The heart rate is very low—only a few beats per minute—but the central blood pressure remains quite high in relation to this bradycardia. Again the pressure trace shows the slow diastolic emptying of the arteries that suggests a peripheral vasoconstriction. There is good evidence that hibernation is a controlled state; when a decrease in the ambient temperature brings a threat of freezing, the animal increases its heat production and usually emerges from hibernation.

The transition periods during which the animal enters or emerges from hibernation are of particular interest. When a ground squirrel or woodchuck goes into hibernation, the heart rate slows down before the body temperature starts to drop, indicating that the drop in metabolic rate is caused—as in asphyxial defense—by a primary vasoconstriction. Arousal from hibernation is easier to study because it can be precipitated at will by disturbing the animal. This triggers an immediate acceleration of the heartbeat to as much as 100 times the hibernating rate. There follows an intense shivering of the front part of the body, which warms up much more quickly than the rest of the body does as measured by the rectal temperature. Midway through arousal the blood flow in the forelegs of the squirrel is sometimes 10 times greater than in the hind legs. The uneven distribution of metabolic and circulatory activity is apparently accomplished by a dilation of the blood vessels that begins in the forward parts. When the vessels in the rest of the animal finally dilate, the over-all metabolic rate sometimes rises as high as when the animal exercises. The entire sequence is consistent with the idea that the onset and termination of hibernation are triggered in the first instance by

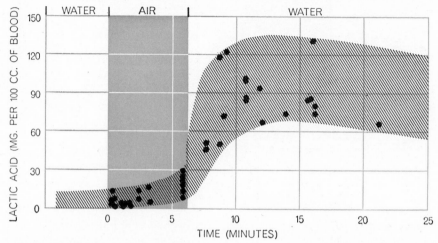

MUSCLE ISCHEMIA, or lack of blood, in grunions results in a lactic acid build-up in muscle while the fish is out of the water. As seen here, the lactic acid does not rise much in the blood until the muscle circulation is restored when the fish re-enters the water.

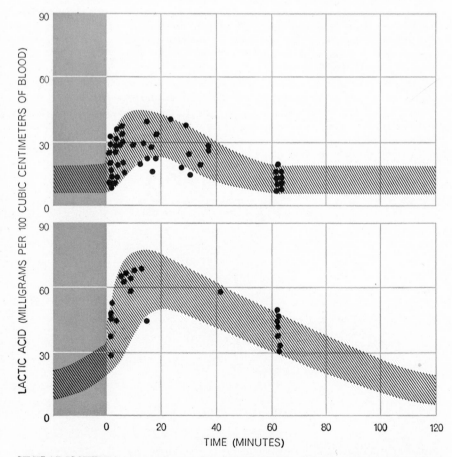

SIMILAR ISCHEMIA apparently protects a baby during the delivery period (color). When breathing begins, the muscle circulation opens up and lactic acid floods the blood. The lactic acid build-up is smaller in a normal delivery (top) than in a long, difficult one (bottom).

vasomotor impulses controlling the size of the small blood vessels. The circulation then throttles metabolism in the tissues to a rate compatible with the blood flow. Going into hibernation seems to call for the same primary vasoconstriction that operates in asphyxial defense.

Any mechanism that operates in many kinds of animals across a wide range of circumstances must be of fundamental physiological significance. In our current work at the Scripps Institution we are trying to learn more about the details of blood flow in animals by implanting ultrasonic measuring devices on arteries and veins. We hope to discover just how the autonomic nervous system responds to environmental changes and the threat of anoxia and what sequence of events actually throws the circulatory switch.

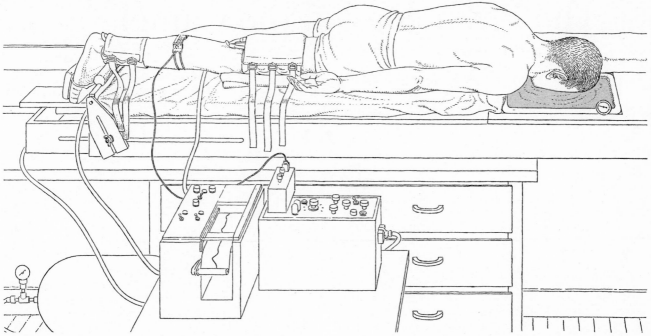

HUMAN DIVING is investigated in the laboratory by having a volunteer immerse his face in a basin of water. In this case the circulation in the lower leg is being measured by plethysmography. The inflatable cuff on the thigh occludes the veins draining the calf but leaves the arteries open. By measuring the circumference of the calf one can determine the blood flow into the lower leg.

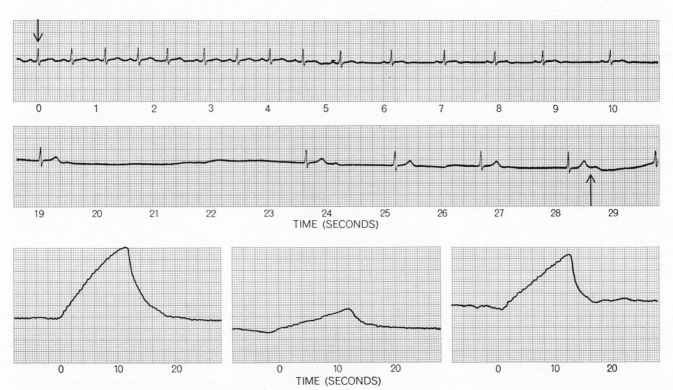

FACE IMMERSION results in bradycardia. The electrocardiogram (*two top strips*) records an extreme case (*arrows mark start and end of dive*). Plethysmographic records (*bottom*) show changes in calf circumference when venous return is occluded for some 12 seconds before (*left*), during (*center*) and after (*right*) face immersion. Blood flow into calf is clearly much reduced during dive.

# The Physiology of the Camel

KNUT SCHMIDT-NIELSEN · December 1959

The camel's ability to go without water for long periods is proverbial. Naturalists since Pliny the Elder have ascribed this talent to a built-in reservoir on which the animal can draw in time of need. Thus the English zoologist George Shaw wrote in 1801: "Independent of the four stomachs which are common to the ruminating animals, the Camels have a fifth bag which serves them as a reservoir for water. . . . This particularity is known to Oriental travelers, who have sometimes found it necessary to kill a Camel in order to obtain a supply of water."

Such tales appear even in modern zoology textbooks (though some writers have shifted the camel's reservoir from its stomach to its hump). There is remarkably little evidence for them. A few years ago I became interested in camel physiology and leafed through every book on the subject I could find. I accumulated a large amount of information on the camel's anatomy, its diseases and its evolution, but discovered that scientific knowledge of its water metabolism was almost nonexistent.

The camel's tolerance for drought is real enough. It can travel across stretches of desert where a man on foot and without water would quickly die of thirst. This fact poses some interesting questions for the physiologist. No animal can get along completely without water. Land animals in particular lose water steadily through their kidneys and from the moist surfaces of their lungs; mammals cool themselves in hot surroundings by evaporating water from their skins or oral membranes.

Desert animals have evolved a variety of mechanisms to minimize these losses. The kangaroo rat, for example, produces urine which contains so little water that it solidifies almost as soon as it is ex-

creted. The animal avoids the heat and thus decreases evaporation by passing the daylight hours in a relatively cool burrow [see "The Desert Rat," by Knut and Bodil Schmidt-Nielsen; SCIENTIFIC AMERICAN offprint 1050].

The camel can hardly escape the heat by burrowing. Does it emulate the desert rat by excreting a highly concentrated urine? Does it store water in its stomach, or anywhere else? For that matter, just how long can a camel go without water?

Our laboratory at Duke University was obviously no place to seek answers to these questions. Accordingly my wife and I, together with T. R. Houpt of the University of Pennsylvania and S. A. Jarnum of the University of Copenhagen, undertook to study camels in the Sahara Desert. The information we were seeking was not only of scientific interest but might also be of practical importance. In many arid lands the camel is the chief domestic animal. It serves not only as a beast of burden but also as a source of milk, meat, wool and leather. A better understanding of camel physiology might benefit the economy of these areas, which include some of the most poverty-stricken regions on earth.

The expedition required a year's planning, because we had to be completely independent of outside supplies in setting up our desert laboratory. Late in 1953 we arrived at the oasis of Béni Abbès, located in the desert south of the Atlas Mountains. To many Americans the word "oasis" suggests a few date palms clustered around a well. Béni Abbès, however, is a community of several thousand people. Its location over an underground river flowing down from the mountains ensures water for drinking and some irrigation.

Camels are valuable beasts in the Sa-

hara, and we had considerable difficulty in securing animals for experimental purposes. With the aid of our native assistant, Mohammed ben Fredj, I managed after considerable haggling to purchase one animal and later to rent two others. Meanwhile we sought to track down the source of some of the abundant camel folklore.

Explorers have often reported that their camels have gone without water for as long as several weeks. Is this possible? Under certain circumstances it is. Much desert exploration has been conducted in winter, because the desert summers are unbearably hot. During the winter the camel can often meet its need for water by browsing on bushes and succulent plants, which flourish after a rain and contain considerable water. Indeed, we found that in the Sahara grazing camels are not watered at all in winter. Some that had not drunk for as much as two months refused water when we offered it to them. When we examined such animals that had been butchered for meat, we found that all their organs contained the normal amount of water.

Thus the camel's drought tolerance in winter seems entirely ascribable to its diet. Even a man would have no difficulty in abstaining from drinking in cool weather if he fed largely on juicy fruits and vegetables. During the winter months the only way to dehydrate a camel is to restrict it to a fodder of dry grass and dried dates (not the soft, sweet dates of the grocery but a hard, fibrous and bitter variety). Even when we kept our camels on this completely dry diet, they could go for several weeks without drinking, though they lost water steadily through their lungs and skin and through the formation of urine and feces. We were able to measure these losses quite accurately simply by weighing the beasts, because unlike most animals deprived of water they continued to eat normally and thus did not lose weight in the usual sense. When we finally offered them water, they would in a few minutes drink enough to bring their weight back to normal. In no case did they drink more water than they had previously lost. Evidently they were not storing up a surplus but replacing a deficit.

Our studies of butchered camels supported this conclusion; we could find no evidence for special water-storing organs. The camel's first stomach, or rumen, does have pouches that are not found in the stomachs of other ruminants. These pouches have been called water sacs by some investigators, but their total fluid capacity is only about a gallon, and they contain coarsely masticated fodder rather than water. The main part of the rumen and the other stomachs contained considerable fluid, but less than the stomachs of other ruminating animals do. Chemical analysis revealed the similarity of the fluid to digestive juices; in salt content it resembled blood rather than water. Though it could furnish no significant reserve of water for the camel, it might well save the life of a thirsty man. The stories of travelers who killed their camels for water may thus be true. However, a man would have to be terribly thirsty to resort to such an expedient, because the fluid is usually a foul-smelling greenish soup. As for other possible sites of water storage, we found that neither the hump nor any other part of the animal's body contained an unusual quantity of fluid.

The tale that the camel stores water has probably gained color from the animal's remarkable capacity for rapid and copious drinking. During a later experiment one of our camels drank more than 27 gallons of water in 10 minutes. Camels are always watered before a long desert journey, and if they have not been watered for some days they will drink greedily. The uncritical observer could easily conclude that the animals are storing water in anticipation of future needs.

Some writers have alleged that the camel's fatty hump, though it contains no water reservoir, nonetheless provides the animal with a reserve of water as well as of food. Their logic is simple enough. All foods contain hydrogen and therefore produce water when they are oxidized in the body; the desert rat obtains all its water from this source. Fat contains a greater proportion of hydrogen than any other foodstuff and yields

CAMEL CAN LOSE WATER amounting to more than 25 per cent of its body weight. A dehydrated camel (*top*) appears emaciated but can still move about; a similarly dehydrated man would be unconscious or dead. The animal can quickly drink back its water losses and resume its normal appearance (*bottom*). Photographs were made about 10 minutes apart.

a correspondingly larger amount of water: about 1.1 pounds of water for each pound of fat. Thus a camel with 100 pounds of fat on its back might seem to be carrying 110 pounds—more than 13 gallons—of water. But in order to turn

the fat into water the camel must take in oxygen through its lungs; in the process it loses water by evaporation from the lung surfaces. Calculation of the rate of loss indicates that the animal will lose more water by evaporation than it can

gain through oxidation.

If the camel possesses no special reserves of water, it must have evolved methods for economizing on water expenditure. Its kidney functions in particular seemed worth investigating. All vertebrates rely on the kidney to rid their bodies of nitrogenous wastes (in mammals primarily urea). Few animals can tolerate any accumulation of these substances in the body. The kangaroo rat conserves water by eliminating a urine very rich in urea, and we were not surprised to find the camel following its example. When we kept our camels on dry fodder, their urine output declined and its urea content rose. In the case of one young animal, however, the urea output dropped sharply along with the volume of urine. The animal did not retain the urea in its blood, because the concentration of urea in the blood plasma also fell. Even the injection of urea into the bloodstream did not raise its concentration in the urine.

Further work revealed that the low level of urea had to do with nutrition rather than water conservation. The dry fodder contained too little protein to meet the nutritional needs of a young and growing camel. Under these circumstances the animal was apparently able to reprocess "waste" urea into new protein. From recent studies of sheep we have found that they share the camel's ability to use nitrogenous compounds over and over again. Experiments with cows by other investigators suggest that these ruminants may husband nitrogen in the same manner [see "The Metabolism of Ruminants," by Terence A. Rogers; SCIENTIFIC AMERICAN, February, 1958].

To determine the maximum efficiency with which the camel can excrete urea, we tried to put one of our camels on a high-protein diet. Unfortunately the camel's taste in food is exceedingly conservative. When we sought to trick the animal into increasing its protein intake by feeding it dates stuffed with raw peanuts, it balked at the first date and refused to accept any more for the rest of the day. Over a period of weeks we gradually accustomed it to the adulterated food, but we were forced to abandon the experiment when we found that we had exhausted the entire stock of peanuts in the oasis!

The kidney of the desert rat has a remarkable capacity for concentrating not only urea but also salt, and one would expect the camel's kidney to operate with similar efficiency. We were not able to test this hypothesis because

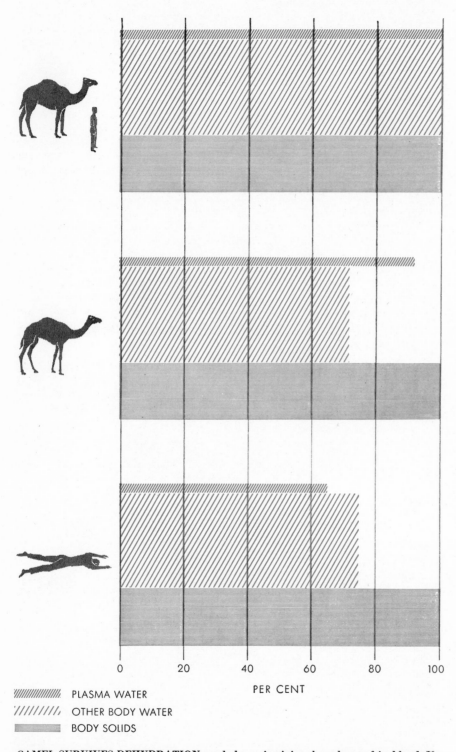

PLASMA WATER

OTHER BODY WATER

BODY SOLIDS

**CAMEL SURVIVES DEHYDRATION** partly by maintaining the volume of its blood. Under normal conditions (*top*) plasma water in both man and camel accounts for about a 12th of total body water. In a camel that has lost about a fourth of its body water (*center*) the blood volume will drop by less than a 10th. Under the same conditions a man's blood volume will drop by a third (*bottom*). The viscous blood circulates too slowly to carry the man's body heat outward to the skin, so that his temperature soon rises to a fatal level.

PER CENT

neither the fodder nor the local wells contained much salt. We were told, however, that camels in other areas could and did drink "bitter waters" containing enough magnesium sulfate (epsom salt) to sicken a man. Camels in coastal regions were said to browse on seaweed along the shore; these plants would of course have a salt content equal to that of sea water. It seems quite possible that the camel can approach the performance of the desert rat, whose efficient kidney permits it to drink sea water without harm.

Even the most efficient kidney cannot explain the camel's ability to get along on low water-rations during the desert summer. In this season the temperature soars to 120 degrees Fahrenheit or more. Since higher animals cannot survive body temperatures much over 100 degrees, they must either seek shelter, as do many small desert creatures, or cool themselves by evaporation of water from the mouth (panting) or from the skin (sweating). On a hot desert day a man may produce more than a quart of sweat an hour.

A man losing water at this rate rapidly becomes intensely thirsty. If the loss passes 5 per cent of his body weight (about a gallon), his physical condition rapidly deteriorates, his perceptions become distorted and his judgment falters. A loss of 10 per cent brings on delirium, deafness and insensitivity to pain.

In cool surroundings a man may cling to life until he has lost water up to 20 per cent of his body weight. In the desert heat, however, a loss of no more than 12 per cent will result in "explosive heat death." As the blood loses water it becomes denser and more viscous. The thickened blood taxes the pumping capacity of the heart and slows the circulation to the point where metabolic heat is no longer carried outward to the skin and dissipated. The internal temperature of the body suddenly increases, and death quickly follows.

How does the camel fare under similar conditions? We kept one camel without water for eight days in the heat of the desert summer. It had then lost 220 pounds—about 22 per cent—of its body weight. It looked emaciated; its abdomen was drawn in against its vertebrae, its muscles were shrunken and its legs were scrawny and appeared even longer than usual. But even though the animal would not have been able to do heavy work or travel a long distance, it was not in serious condition. It had no difficulty in emptying bucket after bucket of water and quickly recovered its normal appearance. Later experiments showed that camels can lose more than 25 per cent of their body weight without being seriously weakened. The lethal limit of dehydration is probably considerably higher, but for obvious humanitarian reasons we did not attempt to determine it.

How does a camel that has lost water amounting to a quarter of its body weight—more than a third of the water in its system—manage to avoid the explosive heat death that would overtake a man long before this point? It can do so because it maintains its blood volume despite the water loss. We were able to

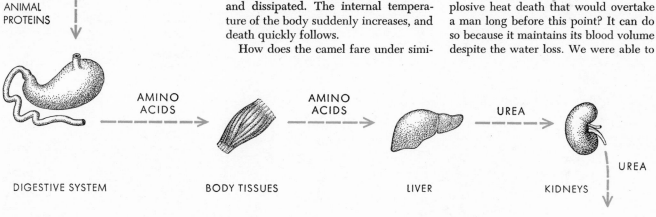

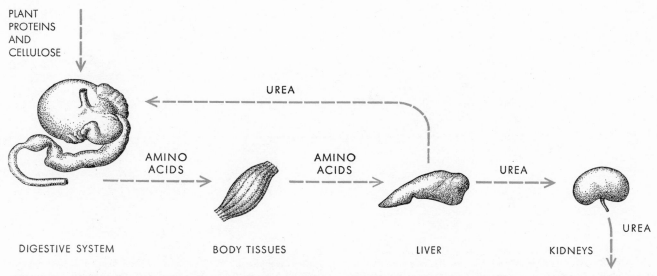

UNUSUAL NITROGEN METABOLISM helps the camel to get along on low-grade fodder. In man (top) nitrogenous metabolic wastes are constantly excreted in the form of urea. In the camel (bottom) urea may return via bloodstream to the stomach, where in combination with broken-down cellulose it is reprocessed into new protein. Sheep and perhaps cattle husband nitrogen similarly.

calculate the blood volume before and after dehydration by injecting a non-poisonous dye into the bloodstream and measuring its concentration when it had become evenly distributed. In the case of a young camel that had lost about 11 gallons of water the reduction in blood volume was less than a quart. The water had been lost not from the blood but from the other body fluids and from the tissues.

One might suppose that the camel has some special physiological mechanism for maintaining its blood volume. In theory, however, a man should be able to do the same thing. When he lacks water, the osmotic pressure of the proteins in his blood plasma should draw it from the rest of his body. Since this does not happen, the real question is not how the dehydrated camel maintains its

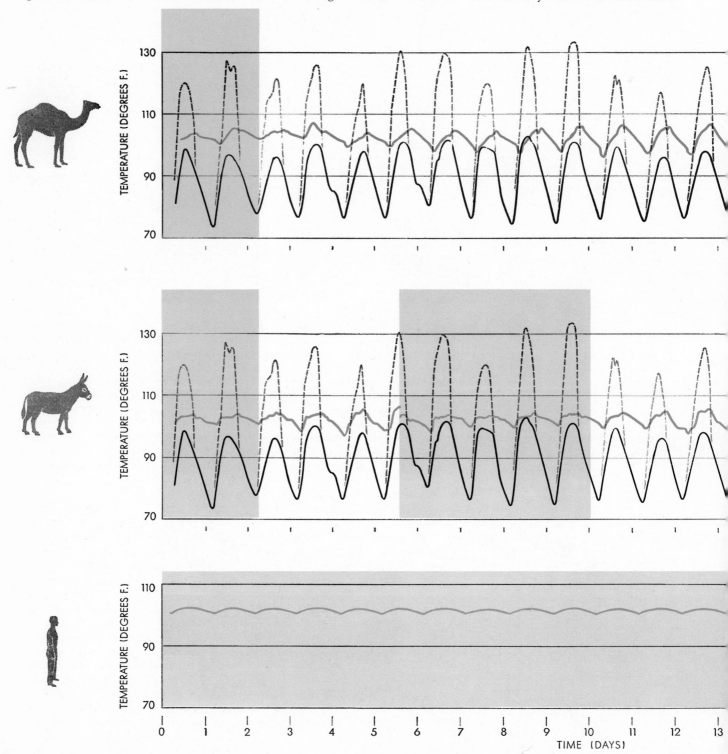

**"FLEXIBLE" BODY TEMPERATURE** partly accounts for the camel's ability to conserve water. Colored curves show variations in body temperature for a camel and a donkey over a 20-day period during the desert summer; a typical temperature curve for a man is shown for comparison. Solid gray curves show variations in air temperature during the same period; the broken curves indicate the additional heat load due to radiation from the sun and ground. The camel's temperature can rise to 105 degrees before the animal begins to sweat freely; during the night its temperature drops as low as 93 degrees, thereby delaying the next day's rise. The camel

blood volume but why a dehydrated man does not.

The camel not only tolerates dehydration much better than a man but also loses water much more slowly. One reason is that it excretes only a small volume

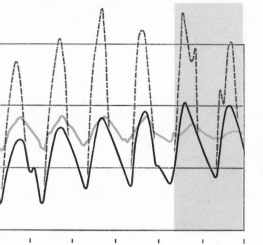

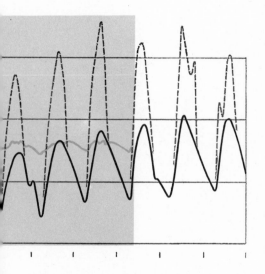

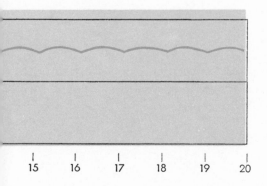

survived though watered (*shading*) only at the beginning and end of the period. Donkey, with a less flexible temperature, sweated more and drank more often. In the desert summer man must drink every day.

of urine—in summer often as little as a quart a day. The animal saves much more water, however, by economizing on sweat.

In the burning heat of the desert an inanimate object such as a rock may reach a temperature of more than 150 degrees F. A camel in such an environment, like a man, maintains a tolerable body temperature by sweating. But where the temperature of the man remains virtually constant as the day grows hotter, the temperature of the camel increases slowly to about 105 degrees. As the temperature of the camel rises, the animal sweats very little; only when its temperature reaches 105 degrees does it sweat freely. The camel's elevated temperature also lessens its absorption of heat, which of course depends on the difference between the temperature of its body and that of the environment.

The camel lowers the heat load on its body still further by letting its temperature fall below normal during the cool desert night. At dawn its temperature may have dropped as low as 93 degrees. Thus much of the day will elapse before the animal's body heats up to 105 degrees and sweating must set in. As a result of its flexible body temperature the camel sweats little except during the hottest hours of the day, where a man in the same environment perspires almost from sunrise to sunset.

These remarkable temperature fluctuations—about 12 degrees for the camel as against two degrees for a man—might seem to indicate a failure of normal heat regulation. This, however, is not so. The camel's body temperature never rises above 105 degrees. Moreover, if the camel has free access to water, the fluctuations are much smaller: about four degrees, comparable to the fluctuations during the cool winter months.

These findings may have implications for animal husbandry in the tropics. Cattle breeders have long sought ways of adapting the highly productive European dairy and beef animals to hot climates. In the process they have generally assumed that animals whose body temperature rises in hot weather will adapt poorly to heat. Although this assumption is often correct, the camel's example suggests that the reverse may sometimes be true.

People in desert areas and outside them have long appreciated the excellent insulating properties of camel hair. The camel employs camel-hair insulation to lower its heat load still fur-

ther. Even during the summer, when the camel sheds much of its wool, it retains a layer several inches thick on its back where the sun beats down. When we sheared the wool from one of our camels, we found that the shorn animal produced 60 per cent more sweat than an unshorn one. To Americans, who wear light clothing during the summer, the idea that a thick layer of wool is advantageous in the desert may seem unreasonable. The Arabs, however, typically dress in several layers of loose clothing, frequently made of wool. I have seen a nomad returning from the desert shed one thick wool burnous after another. We ourselves quickly learned that Arab dress was more comfortable than "civilized" garments.

The camel's hump also helps indirectly to lessen the heat load on the animal. Nearly all mammals possess a food reserve in the form of fat, but in most of them the fat is distributed fairly uniformly over the body just beneath the skin. In having its fat concentrated in one place the camel lacks insulation between its body and its skin, where evaporative cooling takes place. The absence of insulation facilitates the flow of heat outward, just as the insulating wool slows the flow of heat inward.

To clarify the relative importance of insulation and temperature fluctuation in lowering the camel's need for water, we repeated several of our experiments on a donkey. Because the donkey, like the camel, is a native of the arid lands of Asia, it should presumably have developed similar devices for conserving water.

We found that the donkey could tolerate as much water loss as the camel—up to 25 per cent. The donkey, however, lost water three times more rapidly than the camel does; thus it could not go as long without drinking. In one experiment a camel went for 17 days without drinking, while the donkey had to be watered at least once every four days. The difference in water loss seems partly due to the fact that the body temperature of the donkey is more stable than that of the camel. The donkey begins to sweat when its temperature has risen only slightly. Furthermore, the donkey's coat is quite thin in comparison with the camel's and thus does not provide so effective a barrier against heat from the environment.

The donkey outdoes the camel in one respect: its drinking capacity. A camel that has lost 25 per cent of its body weight can drink back the loss in about

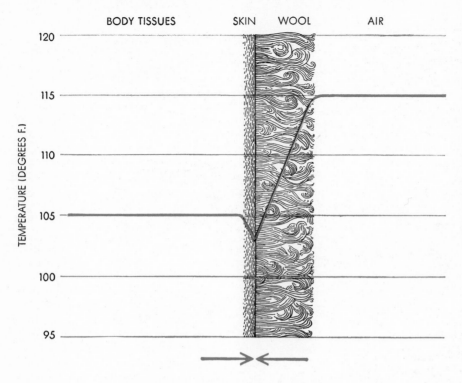

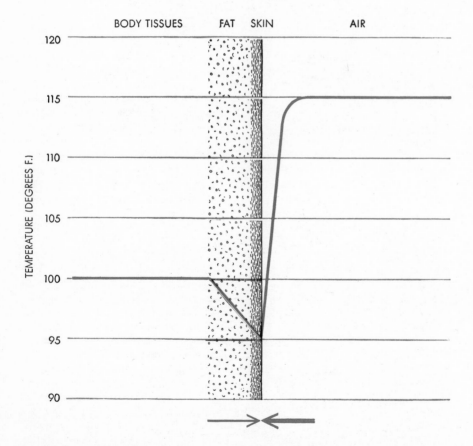

10 minutes; a donkey can perform the same feat in less than two minutes. A man drinks much more slowly; after a day in the desert he will not completely make up his water losses for several hours or until he has eaten (when he tends to drink with his food).

The drinking capacity of both camel and donkey doubtless came about by evolutionary adaptation in the wild state. Water holes are rare in an arid land, and predators often lie in wait near them. The animal that can quickly replenish its water losses and depart is likely to live longer than one that must linger by the water to satisfy its needs.

**HEAT FLOW IN CAMEL AND MAN** is compared in these schematic cross sections of a small portion of body surface. Colored curves show temperature; heat flow, suggested by arrows, increases with the slope of the curves. Camel (*top*) can eliminate heat from its body with an average skin temperature of about 103 degrees; its wool slows the heat flow from the environment. Man (*bottom*), with a lower body temperature and an insulating layer of fat beneath the skin, must maintain a lower skin temperature (that is, must evaporate more sweat) to obtain the same flow of heat from his interior. The lack of insulation between his skin and the air raises heat flow from the air, necessitating still more evaporation.

# 10 Adaptations to Cold

LAURENCE IRVING · January 1966

All living organisms abhor cold. For many susceptible forms of life a temperature difference of a few degrees means the difference between life and death. Everyone knows how critical temperature is for the growth of plants. Insects and fishes are similarly sensitive; a drop of two degrees in temperature when the sun goes behind a cloud, for instance, can convert a fly from a swift flier to a slow walker. In view of the general hostility of cold to life and activity, the ability of mammals and birds to survive and flourish in all climates is altogether remarkable.

It is not that these animals are basically more tolerant of cold. We know from our own reactions how sensitive the human body is to chilling. A naked, inactive human being soon becomes miserable in air colder than 28 degrees centigrade (about 82 degrees Fahrenheit), only 10 degrees C. below his body temperature. Even in the Tropics the coolness of night can make a person uncomfortable. The discomfort of cold is one of the most vivid of experiences; it stands out as a persistent memory in a soldier's recollections of the unpleasantness of his episodes in the field. The coming of winter in temperate climates has a profound effect on human well-being and activity. Cold weather, or cold living quarters, compounds the misery of illness or poverty. Over the entire planet a large proportion of man's efforts, culture and economy is devoted to the simple necessity of protection against cold.

Yet strangely enough neither man nor other mammals have consistently avoided cold climates. Indeed, the venturesome human species often goes out of its way to seek a cold environment, for sport or for the adventure of living in a challenging situation. One of the

marvels of man's history is the endurance and stability of the human settlements that have been established in arctic latitudes.

The Norse colonists who settled in Greenland 1,000 years ago found Eskimos already living there. Archaeologists today are finding many sites and relics of earlier ancestors of the Eskimos who occupied arctic North America as long as 6,000 years ago. In the middens left by these ancient inhabitants are bones and hunting implements that indicate man was accompanied in the cold north by many other warm-blooded animals: caribou, moose, bison, bears, hares, seals, walruses and whales. All the species, including man, seem to have been well adapted to arctic life for thousands of years.

It is therefore a matter of more than idle interest to look closely into how mammals adapt to cold. In all climates and everywhere on the earth mammals maintain a body temperature of about 38 degrees C. It looks as if evolution has settled on this temperature as an optimum for the mammalian class. (In birds the standard body temperature is a few degrees higher.) To keep their internal temperature at a viable level the mammals must be capable of adjusting to a wide range of environmental temperatures. In tropical air at 30 degrees C. (86 degrees F.), for example, the environment is only eight degrees cooler than the body temperature; in arctic air at −50 degrees C. it is 88 degrees colder. A man or other mammal in the Arctic must adjust to both extremes as seasons change.

The mechanisms available for making the adjustments are (1) the generation of body heat by the metabolic burning of food as fuel and (2) the use

of insulation and other devices to retain body heat. The requirements can be expressed quantitatively in a Newtonian formula concerning the cooling of warm bodies. A calculation based on the formula shows that to maintain the necessary warmth of its body a mammal must generate 10 times more heat in the Arctic than in the Tropics or clothe itself in 10 times more effective insulation or employ some intermediate combination of the two mechanisms.

We need not dwell on the metabolic requirement; it is rarely a major factor. An animal can increase its food intake and generation of heat to only a very modest degree. Moreover, even if metabolic capacity and the food supply were unlimited, no animal could spend all its time eating. Like man, nearly all other mammals spend a great deal of time in curious exploration of their surroundings, in play and in family and social activities. In the arctic winter a herd of caribou often rests and ruminates while the young engage in aimless play. I have seen caribou resting calmly with wolves lying asleep in the snow in plain view only a few hundred yards away. There is a common impression that life in the cold climates is more active than in the Tropics, but the fact is that for the natural populations of mammals, including man, life goes on at the same leisurely pace in the Arctic as it does in warmer regions; in all climates there is the same requirement of rest and social activities.

The decisive difference in resisting cold, then, lies in the mechanisms for conserving body heat. In the Institute of Arctic Biology at the University of Alaska we are continuing studies that have been in progress there and elsewhere for 18 years to compare the

ARCTIC ZONE (20 TO −60 DEGREES C.)

TEMPERATE ZONE (20 TO −20 DEGREES C.)

TROPICAL ZONE (35 TO 25 DEGREES C.)

**RANGE OF TEMPERATURES** to which warm-blooded animals must adapt is adicated. All the animals shown have a body temperature close to 100 degrees Fahrenheit, yet they survive at outside temperatures that, for the arctic animals, can be more than 100 degrees cooler. Insulation by fur is a major means of adaptation to cold. Man is insulated by clothing; some other relatively hairless animals, by fat. Some animals have a mechanism for conserving heat internally so that it is not dissipated at the extremities.

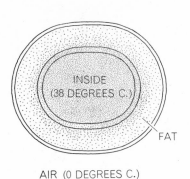

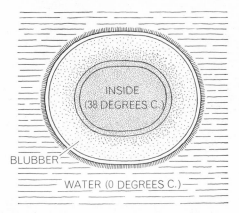

TEMPERATURE GRADIENTS in the outer parts of the body of a pig (*left*) and of a seal (*right*) result from two effects: the insulation provided by fat and the exchange of heat between arterial and venous blood, which produces lower temperatures near the surface.

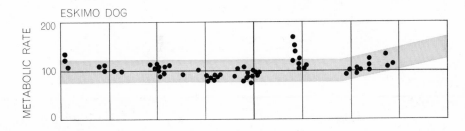

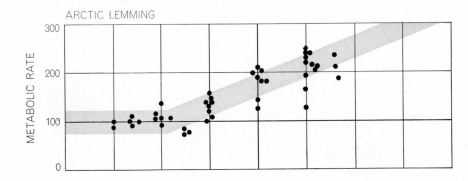

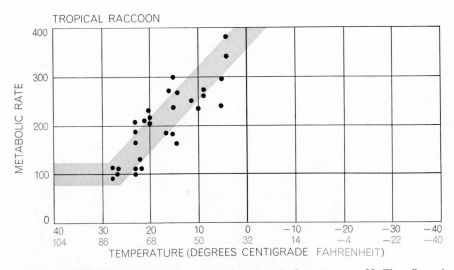

RATE OF METABOLISM provides a limited means of adaptation to cold. The effect of declining temperatures on the metabolic rate is shown for an Eskimo dog (*top*), an arctic lemming (*middle*) and a tropical raccoon (*bottom*). Animals in warmer climates tend to increase metabolism more rapidly than arctic animals do when the temperature declines.

mechanisms for conservation of heat in arctic and tropical animals. The investigations have covered a wide variety of mammals and birds and have yielded conclusions of general physiological interest.

The studies began with an examination of body insulation. The fur of arctic animals is considerably thicker, of course, than that of tropical animals. Actual measurements showed that its insulating power is many times greater. An arctic fox clothed in its winter fur can rest comfortably at a temperature of −50 degrees C. without increasing its resting rate of metabolism. On the other hand, a tropical animal of the same size (a coati, related to the raccoon) must increase its metabolic effort when the temperature drops to 20 degrees C. That is to say, the fox's insulation is so far superior that the animal can withstand air 88 degrees C. colder than its body at resting metabolism, whereas the coati can withstand a difference of only 18 degrees C. Naked man is less well protected by natural insulation than the coati; if unclothed, he begins shivering and raising his metabolic rate when the air temperature falls to 28 degrees C.

Obviously as animals decrease in size they become less able to carry a thick fur. The arctic hare is about the smallest mammal with enough fur to enable it to endure continual exposure to winter cold. The smaller animals take shelter under the snow in winter. Weasels, for example, venture out of their burrows only for short periods; mice spend the winter in nests and sheltered runways under the snow and rarely come to the surface.

No animal, large or small, can cover all of its body with insulating fur. Organs such as the feet, legs and nose must be left unencumbered if they are to be functional. Yet if these extremities allowed the escape of body heat, neither mammals nor birds could survive in cold climates. A gull or duck swimming in icy water would lose heat through its webbed feet faster than the bird could generate it. Warm feet standing on snow or ice would melt it and soon be frozen solidly to the place where they stood. For the unprotected extremities, therefore, nature has evolved a simple but effective mechanism to reduce the loss of heat: the warm outgoing blood in the arteries heats the cool blood returning in the veins from the extremities. This exchange occurs in the *rete mirabile* (wonderful net), a network of small arteries and veins near the junction between the trunk of the animal and the extremity [see " 'The Wonderful Net,' " by P. F. Scholander; Scientific American, April, 1957]. Hence the extremities can become much colder than the body without either draining off body heat or losing their ability to function.

This mechanism serves a dual purpose. When necessary, the thickly furred animals can use their bare extremities to release excess heat from the body. A heavily insulated animal would soon be overheated by running or other active exercise were it not for these outlets. The generation of heat by exercise turns on the flow of blood to the extremities so that they radiate heat. The large, bare flippers of a resting fur seal are normally cold, but we have found that when these animals on the Pribilof Islands are driven overland at their laborious gait, the flippers become warm. In contrast to the warm flippers, the rest of the fur seal's body surface feels cold, because very little heat escapes through the animal's dense fur. Heat can also be dissipated by evaporation from the mouth and tongue. Thus a dog or a caribou begins to pant, as a means of evaporative cooling, as soon as it starts to run.

In the pig the adaptation to cold by means of a variable circulation of heat in the blood achieves a high degree of refinement. The pig, with its skin only thinly covered with bristles, is as naked as a man. Yet it does well in the Alaskan winter without clothing. We can read the animal's response to cold by its expressions of comfort or discomfort, and we have measured its physiological reactions. In cold air the circulation of heat in the blood of swine is shunted away from the entire body surface, so that the surface becomes an effective insulator against loss of body heat. The pig can withstand considerable cooling of its body surface. Although a man is highly uncomfortable when his skin is cooled to 7 degrees C. below the internal temperature, a pig can be comfortable with its skin 30 degrees C. colder than the interior, that is, at a temperature of 8 degrees C. (about 46 degrees F.). Not until the air temperature drops below the freezing point (0 degrees C.) does the pig increase its rate of metabolism; in contrast a man, as I have mentioned, must do so at an air temperature of 28 degrees C.

With thermocouples in the form of needles we have probed the tissues of pigs below the skin surface. (Some pigs, like some people, will accept a little

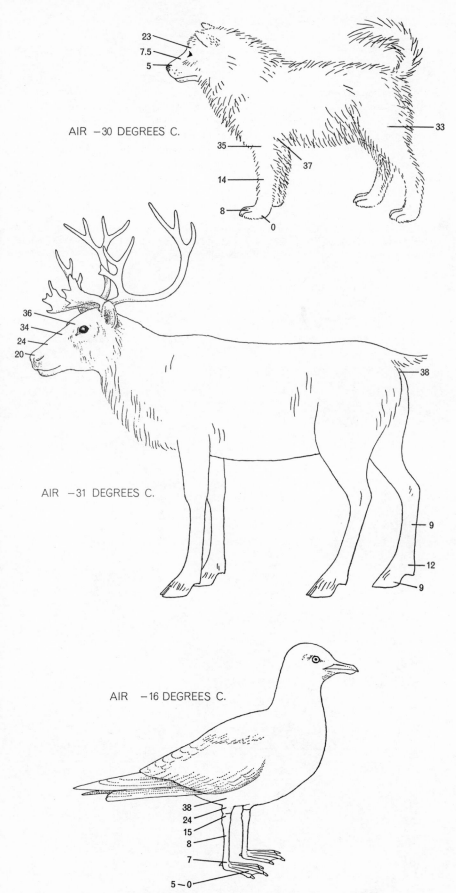

**TEMPERATURES AT EXTREMITIES** of arctic animals are far lower than the internal body temperature of about 38 degrees centigrade, as shown by measurements made on Eskimo dogs, caribou and sea gulls. Some extremities approach the outside temperature.

pain to win a reward.) We found that with the air temperature at −12 degrees C. the cooling of the pig's tissues extended as deep as 100 millimeters (about four inches) into its body. In warmer air the thermal gradient through the tissues was shorter and less steep. In short, the insulating mechanism of the hog involves a considerable depth of the animal's fatty mantle.

Even more striking examples of this kind of mechanism are to be found in whales, walruses and hair seals that dwell in the icy arctic seas. The whale and the walrus are completely bare; the hair seal is covered only with thin, short hair that provides almost no insulation when it is sleeked down in the water. Yet these animals remain comfortable in water around the freezing point although water, with a much greater heat capacity than air, can extract a great deal more heat from a warm body.

Examining hair seals from cold waters of the North Atlantic, we found that even in ice water these animals did not raise their rate of metabolism. Their skin was only one degree or so warmer than the water, and the cooling effect extended deep into the tissues—as much as a quarter of the distance through the thick part of the body. Hour after hour the animal's flippers all the way through would remain only a few degrees above freezing without the seals' showing any sign of discomfort. When the seals were moved into warmer water, their outer tissues rapidly warmed up. They would accept a transfer from warm water to ice water with equanimity and with no diminution of their characteristic liveliness.

How are the chilled tissues of all these animals able to function normally at temperatures close to freezing? There is first of all the puzzle of the response of fatty tissue. Animal fat usually becomes hard and brittle when it is cooled to low temperatures. This is true even of the land mammals of the Arctic, as far as their internal fats are concerned. If it were also true of extremities such as their feet, however, in cold weather their feet would become too inflexible to be useful. Actually it turns out that the fats in these organs behave differently from those in the warm internal tissues. Farmers have known for a long time that neat's-foot oil, extracted from the feet of cattle, can be used to keep leather boots and harness flexible in cold weather. By laboratory examination we have found that the fats in the bones of the lower leg and foot of the caribou remain soft even at 0 degrees C. The melting point of the fats in the leg steadily goes up in the higher portions of the leg. Eskimos have long been aware that fat from a caribou's foot will serve as a fluid lubricant in the cold, whereas the marrow fat from the upper leg is a solid food even at room temperature.

About the nonfatty substances in tissues we have little information; I have seen no reports by biochemists on the effects of temperature on their properties. It is known, however, that many of the organic substances of animal tissues are highly sensitive to temperature. We must therefore wonder how the tissues can maintain their serviceability over the very wide range of temperatures that the body surface experiences in the arctic climate.

We have approached this question by studies of the behavior of tissues at various temperatures. Nature offers many illustrations of the slowing of tissue functions by cold. Fishes, frogs and water insects are noticeably slowed down by cool water. Cooling by 10 degrees

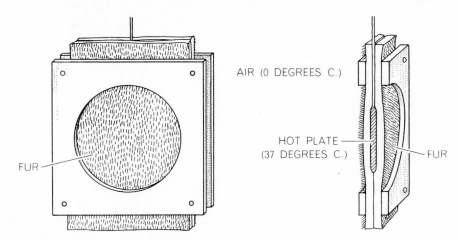

INSULATION BY FUR was tested in this apparatus, shown in a front view at left and a side view at right. The battery-operated heating unit provided the equivalent of body temperature on one side of the fur; outdoor temperatures were approximated on the other side.

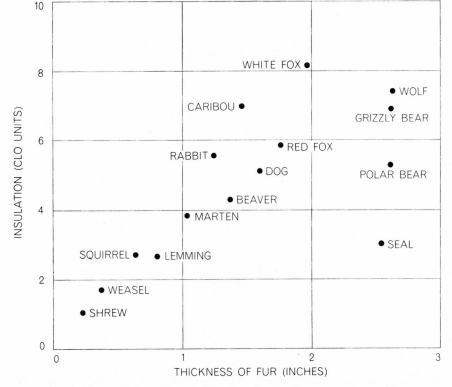

INSULATING CAPACITY of fur is compared for various animals. A "clo unit" equals the amount of insulation provided by the clothing a man usually wears at room temperature.

C. will immobilize most insects. A grasshopper in the warm noonday sun can be caught only by a swift bird, but in the chill of early morning it is so sluggish that anyone can seize it. I had a vivid demonstration of the temperature effect one summer day when I went hunting on the arctic tundra near Point Barrow for flies to use in experiments. When the sun was behind clouds, I had no trouble picking up the flies as they crawled about in the sparse vegetation, but as soon as the sun came out the flies took off and were uncatchable. Measuring the temperature of flies on the ground, I ascertained that the difference between the flying and the slow-crawling state was a matter of only 2 degrees C.

Sea gulls walking barefoot on the ice in the Arctic are just as nimble as gulls on the warm beaches of California. We know from our own sensations that our fingers and hands are numbed by cold. I have used a simple test to measure the amount of this desensitization. After cooling the skin on my fingertips to about 20 degrees C. (68 degrees F.) by keeping them on ice-filled bags, I tested their sensitivity by dropping a light ball (weighing about one milligram) on them from a measured height. The weight multiplied by the distance of fall gave me a measure of the impact on the skin. I found that the skin at a temperature of 20 degrees C. was only a sixth as sensitive as at 35 degrees C. (95 degrees F.); that is, the impact had to be six times greater to be felt.

We know that even the human body surface has some adaptability to cold. Men who make their living by fishing can handle their nets and fish with wet hands in cold that other people cannot endure. The hands of fishermen, Eskimos and Indians have been found to be capable of maintaining an exceptionally vigorous blood circulation in the cold. This is possible, however, only at the cost of a higher metabolic production of body heat, and the production in any case has a limit. What must arouse our wonder is the extraordinary adaptability of an animal such as the hair seal. It swims in icy waters with its flippers and the skin over its body at close to the freezing temperature, and yet under the ice in the dark arctic sea it remains sensitive enough to capture moving prey and find its way to breathing holes.

Here lies an inviting challenge for all biologists. By what devices is an animal able to preserve nervous sensitivity in tissues cooled to low temperatures? Beyond this is a more universal and more

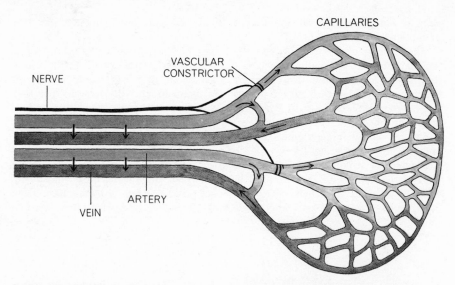

ROLE OF BLOOD in adaptation to cold is depicted schematically. One mechanism, indicated by the vertical arrows, is an exchange of heat between arterial and venous blood. The cold venous blood returning from an extremity acquires heat from an arterial network. The outgoing arterial blood is thus cooled. Hence the exchange helps to keep heat in the body and away from the extremities when the extremities are exposed to low temperatures. The effect is enhanced by the fact that blood vessels near the surface constrict in cold.

interesting question: How do the warm-blooded animals preserve their overall stability in the varying environments to which they are exposed? Adjustment to changes in temperature requires them to make a variety of adaptations in the various tissues of the body. Yet these changes must be harmonized to maintain the integration of the organism as a whole. I predict that further studies of the mechanisms involved in adaptation to cold will yield exciting new insights into the processes that sustain the integrity of warm-blooded animals.

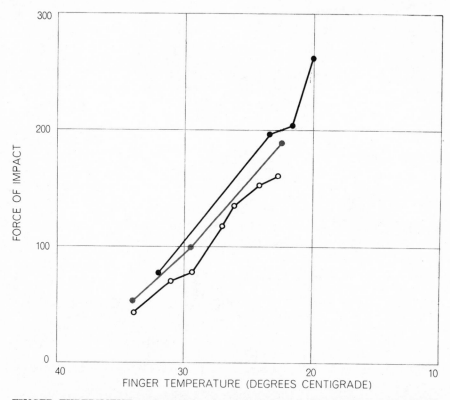

FINGER EXPERIMENT performed by the author showed that the more a finger was chilled, the farther a one-milligram ball had to be dropped for its impact to be felt on the finger. The vertical scale is arbitrary but reflects the relative increase in the force of impact.

# 11 Habitat Selection

STANLEY C. WECKER · October 1964

*Mid pleasures and palaces
'though we may roam,
Be it ever so humble,
there's no place like home.*

If animals were capable of understanding verse, this sentiment would doubtless have as much meaning for the denizens of a rotting log as it does for the inhabitants of the most fashionable suburb. One need only visit the countryside to perceive that the plants and animals in a natural community, like their human counterparts, are not scattered haphazardly over the landscape. Each organism tends to be restricted in distribution by its behavioral and physiological responses to the environment. It follows that living things must be able to locate favorable places in which to live. Their methods of doing so are so numerous and varied, however, that it is difficult to generalize about the selection of habitat.

On the one hand, many small organisms of otherwise low mobility have evolved means for utilizing air and water currents in the dispersion of members of their species. Spores, seeds, ballooning spiders and a surprisingly large number of insects drift in the upper reaches of the atmosphere, and a wide variety of planktonic forms ride the waves of the waters below. Occasionally terrestrial organisms accidentally cross long stretches of sea on pieces of driftwood, and live fish have been transported from pond to pond by hurricanes. The end result of this passive and essentially random dissemination of individuals is that a small number of them eventually reach areas conducive to continued survival and reproduction.

For the majority of animals, on the other hand, choosing a habitat is a more active process. This does not imply that most species can make a critical evaluation of the entire constellation of factors confronting them. More probably they react automatically to certain key aspects of their surroundings. For example, a wide variety of animals, ranging from single-celled protozoans to beetles and salamanders, often select their habitat at least in part by orientation along physicochemical gradients in the environment. These include such factors as temperature, moisture, light and salinity.

Another form of behavior that results in habitat selection is the choice of egg-laying sites by insects. Among certain beetles, butterflies and wasps the gravid female instinctively selects a plant or an animal host that will satisfy the requirements of the developing larva, whether or not the needs of the larva coincide with her own. Among the birds that live in shrubbery or forest the choice of habitat has been found to be associated with the height, spacing and form of the vegetation. Even when the overall character of the vegetation is appropriate for a species, a deficiency of specific environmental cues, such as song perches and nest sites, may exclude the species from an area within its range. The British ornithologist David Lack has called this phenomenon a "psychological factor" in habitat selection. Among the higher forms of life such factors may be fully as important as stimuli more directly related to physiological tolerances.

Although many ecologists have investigated the physical and biological factors that cause mammals to occupy certain habitats and avoid others, little is known about the role of psychological factors. One genus that is particularly well suited for the study of these factors is *Peromyscus,* the deer mouse. To this hardy little mammal almost every conceivable ecological situation, ranging from desert to tropical rain forest, from barren tundra to windblown mountaintops, is home. One species, *P. maniculatus,* is among the most variable of all North American rodents. It has 66 subspecies, which are found in so many habitats that a leading ecologist has remarked that probably no environmental change short of the inundation of the entire continent would eliminate all of them! In spite of this variability, however, in the sense of ecological adaptation the species has just two principal types: the long-tailed, long-eared forest forms, and the smaller short-tailed, short-eared grassland forms.

The prairie deer mouse of the Middle Western and Plains states (*Peromyscus maniculatus bairdi*) is a strictly field-dwelling subspecies that avoids all forested areas, even those with a grassy floor. Studies comparing the food preferences and the requirements for temperature and moisture of this subspecies and a closely related woodland form, *P. m. gracilis,* have not revealed any physiological differences of sufficient magnitude to account for the difference in their choice of habitat. It has therefore been concluded that the absence of the prairie deer mouse from forested areas within its geographic range is primarily a behavioral response to its environment.

The first experimental attempt to identify the environmental cues that cause these mice to choose a place to live was undertaken in 1950 by Van T. Harris, then working with Lee R. Dice at the University of Michigan Laboratory of Vertebrate Biology. Harris presented individual prairie and woodland deer mice with a choice between a laboratory "field" and a laboratory "woods." Each type of mouse exhibited a clear preference for the artificial habitat more closely resembling its natural en-

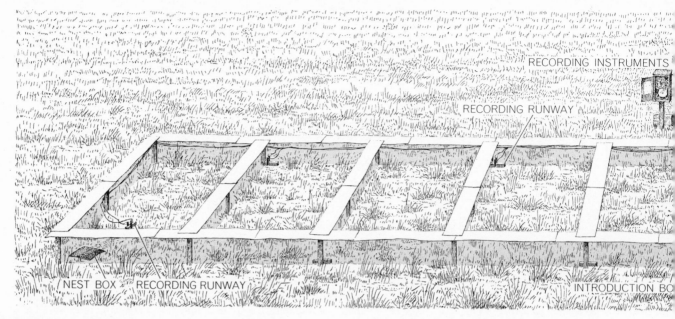

**EXPERIMENTAL ENCLOSURE** for testing habitat preference of prairie deer mice is 100 feet long and 16 feet wide. Five of its 10 compartments are in a field (*left*) and five are in an oak-hickory woodlot. For testing, each mouse is placed in the introduction box near the middle. It can go from there into either the field half or the woods half of the enclosure. Each partition has a run-

vironment. Since the physical conditions throughout the experimental room were uniform, Harris concluded that the mice were reacting to the character of the artificial vegetation. Moreover, laboratory-reared animals with no outdoor experience chose the "correct" artificial habitat as readily as the wild mice did. Harris therefore decided that this behavior was innate.

These experiments were not, however, designed to test the possibility that learning might also be involved. It has recently been established that early experience is of greater importance in the development of adult behavior than had once been thought [see "Early Experience and Emotional Development," by Victor H. Denenberg; SCIENTIFIC

AMERICAN offprint 478]. Since young prairie deer mice are normally born and reared in open fields, one would expect their early experience to reinforce any innate preference for this habitat.

These considerations raise two questions: (1) Does learning actually play a role in habitat selection by *Peromyscus*? (2) Can an innate preference for field conditions be overridden by early experience in a different environment? In order to investigate these problems I constructed a 100-foot-long outdoor pen on the University of Michigan's Edwin S. George Reserve, 26 miles northwest of Ann Arbor. The project was initiated with the support of the Department of Zoology and the Muse-

um of Zoology and was carried out under the auspices of the Laboratory of Vertebrate Biology and its director, Francis C. Evans.

The long axis of the experimental pen crosses a relatively sharp boundary between an open field and an oak-hickory woodlot. The enclosure is divided into 10 compartments, five of which are in the field and five in the woods. There are two underground nest boxes, one at the end that extends farthest into the woods, the other at the end that extends farthest into the field. A third underground box in the middle of the enclosure serves as a chamber for introducing mice. Small metal runways leading from one compartment to another allow the animals to go anywhere with-

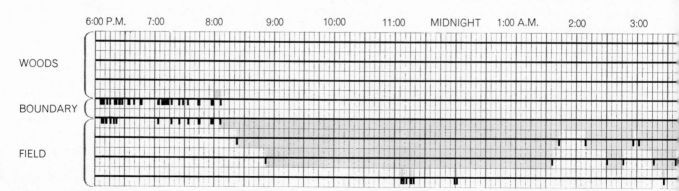

**RECORD MADE BY MOUSE** in two nights shows preference for field. The mouse, from laboratory stock, was in the field for 10 days when quite young, then lived in laboratory for 56 days before test. Daylight hours are omitted here because the mouse was quiet in the field nest box. The eight horizontal lines (*black*) were traced by

pens connected with the various treadles in the enclosure, ranging in order from the woods nest box at top to field nest box at bottom. Short vertical lines along the tracings are "blips" made when mouse crossed treadle. Just after 6:00 P.M. (*far left*) mouse leaves introduction box, runs back and forth across treadles at

way at one end that enables the mouse to go from one compartment to the next. Two of the seven runways with recording treadles are labeled. Nest boxes, both of which have treadles, are in the last compartments at left and right. The instruments that make permanent records of movements of each mouse (*see bottom of these two pages*) are in box at top, just to left of center.

in the entire fenced area. A centrally located electric device records the time at which a mouse passes through the runways and enters the nest boxes. I place each mouse in the experimental enclosure alone and leave it there until it has nested in the same habitat for two consecutive days.

Prairie deer mice are nocturnal and are inactive during the day. I decided, therefore, that it would be most meaningful to consider the length of an animal's active and inactive periods in each environment (woods and field) as separate measures of habitat selection. Three other categories of measurement provide further data for comparing an animal's response to the woods with its response to the field. The five categories used in

this study, then, are (A) *time active*, or time spent outside the nest boxes in woods and field respectively; (B) *time inactive*, or time spent nesting in woods or field; (C) *rate of travel*, or the speed at which a mouse moves about in each of the two habitats; (D) *activity*, or the frequency with which a mouse changes compartments or enters nest boxes in woods or field; and (E) *average penetration* (in feet) into either of the two habitats each time a mouse crosses the boundary between them. In all categories except rate of travel the higher score for woods or field is taken to indicate habitat preference. In the case of rate of travel it was assumed that a mouse travels more slowly in the preferred habitat; presumably the animal

is less subject to stress in its normal environment.

In the course of the study I tested six groups of prairie deer mice, one mouse at a time, in the enclosure. Observing the 132 mice occupied the spring, summer and fall of two successive years. The two control and four experimental groups were each characterized by a different combination of two variables: hereditary background and pretest experience. The hereditary distinction was between field-caught mice (and their immediate offspring) and individuals selected from a laboratory stock. The experience was provided in the field, in the woods and in the laboratory.

The first group to be tested consisted

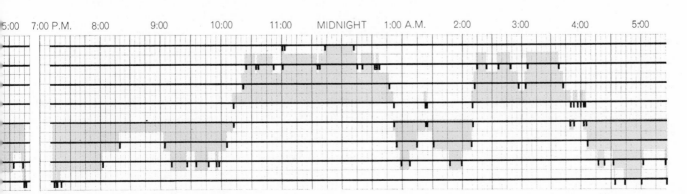

habitat boundary. After brief foray into woods (7:58 P.M.) it returns to field and gradually moves all the way to the nest box (11:07 P.M.). It goes in and out, then moves back several times toward habitat boundary but never crosses it. At 5:16 A.M. it enters field nest box (*end of first night's record*) and remains throughout

the day. Record for second night shows two long periods in the woods, including two entries into the woods nest box. It was usually assumed that the mouse went at least halfway to the next treadle after crossing a treadle, as shown by colored shading. Actually the mouse could have been anywhere between the two treadles.

**INTRODUCTION BOX** opens into the runway (*left*) that crosses the habitat boundary. The two recording treadles for the boundary can be seen in this runway. Tiny door at end of exit tube opens outward only. The two nest boxes resemble the introduction chamber.

of individuals recently caught in old fields of the Edwin S. George Reserve, where earlier studies had clearly demonstrated the strong affinity of prairie deer mice for the field environment. My assumption was that the reactions of these adult animals would provide a basis for evaluating any unnatural effects of the enclosure itself. Accordingly I designated the eight males and four females in the group as Control Series I. At the end of the test it was obvious from all five measurements that the mice much preferred the field half of the enclosure [*see upper illustration on opposite page*]. From this I concluded that the testing situation permitted the animals to exercise their normal habitat preference.

If this preference is innate, field mice reared in the laboratory should also choose the field environment. In order to evaluate this hypothesis I tested seven males and six females from the prairie deer mouse colony of the University of Michigan Mammalian Genetics Center. These were Control Series II. The entire laboratory stock, designated *Peromyscus maniculatus bairdi* Washtenaw (for Washtenaw County), was descended from 10 pairs of animals trapped in the vicinity of Ann Arbor by Harris in 1946. According to the records the 13 individuals of Control Series II were 12 to 20 generations removed from any field experience. Their performance in the enclosure contrasted sharply with that of Control Series I [*see lower illus-*

*tration on opposite page*]. In three of the five categories more Control Series II individuals preferred the woods to the field! The most that can be said of the group as a whole, however, is that it did not demonstrate a well-defined preference for either habitat.

In its laboratory environment the *bairdi* Washtenaw stock has been subjected to different selective pressures from those encountered in fields. Combinations of genes that are advantageous to prairie deer mice in nature, such as those affecting response to the environment, would in the laboratory probably not be selected for and might even be selected against. One can therefore assume that the field and laboratory populations used in my experiments had genetically diverged. Since other investigators have shown that such divergence in laboratory stocks can lead to morphological changes, it seems reasonable to assume that behavioral modifications will arise also. I suggest that these contributed to the highly variable habitat response of the mice in Control Series II. It is of considerable interest that the marked preference for fields displayed by their ancestors has been lost in only 12 to 20 generations.

Thus the data from Control Series II neither support nor refute Harris' contention that the habitat preference of prairie deer mice is normally determined by heredity. The next experiment provided a more rigorous evalua-

tion. For this test I caught more wild field mice and bred them in the laboratory. The offspring, which were separated from their parents shortly after weaning, lived in laboratory cages for an average of about two months. Then I tested eight males and four females in the enclosure as Experimental Series I. None had had any previous outdoor experience.

Among these mice there was no reason to anticipate hereditary modifications of the type postulated for the laboratory stock. Thus if habitat preference is genetically determined, the behavior of the mice in Experimental Series I should approximate that of Control Series I. As the records indicate [*see top illustration on page 84*] these animals did display a pronounced affinity for the field half of the enclosure. Obviously prior experience in this environment is not a necessary prerequisite for habitat selection.

Since the animals were reared by field-caught parents, however, it is possible that some form of noninherited social interaction brought about the results. Unfortunately I have had no opportunity to evaluate this possibility, but other investigators have failed to find evidence in prairie deer mice for transfer of behavioral traits from generation to generation through learning. Litters reared by foster parents do not reveal any consistent indication of maternal, paternal or joint parental influence. It seems likely that, as Harris concluded, the habitat preference of wild populations of prairie deer mice is an expression of an innate pattern of behavior. The pattern may be elicited by certain key environmental stimuli, but it apparently does not depend on a period of habituation to the environment for its expression. This does not mean, however, that early experience has no effect on the selection of habitat by an adult animal. It seems reasonable to assume that a young deer mouse's normal association with open fields will reinforce its innate preference for this environment.

In order to ascertain the role such experience plays, I allowed pairs of laboratory animals to rear litters in a 10-by-10-foot pen constructed in the field. Located a short distance from the main enclosure, this area was divided into two compartments, each of which contained a number of nest boxes. Mice that had mated in the laboratory were moved into the nest boxes soon after they had borne litters and before the eyes of the young had opened. After an average of 31 days in the field pen 13 of the offspring were tested in the main enclosure. I labeled this group Experimental Series II.

These 13 mice—eight males and five females—displayed a well-defined preference for the field habitat. Since the laboratory stock of Control Series II had not particularly preferred the field, the highly contrasting behavior of the offspring of such stock can only be explained by their field experience. Although the laboratory animals have apparently lost the innate preference of the subspecies for fields, they have retained a capacity for learning that enables them to exercise habitat selection if they are exposed to the field environment at an early age. Whether or not early experience in a different environment would reverse normal habitat affinities, however, remained to be determined.

Accordingly field-caught prairie deer mice were allowed to raise litters in a 10-by-10-foot pen in the woods. Subsequently I tested seven of the woods-reared offspring in the large enclosure. These mice—six males and one female—constituted Experimental Series III. The two weeks of woods experience did not noticeably influence their selection of habitat. In all five categories of measurement a majority of the mice exhibited the normal field preference. It thus appears that early experience in the "wrong" environment is not enough to override the innate habitat response. Since learning assumes a more impor-

tant role in the development of a well-defined habitat preference by laboratory animals, it seemed possible that early experience in the woods might lead mice from laboratory stock to prefer the woods habitat.

In order to determine if this was the case I transferred to the woods pen litters born to *bairdi* Washtenaw females. Nine of these offspring, six males and three females, were subsequently tested in the main enclosure as Experimental Series IV. As a whole, in spite of their 24 days of woods experience, these animals did not demonstrate a pronounced tendency to select the woods half of the enclosure. On the other hand, neither did they display any special preference for the field half. One must therefore conclude that prairie deer mice can only learn to respond to

environmental cues associated with the field habitat.

To summarize the six experiments, four groups (Control Series I and Experimental Series I, II and III) consistently selected the field half of the enclosure, whereas the other two (Control Series II and Experimental Series IV) did not exhibit a well-defined habitat preference. All the individuals in the four groups that preferred the field environment had either field-caught parents or field experience or both. The other two groups were offspring of laboratory animals and had had no contact with the natural field environment prior to testing in the enclosure.

The data warrant the following conclusions: (1) The choice of the field environment by *P. m. bairdi* is normally

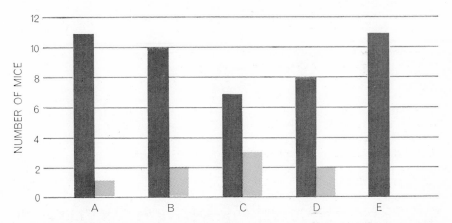

**CONTROL SERIES I,** consisting of 12 adult mice trapped in an open field, showed a clear preference for the field  Gray bars indicate choice of field for each criterion of measurement (*A* through *E*); colored bars denote a preference for the woods. In this and the five bar graphs that follow, a pair of bars for some criteria does not add up to the total number of mice in the group. This results from a failure in the recording apparatus, or from the fact that an animal's score was the same for both woods and field, or because the mouse spent all its time in one habitat, making the comparisons in categories C, D and E impossible.

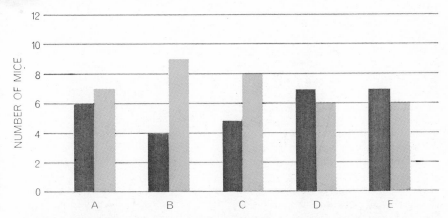

**CONTROL SERIES II,** consisting of 13 animals of laboratory stock, 12 to 20 generations away from the field, preferred the woods according to three categories of measurement. As a whole, however, this group cannot be said to have selected either half of the enclosure. Categories of measurement are (*A*) percent of time active in woods or field, (*B*) percent of time inactive, (*C*) rate of travel in woods or field, (*D*) activity in field or woods and (*E*) average penetration in feet by a mouse into woods or field from the habitat boundary.

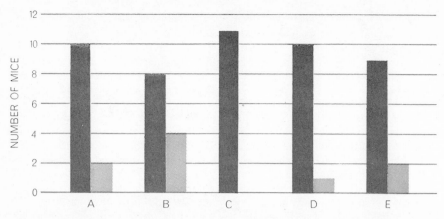

**EXPERIMENTAL SERIES I,** 12 mice, were first-generation offspring of field stock, reared in the laboratory. In all five measurements of habitat selection, they chose the field.

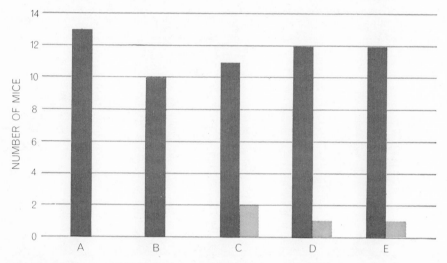

**EXPERIMENTAL SERIES II,** 13 animals, were laboratory stock reared in a pen in the field. By all five criteria of measurement they displayed a strong preference for the field.

determined by heredity. (2) Early field experience can reinforce this innate preference, but it is not a prerequisite for subsequent habitat selection. (3) Early experience in other environments (woods or laboratory) cannot override the normal affinity of field stock for the field habitat. (4) Confinement of the *bairdi* Washtenaw stock in the laboratory for 12 to 20 generations has apparently reduced hereditary control over the habitat response. This genetic change has markedly increased the behavioral variability of these animals when tested in the enclosure. (5) The laboratory stock did retain an innate capacity for learning from early field experience to respond positively to stimuli associated with this environment. Experience in the woods, however, did not cause them, on the whole, to select the woods habitat.

These results indicate that both heredity and experience can play a role in determining the preference of the prairie deer mouse for the field habitat,

which raises an interesting question. Since the same affinity for fields can be learned by each generation, why has natural selection produced an apparently parallel, genetically determined response?

According to the British zoologist C. H. Waddington, evolutionary changes that increase hereditary control are advantageous because they tend to limit the number of possible ways an organism can respond to a particular environmental stimulus. This is beneficial because natural selection favors only those responses conducive to survival. Therefore, as long as the environment remains relatively stable, the population as a whole will eventually become genetically adjusted to the ecological situation it is most likely to encounter and best able to exploit. The innate preference of prairie deer mice for the field environment represents such an adjustment. Why, then, does the mouse retain what appears to be an independent mechanism for habitat selection based

on learning? Furthermore, if we are dealing with two independent mechanisms, why should relaxation of natural selection under laboratory conditions remove one and not the other?

I would suggest that the innate pattern of habitat selection is not independent of the learned pattern but rather is really an extension of the learned pattern. This idea derives support from the observations on *bairdi* Washtenaw stock: the laboratory animals have lost any innate habitat preference but learn to select the "correct," or field, half of the enclosure after being reared in a pen in the field. Presumably a certain number ($X$) of "field-adapting" genes would give the prairie deer mouse the ability to learn to respond positively to the field environment; a larger number of such genes ($X$ plus $Y$) could make this behavior innate. After 12 to 20 generations in the laboratory the mouse reverts from the $X$-plus-$Y$ genotype back to the $X$ genotype.

The behavioral evolution from learned to innate response can be explained as an example of the "Baldwin effect," originally called organic selection when postulated in 1896 by J. M. Baldwin of Princeton University. Recently George Gaylord Simpson of Harvard University has redefined the process to explain how individually acquired, nongenetic adaptations may, under the influence of natural selection, be replaced in a population by similar hereditary characteristics.

As an alternative to accepting the old Lamarckian doctrine that acquired characteristics can be directly inherited, one might apply Simpson's interpretation of the Baldwin effect to the prairie deer mouse situation as follows: As the mice became physiologically and morphologically adapted to existence in the grasslands, patterns of behavior based on some form of learning (homing, for example) tended to confine individuals to the field environment. These patterns, although not exclusively hereditary as such, were still advantageous in that they restricted the animals to the habitat best suited for their survival and reproduction. Then chance mutation created genetic factors that facilitated the development of behavior patterns whose effects resembled those acquired through learning. Finally, since natural selection favored these factors, they spread through the population.

Waddington believes, however, that the Baldwin effect, with its emphasis on chance mutation, involves an oversimplification that ignores the role of the environment in determining the manner in which particular combinations of genes will be expressed. For example, climate or some other aspect of the environment may determine what color certain animals will be, the animals themselves having a genetic potential for more than one color. Waddington maintains that natural selection operates not in favor of genes whose effects happen *by chance* to parallel acquired (nongenetic) adaptations but in favor of factors that control the capacity of an individual to respond to its surroundings. The interaction of organism and environment has the effect of reducing the number of different pathways for genetic expression, thus facilitating the production of better-adapted individuals. The more thorough this "canalization" of developmental possibilities is, the more likely it will be that favorable combinations of genes already present in the population in low frequency will find expression. Once expressed, these combinations of genes can be acted on by natural selection. Since they are favorable, the number of individuals bearing them will ultimately increase. Waddington terms this process the "genetic assimilation" of a character that is initially acquired, or nongenetic.

The results of experiments I am now conducting suggest that the *bairdi* Washtenaw stock learns to respond to the field environment very quickly and may indeed exhibit what the British zoologist W. H. Thorpe has called habitat imprinting. If imprinting is actually operating, one would expect the adult habitat response to be determined during a critical period early in the life of the animal, probably shortly after the young mouse first leaves the nest. It is significant, therefore, that young laboratory animals receiving only 10 days of early field experience still have a marked preference for that environment when they are tested in the enclosure, even after two months of confinement in laboratory cages! On the other hand, exposure of adult laboratory animals to the field environment for as long as 59 days does not cause them to develop a well-defined habitat preference.

In view of the above, it appears that one result of selection for an increased number of "field-adapting" genes has been to shift the development of the behavior patterns involved in habitat selection to earlier and earlier periods in the life of the individual. Obviously survival is enhanced by recognition of a favorable environment over successive generations through learning. It would be even more advantageous to restrict

learning capacity to include only those cues associated with the favorable environment and to reduce to an absolute minimum the time required for such learning. Finally, the necessity for learning could be eliminated altogether by selection for sets of genes that endow an individual with the capacity for making an adaptive response to the critical stimuli as soon as the stimuli are encountered. In this context a hypothetical imprinting stage may have been an important preliminary to the ultimate genetic assimilation of the habitat response of the prairie deer mouse. Indeed, the behavioral differences among the various groups of mice tested during my investigation could be taken to reflect different steps in an evolutionary sequence leading from behavior largely dependent on learning to the development of an innate pattern of control.

This sequence might have occurred as follows: (1) habitat restriction through social factors and homing, (2) recognition of the field environment through learning, (3) learning capacity reduced to cues associated with the field habitat, (4) imprinting to the field environment through exposure very early in life, (5) innate determination of the habitat response.

So far no one has identified the specific cues by which a prairie deer mouse recognizes the field environment. Fortunately the results of my investigations suggest a unique approach to this problem. Young laboratory animals do not develop a well-defined habitat preference in the absence of early field experience. It should therefore be meaningful to expose them in the laboratory to single stimuli designed to simulate different aspects of the natural field en-

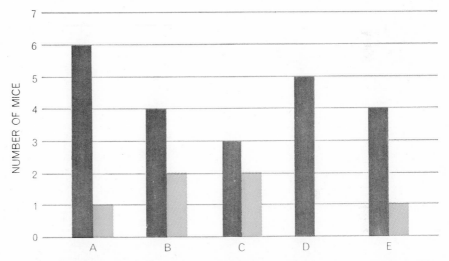

**EXPERIMENTAL SERIES III,** seven mice, offspring of adults trapped in the field, were conditioned by rearing in a pen in the woods. They tended to choose the field habitat.

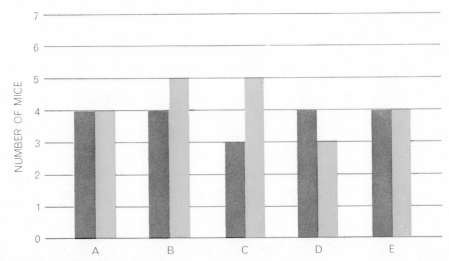

**EXPERIMENTAL SERIES IV,** nine animals, were laboratory stock reared in the pen in the woods. Overall they appeared to have no particular preference for either of the habitats.

vironment. These stimuli include the sight, odor and touch of field vegetation, with artificial grass as the touch stimulus. Groups of animals, each group exposed to only one such factor, could then be tested in the experimental enclosure. In fact, I am now conducting such tests, but the data are not yet extensive enough to warrant any conclusions.

Having considered the role of evolution in habitat selection, I should like to discuss briefly the part that habitat selection plays in the evolutionary process. A diversity of habitat prefer-

ences within a species favors survival by making the species more adaptable to environmental change. Such a diversity, however, might be expected to lead to genetic divergence by selective processes similar to those already described. Nevertheless, most biologists do not believe that new species can arise in this way unless some form of geographical isolation occurs. In Michigan the ranges of the prairie deer mouse and the woodland deer mouse overlap, but there is no evidence of intergradation, or interbreeding, between the two types. It is known, however, that these subspecies did not develop side by side, because

they were formerly isolated geographically. Indeed, the two forms came into close contact only during the past century, when the clearing of forests by man enabled the prairie field mouse to extend its range northward.

Both Harris' experiments and mine provide evidence that the observed difference in habitat preference of these subspecies forms the basis for their continued segregation. As Ernst Mayr of Harvard University points out, ecological differences between two such overlapping forms are to be expected, since competition would otherwise prevent both from coexisting in the same area.

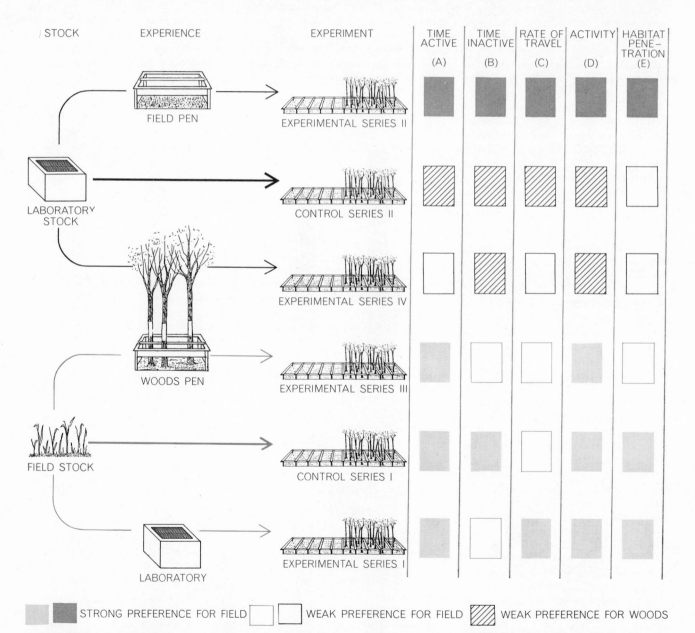

SUMMARY OF OBSERVATIONS reveals preferences of prairie deer mice from various backgrounds. Mice captured in the field were placed in the experimental pen as "Control Series I" (*thick colored arrow*). Offspring of field-caught mice were given conditioning in laboratory cages or in a pen in the woods before testing (*thin colored arrows*). Laboratory stock were tested in the experimental enclosure as "Control Series II" (*thick black arrow*), and their offspring were conditioned in woods or field pens before testing (*thin black arrows*). Results of the tests on the six groups are given in right half of the diagram. The five categories of measurement are explained in the text. Degree of preference is indicated. Results are based on mean response of each group.

# 12 Crises in the History of Life

NORMAN D. NEWELL · February 1963

The stream of life on earth has been continuous since it originated some three or four billion years ago. Yet the fossil record of past life is not a simple chronology of uniformly evolving organisms. The record is prevailingly one of erratic, often abrupt changes in environment, varying rates of evolution, extermination and repopulation. Dissimilar biotas replace one another in a kind of relay. Mass extinction, rapid migration and consequent disruption of biological equilibrium on both a local and a world-wide scale have accompanied continual environmental changes.

The main books and chapters of earth history—the eras, periods and epochs—were dominated for tens or even hundreds of millions of years by characteristic groups of animals and plants. Then, after ages of orderly evolution and biological success, many of the groups suddenly died out. The cause of these mass extinctions is still very much in doubt and constitutes a major problem of evolutionary history.

The striking episodes of disappearance and replacement of successive biotas in the layered fossil record were termed revolutions by Baron Georges Cuvier, the great French naturalist of the late 18th and early 19th centuries. Noting that these episodes generally correspond to unconformities, that is, gaps in the strata due to erosion, Cuvier attributed them to sudden and violent catastrophes. This view grew out of his study of the sequence of strata in the region of Paris. The historic diagram on the opposite page was drawn by Cuvier nearly 150 years ago. It represents a simple alternation of fossil-bearing rocks of marine and nonmarine origin, with many erosional breaks and marked interruptions in the sequence of fossils.

The objection to Cuvier's catastro-phism is not merely that he ascribed events in earth history to cataclysms; many normal geological processes are at times cataclysmic. The objection is that he dismissed known processes and appealed to fantasy to explain natural phenomena. He believed that "the march of nature is changed and not one of her present agents could have sufficed to have effected her ancient works." This hypothesis, like so many others about extinction, is not amenable to scientific test and is hence of limited value. In fairness to Cuvier, however, one must recall that in his day it was widely believed that the earth was only a few thousand years old. Cuvier correctly perceived that normal geological processes could not have produced the earth as we know it in such a short time.

Now that we have learned that the earth is at least five or six billion years old, the necessity for invoking Cuverian catastrophes to explain geological history would seem to have disappeared. Nevertheless, a few writers such as Immanuel Velikovsky, the author of *Worlds in Collision,* and Charles H. Hapgood, the author of *The Earth's Shifting Crust,* continue to propose imaginary catastrophes on the basis of little or no historical evidence. Although it is well established that the earth's crust has shifted and that climates have changed, these changes almost certainly were more gradual than Hapgood suggests. Most geologists, following the "uniformitarian" point of view expounded in the 18th century by James Hutton and in the 19th by Charles Lyell, are satisfied that observable natural processes are quite adequate to explain the history of the earth. They agree, however, that these processes must have varied greatly in rate.

Charles Darwin, siding with Hutton and Lyell, also rejected catastrophism as an explanation for the abrupt changes in the fossil record. He attributed such changes to migrations of living organisms, to alterations of the local environment during the deposition of strata and to unconformities caused by erosion. Other important factors that are now given more attention than they were in Darwin's day are the mass extinction of organisms, acceleration of the rate of evolution and the thinning of strata due to extremely slow deposition.

## The Record of Mass Extinctions

If we may judge from the fossil record, eventual extinction seems to be the lot of all organisms. Roughly 2,500 families of animals with an average longevity of somewhat less than 75 million years have left a fossil record. Of these, about a third are still living. Although a few families became extinct by evolving into new families, a majority dropped out of sight without descendants.

In spite of the high incidence of extinction, there has been a persistent gain in the diversity of living forms: new forms have appeared more rapidly than old forms have died out. Evidently organisms have discovered an increasing number of ecological niches to fill, and by modifying the environment they have produced ecological systems of great complexity, thereby making available still more niches. In fact, as I shall develop later, the interdependence of living organisms, involving complex chains of food supply, may provide an important key to the understanding of how relatively small changes in the environment could have triggered mass extinctions.

The fossil record of animals tells more about extinction than the fossil record of plants does. It has long been known

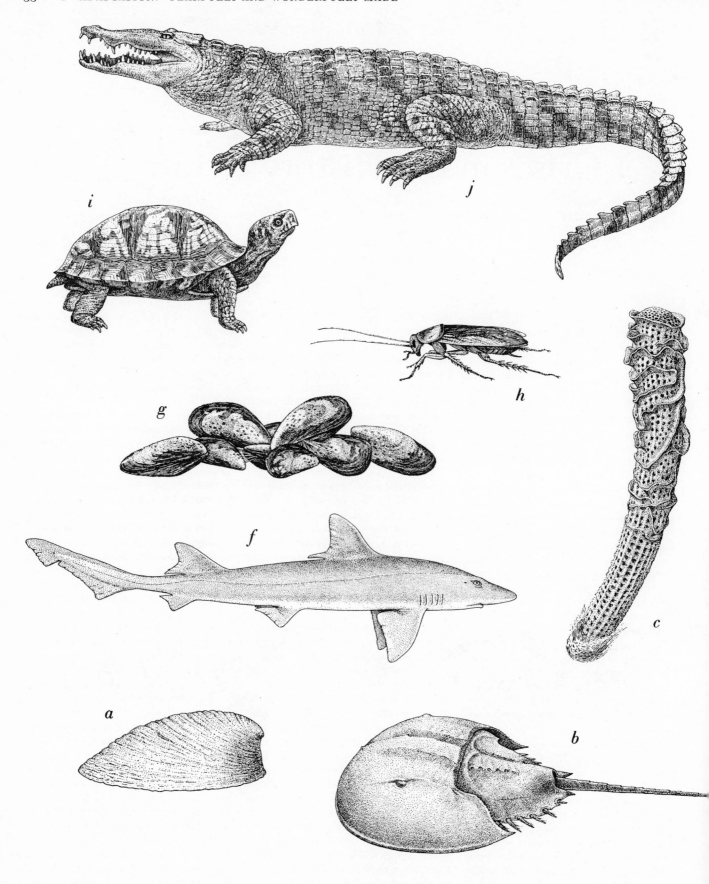

GALLERY OF HARDY ANIMALS contains living representatives of 11 groups that have weathered repeated crises in evolutionary history. Four of the groups can be traced back to the Cambrian period: the mollusk *Neopilina* (*a*), the horseshoe crab (*b*), the Venus's-flower-basket, *Euplectella* (*c*) and the brachiopod *Lingula* (*d*). One animal represents a group that goes back to the Ordovician period: the ostracode *Bairdia* (*e*). Two arose in the Devonian period: the shark (*f*) and the mussel (*g*). The cockroach

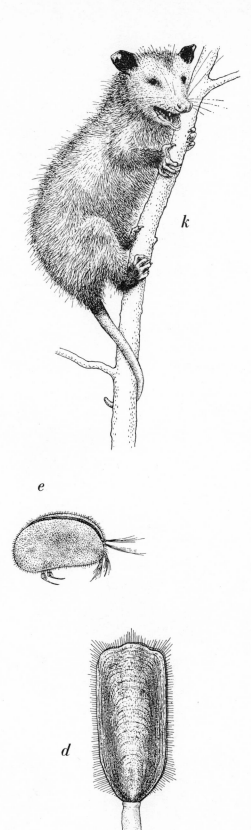

*k*

*e*

*d*

(*h*) goes back to the Pennsylvanian period.
Two arose in the late Triassic: the turtle
(*i*) and the crocodile (*j*). The opossum
(*k*) appeared during the Cretaceous period.

that the major floral changes have not coincided with the major faunal ones. Each of the three successive principal land floras—the ferns and mosses, the gymnosperms and angiosperms—were ushered in by a short episode of rapid evolution followed by a long period of stability. The illustration on page 91 shows that once a major group of plants became established it continued for millions of years. Many groups of higher plants are seemingly immortal. Since green plants are the primary producers in the over-all ecosystem and animals are the consumers, it can hardly be doubted that the great developments in the plant kingdom affected animal evolution, but the history of this relation is not yet understood.

Successive episodes of mass extinction among animals—particularly the marine invertebrates, which are among the most abundant fossils—provide world-wide stratigraphic reference points that the paleontologist calls datums. Many of the datums have come to be adopted as boundaries of the main divisions of geologic time, but there remains some uncertainty whether the epochs of extinction constitute moments in geologic time or intervals of significant duration. In other words, did extinction occur over hundreds, thousands or millions of years? The question has been answered in many ways, but it still remains an outstanding problem.

A good example of mass extinction is provided by the abrupt disappearance of nearly two-thirds of the existing families of trilobites at the close of the Cambrian period. Before the mass extinction of these marine arthropods, which are distantly related to modern crustaceans, there were some 60 families of them. The abrupt disappearance of so many major groups of trilobites at one time has served as a convenient marker for defining the upper, or most recent, limit of the Cambrian period [*see illustration on page 92*].

Similar episodes of extinction characterize the history of every major group and most minor groups of animals that have left a good fossil record. It is striking that times of widespread extinction generally affected many quite unrelated groups in separate habitats. The parallelism of extinction between some of the aquatic and terrestrial groups is particularly remarkable [*see illustration on page 94*].

One cannot doubt that there were critical times in the history of animals. Widespread extinctions and consequent revolutionary changes in the course of

animal life occurred roughly at the end of the Cambrian, Ordovician, Devonian, Permian, Triassic and Cretaceous periods. Hundreds of minor episodes of extinction occurred on a more limited scale at the level of species and genera throughout geologic time, but here we shall restrict our attention to a few of the more outstanding mass extinctions.

At or near the close of the Permian period nearly half of the known families of animals throughout the world disappeared. The German paleontologist Otto Schindewolf notes that 24 orders and superfamilies also dropped out at this point. At no other time in history, save possibly the close of the Cambrian, has the animal world been so decimated. Recovery to something like the normal variety was not achieved until late in the Triassic period, 15 or 20 million years later.

Extinctions were taking place throughout Permian time and a number of major groups dropped out well before the end of the period, but many more survived to go out together, climaxing one of the greatest of all episodes of mass extinction affecting both land and marine animals. It was in the sea, however, that the decimation of animals was particularly dramatic. One great group of animals that disappeared at this time was the fusulinids, complex protozoans that ranged from microscopic sizes to two or three inches in length. They had populated the shallow seas of the world for 80 million years; their shells, piling up on the ocean floor, had formed vast deposits of limestone. The spiny productid brachiopods, likewise plentiful in the late Paleozoic seas, also vanished without descendants. These and many other groups dropped suddenly from a state of dominance to one of oblivion.

By the close of the Permian period 75 per cent of amphibian families and more than 80 per cent of the reptile families had also disappeared. The main suborders of these animals nonetheless survived the Permian to carry over into the Triassic.

The mass extinction on land and sea at the close of the Triassic period was almost equally significant. Primitive reptiles and amphibians that had dominated the land dropped out and were replaced by the early dinosaurs that had appeared and become widespread before the close of the period. It is tempting to conclude that competition with the more successful dinosaurs was an important factor in the disappearance of these early land animals, but what bearing could this have had on the equally impressive and

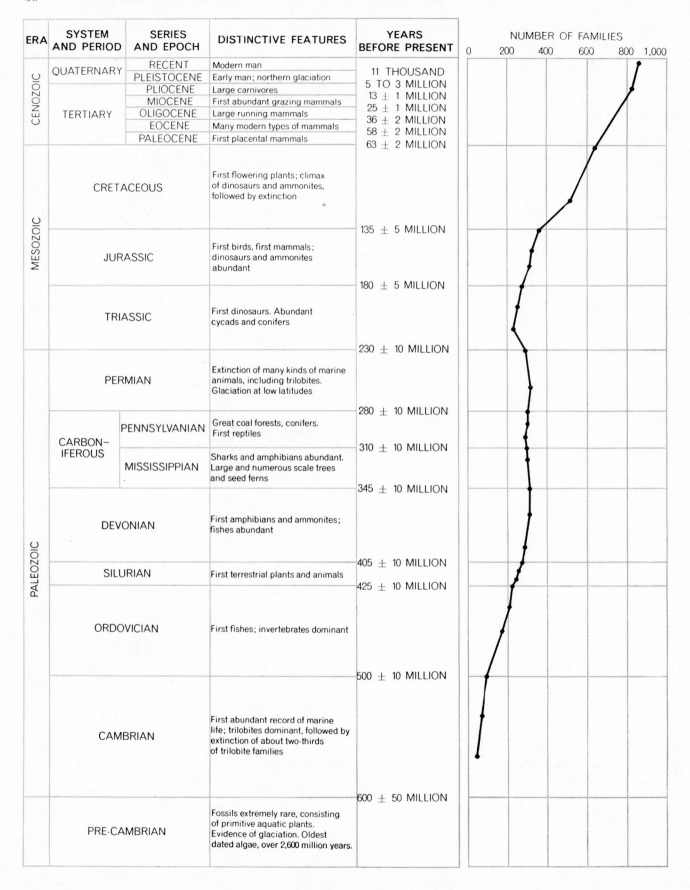

| ERA | SYSTEM AND PERIOD | SERIES AND EPOCH | DISTINCTIVE FEATURES | YEARS BEFORE PRESENT |
|---|---|---|---|---|
| CENOZOIC | QUATERNARY | RECENT | Modern man | 11 THOUSAND |
| | | PLEISTOCENE | Early man; northern glaciation | 5 TO 3 MILLION |
| | TERTIARY | PLIOCENE | Large carnivores | 13 ± 1 MILLION |
| | | MIOCENE | First abundant grazing mammals | 25 ± 1 MILLION |
| | | OLIGOCENE | Large running mammals | 36 ± 2 MILLION |
| | | EOCENE | Many modern types of mammals | 58 ± 2 MILLION |
| | | PALEOCENE | First placental mammals | 63 ± 2 MILLION |
| MESOZOIC | CRETACEOUS | | First flowering plants; climax of dinosaurs and ammonites, followed by extinction | 135 ± 5 MILLION |
| | JURASSIC | | First birds, first mammals; dinosaurs and ammonites abundant | 180 ± 5 MILLION |
| | TRIASSIC | | First dinosaurs. Abundant cycads and conifers | 230 ± 10 MILLION |
| PALEOZOIC | PERMIAN | | Extinction of many kinds of marine animals, including trilobites. Glaciation at low latitudes | 280 ± 10 MILLION |
| | CARBON-IFEROUS | PENNSYLVANIAN | Great coal forests, conifers. First reptiles | 310 ± 10 MILLION |
| | | MISSISSIPPIAN | Sharks and amphibians abundant. Large and numerous scale trees and seed ferns | 345 ± 10 MILLION |
| | DEVONIAN | | First amphibians and ammonites; fishes abundant | 405 ± 10 MILLION |
| | SILURIAN | | First terrestrial plants and animals | 425 ± 10 MILLION |
| | ORDOVICIAN | | First fishes; invertebrates dominant | 500 ± 10 MILLION |
| | CAMBRIAN | | First abundant record of marine life; trilobites dominant, followed by extinction of about two-thirds of trilobite families | 600 ± 50 MILLION |
| | PRE-CAMBRIAN | | Fossils extremely rare, consisting of primitive aquatic plants. Evidence of glaciation. Oldest dated algae, over 2,600 million years. | |

**GEOLOGICAL AGES** can be dated by comparing relative amounts of radioactive elements remaining in samples of rock obtained from different stratigraphic levels. The expanding curve at the right indicates how the number of major families of fossil animals increased through geologic time. The sharp decline after the Permian reflects the most dramatic of several mass extinctions.

simultaneous decline in the sea of the ammonite mollusks? Late in the Triassic there were still 25 families of widely ranging ammonites. All but one became extinct at the end of the period and that one gave rise to the scores of families of Jurassic and Cretaceous time.

The late Cretaceous extinctions eliminated about a quarter of all the known families of animals, but as usual the plants were little affected. The beginning of a decline in several groups is discernible near the middle of the period, some 30 million years before the mass extinction at the close of the Cretaceous. The significant point is that many characteristic groups—dinosaurs, marine reptiles, flying reptiles, ammonites, bottom-dwelling aquatic mollusks and certain kinds of extinct marine plankton—were represented by several world-wide families until the close of the period. Schindewolf has cited 16 superfamilies and orders that now became extinct. Many world-wide genera of invertebrates and most of the known species of the youngest Cretaceous period drop out near or at the boundary between the Cretaceous and the overlying Paleocene rocks. On the other hand, many families of bottom-dwelling sea organisms, fishes and nautiloid cephalopods survived with only minor evolutionary modifications. This is also true of primitive mammals, turtles, crocodiles and most of the plants of the time.

In general the groups that survived each of the great episodes of mass extinction were conservative in their evolution. As a result they were probably able to withstand greater changes in environment than could those groups that disappeared, thus conforming to the well-known principle of "survival of the unspecialized," recognized by Darwin. But there were many exceptions and it does not follow that the groups that disappeared became extinct simply because they were highly specialized. Many were no more specialized than some groups that survived.

The Cretaceous period was remarkable for a uniform and world-wide distribution of many hundreds of distinctive groups of animals and plants, which was probably a direct result of low-lying lands, widespread seas, surprisingly uniform climate and an abundance of migration routes. Just at the top of the Cretaceous sequence the characteristic fauna is abruptly replaced by another, which is distinguished not so much by radically new kinds of animals as by the elimination of innumerable major groups that had characterized the late Cre-

taceous. The geological record is somewhat obscure at the close of the Cretaceous, but most investigators agree that there was a widespread break in sedimentation, indicating a brief but general withdrawal of shallow seas from the area of the continents.

## Extinctions in the Human Epoch

At the close of the Tertiary period, which immediately preceded the Quaternary in which we live, new land connections were formed between North America and neighboring continents. The horse and camel, which had evolved in North America through Tertiary time, quickly crossed into Siberia and spread throughout Eurasia and Africa. Crossing the newly formed Isthmus of Panama at about the same time, many North American animals entered South America. From Asia the mammoth, bison, bear and large deer entered North America, while from the south came ground sloths and other mammals that had originated and evolved in South America. Widespread migration and concurrent episodes of mass extinction appear to mark the close of the Pliocene (some two or three million years ago) and the middle of the Pleistocene in both North America and

Eurasia. Another mass extinction, particularly notable in North America, occurred at the very close of the last extensive glaciation, but this time it apparently was not outstandingly marked by intercontinental migrations. Surprisingly, none of the extinctions coincided with glacial advances.

It is characteristic of the fossil record that immigrant faunas tend to replace the old native faunas. In some cases newly arrived or newly evolved families replaced old families quite rapidly, in less than a few million years. In other cases the replacement has been a protracted process, spreading over tens of millions or even hundreds of millions of years. We cannot, of course, know the exact nature of competition between bygone groups, but when they occupied the same habitat and were broadly overlapping in their ecological requirements, it can be assumed that they were in fact competitors for essential resources. The selective advantage of one competing stock over another may be so slight that a vast amount of time is required to decide the outcome.

At the time of the maximum extent of the continental glaciers some 11,000 years ago the ice-free land areas of the Northern Hemisphere supported a rich

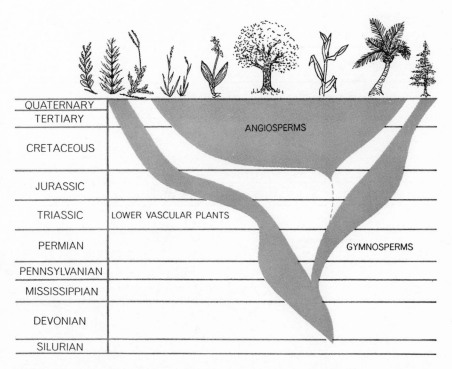

**HISTORY OF LAND PLANTS** shows the spectacular rise of angiosperms in the last 135 million years. The bands are roughly proportional to the number of genera of plants in each group. Angiosperms are flowering plants, a group that includes all the common trees (except conifers), grasses and vegetables. Lower vascular plants include club mosses, quillworts and horsetails. The most familiar gymnosperms (naked-seed plants) are the conifers, or evergreens. The diagram is based on one prepared by Erling Dorf of Princeton University.

and varied fauna of large mammals comparable to that which now occupies Africa south of the Sahara. Many of the species of bears, horses, elks, beavers and elephants were larger than any of their relatives living today. As recently as 8,000 years ago the horse, elephant and camel families roamed all the continents but Australia and Antarctica. Since that time these and many other families have retreated into small regions confined to one or two continents.

In North America a few species dropped out at the height of the last glaciation, but the tempo of extinction stepped up rapidly between about 12,000 and 6,000 years ago, with a maximum rate around 8,000 years ago, when the climate had become milder and the glaciers were shrinking [see illustration on page 98]. A comparable, but possibly more gradual, loss of large mammals occurred at about the same time in Asia and Australia, but not in Africa. Many of the large herbivores and carnivores had been virtually world-wide through a great range in climate, only to become extinct within a few hundred years. Other organisms were generally unaffected by this episode of extinction.

On the basis of a limited series of radiocarbon dates Paul S. Martin of the University of Arizona has concluded that now extinct large mammals of North America began to disappear first in Alaska and Mexico, followed by those in the Great Plains. Somewhat questionable datings suggest that the last survivors may have lived in Florida only 2,000 to 4,000 years ago. Quite recently, therefore, roughly three-quarters of the North American herbivores disappeared, and most of the ecological niches that were vacated have not been filled by other species.

Glaciation evidently was not a significant agent in these extinctions. In the first place, they were concentrated during the final melting and retreat of the continental glaciers after the entire biota had successfully weathered a number of glacial and interglacial cycles. Second, the glacial climate certainly did not reach low latitudes, except in mountainous areas, and it is probable that the climate over large parts of the tropics was not very different from that of today.

Studies of fossil pollen and spores in many parts of the world show that the melting of the continental glaciers was

accompanied by a change from a rainy climate to a somewhat drier one with higher mean temperatures. As a result of these changes forests in many parts of the world retreated and were replaced by deserts and steppes. The changes, however, probably were not universal or severe enough to result in the elimination of any major habitat.

A number of investigators have proposed that the large mammals may have been hunted out of existence by prehistoric man, who may have used fire as a weapon. They point out that the mass extinctions coincided with the rapid growth of agriculture. Before this stage in human history a decrease in game supply would have been matched by a decrease in human populations, since man could not have destroyed a major food source without destroying himself.

In Africa and Eurasia, where man had lived in association with game animals throughout the Pleistocene, extinctions were not so conspicuously concentrated in the last part of the epoch. There was ample opportunity in the Old World for animals to become adapted to man through hundreds of thousands of years of coexistence. In the Americas and

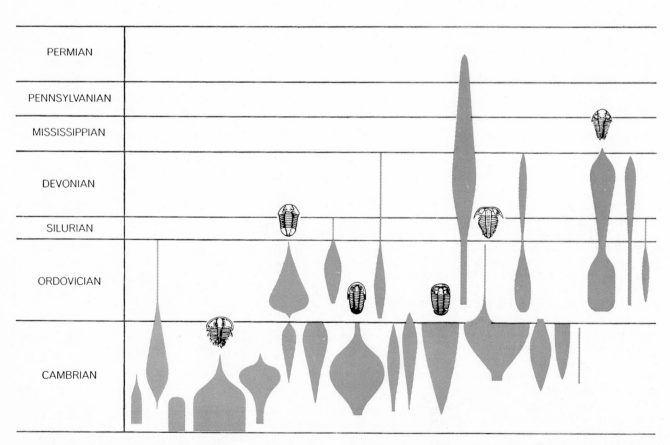

MASS EXTINCTION OF TRILOBITES, primitive arthropods, occurred at the close of the Cambrian period about 500 million years ago. During the Cambrian period hundreds of kinds of trilobites populated the shallow seas of the world. The chart depicts 15 superfamilies of Cambrian trilobites; the width of the shapes is roughly proportional to the number of members in each superfamily. Final extinction took place in the Permian. The chart is based on the work of H. B. Whittington of Harvard University.

Australia, where man was a comparative newcomer, the animals may have proved easy prey for the hunter.

We shall probably never know exactly what happened to the large mammals of the late Pleistocene, but their demise did coincide closely with the expansion of ancient man and with an abrupt change from a cool and moist to a warm and dry climate over much of the world. Possibly both of these factors contributed to this episode of mass extinction. We can only guess.

### The Modern Crisis

Geological history cannot be observed but must be deduced from studies of stratigraphic sequences of rocks and fossils interpreted in the context of processes now operating on earth. It is helpful, therefore, to analyze some recent extinctions to find clues to the general causes of extinction.

We are now witnessing the disastrous effects on organic nature of the explosive spread of the human species and the concurrent development of an efficient technology of destruction. The human demand for space increases, hunting techniques are improved, new poisons are used and remote areas that had long served as havens for wildlife are now easily penetrated by hunter, fisherman, lumberman and farmer.

Studies of recent mammal extinctions show that man has been either directly or indirectly responsible for the disappearance, or near disappearance, of more than 450 species of animals. Without man's intervention there would have been few, if any, extinctions of birds or mammals within the past 2,000 years. The heaviest toll has been taken in the West Indies and the islands of the Pacific and Indian oceans, where about 70 species of birds have become extinct in the past few hundred years. On the continents the birds have fared somewhat better. In the same period five species of birds have disappeared from North America, three from Australia and one from Asia. Conservationists fear, however, that more North American birds will become extinct in the next 50 years than have in the past 5,000 years.

The savannas of Africa were remarkable until recently for a wealth of large mammals comparable only to the rich Tertiary and Pleistocene faunas of North America. In South Africa stock farming, road building, the fencing of grazing lands and indiscriminate hunting had wiped out the wild populations of large grazing mammals by the beginning of the 20th century. The depletion of ani-

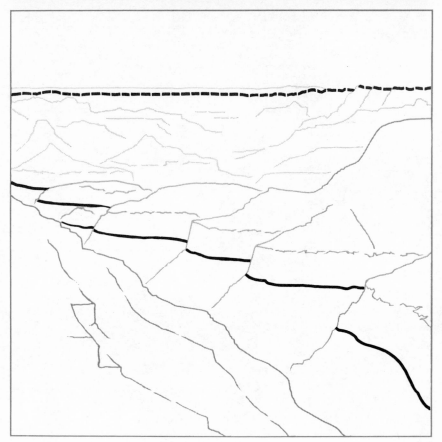

**PALEONTOLOGICAL BOUNDARIES** are clearly visible in this photograph of the Grand Canyon. The diagram below identifies the stratigraphic boundary between the Cambrian and Ordovician periods (*solid line*) and the top of the Permian rocks (*broken line*). These are world-wide paleontological division points, easily identified by marine fossils.

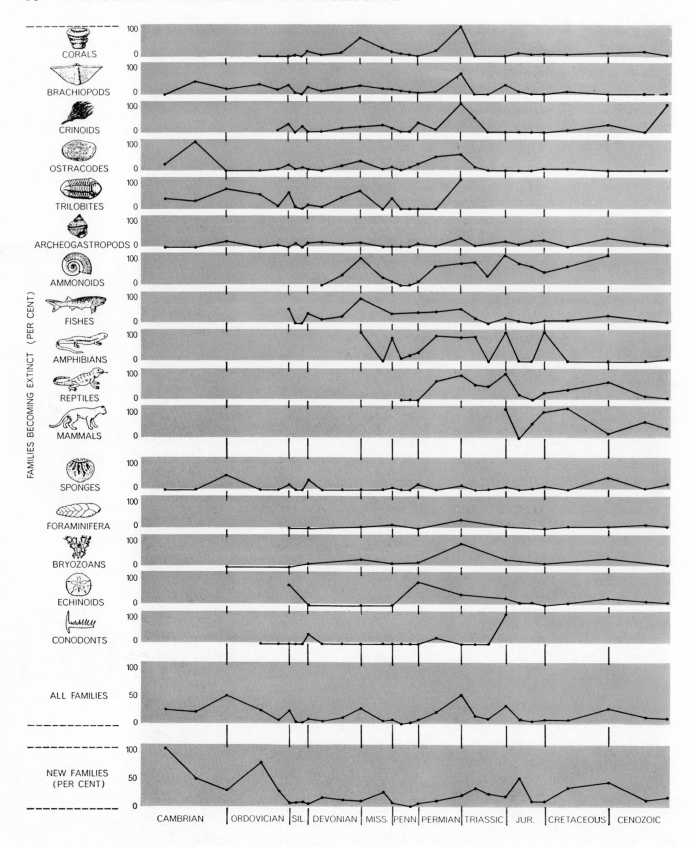

**RECORD OF ANIMAL EXTINCTIONS** makes it quite clear that the history of animals has been punctuated by repeated crises. The top panel of curves plots the ups and downs of 11 groups of animals from Cambrian times to the present. Massive extinctions took place at the close of the Ordovician, Devonian and Permian periods. The second panel shows the history of five other groups for which the evidence is less complete. (Curves are extrapolated between dots.) The next to bottom curve depicts the sum of extinctions for all the fossil groups plotted above (plus bivalves and caenogastropods). The bottom curve shows the per cent of new families in the main fossil groups. It indicates that periods of extinction were usually followed by an upsurge in evolutionary activity.

mals has now spread to Equatorial Africa as a result of poaching in and around the game reserves and the practice of eradicating game as a method of controlling human and animal epidemics. Within the past two decades it has become possible to travel for hundreds of miles across African grasslands without seeing any of the large mammals for which the continent is noted. To make matters worse, the great reserves that were set aside for the preservation of African wildlife are now threatened by political upheavals.

As a factor in extinction, man's predatory habits are supplemented by his destruction of habitats. Deforestation, cultivation, land drainage, water pollution, wholesale use of insecticides, the building of roads and fences—all are causing fragmentation and reduction in range of wild populations with resulting loss of environmental and genetic resources. These changes eventually are fatal to populations just able to maintain themselves under normal conditions. A few species have been able to take advantage of the new environments created by man, but for the most part the changes have been damaging.

Reduction of geographic range is prejudicial to a species in somewhat the same way as overpopulation. It places an increasing demand on diminishing environmental resources. Furthermore, the gene pool suffers loss of variability by reduction in the number of local breeding groups. These are deleterious changes, which can be disastrous to species that have narrow tolerances for one or more environmental factors. No organism is stronger than the weakest link in its ecological chain.

Man's direct attack on the organic world is reinforced by a host of competing and pathogenic organisms that he intentionally or unwittingly introduces to relatively defenseless native communities. Charles S. Elton of the University of Oxford has documented scores of examples of the catastrophic effects on established communities of man-sponsored invasions by pathogenic and other organisms. The scale of these ecological disturbances is world-wide; indeed, there are few unmodified faunas and floras now surviving.

The ill-advised introduction of predators such as foxes, cats, dogs, mongooses and rats into island communities has been particularly disastrous; many extinctions can be traced directly to this cause. Grazing and browsing domestic animals have destroyed or modified vegetation patterns. The introduction of

European mammals into Australia has been a primary factor in the rapid decimation of the native marsupials, which cannot compete successfully with placental mammals.

An illustration of invasion by a pathogenic organism is provided by an epidemic that in half a century has nearly wiped out the American sweet chestnut tree. The fungus infection responsible for this tragedy was accidentally intro-

duced from China on nursery plants. The European chestnut, also susceptible to the fungus, is now suffering rapid decline, but the Chinese chestnut, which evolved in association with the blight, is comparatively immune.

Another example is provided by the marine eelgrass *Zostera*, which gives food and shelter to a host of invertebrates and fishes and forms a protective blanket over muddy bottoms. It is the

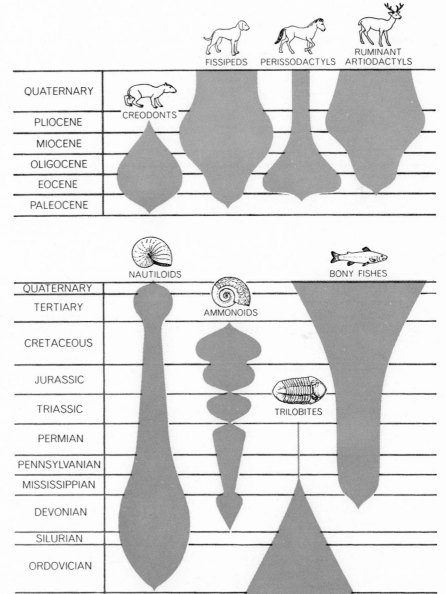

**ECOLOGICAL REPLACEMENT** appears to be a characteristic feature of evolution. The top diagram shows the breadth of family representation among four main groups of mammals over the last 60-odd million years. The bottom diagram shows a similar waxing and waning among four groups of marine swimmers, dating back to the earliest fossil records. The ammonoid group suffered near extinction twice before finally expiring. The diagrams are based on the work of George Gaylord Simpson of Harvard University and the author.

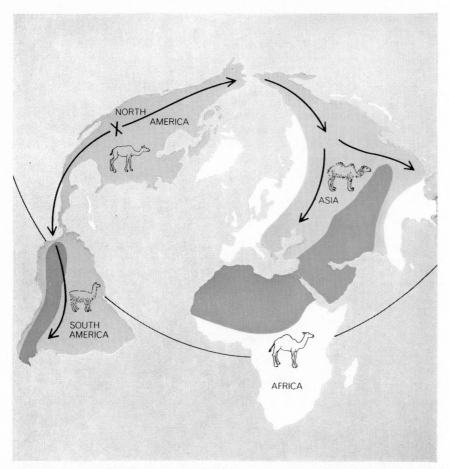

**DISPERSAL OF CAMEL FAMILY** from its origin (*X*) took place during Pleistocene times. Area in light color shows the maximum distribution of the family; dark color shows present distribution. This map is based on one in *Life: An Introduction to Biology*, by Simpson, C. S. Pittendrigh and L. H. Tiffany, published by Harcourt, Brace and Company.

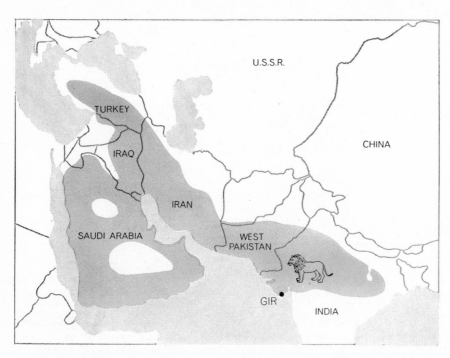

**DISTRIBUTION OF ASIATIC LION** has contracted dramatically just since 1800, when it roamed over large areas (*shown in color*) of the Middle East, Pakistan and India. Today the Asiatic lion is found wild only in Gir, a small game preserve in western India.

most characteristic member of a distinctive community that includes many plant and animal species. In the 1930's the eelgrass was attacked by a virus and was almost wiped out along the Atlantic shores of North America and Europe. Many animals and plants not directly attacked nevertheless disappeared for a time and the community was greatly altered. Resistant strains of *Zostera* fortunately escaped destruction and have slowly repopulated much of the former area. Eelgrass is a key member of a complex ecological community, and one can see that if it had not survived, many dependent organisms would have been placed in jeopardy and some might have been destroyed.

This cursory glance at recent extinctions indicates that excessive predation, destruction of habitat and invasion of established communities by man and his domestic animals have been primary causes of extinctions within historical time. The resulting disturbances of community equilibrium and shock waves of readjustment have produced ecological explosions with far-reaching effects.

### The Causes of Mass Extinctions

It is now generally understood that organisms must be adapted to their environment in order to survive. As environmental changes gradually pass the limits of tolerance of a species, that species must evolve to cope with the new conditions or it will die. This is established by experiment and observation. Extinction, therefore, is not simply a result of environmental change but is also a consequence of failure of the evolutionary process to keep pace with changing conditions in the physical and biological environment. Extinction is an evolutionary as well as an ecological problem.

There has been much speculation about the causes of mass extinction; hypotheses have ranged from worldwide cataclysms to some kind of exhaustion of the germ plasm—a sort of evolutionary fatigue. Geology does not provide support for the postulated cataclysms and biology has failed to discover any compelling evidence that evolution is an effect of biological drive, or that extinction is a result of its failure. Hypotheses of extinction based on supposed racial old age or overspecialization, so popular among paleontologists a few generations ago and still echoed occasionally, have been generally abandoned for lack of evidence.

Of the many hypotheses advanced to explain mass extinctions, most are un-

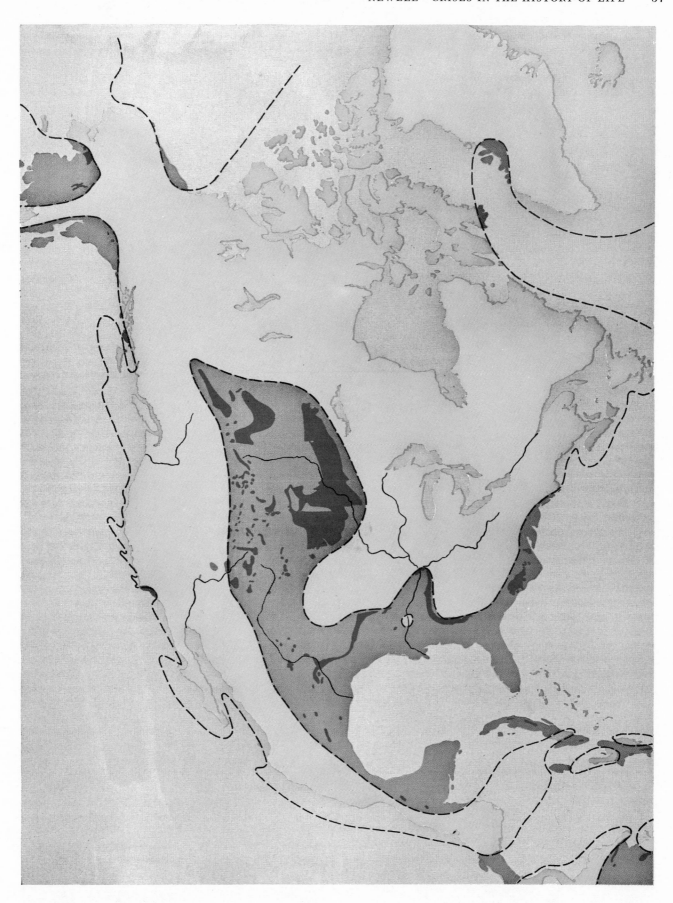

LATE CRETACEOUS SEA covered large portions of Central and North America (*dark gray*). Fossil-bearing rocks laid down at that time, and now visible at the surface of the earth, are shown in dark color. The approximate outline of North America in the Cretaceous period is represented by the broken line. The map is based on the work of the late Charles Schuchert of Yale University.

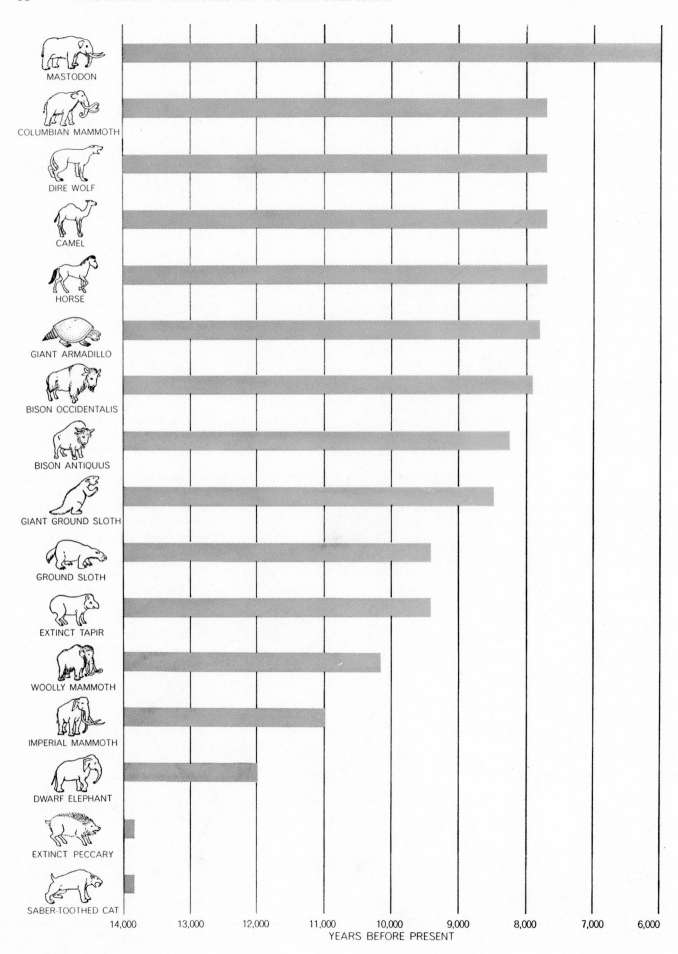

MASTODON

COLUMBIAN MAMMOTH

DIRE WOLF

CAMEL

HORSE

GIANT ARMADILLO

BISON OCCIDENTALIS

BISON ANTIQUUS

GIANT GROUND SLOTH

GROUND SLOTH

EXTINCT TAPIR

WOOLLY MAMMOTH

IMPERIAL MAMMOTH

DWARF ELEPHANT

EXTINCT PECCARY

SABER-TOOTHED CAT

14,000    13,000    12,000    11,000    10,000    9,000    8,000    7,000    6,000

YEARS BEFORE PRESENT

satisfactory because they lack testable corollaries and are designed to explain only one episode of extinction. For example, the extinction of the dinosaurs at the end of the Cretaceous period has been attributed to a great increase in atmospheric oxygen and alternatively to the explosive evolution of pathogenic fungi, both thought to be by-products of the dramatic spread of the flowering plants during late Cretaceous time.

The possibility that pathogenic fungi may have helped to destroy the dinosaurs was a recent suggestion of my own. I was aware, of course, that it would not be a very useful suggestion unless a way could be found to test it. I was also aware that disease is one of the most popular hypotheses for explaining mass extinctions. Unfortunately for such hypotheses, pathogenic organisms normally attack only one species or at most a few related species. This has been interpreted as an indication of a long antecedent history of coadaptation during which parasite and host have become mutually adjusted. According to this theory parasites that produce pathological reactions are not well adapted to the host. On first contact the pathogenic organism might destroy large numbers of the host species; it is even possible that extinction of a species might follow a pandemic, but there is no record that this has happened in historical times to any numerous and cosmopolitan group of species.

It is well to keep in mind that living populations studied by biologists generally are large, successful groups in which the normal range of variation provides tolerance for all the usual exigencies, and some unusual ones. It is for this reason that the eelgrass was not extinguished by the epidemic of the 1930's and that the human race was not eliminated by the influenza pandemic following World War I. Although a succession of closely spaced disasters of various kinds might have brought about extinction, the particular virus strains responsible for these diseases did not directly attack associated species.

Another suggestion, more ingenious

ICE-AGE MAMMALS provided North America with a fauna of large herbivores comparable to that existing in certain parts of Africa today. Most of them survived a series of glacial periods only to become extinct about 8,000 years ago, when the last glaciers were shrinking. The chart is based on a study by Jim J. Hester of the Museum of New Mexico in Santa Fe.

than most, is that mass extinctions were caused by bursts of high-energy radiation from a nearby supernova. Presumably the radiation could have had a dramatic impact on living organisms without altering the climate in a way that would show up in the geological record. This hypothesis, however, fails to account for the patterns of extinction actually observed. It would appear that radiation would affect terrestrial organisms more than aquatic organisms, yet there were times when most of the extinctions were in the sea. Land plants, which would be more exposed to the radiation and are more sensitive to it, were little affected by the changes that led to the animal extinctions at the close of the Permian and Cretaceous periods.

Another imaginative suggestion has been made recently by M. J. Salmi of the Geological Survey of Finland and Preston E. Cloud, Jr., of the University of Minnesota. They have pointed out that excessive amounts or deficiencies of certain metallic trace elements, such as copper and cobalt, are deleterious to organisms and may have caused past extinctions. This interesting hypothesis, as applied to marine organisms, depends on the questionable assumption that deficiencies of these substances have occurred in the ocean, or that a lethal concentration of metallic ions might have diffused throughout the oceans of the world more rapidly than the substances could be concentrated and removed from circulation by organisms and various common chemical sequestering agents. To account for the disappearance of land animals it is necessary to postulate further that the harmful elements were broadcast in quantity widely over the earth, perhaps as a result of a great volcanic eruption. This is not inconceivable; there have probably been significant variations of trace elements in time and place. But it seems unlikely that such variations sufficed to produce worldwide biological effects.

Perhaps the most popular of all hypotheses to explain mass extinctions is that they resulted from sharp changes in climate. There is no question that large-scale climatic changes have taken place many times in the past. During much of geologic time shallow seas covered large areas of the continents; climates were consequently milder and less differentiated than they are now. There were also several brief episodes of continental glaciation at low latitudes, but it appears that mass extinctions did not coincide with ice ages.

It is noteworthy that fossil plants,

which are good indicators of past climatic conditions, do not reveal catastrophic changes in climate at the close of the Permian, Triassic and Cretaceous periods, or at other times coincident with mass extinctions in the animal kingdom. On theoretical grounds it seems improbable that any major climatic zone of the past has disappeared from the earth. For example, climates not unlike those of the Cretaceous period probably have existed continuously at low latitudes until the present time. On the other hand, it is certain that there have been great changes in distribution of climatic zones. Severe shrinkage of a given climatic belt might adversely affect many of the contained species. Climatic changes almost certainly have contributed to animal extinctions by destruction of local habitats and by inducing wholesale migrations, but the times of greatest extinction commonly do not clearly correspond to times of great climatic stress.

Finally, we must consider the evidence that so greatly impressed Cuvier and many geologists. They were struck by the frequent association between the last occurrence of extinct animals and unconformities, or erosional breaks, in the geological record. Cuvier himself believed that the unconformities and the mass extinctions went hand in hand, that both were products of geologic revolutions, such as might be caused by paroxysms of mountain building. The idea still influences some modern thought on the subject.

It is evident that mountains do strongly influence the environment. They can alter the climate, soils, water supply and vegetation over adjacent areas, but it is doubtful that the mountains of past ages played dominant roles in the evolutionary history of marine and lowland organisms, which constitute most of the fossil record. Most damaging to the hypothesis that crustal upheavals played a major role in extinctions is the fact that the great crises in the history of life did not correspond closely in time with the origins of the great mountain systems. Actually the most dramatic episodes of mass extinction took place during times of general crustal quiet in the continental areas. Evidently other factors were involved.

## Fluctuations of Sea Level

If mass extinctions were not brought about by changes in atmospheric oxygen, by disease, by cosmic radiation, by trace-element poisoning, by climatic changes or by violent upheavals of the

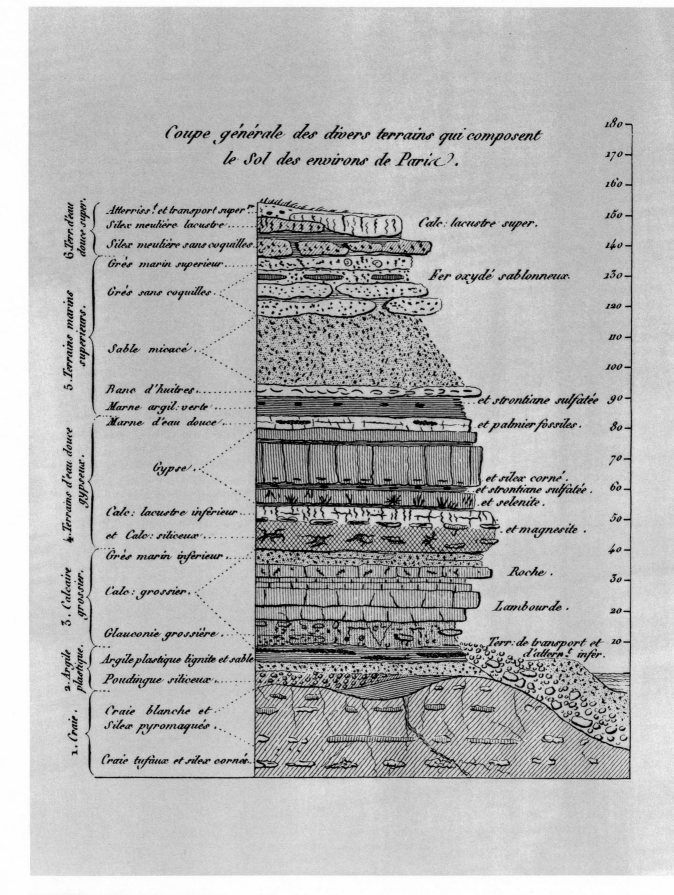

*Coupe générale des divers terrains qui composent le Sol des environs de Paris.*

**"EVIDENCE" FOR CATASTROPHISM** was adduced by the French naturalist Baron Georges Cuvier from his study of the Paris basin. He and Alexandre Brongniart published this diagram in 1822. Cuvier believed that the abrupt changes in the strata bespoke the occurrence of cataclysms. Although his observations were accurate, his conclusions are no longer generally accepted.

earth's crust, where is one to look for a satisfactory—and testable—hypothesis?

The explanation I have come to favor, and which has found acceptance among many students of the paleontological record, rests on fluctuations of sea level. Evidence has been accumulating to show an intimate relation between many fossil zones and major advances and retreats of the seas across the continents. It is clear that diastrophism, or reshaping, of the ocean basins can produce universal changes in sea level. The evidence of long continued sinking of the sea floor under Pacific atolls and guyots (flat-topped submarine mountains) and the present high stand of the continents indicate that the Pacific basin has been subsiding differentially with respect to the land at least since Cretaceous time.

During much of Paleozoic and Mesozoic time, spanning some 540 million years, the land surfaces were much lower than they are today. An appreciable rise in sea level was sufficient to flood large areas; a drop of a few feet caused equally large areas to emerge, producing major environmental changes. At least 30 major and hundreds of minor oscillations of sea level have occurred in the past 600 million years of geologic time.

Repeated expansion and contraction of many habitats in response to alternate flooding and draining of vast areas of the continents unquestionably created profound ecological disturbances among offshore and lowland communities, and repercussions of these changes probably extended to communities deep inland and far out to sea. Intermittent draining of the continents, such as occurred at the close of many of the geologic epochs and periods, greatly reduced or eliminated the shallow inland seas that pro-vided most of the fossil record of marine life. Many organisms adapted to the special estuarine conditions of these seas evidently could not survive along the more exposed ocean margins during times of emergence and they had disappeared when the seas returned to the continents. There is now considerable evidence that evolutionary diversification was greatest during times of maximum flooding of the continents, when the number of habitats was relatively large. Conversely, extinction and natural selection were most intense during major withdrawals of the sea.

It is well known that the sea-level oscillations of the Pleistocene epoch caused by waxing and waning of the continental glaciers did not produce numerous extinctions among shallow-water marine communities, but the situation was quite unlike that which prevailed during much of geological history. By Pleistocene times the continents stood high above sea level and the warm interior seas had long since disappeared. As a result the Pleistocene oscillations did not produce vast geographic and climatic changes. Furthermore, they were of short duration compared with major sea-level oscillations of earlier times.

## Importance of Key Species

It might be argued that nothing less than the complete destruction of a habitat would be required to eliminate a world-wide community of organisms. This, however, may not be necessary. After thousands of years of mutual accommodation, the various organisms of a biological community acquire a high order of compatibility until a nearly steady state is achieved. Each species plays its own role in the life of the community, supplying shelter, food, chemical conditioners or some other resource in kind and amount needed by its neighbors. Consequently any changes involving evolution or extinction of species, or the successful entrance of new elements into the community, will affect the associated organisms in varying degrees and result in a wave of adjustments.

The strength of the bonds of interdependence, of course, varies with species, but the health and welfare of a community commonly depend on a comparatively small number of key species low in the community pyramid; the extinction of any of these is sure to affect adversely many others. Reduction and fragmentation of some major habitats, accompanied by moderate changes in climate and resulting shrinkage of populations, may have resulted in extinction of key species not necessarily represented in the fossil record. Disappearance of any species low in the pyramid of community organization, as, for example, a primary food plant, could lead directly to the extinction of many ecologically dependent species higher in the scale. Because of this interdependence of organisms a wave of extinction originating in a shrinking coastal habitat might extend to more distant habitats of the continental interior and to the waters of the open sea.

This theory, in its essence long favored by geologists but still to be fully developed, provides an explanation of the common, although not invariable, parallelism between times of widespread emergence of the continents from the seas and episodes of mass extinction that closed many of the chapters of geological history.

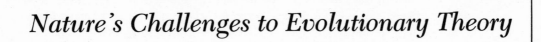 *Nature's Challenges to Evolutionary Theory*

# Nature's Challenges to Evolutionary Theory

## INTRODUCTION

Darwin was raised in an intellectual environment partly created by William Paley (1743–1805). In his *Natural Theology* (1802) Paley gave an eloquent presentation of the idea of "Design in Nature," an idea that had been developing throughout the eighteenth century. Whenever we study an organism closely we see that it is marvelously adapted to the demands of its environment. Clearly, said Paley, it shows *Design*—and, if it has been designed, there must be a Designer, a supernatural being who planned it all. This combined observation-and-argument was regarded as one of the most powerful supports of the belief in God in the eighteenth and nineteenth centuries. Paley agreed with his predecessor Sturmius that an "examination of the eye was a cure for atheism."

The idea of Design in Nature can be considered either as a proof of the existence of God, or as an explanation of the adaptations observed in Nature. As professional biologists we are concerned only with the second issue (though in our nonprofessional moments we may muse upon the former—but that is another matter). As an explanation of adaptation, the argument from Design always works—and that's just the trouble. An explanation which explains everything, explains nothing. It is a *panchreston*, an explain-all, which is no more credible than a panacea, a cure-all. A fundamental aspect of scientific method is that a panchreston is not an admissible element in a scientific theory. As the twentieth-century philosopher Karl Popper put it, *falsifiability, or refutability, is a criterion of the scientific status of a theory.* By this criterion the explanation implied by Design in Nature is not a scientific explanation, since it cannot possibly be refuted.

Darwin's theory of evolution by natural selection stands in sharp contrast to the idea of Design in Nature. It asserts that spectacular adaptations have their origins in myriads of minute mutations, the vast majority of which are harmful to the organism; that natural selection acts like a ratchet to preserve each useful mutation selected while new mutational changes are being tried out. Ever since the Darwinian theory was published it has been attacked as setting impossibly severe restrictions on the mechanism of change. The eye, it has been argued, is useful only if it is almost perfect, if it includes hundreds of correlated adaptations: how could the earliest changes in the direction of a functioning eye have been preserved by natural selection since they would have been of no use? This question bothered Darwin, and it has bothered many biologists since.

Adhering to Popper's criterion of falsifiability, biologists are not impressed by contemporary critics who (following Sturmius and Paley) think that the difficulties of Darwinian theory justify the argument from Design (because it cannot be falsified). Nevertheless, we must admit that some of the more bizarre examples of adaptation in nature are so remarkable that they cannot *easily* be explained in Darwinian terms. Some of the best of these embarrassing examples are assembled in this section: the student is urged to try his wits on them.

First, Alexander Petrunkevitch introduces us to the interactions of "The Spider and the Wasp." Query: why, under Darwinian principles, doesn't the spider try to escape its Nemesis, the wasp? (Even the believers in Design may find the spider's behavior somewhat perverse!)

"The Evolution of Bowerbirds," as told by E. Thomas Gilliard, presents to our awed sight a spectacle so beautiful (by human standards) that we really wonder if it could have been evolved solely by natural means. (We tend to think of "Nature" as being rigidly utilitarian—but is this assumption justified?)

Conrad Limbaugh, a biologist who lost his life skin-diving, tells us of one of the more fantastic sights he saw beneath the surface of the sea, the "Cleaning Symbiosis" that exists between members of different phyla. We can grant that the cleaning service is of advantage to the "host" species as a whole—but is the relationship a stable one? Suppose an occasional host cheated and ate his valet after the service: would he not thereby have the best of both worlds? Would not natural selection, operating along these lines, result in the destruction of the symbiotic relationship? If this reasoning is correct, then how has the symbiosis survived?

Logically less spectacular, but visually no less so, is the phenomenon of "Biological Luminescence" discussed by William D. McElroy and Howard H. Seliger. Few people today are aware of how common the phenomenon of living luminescence is, because they almost never take a walk in the dark through the woods or along the seashore. (It is seldom really dark—particularly at the seashore—but people will never discover this as long as they keep their flashlights switched on.) What is the adaptive significance of luminescence? The authors discuss the mechanistic reason for it (its biochemistry) and suggest that in many organisms it may have no teleological significance at all.

In the final article of this section, "The Navigation of the Green Turtle," Archie Carr discusses a particular instance of biological navigation by unknown means. Is Darwinian evolution capable of producing a navigational ability so subtle that even contemporary man, with his very great knowledge of chemistry and physics, is unable to decipher the mechanism?

Such are only a few of the unsolved puzzles facing biologists who are committed to the Darwinian theory. Are they beyond solution within the framework of this theory or not? Is the framework wrong? Should Popper's criterion be modified? Was Paley right? Think about it!

# 13 The Spider and the Wasp

ALEXANDER PETRUNKEVITCH · August 1952

**SPIDER AND WASP** are the tarantula *Cyrtopholis portoricae* (*top*) and the digger wasp *Pepsis marginata* (*bottom*). The tarantula is shown in an attitude of defense. The wasps of the genus Pepsis are either a deep blue or blue with rust-colored wings. The largest species of the genus have a wingspread of about four inches.

TO HOLD ITS OWN in the struggle for existence, every species of animal must have a regular source of food, and if it happens to live on other animals, its survival may be very delicately balanced. The hunter cannot exist without the hunted; if the latter should perish from the earth, the former would, too. When the hunted also prey on some of the hunters, the matter may become complicated.

This is nowhere better illustrated than in the insect world. Think of the complexity of a situation such as the following: There is a certain wasp, *Pimpla inquisitor*, whose larvae feed on the larvae of the tussock moth. *Pimpla* larvae in turn serve as food for the larvae of a second wasp, and the latter in their turn nourish still a third wasp. What subtle balance between fertility and mortality must exist in the case of each of these four species to prevent the extinction of all of them! An excess of mortality over fertility in a single member of the group would ultimately wipe out all four.

This is not a unique case. The two great orders of insects, Hymenoptera and Diptera, are full of such examples of interrelationship. And the spiders (which are not insects but members of a separate order of arthropods) also are killers and victims of insects.

The picture is complicated by the fact that those species which are carnivorous in the larval stage have to be provided with animal food by a vegetarian mother. The survival of the young depends on the mother's correct choice of a food which she does not eat herself.

In the feeding and safeguarding of their progeny the insects and spiders exhibit some interesting analogies to reasoning and some crass examples of blind instinct. The case I propose to describe here is that of the tarantula spiders and their arch-enemy, the digger wasps of the genus Pepsis. It is a classic example of what looks like intelligence pitted against instinct—a strange situation in which the victim, though fully able to defend itself, submits unwittingly to its destruction.

MOST tarantulas live in the Tropics, but several species occur in the temperate zone and a few are common in the southern U. S. Some varieties are large and have powerful fangs with which they can inflict a deep wound. These formidable looking spiders do not, however, attack man; you can hold one in your hand, if you are gentle, without being bitten. Their bite is dangerous only to insects and small mammals such as mice; for a man it is no worse than a hornet's sting.

Tarantulas customarily live in deep cylindrical burrows, from which they emerge at dusk and into which they retire at dawn. Mature males wander about after dark in search of females and

**NEST OF THE MUD DAUBER WASP** illustrates an intricate predatory relationship. A single cell of the nest, enlarged 10 times, contains one pupa of a secondary predator and five smaller pupae of a tertiary predator.

**DEATH OF THE SPIDER** is shown in these drawings. In the first drawing the wasp digs a grave, occasional-

occasionally stray into houses. After mating, the male dies in a few weeks, but a female lives much longer and can mate several years in succession. In a Paris museum is a tropical specimen which is said to have been living in captivity for 25 years.

A fertilized female tarantula lays from 200 to 400 eggs at a time; thus it is possible for a single tarantula to produce several thousand young. She takes no care of them beyond weaving a cocoon of silk to enclose the eggs. After they hatch, the young walk away, find convenient places in which to dig their burrows and spend the rest of their lives in solitude. Tarantulas feed mostly on insects and millepedes. Once their appetite is appeased, they digest the food for several days before eating again. Their sight is poor, being limited to sensing a change in the intensity of light and to the perception of moving objects. They apparently have little or no sense of hearing, for a hungry tarantula will pay no attention to a loudly chirping cricket placed in its cage unless the insect happens to touch one of its legs.

But all spiders, and especially hairy ones, have an extremely delicate sense of touch. Laboratory experiments prove that tarantulas can distinguish three types of touch: pressure against the body wall, stroking of the body hair and riffling of certain very fine hairs on the legs called trichobothria. Pressure against the body, by a finger or the end of a pencil, causes the tarantula to move off slowly for a short distance. The touch excites no defensive response unless the approach is from above where the spider can see the motion, in which case it rises on its hind legs, lifts its front legs, opens its fangs and holds

this threatening posture as long as the object continues to move. When the motion stops, the spider drops back to the ground, remains quiet for a few seconds and then moves slowly away.

The entire body of a tarantula, especially its legs, is thickly clothed with hair. Some of it is short and woolly, some long and stiff. Touching this body hair produces one of two distinct reactions. When the spider is hungry, it responds with an immediate and swift attack. At the touch of a cricket's antennae the tarantula seizes the insect so swiftly that a motion picture taken at the rate of 64 frames per second shows only the result and not the process of capture. But when the spider is not hungry, the stimulation of its hairs merely causes it to shake the touched limb. An insect can walk under its hairy belly unharmed.

The trichobothria, very fine hairs growing from disklike membranes on the legs, were once thought to be the spider's hearing organs, but we now know that they have nothing to do with sound. They are sensitive only to air movement. A light breeze makes them vibrate slowly without disturbing the common hair. When one blows gently on the trichobothria, the tarantula reacts with a quick jerk of its four front legs. If the front and hind legs are stimulated at the same time, the spider makes a sudden jump. This reaction is quite independent of the state of its appetite.

These three tactile responses—to pressure on the body wall, to moving of the common hair and to flexing of the trichobothria—are so different from one another that there is no possibility of confusing them. They serve the tarantula adequately for most of its needs and enable it to avoid most annoyances and

dangers. But they fail the spider completely when it meets its deadly enemy, the digger wasp Pepsis.

These solitary wasps are beautiful and formidable creatures. Most species are either a deep shiny blue all over, or deep blue with rusty wings. The largest have a wing span of about four inches. They live on nectar. When excited, they give off a pungent odor—a warning that they are ready to attack. The sting is much worse than that of a bee or common wasp, and the pain and swelling last longer. In the adult stage the wasp lives only a few months. The female produces but a few eggs, one at a time at intervals of two or three days. For each egg the mother must provide one adult tarantula, alive but paralyzed. The tarantula must be of the correct species to nourish the larva. The mother wasp attaches the egg to the paralyzed spider's abdomen. Upon hatching from the egg, the larva is many hundreds of times smaller than its living but helpless victim. It eats no other food and drinks no water. By the time it has finished its single gargantuan meal and become ready for wasphood, nothing remains of the tarantula but its indigestible chitinous skeleton.

The mother wasp goes tarantula-hunting when the egg in her ovary is almost ready to be laid. Flying low over the ground late on a sunny afternoon, the wasp looks for its victim or for the mouth of a tarantula burrow, a round hole edged by a bit of silk. The sex of the spider makes no difference, but the mother is highly discriminating as to species. Each species of Pepsis requires a certain species of tarantula, and the wasp will not attack the wrong species. In a cage with a tarantula which is not its normal prey the wasp avoids the spider, and is usually killed by it in the night.

Yet when a wasp finds the correct species, it is the other way about. To

ly looking out. The spider stands with its legs extended after raising its body so the wasp could pass under it. In the second drawing the wasp stings the spider, which falls on its back. In the third the wasp licks a drop of blood from the wound. In the final drawing the spider lies in its grave with the egg of the wasp on its abdomen.

identify the species the wasp apparently must explore the spider with her antennae. The tarantula shows an amazing tolerance to this exploration. The wasp crawls under it and walks over it without evoking any hostile response. The molestation is so great and so persistent that the tarantula often rises on all eight legs, as if it were on stilts. It may stand this way for several minutes. Meanwhile the wasp, having satisfied itself that the victim is of the right species, moves off a few inches to dig the spider's grave. Working vigorously with legs and jaws, it excavates a hole 8 to 10 inches deep with a diameter slightly larger than the spider's girth. Now and again the wasp pops out of the hole to make sure that the spider is still there.

When the grave is finished, the wasp returns to the tarantula to complete her ghastly enterprise. First she feels it all over once more with her antennae. Then her behavior becomes more aggressive. She bends her abdomen, protruding her sting, and searches for the soft membrane at the point where the spider's leg joins its body—the only spot where she can penetrate the horny skeleton. From time to time, as the exasperated spider slowly shifts ground, the wasp turns on her back and slides along with the aid of her wings, trying to get under the tarantula for a shot at the vital spot. During all this maneuvering, which can last for several minutes, the tarantula makes no move to save itself. Finally the wasp corners it against some obstruction and grasps one of its legs in her powerful jaws. Now at last the harassed spider tries a desperate but vain defense. The two contestants roll over and over on the ground. It is a terrifying sight and the outcome is always the same. The wasp finally manages to thrust her sting into the soft spot and holds it there for a few seconds while she pumps in the poison. Almost immediately the tarantula falls paralyzed on its back. Its legs stop twitching; its heart stops beating. Yet it is not dead, as is shown by the fact that if taken from the wasp it can be restored to some sensitivity by being kept in a moist chamber for several months.

After paralyzing the tarantula, the wasp cleans herself by dragging her body along the ground and rubbing her feet, sucks the drop of blood oozing from the wound in the spider's abdomen, then grabs a leg of the flabby, helpless animal in her jaws and drags it down to the bottom of the grave. She stays there for many minutes, sometimes for several hours, and what she does all that time in the dark we do not know. Eventually she lays her egg and attaches it to the side of the spider's abdomen with a sticky secretion. Then she emerges, fills the grave with soil carried bit by bit in her jaws, and finally tramples the ground all around to hide any trace of the grave from prowlers. Then she flies away, leaving her descendant safely started in life.

IN ALL THIS the behavior of the wasp evidently is qualitatively different from that of the spider. The wasp acts like an intelligent animal. This is not to say that instinct plays no part or that she reasons as man does. But her actions are to the point; they are not automatic and can be modified to fit the situation. We do not know for certain how she identifies the tarantula—probably it is by some olfactory or chemo-tactile sense—but she does it purposefully and does not blindly tackle a wrong species.

On the other hand, the tarantula's behavior shows only confusion. Evidently the wasp's pawing gives it no pleasure, for it tries to move away. That the wasp is not simulating sexual stimulation is certain, because male and female tarantulas react in the same way to its advances. That the spider is not anesthetized by some odorless secretion is easily shown by blowing lightly at the tarantula and making it jump suddenly.

What, then, makes the tarantula behave as stupidly as it does?

No clear, simple answer is available. Possibly the stimulation by the wasp's antennae is masked by a heavier pressure on the spider's body, so that it reacts as when prodded by a pencil. But the explanation may be much more complex. Initiative in attack is not in the nature of tarantulas; most species fight only when cornered so that escape is impossible. Their inherited patterns of behavior apparently prompt them to avoid problems rather than attack them. For example, spiders always weave their webs in three dimensions, and when a spider finds that there is insufficient space to attach certain threads in the third dimension, it leaves the place and seeks another, instead of finishing the web in a single plane. This urge to escape seems to arise under all circumstances, in all phases of life and to take the place of reasoning. For a spider to change the pattern of its web is as impossible as for an inexperienced man to build a bridge across a chasm obstructing his way.

In a way the instinctive urge to escape is not only easier but often more efficient than reasoning. The tarantula does exactly what is most efficient in all cases except in an encounter with a ruthless and determined attacker dependent for the existence of her own species on killing as many tarantulas as she can lay eggs. Perhaps in this case the spider follows its usual pattern of trying to escape, instead of seizing and killing the wasp, because it is not aware of its danger. In any case, the survival of the tarantula species as a whole is protected by the fact that the spider is much more fertile than the wasp.

# 14 The Evolution of Bowerbirds

E. THOMAS GILLIARD · August 1963

A 19th-century naturalist once suggested that just as mammals were commonly divided into two groups—man and the lower forms—all birds should be split into two categories: bowerbirds and other birds. No one who has observed the behavior of these remarkable creatures of Australia and New Guinea and examined their artifacts can scoff at this proposal. The males of some species build elaborate walled bowers of sticks and decorate them with bright objects and even with paint. Others construct towers up to nine feet high, some with tepee-like roofs and internal chambers, on circular lawns that they tend carefully and embellish with golden resins, garishly colored berries, iridescent insect skeletons and fresh flowers that are replaced as they wither. The bowers are stages set by the males on which to perform intricate routines of sexual display and to mate with the females of their species. The bowerbirds' architectural, engineering and decorating skills and their courtship displays constitute behavior that, as G. Evelyn Hutchinson of Yale University has said, "in its complexity and refinement is unique in the nonhuman part of the animal kingdom."

The student of evolution inevitably asks how such extremely specialized behavior came about. The answer, I suspect, can be unmasked if one steps back to survey all the birds with behavioral affinities to the bowerbirds, that is, those birds that practice the pattern of courtship behavior known as arena behavior. There are only 18 species called bowerbirds, at least 12 of which actually build bowers, but there are in all some 85 species that have been described as arena birds. This is still a small proportion—about 1 per cent—of the avian species of the world. But arena birds are a world-wide assemblage including

species in such disparate families as sandpipers, grouse, bustards, blackbirds, small tropical manakins and the bizarrely beautiful birds of paradise.

It has fallen to my lot to be able to make comparative ethological investigations of many of these species in the tropics of New Guinea and South America. As a result I have been able to reach some conclusions that seem to be new. I believe that arena behavior, wherever it appears, probably has a common origin and that it represents an advanced stage in avian development. Once set in motion, I think, it has a predictable evolution leading rather quickly to the development of the highly specialized combinations of structure and behavior found in all the far-flung arena species. The bowerbirds are at the pinnacle of arena evolution. They have gone a step beyond the most richly ornamented arena birds, substituting fancy houses and jewelry for colorful plumage.

Arena behavior was defined by the ornithologist and student of evolution Ernst Mayr as a pattern of territorial behavior in which the males establish a mating station that has no connection with feeding or nesting. I would add that it is a rather rare form of courtship behavior involving a group of males usually living in an organized band on or about a long-established mating space: the arena. Each arena is composed of a number of courts, the private display territories of individual males. To establish their right to a territory the males go through ritualistic combat routines, fighting, charging, displaying their plumage or brandishing twigs, singing or producing "mechanical" sounds. Once territories are established there is little fighting for mates because the females do the choosing. The sexes live apart for long periods of the year and are often

so dissimilarly dressed as to look like different species. Since there is no true pair bond, the males play no part whatever in building or defending the nest or in rearing the young.

This advanced courtship pattern is in sharp contrast to the less advanced behavior of the other 99 per cent of the world's birds. For them the central event is the establishment of a pair bond between a male and a female, with the pair proceeding to share the work of raising the young. (The word "advanced" is not intended to imply a value judgment on the state of matrimony. Ornithologists simply assume that pair-bonding and work-sharing habits represent the less advanced evolutionary condition in birds because these habits are so nearly universal.) The pair-bond pattern is found regularly not only in the phylogenetically recent passerine (perching) order of songbirds, which is currently the most numerous and highly differentiated avian group, but also in the older nonpasserine birds; it is a "conservative" behavioral pattern that has resisted modification. Yet the breakthrough to arena behavior seems to occur, apparently at random, just about anywhere in the world and at scattered points on the family tree of birds [see illustration on page 114].

The characteristics that define arena behavior and argue for its common origin and line of evolution emerge from the study of a fairly large number of arena birds. The pattern is most evident when the arena is small, as in the case of the ruff, a sandpiper of northern Europe and Asia whose behavior has been described in detail by C. R. Stonor. The males and females apparently live apart except for a few minutes in the breeding season. Each spring the males gather in isolated clans, each of which populates

MALE COCK OF THE ROCK (*Rupicola rupicola*) perches above its court in a British Guiana forest. Like the bowerbirds, this member of the cotinga family is an arena bird: the males live apart from the females in clans and establish individual breeding stations.

THREE COCKS occupying adjacent courts in a small arena were watched by the author for 20 days as they defended their territories and displayed to visiting females. The cock at left is posturing on its terrestrial court; the others perch above their courts.

CRESTED BOWERBIRD (*Amblyornis macgregoriae*) of New Guinea is a member of a remarkable genus that builds high towers of sticks surrounded by courtyards. *A. macgregoriae*, the most colorfully plumed of the genus, builds the least complex bower.

GREATER BIRD OF PARADISE (*Paradisaea apoda*) is native to the New Guinea region. This bird is a member of a breeding colony established in 1909 on Little Tobago in the Caribbean Sea. Photographs on this page and preceding one were made by author.

a small, grassy hillock in rolling meadowland. After a period of fighting and display among themselves the males learn to recognize one another as individuals, and arrange themselves on the mound in a social order that presumably remains fairly fixed throughout the breeding season. Each male's territory is a private court about two feet in diameter that he defends vigorously against other males. The clan waits day after day for the visits of occasional females in search of mates. When one appears, the males go to their courts and assume strangely stiff postures, extending the colorful plumage of their neck ruffs. Displaying in this manner they reminded Stonor of a bed of flowers. The female wanders through this cluster and pecks at the neck feathers of the bird she prefers. Mating occurs immediately—whereupon the rejected males immediately collapse on their courts as if in a fainting spell.

Arena behavior of a similar sort but on a larger scale is practiced by the sage grouse and prairie chicken of North America. The grouse's arena may be half a mile long and 200 yards wide, with 400 males within its boundaries, each standing 25 to 40 feet apart on its private court. The zoologist John W. Scott was able to study the breeding hierarchy in a clan of these grouse. He found that the great majority of matings went to four "master" and a few "submaster" cocks with courts located along the center line of the long, narrow arena. Of 114 observed matings involving males whose place in the hierarchy had been determined, 74 per cent went to the four master cocks. Only after these birds had become satiated did 13 per cent of the matings go to the submasters, and the few remaining matings went to scattered owners of peripheral courts. These and other observations make it clear that arena matings are not random: the coordinated clan activities that serve to establish the territorial hierarchy, and thus the breeding rights, are of primary evolutionary importance.

Some years ago on an expedition to South America I studied arena behavior in a very different bird, a cotinga called cock of the rock (*Rupicola rupicola*). I found a clan of these brilliant orange birds, which wear a great semicircular crest resembling that of a Roman helmet, in the Kanuku Mountains of British Guiana. The males held and defended an arena some 40 by 80 feet in extent including about 40 small courts—cleared areas on the ground under saplings and vines that provided convenient perches. For 20 consecutive days I watched three

members of the clan, readily recognizable as individuals, that held adjacent courts in one part of the arena. I was struck by the silence and deliberateness of movement that characterized their behavior on the courts; it was reminiscent of the behavior of a pair-bonded male at its nest. During the period of observation females visited the arena several times. Whenever a female arrived, the three males, if they were not already on the ground, would fall almost like stones from their perches to their courts. There, with bodies flattened and heads tilted so that the crests were silhouetted against the bare ground, they would posture stiffly for many minutes. Again there was a resemblance to the attitude of a male attending a nest. The three birds jealously defended from one

another their own courts and a cone-shaped space above them. But when a wandering nonclan male visited them, they would fly up and attack him as a team with violent chasing displays, wing-buffeting, strange cries and whinnying sounds.

The 24 species of birds of paradise in which arena behavior is seen vary widely in physical characteristics and in the details of their displays. Some clear courts on or near the ground, some inhabit the middle levels of tropical forests and some display high in the treetops. In many of them the arena is so large that it has not usually been considered an arena at all. The distances between the individual courts can mislead one into believing that each male is operating in solitude, but this is almost cer-

MALE RUFFS display on small private courts close to one another in a tight arena. When reeves (female ruffs) are in the vicinity, the males posture stiffly on their courts, extending their colorful plumage (*top*). Two reeves approach (*middle*); one selects a mate by pecking at its neck feathers (*bottom*). The photographs were made by Arthur Christiansen.

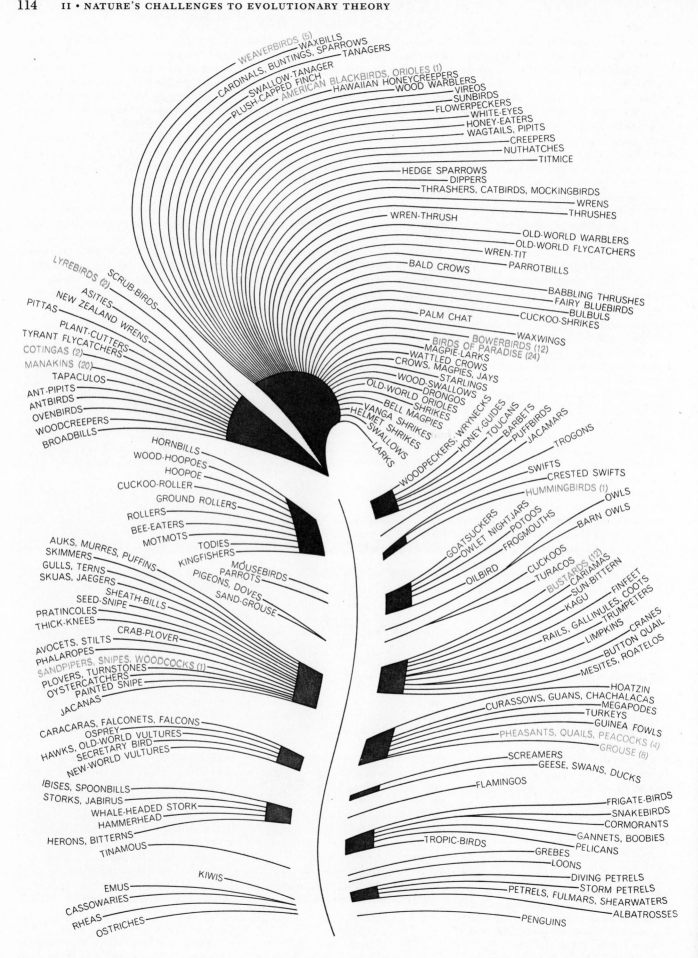

tainly not the case. Apparently these species have "exploded" arenas; the birds' calls and mechanisms for the production of other sounds are always highly developed and powerful, so that the males can interact in spite of their seeming isolation. Strong evidence in favor of the exploded-arena hypothesis is the fact that in many of these species the courts have been found to be concentrated in certain areas of the forest year after year.

I have studied two of the species that clear courts on or near the ground beneath low branches, vines and saplings: the magnificent bird of paradise (*Diphyllodes magnificus*) and Queen Carola's bird of paradise (*Parotia carolae*). For both species the court is the property of a single male that remains in attendance many hours a day, probably for several months a year. Austin L. Rand of the Chicago Natural History Museum has described how the magnificent bird of paradise spends countless hours trimming away the forest leaves above its court, thereby enabling a shaft of sky light to enhance the bird's iridescent coloring. Similar but less well developed court-clearing is practiced by other arena birds. In an arena of blue-backed manakins on Tobago in the West Indies I saw that much of the foliage had been cut around the arboreal courts. Frank M. Chapman of the American Museum of Natural History studied clans of Gould's manakins located miles apart in Panama that had cleared many small, platelike clearings in 200-foot-long strips of the rain-forest floor. The cock of the rock clears its court with violent wing-thrashing, whereas most other arena birds use their bills for this purpose. However it is done, the court of many arena birds is swept clean of fallen debris if it is terrestrial, and stripped of many leaves and twigs if it is arboreal.

It seems not too big a step from the court-clearers to such elementary bower-builders as Archbold's bowerbird (*Archboldia papuensis*). These are clearly arena birds: the males and females apparently live apart most of the year. The males spend the breeding season

ARENA BEHAVIOR has developed at a number of apparently unrelated points on the tree of avian evolution. Families that include arena birds are shown in color, together with the number of known arena species in each, a number that is subject to upward revision. In this highly schematic diagram the major families have been grouped into 28 orders of birds, from the oldest (*bottom*) to the most recent (*top*).

on or close to table-sized stages on the ground in high mountain forests of New Guinea. Each stage is owned and defended by a single male who carpets it with ferns, decorates it with shafts of bamboo, piles of resin, beetle skeletons, snail shells and lumps of charcoal. Each is within audible range of other stage-tending males. On one slope of Mount Hagen I found five stages concentrated in a zone about two miles in diameter, and my native hunters reported others I did not see. Although the species seemed rather common, a number of expeditions failed to find any of these birds elsewhere on Mount Hagen; however, a similar group was discovered on another mountain some 20 miles away. In my opinion each of these groups represents a clan, and its gathering place is the clan's arena. The males within each clan maintain contact with one another by uttering mighty whistles and harsh, rasping notes, and it seems likely that they all know when a female is in the arena and act in concert as many other arena birds do.

I watched one male receiving a visit from a female. As soon as the female arrived near the court the male dropped to its colorful stage and began to act in a manner resembling that of a young bird begging food. With its wings outstretched and its tail spread, it crawled tortuously toward the female, which perched at the edge of the court and kept moving around its periphery. The male held its head up like a turtle, made gasping movements with its bill and kept up a deep, penetrating "churr" song. In spite of the vigor of this display the ceremony was apparently not consummated by mating. After 22 minutes something disturbed the birds and the female flew off. Soon the male began rearranging the piles of ornaments and resumed its long, solitary wait.

Another New Guinea bowerbird with an exploded arena is the extraordinary gardener bowerbird (*Amblyornis*). A male of this genus builds its bower by piling sticks against a sapling on the floor of a mountain rain forest and clearing a mossy saucer around the tower. Some species build large towers with roofs and internal chambers and decorate the moss court with snail shells, insect and spider silk and fresh flowers changed daily for months on end. Others build only a small roof and use fewer ornaments, and still others merely maintain a clearing around a modest tower of intertwined sticks.

Some years ago I noticed that there is an inverse ratio in the three known *Amblyornis* species between the complexity of the bower and the plumage of

the male bird (the three females are virtually indistinguishable). In the species *A. macgregoriae*, which builds the simple bower, the adult male wears a long golden-orange crest [*see top illustration on page 112*]. In *A. subalaris*, which builds the somewhat more complex bower, the male wears a shorter crest. And in the aptly named species *A. inornatus,* which builds the most elaborate bower (with a broad roof overhanging a court decorated with berries, shells and piles of flowers), the male wears no crest at all and cannot be distinguished from any of the females!

I believe that in these birds the forces of sexual selection have been transferred from morphological characteristics—the male plumage—to external objects and that this "transferral effect" may be the key factor in the evolution of the more complex bowerbirds. This would explain the extraordinary development and proliferation of the bowers and their ornaments: these objects have in effect become externalized bundles of secondary sexual characteristics that are psychologically but not physically connected with the males. The transfer also has an important morphological effect: once colorful plumage is rendered unimportant, natural selection operates in the direction of protective coloration and the male tends more and more to resemble the female.

Further evidence of this sort came from observations of Lauterbach's bowerbird (*Chlamydera lauterbachi*), a grassland and forest-edge species of New Guinea. In an area several miles in diameter I once found 16 bowers of this "avenue-building" species hundreds to many thousands of feet apart. One bower I examined contained almost 1,000 pale pebbles weighing nearly 10 pounds. More than 3,000 sticks and 1,000 hairlike strands of grass had gone into the four-walled structure. The sticks were interlocked to form a rigid structure and the grass was used to line the vertical walls facing the inner court. Three times during the many days I watched a female entered a bower. The male became highly excited and began to dance. The female jumped quickly within the walls and then stood still and alert. Almost as soon as she was in the bower the male picked up with its bill a marble-sized red berry, held it high and displayed it to the female in much the same manner as it would have displayed its bright crest feathers—if it had had any. *C. lauterbachi*, like *A. inornatus*, is the most advanced builder of its genus. It is also a species in which the male and

INVERSE RATIO was noted by the author between the complexity of gardener bowerbirds' bowers and the brilliance of their plumage. The most complex bower, seen at left in a photograph made by S. Dillon Ripley of Yale University, is built by the crestless *Amblyornis inornatus*. The simplest bower *(right)* is that of the orange-crested *A. macgregoriae* [see top illustration on page 112].

female cannot be told apart except by dissection. The transferral effect seems to be operating in this case too.

It appears that once the female has selected a bower-owner she stays for several days. (This has also been reported in some arena birds, such as the argus pheasant.) These stays may be responsible for the assumption made by many investigators that there is a pair bond in bowerbirds. Pair-bonding cannot be proved or disproved except by marking and observing females; my investigations indicate that at least most of the bower-building bowerbirds are polygynous, with exploded arenas like those of their close relatives, the birds of paradise.

One further observation bearing on the transferral effect should be mentioned. In the Finisterre Mountains of New Guinea I watched and filmed the courtship behavior of the fawn-breasted bowerbird (*Chlamydera cerviniventris*), in which both sexes are an identical drab

brown. When a female entered the two-walled avenue bower and squatted on the floor, the male immediately approached. On the ground several feet from the bower the male suddenly appeared to be overcome by a spasm. Its head seemed to turn involuntarily away from the female again and again. Finally the bird appeared to regain control, seized a sprig of green berries in its bill, faced the female and waved the berries up and down as it slowly approached the bower. I saw several more such visits by a female, and each time the male went through the curious twisting motions that presented the back of its head to the female.

Later, watching the films I had made of these movements, I was struck by the thought that the head-screwing might constitute crest display—except for the fact that *C. cerviniventris* has no crest! But many males closely related to this species do have glittering violet-to-pink

crests at the nape of the neck and the Australian ornithologist John Warham has described how they twist their necks to display the crest to a female in the bower. I concluded that the head-twisting of *C. cerviniventris* is a relict movement dating from the time when the species had such a crest. With the later incorporation of the berries as ornaments in the courtship ceremony, I postulated, the crest became unimportant. Since it was now simply a liability in terms of protective coloration, it was lost through natural selection—but the movement associated with it persists. This I consider a strong second line of evidence for the transferral effect.

Again it must be emphasized that the courtship behavior of this species and probably that of all other ground-displaying bowerbirds, even though complicated and camouflaged by refinements of ornamentation and stick architecture, follows the basic pattern of

COURTSHIP BEHAVIOR of avenue-building bowerbirds is shown in this sequence of drawings. The male builds a walled bower by inserting thousands of sticks into a foundation mat *(left)* and decorates it with pebbles and berries *(second from left)*.

arena behavior the world around. It is the behavior of a clan of males interacting in an arena, each on its own territory and competing with the other males for itinerant females. Many arena species clear courts and some do it more effectively than others; some build stages or erect walls, towers or houses. All these actions, I believe, are merely levels of refinement of the same basic behavior.

Is the history of the bower, then, the same as the history of the arena bird's court? I think so. Arena behavior, I suggest, can develop fortuitously at any period in the history of any bird group as a result of a shift in the work load shared by a pair-bonded male and female. The division of labor in nest construction and care and the rearing of the young varies from species to species. In extreme cases the males may be completely released from all nesting duties—perhaps because natural selection favors a stock in which brightly colored males stay away from the nest. Emancipated from the pair bond, the males can live apart from the females in bachelor clans. Now sexual selection can operate freely, tending in the direction of brighter plumage and more complex display behavior that will attract more females.

The next step, from elementary arena behavior to bower-building, may not be so great as it seems at first. I have pointed out that most arena birds clear some sort of display space for themselves. In the species that have come down from the trees to the ground, such as the cock of the rock and some birds of paradise, the males spend much of their time clearing away twigs and leaves and perhaps berries, stones and shells, if there are any about. A. J. Marshall of Monash University in Australia and Erwin Stresemann of the Berlin Natural History Museum have speculated that

the handling of these objects may accidentally have become incorporated in and important to the courtship ceremony for which the court is maintained, and so have led to bower-building. I think it likely that both court-clearing and bower-building are deeply rooted in the nesting impulses of the male birds. Nest-building and the actions associated with it by each species constitute fixed behavioral patterns that are not easily abandoned and are more likely to be diverted into new directions. Other investigators have noted actions in arena birds, and particularly in bowerbirds, that reminded them of nesting behavior. V. G. L. van Someren remarked some years ago that in shaping its court the male of the weaverbird species known as Jackson's dancing whydah "creates recesses resembling the early stages of a nest, butting into the grass and smoothing it down with his breast." Edward A. Armstrong commented in his classic book on bird behavior that "this performance would seem to be due to the survival of the nest-building impulse."

Marshall, a leading student of the bowerbirds, has called attention to many activities he believes stem from displaced nesting habits. Certainly as one looks at a New Guinea stick bower, particularly that of Lauterbach's bowerbird, one cannot but feel it is some sort of monstrous nest. The wall of sticks, the lining of grass, even the way the male places egg-sized berries or pebbles near the center of the basket-like structure—all suggest aspects of nest-building that still survive in males that have had no nesting responsibilities for tens of thousands of years and probably much longer. In other bowerbirds and arena birds this impression of a physical nest is, to be sure, not so vivid. But, as noted in the case of the cock of the rock, I have often been impressed by the male's strangely

quiet and attentive manner when it visits its court or bower, a manner that reminds an ornithologist of a parent bird arriving at its nest.

To sum up, I would define arena behavior as courtship behavior reshaped by emancipated males to include their nondiscardable nesting tendencies. I would further suggest that bower behavior has developed in certain arena birds under the influence of natural and sexual selection, that some of the ground-clearing arena birds are even now on the way to becoming builders of bowers, and that the dully dressed bowerbirds that build the most complex and ornamented structures are at the leading edge of avian evolution.

This hypothesis does not in itself explain the great variety and variability of bowers or the complexities of behavior and plumage in arena birds, all of which seem to imply that these birds are evolving at an accelerated rate compared with other birds. The biological advantage of arena behavior may be precisely that it does speed up evolution. Because of promiscuous polygyny a few males in each generation are enough to propagate a species. Losses by predation can be very acute (and indeed must be in the case of terrestrially displaying males), and both natural and sexual selection can operate more severely than usual.

An indication that some such process may be at work is the fact that "intergeneric hybrids," although extremely rare in all animals, are rather more common in arena birds. Since a species—a limb-tip on the avian tree of evolution—is identified as such by its "reproductive isolation" from the other limb-tips, it is difficult to explain even one case of interfertility between genera, the main limbs of the tree. Yet in our collection at the American Museum of Natural History

With the male in attendance, a female enters the bower (*third from left*) and, after the male displays, sits on the floor (*third from right*). The two birds mate (*second from right*). Then the female leaves to build a nest and rear her young by herself (*right*).

"TRANSFERRAL EFFECT" is illustrated by a relict head-turning movement in a bowerbird. *Chlamydera nuchalis* (*left*) displays to the female a bright pink crest at the nape of its neck. *C. cer-* *viniventris* (*right*) makes a similar movement although it has no crest. This bird's use of berries as ornaments made the crest unnecessary and it disappeared, but the turning motion persists.

we have no less than 11 adult male intergeneric hybrid offspring of the magnificent bird of paradise (*Diphyllodes magnificus*) and the king bird of paradise (*Cicinnurus regius*), which were long ago classified in different genera. The number of hybrids occurring between these birds leads me to suspect that *Diphyllodes* and *Cicinnurus* may not be nearly so distantly related as their fundamental structures seem to indicate. Perhaps arena behavior, once it takes hold of a species, fashions structural changes (body form) more rapidly than it does genetic changes (reproductive barriers). Such uneven radiation

might explain the hybrids between arena birds so different in size, shape and color that any taxonomist would accept them as distinct genera. Is there perhaps a correlation between such birds and the many varieties of domestic dogs, in the case of which man has acted as the agent of rapid selection and has bred such different but interfertile forms as the Pekingese and the great Dane?

This idea is probably premature and may be fanciful. Keeping to firmer ground, it is safe to say that the highly specialized combinations of structure and behavior seen in arena birds argue most eloquently that these birds are

evolving at a faster rate than most birds and that this accelerated evolution is due to their behavior. One has only to consider the magnificent plumage of the argus pheasant, the great inflatable bibs of the bustard, the radiant orange paraphernalia of the cock of the rock and the lacy plumage of the birds of paradise to be seized by the notion that some rapidly operating mechanism is directing the evolution of these birds. The same holds true for the even more wonderful arena birds called bowerbirds, with their houses and ornamented gardens and their courtship displays that replace plumage with glittering natural jewelry.

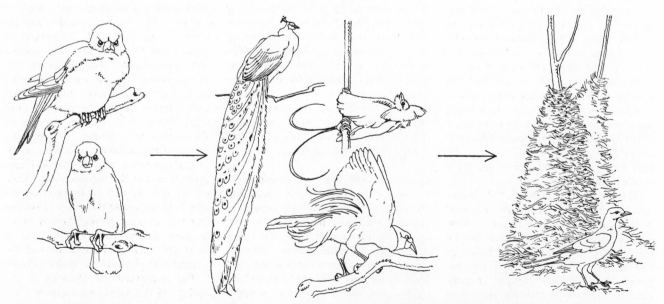

EVOLUTION OF BOWERBIRDS is diagramed here according to the author's hypothesis in highly simplified form. "Ordinary" birds (*left*) develop a pair bond, with a male and female mating and then tending the nest. If that pair bond is broken, there is a breakthrough to arena behavior (*center*) and a consequent proliferation of specialized plumage and courtship behavior. A few arena birds go one step further, to bower-building (*right*). With sexual selection transferred to objects, males may become dully colored.

# 15 Cleaning Symbiosis

CONRAD LIMBAUGH · August 1961

While skin diving in the cool water off the coast of southern California in the spring of 1949, I observed a brief and seemingly casual meeting between a small golden kelp perch (*Brachyistius frenatus*) and a walleye surfperch (*Hyperprosopon argenteum*) twice its size. The walleye had separated itself from a milling school of its fellows several yards away and was holding itself rigid with fins extended, its body pointed at an unnatural angle to the surface of the water. The three-inch kelp perch spent several minutes picking at the silver sides of the walleye with its pointed snout. Then the kelp perch darted into the golden leaves of a nearby kelp plant, and the walleye returned to lose itself in the activity of the school. At the time I recorded this event in my notes only as an interesting incident.

Since then my studies and the observations of others have convinced me that this was not an isolated episode. On the contrary, it was an instance of a constant and vital activity that occurs throughout the marine world: cleaning symbiosis. Certain species of marine animal have come to specialize in cleaning parasites and necrotic tissue from fishes that visit them. This mutually beneficial behavior promotes the well-being of the host fishes and provides food for those that do the cleaning.

The relationship between the cleaner and the cleaned is frequently so casual as to seem accidental, as in the encounter that first caught my attention. On the other hand, one finds in the Bahamas the highly organized relationship between the Pederson shrimp (*Periclimenes pedersoni*) and its numerous clients. The transparent body of this tiny animal is striped with white and spotted with violet, and its conspicuous antennae are considerably longer than its body. It establishes its station in quiet water where fishes congregate or frequently pass, always in association with the sea anemone *Bartholomea annulata*, usually clinging to it or occupying the same hole. When a fish approaches, the shrimp will whip its long antennae and sway its body back and forth. If the fish is interested, it will swim directly to the shrimp and stop an inch or two away. The fish usually presents its head or a gill cover for cleaning, but if it is bothered by something out of the ordinary, such as an injury near its tail, it presents itself tail first. The shrimp swims or crawls forward, climbs aboard and walks rapidly over the fish, checking irregularities, tugging at parasites with its claws and cleaning injured areas. The fish remains almost motionless during this inspection and allows the shrimp to make minor incisions in order to get at subcutaneous parasites. As the shrimp approaches the gill covers, the fish opens each one in turn and allows the shrimp to enter and forage among the gills. The shrimp is even permitted to enter and leave the fish's mouth cavity. Local fishes quickly learn the location of these shrimp. They line up or crowd around for their turn and often wait to be cleaned when the shrimp has retired into the hole beside the anemone.

Such behavior has been considered a mere curiosity for many years. The literature contains scattered reports of cleaning symbiosis, including a few examples among land animals: the crocodile and the Egyptian plover, cattle and the egret, the rhinoceros and the tickbird. As early as 1892 the German biologist Franz von Wagner had suggested that the pseudoscorpion, a tiny relative of the spider that is frequently observed stealing a ride on larger insects, is actually engaged in removing parasitic mites from these insects. The U.S. biologist William Beebe in 1924 saw red crabs remove red ticks from sunbathing marine iguanas of the Galápagos Islands. While diving in the coral waters off Haiti four years later, Beebe also saw several small fishes of the wrasse family cleaning parrot fish. Mexican fishermen in the Gulf of California refer to a certain angelfish (*Holacanthus passer*) as *El Barbero*. They explain that this fish "grooms the other fishes" and so deserves its title as "The Barber."

Recognition of cleaning symbiosis and its implications has come only in recent years. The gear and the technique of skin diving have given marine biologists a new approach to the direct observation of undersea life. They have discovered numerous examples of cleaning behavior, enough to establish already that the behavior represents one of the primary relationships in the community of life in the sea. The known cleaners include some 26 species of fish, six species of shrimp and Beebe's crab. This number will undoubtedly increase when the many marine organisms now suspected of being cleaners have been studied more closely. It now seems that most other fishes seek out and depend on the service they render. The primary nature of the behavior is evident in the bright coloration and anatomical specialization that distinguish many cleaners. It appears that cleaning symbiosis may help to explain the range of species and the make-up of populations found in particular habitats, the patterns of local movement and migration and the natural control of disease in many fishes.

The importance of cleaning in the ecology of the waters off southern California became more and more apparent to me during the early 1950's as I accumulated observations of cleaners at work. My notes are particularly concerned with

CALIFORNIA MORAY EEL (*Gymnothorax mordax*) has its external parasites removed by four California cleaning shrimps (*Hippolysmata californica*). At upper left is a fifth shrimp. This photograph and the one at right below were made by Ron Church.

SPANISH HOGFISH (*top*) in process of cleaning ocean surgeon (*Acanthurus bahianus*) was photographed by author in Bahamas.

LIONFISH (*Pterois volitans*) is host to a very much smaller cleaning wrasse (*purple fish in center*) of undetermined species.

**THREE PAIRS OF MARINE ORGANISMS** are shown in the illustration above. The smaller organism in each pair lives partly by cleaning the larger one, eating parasites and dead tissue. Skin-diving marine biologists have recently discovered that this "cleaning symbiosis" is quite common among organisms that live in the sea. In the pair at top left a smooth trunkfish *(Lactophrys triqueter)* is cleaned by a bluehead *(Thalassoma bifasciatum)*. In the pair at center right the larger fish is a black angelfish *(Pomacanthus paru)*; the smaller one, a neon goby *(Elecatinus oceanops)*. In the pair at the bottom a longjaw squirrelfish *(Holocentrus marianas)* is attended by a tiny, violet-spotted Pederson cleaning shrimp *(Periclimenes pedersoni)*.

the performance of the golden-brown wrasse *(Oxyjulis californica)*, commonly called the señorita. This cigar-shaped fish is abundant in these waters and well known to fishermen as a bait-stealer.

Certain fishes, such as the opaleye *(Girella nigricans)*, the topsmelt *(Atherinops affinis)* and the blacksmith *(Chromis punctipinnis)*, crowd so densely about a señorita that it is impossible to see the cleaning activity. When I first saw these dense clouds, often with several hundred fish swarming around a single cleaner, I thought they were spawning aggregations. As the clouds dispersed at my approach, however, I repeatedly observed a señorita retreating into the cover of the rocks and seaweed nearby. Often the host fishes, unaware of my approach, would rush and stop in front of the retreating señorita, temporarily blocking its path. In less dense schools I was able to observe the señorita in the act of nibbling parasites from the flanks of a host fish. While being cleaned blacksmiths would remain motionless in the most awkward positions—on their sides, head up, head down or even upside down.

The material cleaned from fishes by the señorita and other cleaners has not been thoroughly studied. Among the organisms I have noted in the stomach contents of cleaners are copepods and isopods: minute parasitic crustaceans that attach themselves to the scales and integument of fishes. I have also found bacteria, and on several occasions I have seen señoritas in the act of nibbling away a white, fluffy growth that streamed as a milky cloud from the gills of infected fishes. Especially in the spring and summer months off California and farther south in the warmer waters off Mexico, many fishes display this infection; it ranges from an occasional dot of white to large ulcerated sores rimmed with white. Carl H. Oppenheimer, now at the University of Miami, has shown that this is a bacterial disease by infecting healthy individuals with material taken from diseased fishes.

Judging by the diversity of its clientele, the señorita is well known as a cleaner to many members of the marine community. Among the species that seek out its services I have counted pelagic (deep ocean) fishes as well as the numerous species that populate the kelp beds nearer shore. The black sea bass

SPOTTED GOATFISH (*Pseudupeneus maculatus*) is host to the smaller Spanish hogfish. The hogfish is found in the tropical waters from Bermuda and Florida to Rio de Janeiro, in the Gulf of Mexico and around Ascension and St. Helena islands in the South Atlantic.

GARIBALDI (*Hypsypops rubicunda*) at top holds itself at an unnatural angle while being cleaned by a señorita. The latter, which is found in temperate waters from central California to central Lower California, cleans more than a dozen species of fish.

(*Stereolepis gigas*) and the even larger ocean sunfish (*Mola mola*) seem to come purposely to the outer edge of the kelp beds, where they attract large numbers of señoritas, which flock around them to pick off their parasites. I have also observed the señorita at work on the bat ray (*Holorhinus californicus*), showing that the symbiosis embraces the cartilaginous as well as the bony fishes.

Since first recognizing cleaning behavior in these southern California fishes, I have studied it in numerous places down the Pacific Coast of Mexico, in the Gulf of California, in the Bahamas and in the Virgin Islands. Observations such as mine have been paralleled in the literature by other skin-diving biologists and by underwater photographers. From 1952 to 1955 Vern and Harry Pederson

**JUVENILE GRAY ANGELFISH** (*Pomacanthus aureus*) at right cleans external parasites from the tail of a bar jack (*Caranx ruber*). Below the jack is another cleaner, the Spanish hogfish. This photograph and those on the opposite page were made by the author.

**"CLEANING STATION,"** consisting of a sponge (*light area with small, dark protuberances*) surrounded by turtle grass, is manned by a juvenile gray angelfish. The station, located off New Providence Island in the Bahamas, was photographed by the author's wife.

FOUR CLEANING RELATIONSHIPS are depicted in this drawing by Rudolf Freund. In each the cleaner is in color. At top left a señorita (*Oxyjulis californica*) cleans a group of blacksmiths (*Chromis punctipinnis*). At top right are a butterfly fish (*Chaetodon* *nigrirostris*) and two Mexican goatfish (*Pseudupeneus dentatus*); in center, two neon gobies (*Elecatinus oceanops*) and a Nassau grouper (*Epinephelus striatus*); at bottom, a Spanish hogfish (*Bodianus rufus*) in the mouth of a barracuda (*Sphyraena barracuda*).

made motion pictures in the Bahamas of cleaning behavior in a number of species of fish and in the violet-spotted shrimp that bears their name. In 1953 the German skin diver Hans Hass suggested that the pilot fish associated with manta rays ate the parasites of their hosts. Irenäus Eibl-Eibesfeldt, a German biologist, published notes in 1954 on cleaning behavior he had witnessed in fishes in Bahamian waters; he expressed the belief that it is common in the oceans of the world. In the Hawaiian and Society islands John E. Randall of the University of Miami identified as cleaners four fishes of the genus *Labroides*, two of which were new species.

A few generalizations about cleaning symbiosis may now be attempted. In the first place, the phenomenon appears to be more highly developed in clear tropical waters than in cooler regions of the seas. The tropical cleaner species are more numerous and include the young of the gray angelfish (*Pomacanthus aureus*), the butterfly fish (*Chaetodon*), gobies (*Elecatinus*) and several wrasses such as the Spanish hogfish (*Bodianus rufus*) and the members of the genus *Labroides*. Even distantly related species have analogous structures for cleaning, such as pointed snouts and tweezer-like teeth; this suggests convergent evolution toward specialization in the cleaning function. In the tropical seas the cleaning fish are generally brightly colored and patterned in sharp contrast to their backgrounds; it appears that most fishes that stand out in their environment are cleaners. Since cleaning fishes must be conspicuous, it is logical that they should have evolved toward maximum contrast

with their surroundings. (The parasites on which they feed have evolved toward a maximum of protective coloration, matching the color of their hosts, and are usually invisible to the human observer of cleaning behavior.) In general these fishes are not gregarious and live solitarily or in pairs. In Temperate Zone waters, on the other hand, the cleaners are not so brightly colored or so contrastingly marked. They tend to be gregarious, to the point of living in schools, and are more numerous, though the number of species is smaller.

The cleaning behavior of the tropical forms is correspondingly more complex than that of the Temperate Zone species. Whereas the latter simply surround or follow a fish in order to clean it. the tropical cleaners put on displays not

**BLACKSMITHS IN GROUP** waiting to be cleaned by a single señorita (*slender fish in nearly horizontal position at right center*) assume various positions. This photograph was made by Charles H. Turner of the State of California Department of Fish and Game.

unlike those shown in courtship by some male fishes. They rush forward, turn sideways and then retreat, repeating the ritual until a fish is attracted into position to be cleaned. Frequently they sense the presence of a fish before a human observer can, and they hasten to take up their station before the fish arrives to be cleaned.

Some species clean only in their juvenile stage; none of them appears to depend exclusively on the habit for its food. Again, however, the tropical species come closer to being "full time" cleaners. One consequence of their higher degree of specialization is that they enjoy considerable immunity from predators. In an extensive investigation of the food habits of California kelp fishes I never found a señorita, a close cousin of the numerous cleaning wrasses of the tropics, in the stomach contents of other fishes. I have seen it safely enter the open mouth of the kelp bass, a fish that normally feeds on señorita-size fishes. On the other hand, the kelp perch, a more typical Temperate Zone cleaner, frequently turns up in the stomachs of fishes that it cleans. The immunity of certain cleaners is so well established that other fishes have come to mimic them in color and conformation and so share their immunity. Some mimics reverse the process and prey on the fish that mistake them for cleaners!

The same generalizations may be made in contrasting the cleaning shrimps of the Tropical and Temperate zones. Only one of the six known species occurs outside the tropics; this is the California cleaning shrimp (*Hippolysmata californica*). It is a highly gregarious and wandering animal, at the other pole of behavior from the tropical species as represented by the solitary and sedentary Pederson shrimp of the Bahamian waters. The California cleaning shrimp does not have the coloration and marking to make it stand out from its environment. So far as I have been able to determine, it does not display itself to attract fishes. These California shrimps wander abroad in troops numbering in the hundreds, feeding on the bottom at night and retiring to cover during the day. They act as cleaners when they come upon an animal, say a lobster, in need of cleaning or when a fish, perhaps a moray eel, swims into the crevice where they have found shelter. They will crawl rapidly over the entire outside surface of the animal, cleaning away everything removable, including decaying tissue. A lobster that has been worked over by a team of these

PEDERSON CLEANING SHRIMP (*Periclimenes pedersoni*) attracts hosts by waving its antennae, which are longer than its body. Shell-like objects (*upper right*) are shrimp's uropods, or "flippers." Photograph was made by F. M. Bayer of Smithsonian Institution.

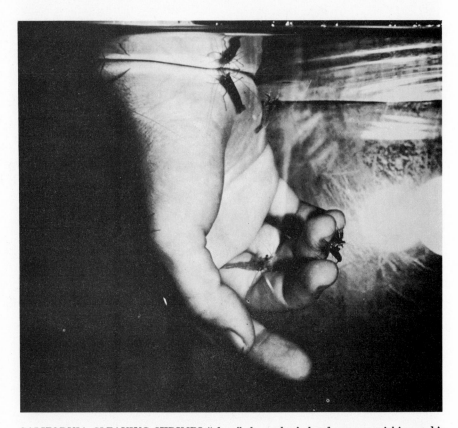

CALIFORNIA CLEANING SHRIMPS "clean" the author's hand, even to picking at his fingernails. These shrimps clean everything that is removable from the exterior of a host.

shrimps comes out with a clean shell; a human diver's hand will receive the same treatment. Fishes do not seem to be bothered by these rough attentions, although the moray may occasionally jerk its head as if annoyed.

In some cases the shrimps may enter the mouth of the moray to get at parasites there, but not without risk; the stomachs of morays have yielded a considerable number of these shrimps. In contrast, the tropical cleaning shrimps, all of them more exclusively specialized as cleaners, seem to have the same immunity from predation as the tropical cleaning fishes. With their bright colors, their fixed stations and their elaborate display behavior, they are plainly advertised to the community as cleaners and attract hosts rather than predators. It is easy to visualize the evolutionary path by which the more complex cleaning symbiosis may have developed from the imperfect cleaner-host relationships such as that of the California shrimp.

In the summer of 1955, in the Gulf of California near Guaymas, I noted that cleaning behavior appeared to be concentrated at rocky points: each point was manned by two butterfly fish and one angelfish. I assumed that the concentration of other fishes arose from the fact that these points constitute the intersection of the communities of fishes on each side. In 1958 Randall, reporting on his studies of the cleaning wrasses in the Society Islands, observed that fishes came from comparatively long distances to the sites occupied by the cleaners, not just from the immediate community. The Pederson brothers made the same observation in the Bahamas, reporting that the cleaners congregate in regular "cleaning stations" in the coral reefs and attract host fishes from large areas.

Subsequent studies have confirmed these observations. The various species of cleaning fish and shrimp tend to cluster in particular ecological situations: at coral heads, depressions in the bottom, ship wreckage or the edge of kelp beds. Their presence in these localities accounts in great part for the large assemblages of other fishes that are so frequently seen there. Even a small cleaning station in the tropics may process a large number of fish in the course of a day. I saw up to 300 fish cleaned at one station in the Bahamas during one six-hour daylight period. Some of the fishes pass from station to station and return many times during the day; those that could be identified by visible marks, such as infection spots, returned day after day at regular time intervals. Altogether it seemed that many of the fishes spent as much time at cleaning stations as they did in feeding.

At cleaning stations inhabited by thousands of cleaning organisms, cleaning symbiosis must assume great numerical significance in determining the distribution and concentration of marine populations. In my opinion, it is the presence of the señorita and the kelp perch that brings the deep-water coastal and pelagic fishes inshore to the edge of the kelp beds on the California coast. Most concentrations of reef fishes may similarly be understood to be cleaning stations. Cleaning symbiosis would therefore account for the existence of such well-known California sport-fishing grounds as the rocky points of Santa Catalina Island, the area around the sunken ship *Valiant* off the shore of Catalina, the La Jolla kelp beds and submarine canyon and the Coronado Islands.

These generalizations of course call for further observation and perhaps experimental study. In a modest field experiment in the Bahamas I once removed all the known cleaning organisms from two small, isolated reefs where fish seemed particularly abundant. Within a few days the number of fish was drastically reduced; within two weeks almost all except the territorial fishes had disappeared.

This experiment also demonstrated the importance of cleaning symbiosis in maintaining the health of the marine population. Many of the fish remaining developed fuzzy white blotches, swelling, ulcerated sores and frayed fins. Admittedly the experiment was a gross one and not well controlled, but the observed contrast with the fish populations of the nearby coral heads was very striking. Certainly it appeared that the ailments occurred because of the absence of cleaning organisms. This impression was strengthened when a number of local fishes that had been maintained in an aquarium were found to be developing bacterial infections. I placed a cleaner shrimp in the aquarium, and it went to work at once to clean the infected fishes.

Symbiotic cleaning has some important biological implications. From the viewpoint of evolution it provides a remarkable instance of morphological and behavioral adaptation. Ecologically speaking, cleaners must be regarded as key organisms in the assembling of the species that compose the populations of various marine habitats. Cleaning raises a great many questions for students of animal behavior; it would be interesting to know what mechanism prevents ordinarily voracious fishes from devouring the little cleaners. In zoogeography the cleaning relationships may provide the limiting factor in the dispersal of various species. In parasitology the relationship between the cleaning activities on the one hand and host-parasite relations on the other needs investigation. The beneficial economic effect of cleaners on commercially important marine organisms must be considerable in some areas. The modern marine-fisheries biologist must now consider cleaners in any thorough work dealing with life history and fish population studies. From the standpoint of the philosophy of biology, the extent of cleaning behavior in the ocean emphasizes the role of co-operation in nature as opposed to the tooth-and-claw struggle for existence.

# 16 Biological Luminescence

WILLIAM D. McELROY and HOWARD H. SELIGER · December 1962

The light of fireflies and other luminescent organisms has always charmed human observers. What benefit does the ability to produce light confer on an organism? Is the light completely "cold," that is, is its production 100 per cent efficient? Exactly how is the light produced? In spite of much study, dating back more than a century, these questions cannot be answered completely. But the main steps in the process have been established, its efficiency has been measured and the principal substances involved in it have been identified. With this knowledge in hand it is possible to make a reasonable guess as to how biological luminescence, or bioluminescence, arose in the course of evolution.

Bioluminescence is not only of interest in itself but also provides a sharp tool for studying other biological processes. This has resulted in part from the development of highly sensitive and rapid recording devices for the measurement of light. Because the emission of light by an organism is a chemical reaction catalyzed by an enzyme, the intensity of the light provides direct evidence of the rate of a kind of reaction that is common to all life processes. Consequently light emission by cells or cell extracts can be studied under various conditions and can serve as a valuable quantitative tool for biochemical and biophysical investigations.

One of the most striking features of bioluminescence is the sheer diversity of organisms that have developed the ability to emit light. They include certain bacteria, fungi, radiolarians, sponges, corals, flagellates, hydroids, nemerteans (vividly colored marine worms), ctenophores (small jellyfish-like animals), crustaceans, clams, snails, squids, centipedes, millepedes and insects. Among the last are of course the insects familiarly known as fireflies and glowworms. Many fishes are also luminous, but there are no self-luminous forms among amphibians, reptiles, birds or mammals. None of the higher plants is luminous. With the possible exception of a few strains of luminous bacteria, no freshwater organism is luminous, even though many of them are closely related to light-emitters that live in the sea.

Light emission can occur whenever a physical system undergoes a discrete change in free energy. The source of the original excitation of the system can be thermal, as in an incandescent lamp; electrical, as in a flash of lightning; mechanical, as in the scintillation that attends the breaking of a sugar crystal; or chemical, as in the glow of phosphorus. Bioluminescence is chemical luminescence, or chemiluminescence.

In a secluded bay in Jamaica certain protozoa that glow when they are disturbed are so abundant that they brightly illuminate the fish swimming in their midst. In Thailand one species of firefly congregates on certain trees, and all the fireflies flash on and off in unison like Christmas-tree lights. In Brazil the "railroad worm," the larva of a large beetle, bears green lights along its sides and a red light on its head. In the waters off Bermuda the female of a species of marine worm comes to the surface three days following a full moon and secretes a glowing circle of luminous material. The male, emitting puffs of light, heads straight for the circle of light, and both eggs and sperm are discharged into the water. A deep-sea angler fish carries a luminous organ at the tip of a retractable rodlike appendage with which it lures victims into its jaws. One deep-sea member of the squid family, quite unlike its ink-emitting cousins, spurts a luminous cloud when it wants to hide. In this symphony of living light most chords are blue. The greens and yellows of the fireflies and the green and red of the railroad worm are grace notes ornamenting the azure theme of the luminous bacteria and larger marine organisms.

## The Luminous Clams

Probably the best known of the luminous mollusks is the boring clam *Pholas dactylus,* which men have regarded as a delicacy since antiquity. In Greek *pholas* means lurking in a hole, which describes the mollusk's habit of boring into soft rock and hiding there with only its siphon exposed. In 1887 the French physiologist Raphaël Dubois used *Pholas* in his pioneering studies of the substances involved in bioluminescence. Dubois demonstrated that a cold-water extract of *Pholas* would continue to emit light for several minutes. He found that after the light emission had ceased it could be restored by adding a second extract obtained by washing a fresh clam in hot water and cooling the juice. Dubois concluded that there was some substance in the hot-water extract that was essential for light emission and that it was not affected by heating. He called this material luciferin, a name he coined from Lucifer, meaning light-bearer. The substance in the cold-water extract he called luciferase, indicating by the suffix "-ase" that it had the properties of an enzyme. Enzymes are biological catalysts, and like most enzymes luciferase is heat-sensitive. Dubois reasoned that both luciferin and luciferase were extracted by water—hot or cold—but that hot water inactivated the luciferase, leaving only the luciferin active.

The other pioneer in the field of bioluminescence was the late E. Newton

**GLOWING TOADSTOOLS** of the genus *Mycena* were photographed by self-emitted light. The light is given off principally from the gills beneath the caps of the fungus. Luminous mold is often seen in the vegetative state on rotting logs, but it is rare for luminescence to continue into the fruiting state shown here. The photograph was made by Yata Haneda of the Yokosuka City Museum.

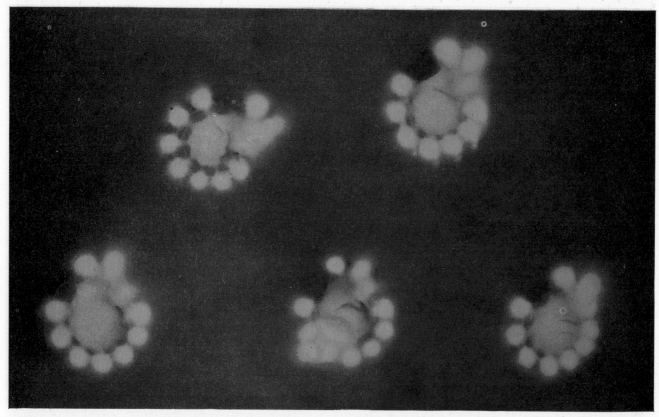

RAILROAD WORM is the larval form of a South American beetle. F. W. Goro made this unusual photograph by pressing a sheet of Kodachrome directly against a single larva several times to obtain multiple images. The picture is consequently a true autograph, made without the intervention of lens or camera. It is reproduced through the courtesy of *Life*. Copyright 1945 by Time Inc.

HATCHET FISH, *Argyropelecus hemigymnus,* is one of the more than 100 species of light-emitting fish. The photograph is by Haneda. In classifying many thousands of fish netted below 400 meters, the deep-sea investigator William Beebe found that more than 95 per cent were luminous. It seems likely that the light patterns found in various species play a role in hunting and recognition.

Harvey of Princeton University. Following Dubois's observations Harvey did much to show clearly that light emission in organisms is an enzymatic process. He described luciferin-luciferase reactions in a variety of organisms and demonstrated that they were of several different types. On a field trip to Japan he found a crustacean (*Cypridina hilgendorfii*) that, when dried, provided a convenient source of both luciferin and luciferase. Harvey and his students used many pounds of the material in their studies. *Cypridina* is a small crustacean with two hinged valves covering its body. It is found in both fresh and salt water, but only the marine forms are luminous. During World War II, Japanese soldiers used dried *Cypridina* as a source of low-intensity light when they did not want to run the risk of using a flashlight. A small quantity of *Cypridina* powder placed in the palm of the hand and moistened provided enough light for reading a map or a message.

*Cypridina* live in the sea bottom near the shore and come out to feed at night. The organism is not itself luminous; it excretes luciferin and luciferase into the surrounding water, and the interaction of the two substances produces a blue light. The luciferin is apparently synthesized in one gland and the luciferase in another. Japanese biochemists have recently purified the luciferin from *Cypridina* and have published a tentative description of its molecular structure. This appears to resemble the structure of firefly luciferin, about which we will have more to say.

### Fireworms of the Sea

There are a large number of luminous forms among the annelid worms, which range in length from a fraction of an inch to several inches. The luminescence is particularly striking during the mating period of the "fireworms," annelids of the order Polychaeta. It seems likely that Columbus saw fireworms on his first voyage to the New World. He wrote of seeing lights in the water resembling moving candles as he approached the Bahamas. The relation between luminescence, the phase of the moon and periodicity in the breeding of these marine organisms is beautifully illustrated by the Bermuda annelid *Odontosyllis enopla*. The worms begin to swarm two or three days after the full moon, the females appearing first. Each swims in a small circle at the surface, emitting a greenish light. Invariably the performance reaches a peak between 55 and 56 minutes after

sunset. The circles of light evidently attract the male worms, which normally stay well below the surface. As the males swim toward the females, traveling 15 to 20 feet with remarkable accuracy, they emit short flashes of light. Commonly several males will converge on a single female; the whole group then rotates in a tight, glowing circle as its members discharge eggs and sperm into the water. The eggs are accompanied by a secretion that leaves a luminous cloud in the wake of the female. The females, which range up to 35 millimeters in length, are often twice as long as the males. The body of the female glows strongly and almost continuously. The male continues to glow with sharp intermittent flashes.

After the mating process has begun the males exhibit an additional positive response to light. For example, if a flashlight is aimed into the water, males will start swimming toward its beam. There is no evidence to indicate that the females will respond positively to the light, although they are obviously stimulated to release their eggs by the presence of the males. Recently we have been able to obtain from *Odontosyllis* extracts of luciferin and luciferase that give off light when the two are mixed together. We do not yet have enough of the two materials, however, to study the chemistry of the bioluminescent reaction in detail.

### Marine Dinoflagellates

The "burning of the sea" presented a mystery to fishermen and other observers for centuries. The "burning" refers to the glow sometimes seen in the wake of a ship as it moves through tropical waters. The glow is due to the presence of large numbers of dinoflagellates that luminesce when they are disturbed. These one-celled organisms often develop in large quantities at favorable seasons of the year. In secluded bays a permanent heavy culture can develop; the waters of the bay can become so thick with dinoflagellates that the water itself is colored. Such luminescent bays have become famous tourist attractions. One of the most spectacular is Oyster Bay, near Falmouth on the northern coast of Jamaica; another is on the southern coast of Puerto Rico near Parguera. The two bays are inhabited chiefly by the luminous dinoflagellate *Pyrodinium bahamense*. If one travels across one of the bays at night, looking down from the bow of a moving boat, one can see fish sharply silhouetted against the glowing water as they dart out of the way. The movement of the fish

triggers the luminescence, and every wave looks as if it were aflame.

The discovery that this luminescence comes always from living things was only slowly appreciated because most of the dinoflagellates are invisible to the naked eye. The mystery of the burning sea was not definitely settled until about 1830. In recent years dinoflagellates have been grown in the laboratory and their bioluminescence has been studied in great detail.

The "red tides" of the sea are due in most cases to dinoflagellates, which are also capable of forming patches of brown and yellow. The color of their nighttime luminescence, however, is always blue. On occasion the daytime red patches are due to the flagellate *Noctiluca*, which is large enough to be seen without a microscope. Along the Pacific coast of the U.S. it is not unusual to find patches of *Gonyaulax polyhedra*, a quite luminous dinoflagellate. The red tides reported along the Gulf Coast of Florida in recent years are produced by an organism (*Gymnodinium brevis*) that is unrelated to the flagellates and is nonluminous.

By growing cultures of *Gonyaulax* in the laboratory it has been found that they stop producing light at dawn and luminesce again in the evening. In addition to being luminescent *Gonyaulax* is a photosynthetic organism requiring light for growth. Under laboratory conditions one can readily obtain cultures of 10,000 to 20,000 cells per liter. When the culture vessel is shaken, the cells emit bright flashes of light lasting less than a tenth of a second. If the organisms are illuminated continuously with a dim light, so that they are no longer exposed to a normal day-night cycle, an interesting phenomenon takes place. When one shakes the culture to measure the maximum light output, one finds that the maximum output continues to occur each night at about 1 a.m. and decreases to a minimum some 12 hours later. In other words, the organism's normal day-night rhythm will continue unbroken for weeks under a steady weak light sufficient to supply energy. This remarkable biological clock can be altered, however, by subjecting the cells to an artificial light-dark cycle. For example, if *Gonyaulax* cells are exposed to eight hours of darkness followed by eight hours of light, they adopt a new rhythm in which they can emit light during the eight hours of darkness and are nonluminous for the eight hours of light. When the cells are removed from this artificial 16-hour cycle and are again placed under a continuous light of low intensity, the original

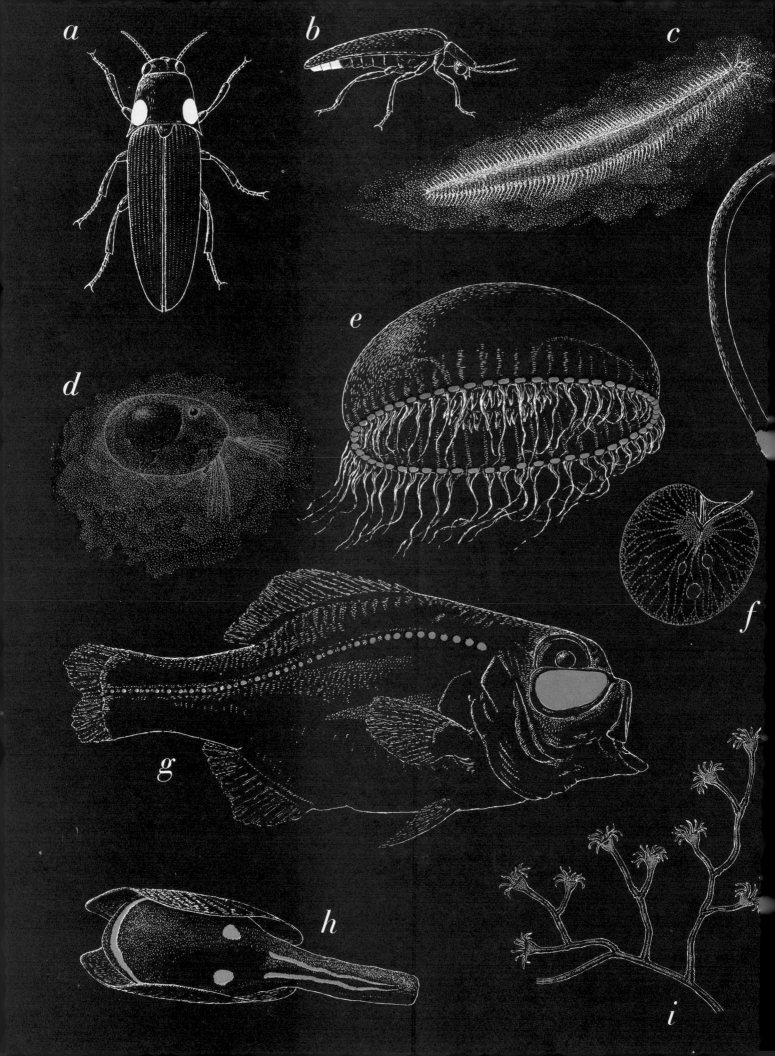

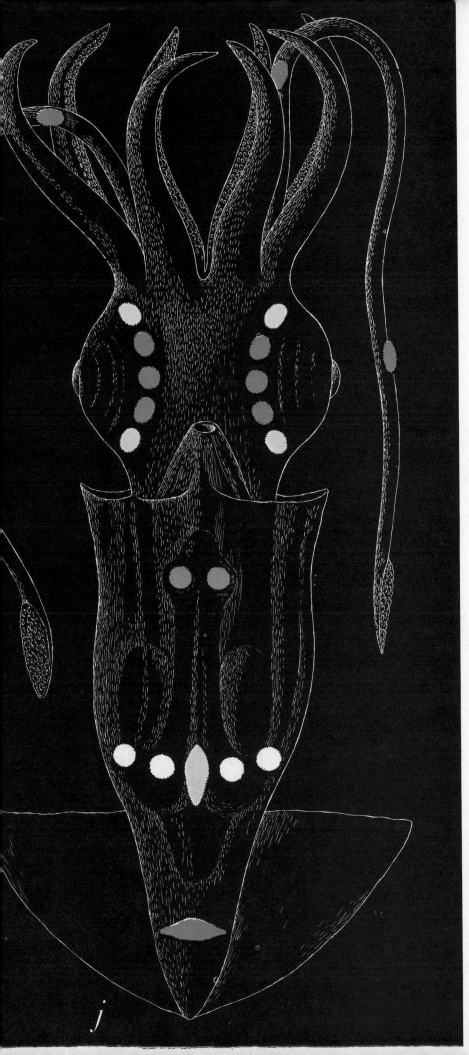

24-hour rhythm resumes. The mechanism underlying this behavior has not been discovered.

Recently we have looked for rhythmic behavior in dinoflagellates under natural conditions and have found that some species show a night-day rhythm and that others do not. In *Gonyaulax* both luciferin and luciferase, the necessary components for light production, are found in greater amounts in cell-free extracts prepared during the night hours than during the day, showing that the rhythm of luminescence reflects rhythmic biochemical processes. It would appear that the luminescent system is not the clock but rather that it is controlled by a master clock that regulates other physiological processes.

### Luminous Fungi and Bacteria

If you should chance to stumble over a rotten log in the woods at night, you might be surprised to find that freshly exposed parts of the log were glowing brilliantly. Luminescence of this sort is caused by fungi. The phenomenon was known to Aristotle, and it was studied by such illustrious figures as Francis Bacon and Robert Boyle. Not until early in the 19th century, however, was the role of the fungus properly appreciated.

One of the best known luminous fungi is *Panus stipticus*, which exists in two varieties: a North American form that is luminous and a European form that is not. The threadlike mycelia of the two varieties are able to fuse, and it can be shown by this mating technique that luminescence is under genetic control. Evidently the European variety lacks one or more genes needed to produce enzymes required for bioluminescence.

GALLERY OF ANIMALS at left suggests the diversity of bioluminescent organisms. Roughly speaking, bioluminescent organisms exist in about a third of the 33 phyla and a third of the 80 classes given in the official American classification of the animal kingdom. The 10 luminous animals at left are: *a,* a click beetle (*Pyrophorus noctilucus*); *b,* a common North American firefly (*Photuris pennsylvanica*); *c,* the Bermuda fireworm (*Odontosyllis enopla*); *d,* a Japanese crustacean (*Cypridina hilgendorfii*); *e,* a jellyfish (*Aequorea aequorea*); *f,* a protozoan (*Noctiluca miliaris*); *g,* a fish (*Photoblepharon*) in which the light is supplied by symbiotic bacteria; *h,* an edible clam (*Pholas dactylus*); *i,* one of the luminous hydroids (*Campanularia flexuosa*); *j,* deep-sea squid (*Thaumatolampas diadema*).

At least one of these enzymes is luciferase, which is found in the North American *Panus* but not in the European.

Before electric refrigerators came into general use there were often reports in the newspapers about "mystery meat" that gave off light. There should have been no mystery about the light; it has been known for a long time that luminous bacteria—all quite harmless—readily grow on meat and dead fish. Boyle experimented with such bacteria and in 1668 demonstrated that they need air if they are to emit light. Subsequently luminescent bacteria found in salt water became a favorite subject for studying bioluminescence. Most of these forms will grow easily on ordinary nutrient agar containing 3 per cent sodium chloride (the salinity of sea water) and

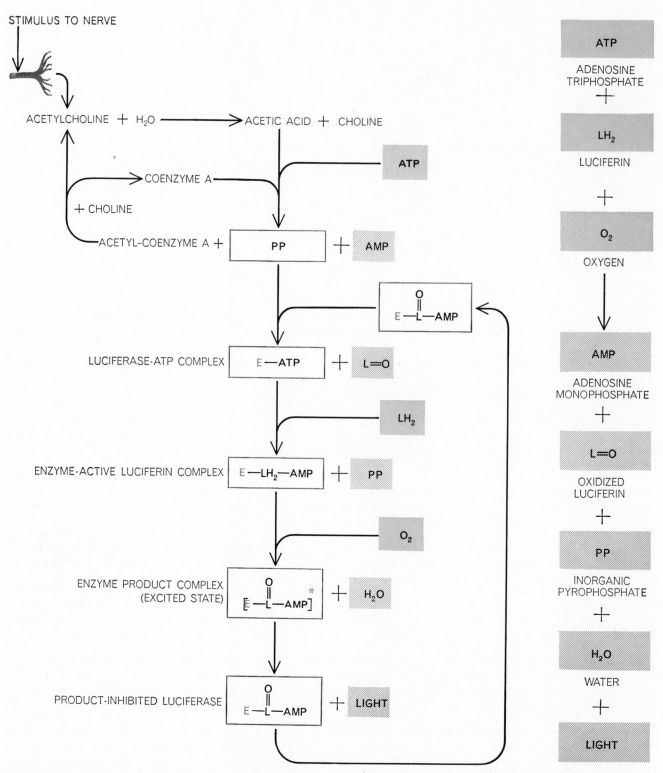

**FIREFLY FLASH** is probably triggered by a nerve impulse delivered to the luminous gland. A sequence of chemical reactions then produces light. The substances consumed in the reaction, as shown in the summary at right, are adenosine triphosphate ($ATP$), luciferin ($LH_2$) and oxygen ($O_2$). The products are oxidized luciferin ($L=O$), two phosphate compounds, water and light. The reaction is catalyzed by the enzyme luciferase, represented by $E$. One quantum of light is produced for each molecule of luciferin oxidized.

glucose or glycerol. Among the best sources of salt-water luminous bacteria are dead fish or squids that have not been washed in fresh water. If such material is incubated overnight at 15 or 20 degrees centigrade, it is usually covered with colonies of luminous bacteria by morning. The bacteria can then be transferred to agar plates and readily developed into pure cultures that emit a strong blue or blue-green light. This culture technique was exploited by Dubois, who wrote: "In 1900, at the Palace of Optics, at the International Exposition in Paris, I have been able to illuminate, as from the clearest light of the moon, a vast chamber using large glass flasks of 25-liter capacity... containing very brilliant photobacteria... In the evening as soon as one entered the chamber one could read and see all the people in the room." The light emitted by luminous bacteria is usually a broad band in the blue or blue-green region of the spectrum (wavelengths between 480 and 500 millimicrons).

Some of the most interesting luminous bacteria live in symbiosis with other organisms, frequently squids and fishes. The host often has a complicated luminous organ in which the light is supplied by bacteria. Although the bacteria emit light continuously, the fish or squid may develop a special device, such as a movable screen, that serves to turn the light on and off. One of the most striking instances of bacterial symbiosis occurs in the Indonesian fish *Photoblepharon*. This fish has under each eye an oval white spot, richly supplied with blood vessels, in which the luminous bacteria grow. To turn off the light there is a black fold of skin that can be drawn over the luminous spot like an eyelid [see *illustration on pages 132 and 133*].

The physiology and biochemistry of bacterial luminescence have been studied in great detail. Although we do not know the exact mechanism for creating the luminescent state, we are reasonably certain of the compounds involved. It is now clear that the light-emitting reaction is intimately related to the oxidative, or electron-transport, processes of the bacterial cell. The top illustration on the next page outlines the current hypothesis, in which the light-emitting reaction is a side branch of the general electron-transport process by which the cell extracts energy from food. The requirements for luminescence are a reduced form of riboflavin, an aldehyde, oxygen and an enzyme.

Luminous bacteria have been favored organisms for studying the action of

LUCIFERIN (LH₂)

OXIDIZED LUCIFERIN (L=O)

**STRUCTURE OF LUCIFERIN** in the firefly has been established by the authors and their associates at Johns Hopkins University. In the light-producing reaction it combines with one molecule of oxygen to form oxidized luciferin and water. Other luciferins are known.

drugs and other inhibitors of cell respiration because the effects are observable externally by means of a photoelectric cell. It is also possible to obtain mutant strains of luminescent bacteria that are nonluminous or only weakly luminous. One can then examine the ability of various chemicals to restore luminescence. The illustration on page 137 shows how the dim light emitted by a suspension of certain mutant bacteria can be increased by the addition of a long-chain aldehyde such as dodecanal. To determine the rate at which the aldehyde penetrates the cell membrane one simply uses a photocell to measure the rate at which the light intensity increases.

## Fireflies and Glowworms

Among the insects true instances of self-luminescence are to be found in the springtails, lantern flies, click beetles, the larvae of certain flies and, of course, in the fireflies and their larvae, called glowworms. It is a spectacular sight to see the glowworms that live in caves in New Zealand, the most famous being at Waitomo, about 200 miles north of Wellington. The ceilings of these caves are covered with thousands of glowing larvae, and from each is suspended a long luminescent thread that apparently

serves to catch food particles or small insects. If one talks loudly, or if the wall of the cave is tapped sharply, the larvae turn off their lights virtually as one. After a brief period the lights come on again, tentatively at first and then more boldly, until the whole ceiling is once again ablaze.

The true fireflies, or lightning bugs, are found in many parts of the world and provide perhaps the most familiar example of bioluminescence. (Curiously, fireflies are almost unknown in England.) The scientific literature on this group of insects far exceeds that of any other luminous organism. The old hypothesis that the light of the firefly is a mating device to attract the sexes is now universally accepted. Nothing could be simpler than a flashing light to advertise the whereabouts of a flying male to a responsively flashing female waiting in the grass.

Each species of firefly has a characteristic flash that the female of the species can recognize. The signaling system of one common American species of firefly, *Photinus pyralis*, is fairly typical of the mating behavior of a number of species. At dusk the male and female emerge separately from the grass. The male flies about two feet above the ground and emits a single short flash at

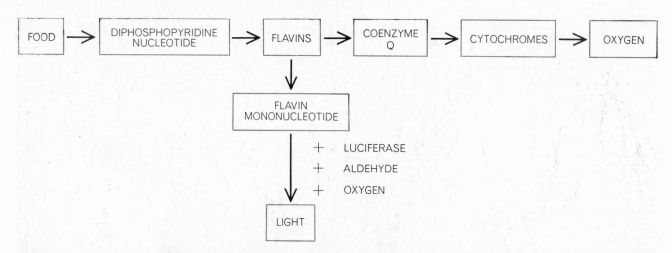

**SOURCE OF BACTERIAL LIGHT** is a side branch of the oxidation-reduction reactions that extract energy from nutrients. In this sequence hydrogen atoms (or their equivalent electrons) are removed from nutrient and passed along (*colored arrows*) to a series of compounds. The final hydrogen-acceptor is oxygen and the final product is water. At certain steps in the sequence energy is removed from the reactants and stored in the form of ATP (*not shown*). Light is emitted when one of the reduced flavins (flavin mononucleotide) reacts with luciferase and oxygen in the presence of an aldehyde. In this reaction flavin takes the role of luciferin.

regular intervals. The female climbs some slight eminence, such as a blade of grass, and waits. Ordinarily she does not fly at all, and she never flashes spontaneously. If a male flashes within three or four yards of her, she will usually wait a decorous interval, then flash a short response. At this the male turns in her direction and glows again. The female responds once more with a flash, and the exchange of signals is repeated—usually not more than five or 10 times—until the male reaches the female, waiting in the grass, and the two mate.

Recognition apparently depends on the time interval between the male flash and that of the female. This interval in certain species is approximately two seconds at 25 degrees centigrade (77 degrees Fahrenheit) and varies with temperature. A flash of artificial light of about a second's duration, simulating the delayed response of a female firefly, will usually induce a male to fly toward it.

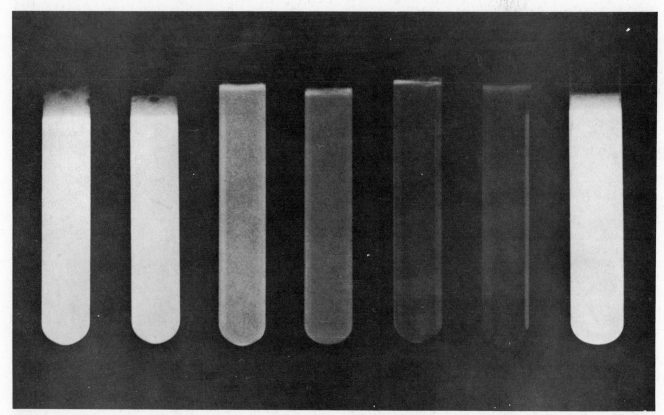

**ROLE OF OXYGEN** in bioluminescence can be nicely demonstrated with suspensions of luminous bacteria. The first two tubes at left had been aerated continuously prior to the making of the photograph. The next four tubes had been standing unaerated for two, three, four and five minutes respectively. With the passage of time their light emission declined. The last tube at the right, which had been standing undisturbed for 10 minutes, was shaken vigorously to introduce fresh oxygen just before the photograph was made. For a brief period it glows even more brightly than the two tubes that had been supplied with oxygen continuously.

Other species of fireflies have other systems and types of flashes. Synchronous flashing of a number of males to one female has been observed, but it is rare in North American species. Among tropical fireflies, however, it is fairly common. In Burma and Thailand, for example, all the fireflies on one tree may flash simultaneously, whereas those on another tree some distance away may also flash in unison but out of step with those on the first tree. It is conceivable that all the fireflies on one tree are males and those flashing out of phase nearby are all females, but this has not been established.

The eggs of American fireflies are laid on or near the ground and hatch in about three weeks. The larvae differ considerably in habit. They live mostly in damp places among fallen leaves, becoming active at night and feeding on slugs, snails and the larvae of smaller insects. The firefly larvae usually winter under stones or a short distance underground, often in specially constructed chambers. The larvae metamorphose into pupae near the surface.

The first indication of the formation of the light organ takes place about 15 days after egg development begins. After about 22 days of development the light organ has become functional and appears as two bright spots of light. The larvae emerge on about the 26th day of incubation and become glowworms, with the two small lights at one end. In about two years they reach maturity as pupae. During pupation additional light organs develop, which are to become the light organs of the adult firefly. The light organs of both the larva and the adult develop out of fatty bodies that differentiate into specialized luminescent and reflector layers.

The light emission of fireflies depends on a rich supply of oxygen. The light organs are supplied with blood through an extensive capillary system and with oxygen through an extensive system of tracheal tubes. Unfortunately it is difficult to trace the air-supplying tracheae into the photogenic tissue; it is equally difficult to trace the nerve fibers that must control the flashing of the firefly. Investigators have been able to isolate an individual nerve fiber going to the luminous gland and have been able to stimulate light emission by applying an electric current to the nerve. Probably the best indication of nervous control of the flash is to be observed, however, when the animal is decapitated. Flashing ceases immediately. Subsequently the light organ may glow dimly, with random scintillations, for a long time. The

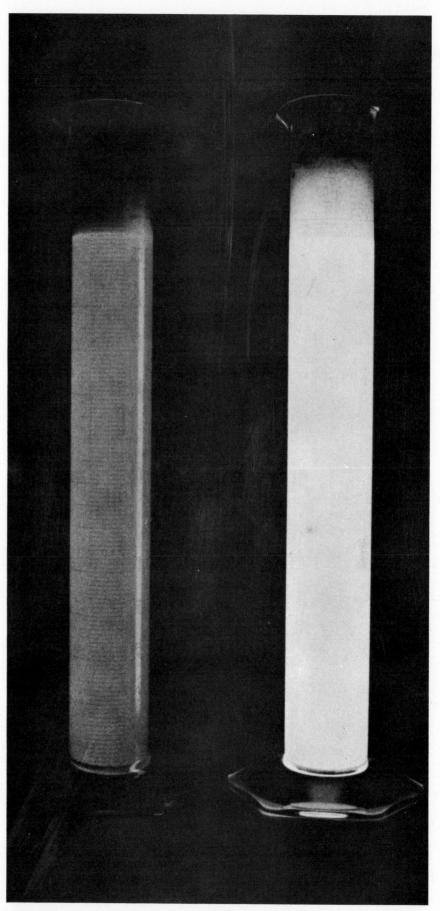

DARK MUTANT BACTERIA, in the cylinder at left, are barely luminous because they cannot make a long-chain aldehyde (dodecanal) essential for high luminosity. When this aldehyde is added to a suspension of the mutant organisms, they glow brightly (*right*).

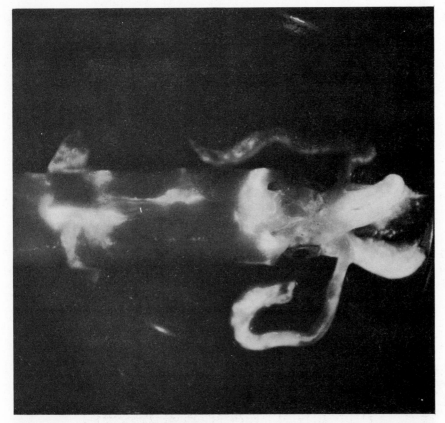

LUMINOUS BACTERIA will usually develop on the surface of a salt-water squid kept over-night in a warm place. Only salt-water varieties of bacteria are luminous. The photograph, made by the authors, required a 15-second exposure at $f/4.7$ with Polaroid 3,000-speed film.

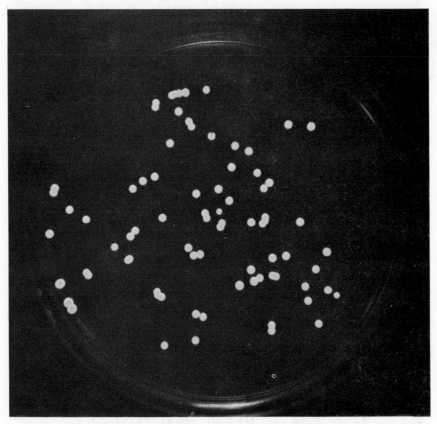

COLONIES OF LUMINOUS BACTERIA can readily be produced by removing bacteria from a decaying sea animal, such as the squid shown at the top of the page, and transferring them to a saline nutrient agar. Robert Boyle experimented with such bacteria in 1668.

exact mechanism of nervous control remains unknown. According to one hypothesis the nerve impulse simply liberates oxygen into the luminous gland, thereby stimulating luminescence. A second hypothesis, which we favor, proposes a series of steps triggered by the release of acetylcholine at a nerve ending in the luminous organ [*see illustration on page 134*].

The chemistry of the firefly light has been worked out in considerable detail since Harvey first established in 1916 that the glow of the firefly results from the same luciferin-luciferase reaction that Dubois had found in the luminous clam. We now know that firefly luminescence requires, in addition to oxygen, the ubiquitous energy-supplying substance adenosine triphosphate (ATP). If a cold-water extract obtained from firefly lanterns is allowed to stand until the light disappears, the light can be restored to more than its original intensity with the addition of ATP.

Within the past few years we have isolated firefly luciferin in our laboratory at Johns Hopkins University. We have established its chemical structure and have confirmed its validity by synthesizing the compound and showing that under the appropriate conditions it luminesces. We have also isolated and obtained in pure form the light-stimulating enzyme of the firefly, luciferase. It appears to contain about 1,000 amino acid subunits and is therefore larger than any of the proteins whose structure has so far been established.

The peak wavelength of the light emitted by the firefly *Photinus pyralis* is 562 millimicrons, in the yellow-green part of the spectrum. We have found that extracts of firefly lanterns emit light at the same wavelength when the acid-alkaline balance of the solution is neutral. If the solution is made acid, or if high concentrations of inorganic phosphate are added, the light shifts to red, with a peak emission at 614 millimicrons. Presumably shifts of this sort can explain the slight differences in the color of the light emitted by various fireflies.

The availability of luciferin in pure form has also enabled us to determine the efficiency of the light-emitting process. To do this we compare the number of luciferin molecules oxidized with the number of light quanta produced. It turns out that for each molecule of luciferin consumed exactly one light quantum is emitted. It has been fashionable for many years to describe bioluminescence as "cold light" to distinguish it from thermal luminescence. The finding that the quantum efficiency

"INSTANT" BIOCHEMICAL LIGHT is produced simply by adding water to the powder obtained by drying and pulverizing a small marine crustacean called *Cypridina*. Rich in luciferin and luciferase, dried *Cypridina* was sometimes used as a light source by Japanese soldiers during World War II when the use of a flashlight under battle conditions might have revealed their position.

SENSITIVE ASSAY FOR ATP uses the lanterns from four or five fireflies as the indicating agent. A small sample containing an unknown amount of ATP is added to a suspension of the pulverized lanterns. The more ATP present, the more intense the light emitted. The photograph shows the light produced by .1-milliliter samples containing various microgram amounts of ATP.

DIMMING OF BACTERIA is observed when a well-aerated suspension is allowed to stand undisturbed. The dimming begins at the bottom, as oxygen is depleted, and works upward. Rising air bubbles postpone the dimming in the upper part of the cylinder.

of firefly light production is indeed 100 per cent makes the term "cold light" strictly accurate.

One of the few creatures to luminesce in two colors is the Central and South American beetle *Phrixothrix*. The larva of these insects is decorated with 11 pairs of luminous green spots that form two parallel rows running along the sides of the body; on the head of the larva are two luminous spots that glow a bright red. At night, when only the red spots are shining, the animal looks like a glowing cigarette. When the animal is disturbed and crawling, however, the green lights flash on, so that it rather resembles a railroad train with red head lamps. Not surprisingly, *Phrixothrix* is commonly called the railroad worm.

Other luminescent insects are found among the click beetles, the Elateridae. In some ways they look much like ordinary fireflies. Most of them, however, are decorated with two oval greenish spots, one on each side of the front part of the body. Because these luminous spots have the appearance of automobile headlights the insects are sometimes called "automobile bugs." In addition the click beetle usually has on its first abdominal segment a heart-shaped spot that glows orange and that is visible only when the beetle is in flight.

### Luminescence in Evolution

Among the more advanced multicellular organisms, light emission has been adapted to fulfill very definite functions: as a mating signal for the fireworms and the fireflies, as a lure for the deep-sea angler fish and as a protective screen for certain squids and other marine animals. What function, if any, light emission has in the lower organisms such as the bacteria, the fungi and the dinoflagellates is not immediately obvious. The wide distribution of this large variety of different luminous organisms with entirely different chemical reactions for light emission would indicate that at some time this mechanism must have had some selective advantage.

Even though the luciferins from various luminous organisms are different, we are reasonably certain that all are associated either directly or indirectly with the energy-liberating reactions of the cell. In all cases where the detailed chemistry of the reactions leading to light emission has been examined, oxygen is an essential ingredient. For example, in the luminous bacteria the light-emitting reaction is a branch of the electron-transport system that is essential for growth and reproduction. It

seems reasonable to expect that the origin of the light-emitting processes was in some way closely associated with the early evolution of life on earth. Furthermore, it is our belief that various "practical" adaptations of bioluminescence in the more advanced organisms came late in evolution.

We propose that bioluminescence was originally an incidental concomitant of the chemical reactions that were most efficient in removing oxygen from living systems. It is generally believed that the earliest forms of life on earth developed in the absence of oxygen. The first organisms, therefore, were anaerobes. When in the course of the millenniums free oxygen slowly appeared—as a result of solar decomposition of water vapor, augmented, perhaps, by primitive photosynthesis—it would have been highly toxic to anaerobic organisms that could not quickly get rid of it. Chemically the most efficient way to remove oxygen is to reduce it to form water. In the forms of life then present, the most likely reducing agents would have been those organic compounds that were already part of the hydrogen-transport system of the primitive anerobes. When oxygen is converted to water by such compounds, enough energy is liberated in single packets, or quanta, to excite organic molecules to emit light. Low-energy packets will not do. Thus all the successful oxygen-removing organisms would have been potentially luminescent.

During subsequent evolution anaerobic organisms evolved that could use oxygen directly in their metabolic machinery. Then the oxygen-removing light reaction was no longer a selective advantage. But since it had evolved with the primitive electron-transport process, it was not easily lost. In most cases where it has been studied carefully bioluminescence is produced by a nonessential enzyme system. It is possible, for example, to grow luminous bacteria and luminous fungi under conditions that inhibit light emission without affecting growth. And it is possible to obtain mutant strains of luminous fungi and bacteria that are fully vigorous although nonluminous. We find additional support for our hypothesis in the observation that all luminescent reactions can detect and use oxygen at extremely low concentrations. Bacteria can easily produce measurable light when the oxygen concentration is as low as one part in 100 million. Thus we argue that bioluminescence is a vestigial system in organic evolution and that through the secondary processes of adaptation the system has been preserved in various and unrelated species.

# 17 The Navigation of the Green Turtle

ARCHIE CARR · May 1965

One of the stubborn puzzles of animal behavior is the ability of some animals to travel regularly to remote oceanic islands. The best-known of the blue-water navigators are birds; recently, however, the green turtle (*Chelonia mydas*) has given evidence of being as keen an island-finder as the sooty tern or the albatross. Because green turtles swim slowly, and do so at the surface of the water or a little below it, they are potentially easier to follow in their journeys than either birds or migratory fishes, seals and whales. The green turtle may therefore prove to be an important experimental subject for students of animal navigation.

The evidence that green turtles can find their way to remote oceanic islands is provided by female green turtles that normally inhabit feeding grounds along the coast of Brazil. It appears that once every two or three years these turtles swim all the way to Ascension Island—a target five miles wide and 1,400 miles away in the South Atlantic—to lay their eggs. By the processes of natural selection this population seems to have evolved the capacity to hold a true course across hundreds of miles of sea, using only animal senses as instruments of navigation. The difficulties facing such a voyage would seem insurmountable if it were not so clear that the turtles are somehow surmounting them.

The green turtle is one of the five kinds of sea turtle found throughout the warmer oceans of the world [*see illustration on next two pages*]. Adult green turtles, which may weigh more than 500 pounds, are herbivorous; they feed on the so-called turtle grass that grows abundantly in sheltered tropical shallows. Although the green turtles of the world are separated into reproductively isolated breeding colonies, they show little tendency to evolve into recognizable local races and species. The green turtles of the Pacific, for example, show only minor differences in form and color from those of the Atlantic. The one area in which what appears to be a well-differentiated species has evolved is the northern coast of Australia, where the form *Chelonia depressa* is found. Green turtles nest only in places where the average temperature of the surface water during the coldest month of the year is above 68 degrees Fahrenheit. In the Atlantic the northern limit of their nesting range seems to have been Bermuda; early voyagers to the New World destroyed the colony there. The most northerly nesting site known in the Pacific is French Frigate Shoal, an outlier of the Hawaiian Islands.

Until a few years ago what was known about the green turtle consisted mainly of cooking recipes and a sea of folklore from which rose only a few islands of fact. Among these were studies by Edward Banks in the Turtle Islands of Sarawak, by James Hornell in the Seychelles Islands off the east coast of Africa, by P. E. P. Deraniyagala in Ceylon and by F. W. Moorhouse along the Great Barrier Reef of Australia. More recently in Sarawak, Tom Harrisson and John R. Hendrickson have independently uncovered a great deal of information on the nesting ecology and reproductive cycles of the huge breeding colony there. Since 1955 my colleagues at the University of Florida and I have been working, with the aid of a series of National Science Foundation grants, at the only green turtle nesting beach that remains in the western Caribbean: Tortuguero in Costa Rica. What is now known about *Chelonia* from all these studies permits the piecing together of a coherent—albeit still somewhat fragmentary—account of its life.

Although green turtles are primarily sea animals, in a few places in the Pacific they sometimes go ashore to bask. They have been seen lying in the sun along with albatrosses and basking monk seals on such small Pacific islands as Pearl and Hermes Reef, Lisianski and Kure Atoll. The females of the Pacific populations sometimes even nest during the day. Neither nesting during the day nor basking appears to be the habit of green turtles in any Atlantic population. Once the Atlantic hatchlings leave the beach the males remain at sea for the rest of their lives. The females come ashore only to nest, and they do so after dark. They always return to the same general nesting area and often to the same narrow sector of beach.

The green turtle is one of the few reptiles that are known to reproduce at intervals of more than a year. In Sarawak the entire turtle population nests in a three-year cycle. At Tortuguero about a third of the colony returns to nest every two years and the other two-thirds follows a three-year schedule. In our eight years of tagging turtles at this site no turtle has returned after an absence of only one year. When the Tortuguero turtles finish nesting, they travel back to their home pastures of turtle grass and evidently remain there feeding until their reproductive rhythm directs them to return to the nesting beach. Such a feeding ground may be within a few dozen miles of the nesting beach or many hundreds of miles away.

The time of year at which the nesting season begins and the duration of the season vary from one region to another. In some places nesting is restricted to three or four months of the year; in others it may run through the entire year, with a peak during two or three months or even with two separate peaks. Mating takes place at the nesting ground and apparently nowhere else. Either the males accompany the females during their journey from the home pasture or they make an exactly timed rendezvous with them at the nesting beach. In any case, as soon as the first tracks of nesting turtles appear on the shore the animals can be seen at sea just beyond the surf, courting, fighting and mating. Because these activities are mostly out of sight little is known about them. From a low-flying airplane one sometimes gets a glimpse of two males splashing around a single female. Many females come ashore scratched and lacerated, evidently because of the violent attentions of the males.

Some females apparently mate just before their first nesting trip ashore; others do so later. At Tortuguero mating activity appears to end after the third or fourth week of the nesting season. Even when mating precedes the first landing, it must take place after at least some of the female's eggs have formed shells. It therefore seems unlikely that any of the eggs of the current season are fertilized as a result of current mating. The encounter probably serves to fertilize eggs for the next nesting season, two or three years ahead.

Once at the nesting beach the female goes ashore from three to seven times to deposit clutches of eggs in the sand. The interval between nesting trips is about 12 days, and the number of eggs laid on each occasion is 100 or so. Each egg is about two inches in diameter. The shell is flexible, and when the egg is first laid it has a curious dent in it that no amount of pressing will smooth out. The incubation period is about 57 days.

On hatching and emerging from the nest the young green turtles nearly always set off on a direct course for the sea, even when the water itself is completely hidden by dunes or other obstacles. Experiments with a number of different kinds of marine and freshwater turtles indicate that the mechanism of this orientation is an innate response to some quality of the light over open water. It is clear that no compass-like sense is involved: in a series of tests we flew little turtles from Caribbean nests across Costa Rica and allowed them to emerge from artificial nests on a Pacific beach. Even though the sea now lay in the opposite direction the young turtles reached the water as easily as their siblings on the home beach did.

After the hatchlings enter the water, either their sea-finding drive gives way to other orienting mechanisms or they simply keep swimming until whatever

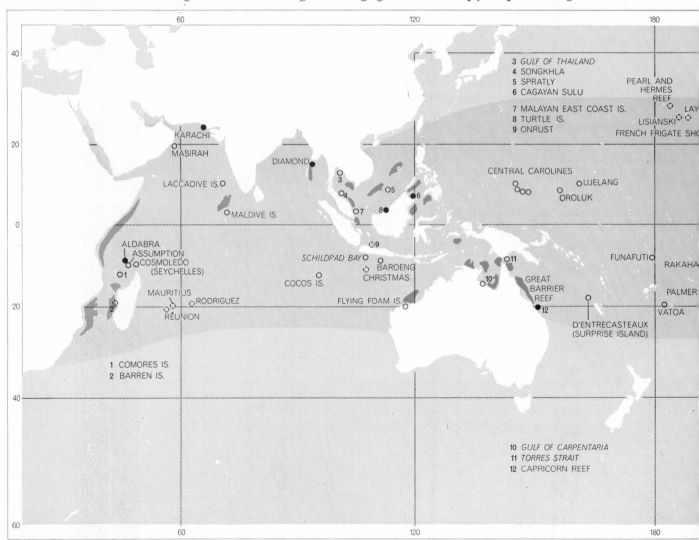

● MAJOR NESTING BEACHES
○ MINOR NESTING BEACHES
◔ ⊗ FORMER NESTING BEACHES
◣ PRINCIPAL FEEDING GROUNDS

**PAST AND PRESENT RANGE** of the green turtle was compiled from the accounts of early explorers and later sources by James J. Parsons of the University of California at

difference they perceive between sea light and land light becomes too slight to provide a guiding stimulus. By this time they will probably have been picked up by a longshore current. Since the adults navigate over long distances, they must have some kind of compass sense. This sense may be latent in the hatchlings: recent laboratory experiments at Duke University by Klaus Fischer seem to show that this is the case. In nature, however, this sense evidently does not come into operation until the light-beacon sense fails. In any case, tests have shown that the sea-finding drive is not lost even when turtles are kept away from water for as long as a year after hatching. It is also evident that both capacities are present in the mature female. The compass sense must guide her from feeding ground to nesting beach, and the sea-finding drive directs her back to the

ocean after she has nested—even though it is out of sight of her nesting place.

A recent experiment demonstrates the kind of ambiguity that can arise in the study of orientation among young green turtles. Several hundred 20-day-old hatchlings from Tortuguero were placed in a circular tank at the Lerner Marine Laboratory on the island of Bimini in the Bahamas. The nearest water was on the bay side of the island, some 40 yards away. The ocean was some 200 yards away in the opposite direction. From turtle's-eye level the rim of the tank blocked any view of either bay or ocean. The skyline was broken by trees and buildings.

The distribution of the young turtles in the tank was recorded over a three-day period, at 9:00 A.M., 4:00 P.M. and 11:00 P.M. each day. During most of that time the wind blew steadily from the bay side of the tank. At night, while

the sleeping turtles floated on the surface, the steady breeze piled them up on the ocean side of the tank. Once awake in daylight, however, the turtles showed a marked orientation in the opposite direction. There was active—at times frantic—swimming toward and crowding along the wall nearest the bay [see illustration on page 145]. This bias was not simply a tendency to swim upwind; the bay side of the tank was equally favored during a few windless periods. The response could have been an innate direction preference based on a compass sense, but it was more probably the same light-seeking urge that guides hatchlings from the nest to the water. Two months later, however, when the same test was repeated with the same animals, they showed no seaward orientation at all.

Almost nothing is known about the movements and habits of green turtles

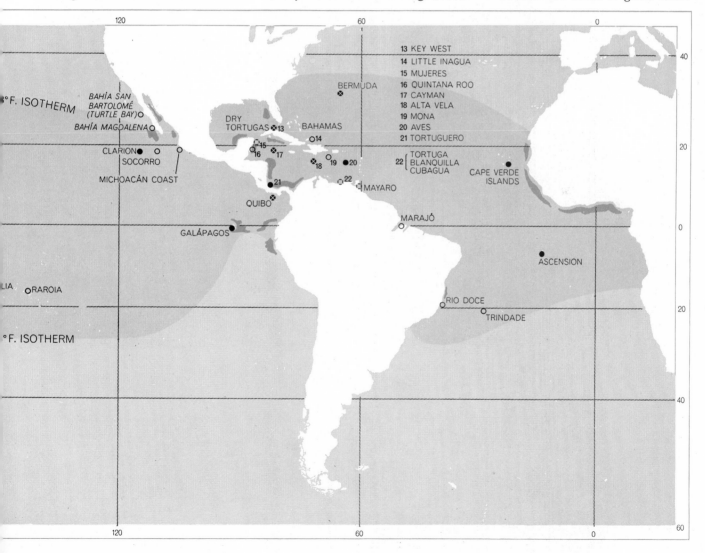

during the first year of life. They are mainly carnivorous at this age, but they are able to feed only on small, weak marine invertebrates. Such prey is scarce both at the nesting beaches and at the turtle-grass pastures that feed the grown turtles, and very young turtles are almost never seen in these places. It seems likely that the hatchlings must spend their first months moving from location to location at sea as growth qualifies them to feed on invertebrates of increasing size. All we really know is that the hatchlings disappear.

The only place in the Atlantic and Caribbean regions where we have been able to study green turtles of an age between hatching and maturity is off the west coast of Florida. There a migrating population of young turtles, ranging in weight from 10 to 90 pounds, shows up each April. At this stage most of them have become herbivorous, and they spend the summer months browsing in the turtle-grass flats between

Tarpon Springs and the mouth of the Suwannee River. In November they move away to an unknown destination. These Florida visitors may have come from the Costa Rican nesting ground. We have no proof of this, however, because of the difficulty of devising a marking system that will survive the changes in size and proportion of the growing animals.

As recently as 10 years ago it was not definitely known that green turtles migrated long distances from home range to nesting beach. The first clear evidence of periodic long-range migrations came from the tagging program conducted at Tortuguero. During the past eight years 3,205 adult turtles have been tagged; 129 of these have later been recovered. Most of the tags have come to us from professional turtle fishermen operating off the coast of Nicaragua, but other recovery sites are distributed over an area more than 1,500 miles across at its widest point. The eight most distant recoveries are as fol-

lows: one from the Marquesas Keys off the tip of Florida, one from the northern coast of Cuba, four from the Gulf of Mexico off the Yucatán Peninsula and two from the Gulf of Maracaibo in Venezuela [see illustration below].

These returns furnish grounds for some generalizations that support the reality of migratory travel by Chelonia. One such generalization is that no turtle tagged at Tortuguero has ever been recovered there after the end of the nesting season. Another is that no turtle tagged at Tortuguero has ever been found nesting anywhere else. A third is that there is very little correlation between the time elapsed after tagging and the distance the tagged turtle traveled from Tortuguero. This strongly suggests that the turtles are not random wanderers but migrants following a fixed travel schedule between the nesting beach and their restricted home range. Otherwise the animals would tend to cover the same distance in the same time.

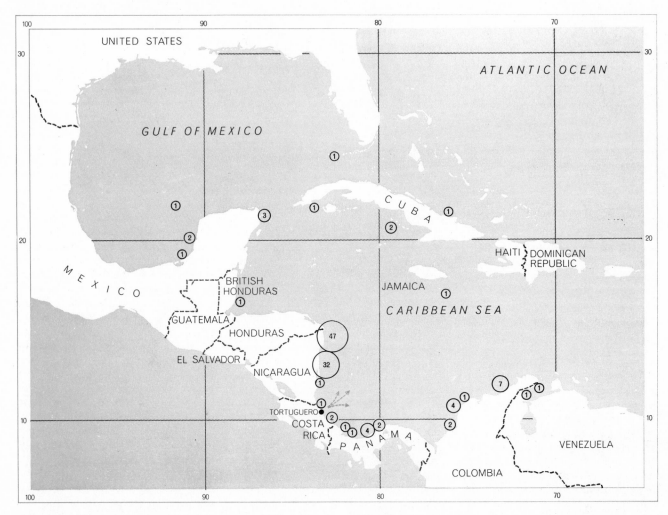

**TAGGING AT TORTUGUERO**, the nesting beach in Costa Rica, has marked 3,205 adult green turtles in the past eight years. So far 129 tags have been recovered. As the relative size of the circles indicates, most of the recoveries have been made along the coast of Nicaragua, but turtles from Tortuguero have also appeared as far away as Venezuela, the Gulf coast of Yucatán and Florida.

Although such findings make a strong case for periodic migration and homing by the green turtles that nest at Tortuguero, they do not prove a capacity for true navigation, that is, oriented travel involving something more than piloting by landmarks and an ability to keep headed in a fixed direction by using the sun or stars for a compass; such piloting is accomplished by many different kinds of animals. The beach at Tortuguero is part of a mainland shore. The green turtles could simply leave their distant pastures on an initially correct compass heading and, on making landfall, follow the coast until things look, smell or taste in ways that mean the ancestral breeding ground has been reached. In their successive nestings during a single season females often return to the same 200-yard stretch of nesting shore they had used earlier.

Indeed, it appears certain that once the turtles have reached the Tortuguero area, they do search the shore for cues to guide them to a nesting site. At the start of the nesting season distinctive "half-moon" turtle tracks appear, usually toward one end of the 22-mile length of nesting beach. These are semicircular or U-shaped trails left by females that have come out of the water, made a short trip toward the upper beach and then turned back to the surf without nesting. Such behavior implies that some sort of discriminatory process is involved in the selection of a nesting site. In the course of coming ashore a female nearly always stops in the backwash of the surf and presses her snout deliberately against the sand, sometimes repeating the process as she moves up the wet lower beach. This behavior appears to be an olfactory assessment of the shore, although it could also be tactile. Little more is known about the senses involved in the selection of nesting sites.

In searching for an instance of turtle migration that clearly involves an ability to make a long, oriented sea voyage in the absence of landmarks, I thought of the green turtle colony that nests on Ascension Island. The capacity for open-sea orientation is the ultimate puzzle in the study of animal navigation. Even human navigators, with their ability to measure the position of the sun and the stars, were unable to calculate positions at sea accurately until the development of precise chronometers in the 18th century. Work with various animals, notably homing pigeons and migratory birds, suggests that there

OCEAN-FINDING ABILITY is demonstrated by free-swimming green turtle hatchlings in a circular tank. Although the rim blocks any direct view, most of the turtles have gathered along the side nearest the water, guided by some difference in the light from that direction.

are three inherent aids to navigation: a clock sense, a map sense and a compass sense. On the basis of these senses the navigation feats of animals that migrate overland can be explained, at least in theory. On the featureless open sea, however, the situation is quite different.

One difficulty in the study of open-sea navigation by animals is the dearth of information on routes and schedules of travel. I am not aware of a single instance in which the journey of an oceanic migrant has been traced in detail, with data on headings and speeds. Only when this has been done will it be possible to say that here piloting by visual guideposts is taking place, there celestial navigation can be assumed and elsewhere some cryptic signal must be involved.

Before we could use the green turtle nesting colony on Ascension Island for a study of open-sea navigation it was necessary to establish whether the turtles traveled there from some distance away or were merely a local population. That they were not local residents seemed certain on two grounds: (1) the turtles arrive to nest in substantial numbers each February but disappear by June and (2) there are no beds of turtle grass anywhere in the vicinity of Ascension. It was then necessary to find out where the feeding grounds of the Ascension nesting colony were located. A survey of the coasts of Argentina and Brazil in 1957 yielded no evidence that the abundant green turtle population of the Brazilian coast came from nesting grounds on the South American mainland. Turtles were known to nest on the island of Trindade, some 700 miles off the Brazilian coast, but their

numbers were small. It therefore seemed likely that the green turtles that nest on Ascension feed along the coast of Brazil. The next step was to test the reality of this apparent instance of open-sea migration by means of a tagging program.

The green turtles at Ascension, like those at Tortuguero, breed in either two-year or three-year cycles. During February, March and April of 1960 Harold Hirth, then a graduate student at the University of Florida, tagged 206 female turtles at the six nesting beaches on the island. In 1963, when that part of the 1960 population which nests every three years was due to return to Ascension, a tag patrol was set up at the beaches. Three of the turtles Hirth had tagged were found again. In 1964, when the two-year group was due to return for the second time, two more of Hirth's turtles showed up [see lower illustration on next page]. Four of these five females had landed on the same short section of beach where Hirth had tagged them; the fifth went ashore on an adjacent beach recently formed by high seas. During the past five years nine more of Hirth's 1960 tags have been recovered from turtles captured by fishermen along the Brazilian coast.

A skeptical statistician might attribute these findings to random wandering. Short of tracking a turtle all the way, clinching proof that green turtles travel from Brazil to Ascension will be obtained only when a turtle tagged on Ascension is recaptured in Brazilian waters, released there and then captured again on Ascension. This is not likely to happen; by the time a tag reaches the University of Florida from Brazil the turtle that carried it has usually been eaten. Thus the evidence remains circumstantial: turtles tagged on Ascension have been captured off Brazil; others have disappeared for three or four years only to return to the same Ascension beaches on which they were first encountered. This does not prove the reality of the migratory pattern beyond all possible doubt, but I think it does so beyond reasonable doubt.

There are three basic questions to be asked about this particular migratory journey: How was it originally established as a behavioral adaptation? What route does it follow? What guides the turtles? With respect to the first question, the establishment of a nesting colony on a tiny mid-ocean island such as Ascension seems an evolutionary venture most unlikely to succeed. The problem is to visualize the selective process and the survival values in the earliest stages of the evolution of such a migratory pattern. If Ascension had once been a much more extensive area of land, the navigational equipment with which the green turtles now find the island could have been slowly refined by natural selection as the area shrank to a small island. I have found no one, however, who believes the area of Ascension can have become appreciably smaller during the past 50 million years or so. Certainly the water around it today is so deep that such a change seems unlikely.

There is one possibility that may decrease the theoretical difficulty to some degree. Perhaps the island was originally colonized by green turtles that had been accidentally carried from West Africa by the South Equatorial Current, which flows from east to west. Another kind of sea turtle—the West African ridley (*Lepidochelys olivacea*)— has colonized the coast of the Guianas, north of Brazil, in just this fashion. If egg-bearing green turtles had landed by chance on Ascension and nested there, the process of selection would have had good material to work on. The hatchlings leaving the island would have been carried to the coast of Brazil by the South Equatorial Current and at the same time could have borne with them "imprinted" information that would help them to retrace their journey at maturity. Such a hypothesis of course does no more than get the nesting colony established on Ascension. It makes no attempt to solve the navigation puzzle.

The next question concerns the route followed from Ascension to Brazil and back. Apart from inference, nothing is known about this. The South Equatorial Current presumably carries the hatchlings to Brazil; the shortest path for mature turtles returning to the island would be directly eastward from Brazil against the thrust of the same current. Such a route would conform to a classic pattern for aquatic migrations: upstream movement for the strong adult animals and downstream travel for the weak and inexperienced young.

There are two other routes that would allow the entire round trip to be

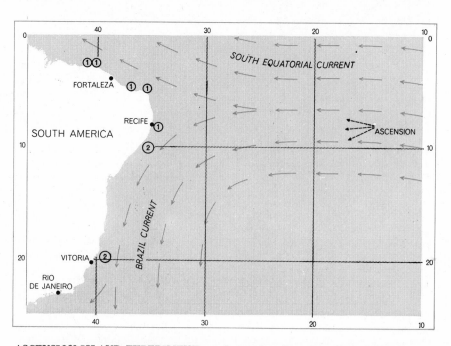

**ASCENSION ISLAND EXPERIMENT** was designed to determine if the turtles that nest there are the same animals that feed along the coast of Brazil, 1,400 miles or more away. In 1960, 206 turtles were tagged at Ascension; so far nine have been captured at the coastal points noted, proving that at least some Ascension turtles do travel to Brazil.

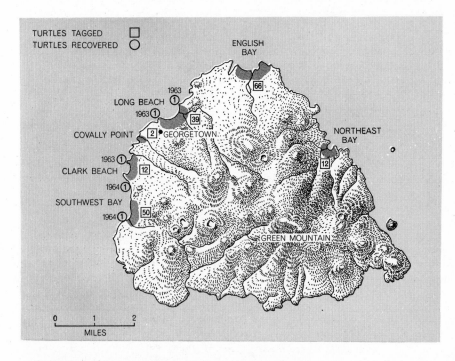

**REPEATED NESTING AT ASCENSION** has also been proved by the tagging experiment. In 1963 three of the turtles tagged in 1960 returned to the island and dug their nests in the same beaches they had used before. In 1964 two more tagged turtles appeared; one of them missed its home beach by a few hundred yards. All had presumably come from Brazil.

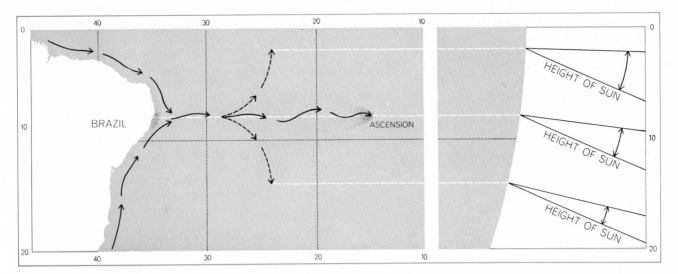

**MEANS OF NAVIGATION** available to the green turtles for their ocean voyage to Ascension remain conjectural. Distinctive chemical cues from the island, carried westward by the currents, may help the turtles to make final landfall; chemical or visual cues unique to the Brazilian coast may also guide them to the latitude of Ascension before they set out to sea. In the open ocean, however, some kind of guidance beyond a simple compass sense must be required if the turtles are to be able to correct for drift and reach the zone of chemical guidance. In this illustration the hypothetical cue is the sun's height above the horizon at noon.

made with the aid of favorable currents. If the Ascension-bound migrants swam northward from Brazil, they would enter the part of the Equatorial Current destined to become the Gulf Stream and could stay in this current until a full circle brought them westward to Ascension from the coast of West Africa. If instead they rode the Brazil Current southward, they could then travel the West Wind Drift to South Africa, catch the northward-flowing Benguela Current and rejoin the South Equatorial Current on its way to Ascension and beyond. The time required for these journeys seems prohibitive. Both would have to be negotiated without food, and the temperature of the West Wind Drift waters can drop to a chilling 40 degrees F. The direct easterly course, or some modification of it, appears to be the most logical route from Brazil to Ascension.

As for the final question, in attempting to judge how the Brazil-to-Ascension migration is guided the first step will be to determine how and where some sort of contact—direct or indirect —is established with the island. Even with a pinpoint target such as Ascension, migrating birds would be able to correct a fairly gross navigational error by visual means. To a turtle, however, an island is out of sight a few miles away. Green Mountain on Ascension stands 5,000 feet high and often has a corona of cloud that rises much higher. The sight of birds converging on the island from miles away at sea might provide an approaching turtle with still another visual guide. Such signals, how-

ever, would probably be picked up only in the last 20 miles or so. What cues might there be at longer range?

Very little is known about nonvisual phenomena associated with the presence or direction of an island, nor is anyone sure about what a green turtle can taste, smell or hear. It seems a point in favor of the upstream hypothesis of travel to Ascension, however, that such a route would allow the approaching turtles to detect an olfactory gradient— if indeed such a chemical cue is given off by the island. Perhaps when the hatchlings leave the island they take with them an imprinted memory of the taste or smell of Ascension water. Coming back as mature adults they may be able to detect this Ascension effusion in the westbound current far downstream from the island and to follow it until they make a visual landfall. There are two basic weaknesses in this proposal: no one knows how far downstream a green turtle can taste or smell an island, and there is no information to indicate the direction from which the migrants approach Ascension.

Even if we assume that far-reaching cues guide the final homing of the turtles to Ascension, there remain hundreds of miles of open ocean to be crossed—and crossed with precision— before such signs could conceivably be detected. For the greater part of this distance the animals must be navigating, and the most logical assumption appears to be that the navigating is done with information from celestial guideposts. Colin Pennycuick of the University of Cambridge has recently

called my attention to an old island-finding technique used by human navigators before the accurate calculation of longitude was possible. Knowing the latitude of his target, the navigator would sail north or south by compass until the noon position of the sun showed that he had reached the desired latitude; he would then simply sail due east or west (depending on the location of his target) until he made landfall.

This human technique seems particularly worth considering in connection with the migration of green turtles to Ascension. Possibly the turtles go north or south along the Brazilian coast until they reach the vicinity of their first landfall as hatchlings. Visual or olfactory impressions from this first contact with the mainland would identify that coastal point, which should be close to the latitude of Ascension. Thereafter compass sense alone might conceivably guide the turtles on a journey due east to a point where cues from the island could be detected.

This proposal too has weaknesses. Any drifting due to wind or current during the hundreds of miles of open-sea swimming could put the migrant hopelessly off course in spite of a constant compass heading. Unless the turtle were able to make corrections by one means or another the landfall at Ascension would never take place. For human navigators today the ability to make such corrections requires finding not only latitude but longitude as well. Latitude can be judged from the height

**GREEN TURTLE HATCHLINGS,** with colored tags attached to their left hind flippers, scramble across the beach at Ascension Island, headed for the waters of the South Atlantic. In order to trace turtle migrations the author and his colleagues have tagged young and adult green turtles both at Ascension and in Costa Rica at the only nesting beach still frequented in the western Caribbean.

**RADIO-EQUIPPED TURTLE** was used by the author to test the feasibility of tracking movements at sea from shore. To track the green turtles' long journey from Brazil to Ascension Island might require such advanced techniques as satellite-relayed telemetry.

promising for short runs. With the support of the Office of Naval Research we are trying to work out procedures for tracking longer trips by mounting a radio transmitter on the back of a turtle [*see illustration at left*], on the floats or preferably on the balloons. The length of the journey from Brazil to Ascension, however, has so far made the task of keeping in touch with these migrants a formidable one.

This may soon no longer be the case. The National Aeronautics and Space Administration intends to load apparatus for a number of scientific experiments aboard space vehicles connected with the Apollo program. Tracking the Ascension migrants by satellite could easily prove to be the most efficient method of learning the route they follow. The green turtle could without inconvenience tow a raft, bearing a radio transmitter and power source, for long distances. Each time the satellite passed within range of the towed transmitter a signal would be received; these signals, rebroadcast to a control station, would allow a precise plotting of the position of the turtle.

One key experiment making use of such facilities comes quickly to mind. Several radio-equipped turtles could be released a few hundred miles east of Ascension, where because of the prevailing current no chemical cues from the island could possibly be present. If the turtles nonetheless made their way to the Ascension nesting beaches, this would prove that their feat of navigation is not chemically guided. If satellite-tracking can pin down facts such as that, what may be discovered about animal navigation in general should abundantly repay the effort.

of the sun at noon, but reckoning longitude requires the measurement not only of some celestial body's altitude but also of its azimuth. It is hard to see how this can be done effectively by an animal in the open sea; the azimuth measurement —the horizontal component of the movement of the sun and the stars—could not be made against a featureless horizon. Pennycuick's suggestion nonetheless has hypothetical merit in regard to the Ascension migration. Eastbound turtles that were displaced north or south during the journey could conceivably correct for drift on the basis of latitude reckoning alone. Even this, of course, would be an astounding animal adaptation.

It is clear that an adequate analysis of the travel orientation of the green turtle will require tracking the animals throughout entire migratory journeys. At the University of Florida we have made preliminary tracking tests in which a turtle tows a float from which a helium-filled balloon rises to mark the position of the migrant. This seems

*Elements of Sociality*

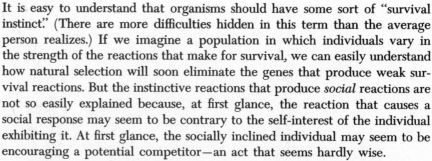

# Elements of Sociality

## INTRODUCTION

It is easy to understand that organisms should have some sort of "survival instinct." (There are more difficulties hidden in this term than the average person realizes.) If we imagine a population in which individuals vary in the strength of the reactions that make for survival, we can easily understand how natural selection will soon eliminate the genes that produce weak survival reactions. But the instinctive reactions that produce *social* reactions are not so easily explained because, at first glance, the reaction that causes a social response may seem to be contrary to the self-interest of the individual exhibiting it. At first glance, the socially inclined individual may seem to be encouraging a potential competitor—an act that seems hardly wise.

Biologists have long felt that some basic principles of sociality must be involved in the aggregation of individual cells of the same genotype to form a cooperating mass of cells to which we again give the name "individual." The phenomenon as it occurs in slime-molds is described by John Tyler Bonner in "Differentiation in Social Amoebae." In the formation of a successful multicellular organism, competition among the constitutive cells is largely avoided since these cells differentiate and become specialized for different functions. This principle is not without application at higher levels of organization.

The integration of the actions of separate individuals must be brought about by messages of some sort that pass from one individual to another. Transmission may be by way of sight or sound waves; or by diffusion of meaningful chemicals through a liquid or gaseous medium. The last mentioned possibility is discussed by Edward O. Wilson in "Pheromones." The new term is designed to call attention to the similarity of the pheromones to the "hormones," substances that integrate the actions of cells and tissues within a single individual. Do pheromones have a significant function in human sociality? One suspects they did in the past; but because of taboo and selective inattention it is difficult to be sure about their relevance in the present. How would you test this possibility?

As a contrast to chemical messages, Adrian M. Wenner relates how "Sound Communication in Honeybees" integrates the actions of the bees of a hive. Other mechanisms have also been proposed: for example, the "dance" of the bees, which is perceived by other bees, presumably by touch. The subject is a controversial one; Wenner's article shows us how the investigation of it is aided by modern physical apparatus.

N. Tinbergen's classical study of "The Curious Behavior of the Stickleback" makes us keenly aware of the essential antagonism of the defensive and the sexual reactions of an organism. If the species is to continue, these antagonisms must somehow be reconciled (though the antagonisms remain, as Freudian psychology makes clear). In the stickleback the adjustment is made at a rigidly instinctive level. Man is not rigidly instinctual; but you may find it interesting, as you observe the courtship of human beings, to see if you can place the sequence of responses into a Tinbergian pattern.

In "The Behavior of Lovebirds," William C. Dilger demonstrates how vulnerable instinctive reactions are to slight derangements. By crossing species that had different instinctive patterns he produced a hybrid with a poorly adapted constellation of instinctive elements. The example is a particular instance of the general principle that the hybrid between two well-adjusted constellations of genes is itself an inharmonious constellation.

Traditionally, instinct has been contrasted with learning. In recent years, an intermediate possibility has been described: "'Imprinting' in Animals," which is discussed by Eckhard H. Hess. It is a worthwhile educational exercise to make a detailed table showing the similarities and differences between instinct, imprinting, and learning. The idea of a "critical period" for imprinting cannot help but make us speculate about the possible existence of critical periods in human learning, and (if they exist) mull over their immense importance to educational theory and social structure.

The literature on "instinct" is, of course, rich in controversy. How we can most usefully define the word has been a matter of debate for a long time. There is a natural tendency to name instincts in terms of the end results they produce (or supposedly produce) rather than in terms of the immediately sufficient stimulus-and-response. There are dangers in this practice. To speak of a "survival instinct" is to imply—or at any rate to cause one's less sophisticated hearers to *infer*—that the organism has some knowledge of the lifetime significance of its instinctive reactions of fleeing from one stimulus, of fighting in response to another, and so on. Experimental studies cast doubt on these naive assumptions.

It is natural to assume that instinctive reactions that are closely related to the most basic requirements for survival will have precedence over reactions less closely related. Harry F. Harlow's study of "Love in Infant Monkeys" showed us that "it ain't necessarily so." A priori one would expect the nursing reaction of an infant to take precedence over mere attempts at bodily contact, but such is not the case. The reactions of Harlow's monkeys to terry-cloth mother-surrogates immediately make us think of Linus and his blanket in the comic strip. Keenly aware of the human implications of his findings, Harlow reintroduced the word "love" into a scientific field from which it had long been absent. Query: was this a wise change to make?

As science becomes replete with knowledge, those entering or thinking of entering the field come to doubt if there are still any discoveries to be made without spending a fortune on expensive equipment. The doubt is justified, of course. Eckhard H. Hess's study of "Attitude and Pupil Size" shows us, however, that it is still possible for an observant and thoughtful person to discover new things with no equipment whatsoever (though the thorough investigation of them is usually much aided by equipment). Outside the world of self-conscious science it is probable, as Hess indicates, that the phenomenon he describes has been known for a long time. Perhaps it was something of this sort that the dramatist John Heywood had in mind when he said (in 1546): "They do not love that do not show their love."

Sociality clearly must have survival value for the species, or it would not exist. Yet some of the consequences of sociality, "responsibility" for instance, can sometimes be rather hard on the individual. Joseph V. Brady describing "Ulcers in 'Executive' Monkeys" inevitably makes us think of human situations. We recall the somber saying of another sixteenth-century Englishman, the ecclesiastic Richard Hooker: "Ministers of good things are like torches, a light to others, waste and destruction to themselves." The interaction of natural selection and the effects of responsibility on the individual, in the course of a long period of time, creates stability problems for society.

# 18 Differentiation in Social Amoebae

JOHN TYLER BONNER · December 1959

Recently I was asked to talk to two visiting Russian university rectors (both biologists) about the curious organisms known as slime molds. Communication through the interpreter was somewhat difficult, but my visitors obviously neither knew nor really cared what slime molds were. Then, without anticipating the effect, I wrote on the blackboard the words "social amoebae," a title I had used for an article about these same organisms some years ago [see "The Social Amoebae," by John Tyler Bonner; SCIENTIFIC AMERICAN, June, 1949]. The Russians were electrified with delight and curiosity. I described how individual amoebae can come together under certain conditions to form a multicellular organism, the cells moving into their appropriate places in the organism and differentiating to divide the labor of reproduction. Soon both of my guests were beaming, evidently pleased that even one-celled animals could be so sophisticated as to form collectives.

Of course there are other reasons why slime molds hold the interest of biologists. The transformation of free-living, apparently identical amoebae into differentiated cells, members of a larger organism, presents some of the same questions as the differentiation of embryonic cells into specialized tissues. In the budding embryo, moreover, cells go through "morphogenetic movements" which seemingly parcel them out to their assigned positions in the emergent organism. The only difference is that the simplicity of the slime molds provides excellent material for experiments.

The slime-mold amoebae, inhabitants of the soil, do their feeding as separate, independent individuals. Flowing about on their irregular courses they engulf bacteria, in the manner of our own amoeboid white blood cells. At this stage they reproduce simply by dividing in two. Once they have cleared the food away, wherever they are fairly dense, the amoebae suddenly flow together to central collection points. There the cells, numbering anywhere from 10 to 500,000, heap upward in a little tower which, at least in the species *Dictyostelium discoideum*, settles over on its side and crawls about as a tiny, glistening, bullet-shaped slug, .1 to two millimeters long. This slug has a distinct front and hind end (the pointed end is at the front) and leaves a trail of slime as it moves. It is remarkably sensitive to light and heat; it will move toward a weak source of heat or a light as faint as the dial of a luminous wrist watch. As the slug migrates, the cells in the front third begin to look different from the cells in the two thirds at the rear. The changes are the early signs of differentiation; eventually all the hind cells turn into spores—the seeds for the next generation—and all the front cells cooperate to make a slender, tapering stalk that thrusts the mass of spores up into the air.

To accomplish this transformation the slug first points its tip upward and stands on end. The uppermost front cells swell with water like a bit of froth and become encased in a cellulose cylinder which is to form the stalk. As new front cells arrive at the frothy tip of the stalk they add themselves to its lengthening structure and push it downward through the mass of hind-end cells below. When this process, like a fountain in reverse, has brought the stalk into contact with the surface, the continued upward migration of pre-stalk cells heightens the stalk lifting the presumptive spore cells up into the air. Each amoeba in the spore mass now encases itself in cellulose and becomes a spore. The end result is a delicate tapering shaft capped by a spherical mass of spores. When the spores are dispersed (by water or by contact with some passing creature such as an insect or a worm), each can split open to liberate a tiny new amoeba.

What mechanism brings the independent slime-mold amoebae together in a mass? More than a decade ago we found that they are attracted by the gradient of a substance which they themselves produce. In our early experiments we were unable to obtain cell-free preparations of this substance (which we named acrasin); cells actively secreting it were always necessary to start an aggregation. Later B. M. Shaffer of the University of Cambridge got around this barrier in an ingenious experiment. He took water that had been near acrasin-producing cells (but was itself free of cells) and applied it to the side of a small agar block placed on top of some amoebae. The amoebae momentarily streamed toward the side where the concentration of acrasin was higher. Shaffer found that the water must be used immediately after it is collected in order to achieve this effect, and that it must be applied repeatedly. He therefore concluded that acrasin loses its potency rapidly at room temperature. The loss of potency, he showed, is caused by enzymes that are secreted by the amoebae along with acrasin; when he filtered the fluid through a cellophane membrane to hold back the large enzyme molecules, he was able to secure a stable preparation of acrasin. Presumably the enzymes serve to clear the environment of the substance and so enhance the establishment of a gradient in the concentration of acrasin when it is next secreted. Maurice Sussman and his

**SPHERICAL MASSES OF SPORES** of the social amoeba *Dictyostelium discoideum* are held aloft by stalks composed of other amoebae of the same species. When the spores are dispersed, each can liberate a new amoeba. The stalks are about half an inch high.

AGGREGATING AMOEBAE of *Dictyostelium discoideum* move in thin streams toward central collection points. Each of the centers comprises thousands of cells. This photograph and facing one were made by Kenneth B. Raper of the University of Wisconsin.

co-workers at Brandeis University in Waltham, Mass., have confirmed Shaffer's work and are now attempting the difficult task of fractionating and purifying acrasin, steps leading toward its identification.

Meanwhile Barbara Wright of the National Institutes of Health in Bethesda dropped a bombshell. She discovered that urine from a pregnant woman could attract the amoebae under an agar block just as acrasin does. The active components of the urine turned out to be steroid sex hormones. This does not necessarily mean that acrasin is such a steroid. Animal embryologists were thrown off the track for years when they found that locally applied steroids induce the further development of early embryos. Only after much painful confusion did it become clear that steroids do not act directly on the embryo, but stimulate the normal induction substance. We must therefore consider the possibility that the steroids act in a similarly indirect manner on the amoebae. The purification of acrasin will, we hope, soon settle the question.

From observations of the cells during aggregation, Shaffer has come to the interesting conclusion that the many incoming amoebae are not responding to one large gradient of acrasin but to relays of gradients. That is, a central cell will release a puff of acrasin that produces a small gradient in its immediate

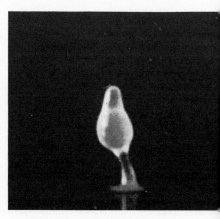

DEVELOPMENT OF THE FRUITING BODY of a slime mold is shown in this series of photographs made at half-hour intervals. At far left the tip cells are starting to form a stalk. In the next two pictures the stalk has pushed down through the mass to the

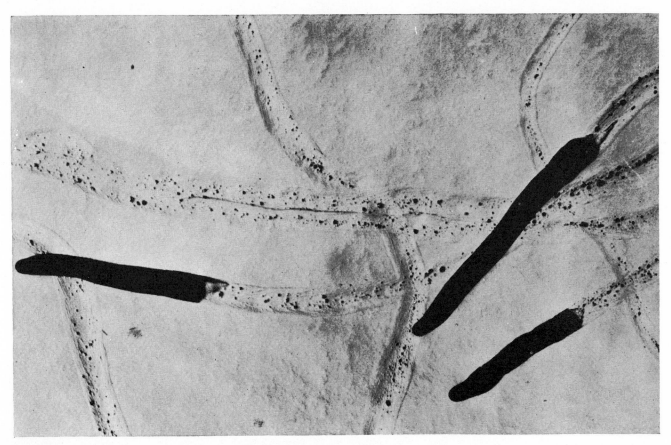

MIGRATING SLUGS of *Dictyostelium discoideum* leave trails of slime behind them as they move. The photographs in this article appear in *The Cellular Slime Molds*, by John Tyler Bonner, and are reproduced with permission of Princeton University Press.

vicinity. The surrounding cells become oriented, and now produce a puff of their own. This new puff orients the cells lying just beyond, and in this way a wave of orientation passes outward. Time-lapse motion pictures show the amoebae moving inward in waves, which could well represent the relay system. If this interpretation is sound, then the rapid breakdown of acrasin by an enzyme plainly serves to clear the slate after each puff in preparation for the next. The cells do not depend entirely on acrasin for orientation; once they are in contact they tend to stick to one another and the pull-tension of one guides the cells that follow. This is a special case of contact guidance, a phenomenon well known in the movements of embryonic cells of higher animals.

After the amoebae have gathered together, what determines their position within the bullet-shaped slug? One might assume that the cells that arrive at the center of the heap automatically become the tip of the slug, and that the last cells to come in from the periphery make up the hind end. If this were the case, chance alone would determine whether a cell is to become a front-end cell and enter into the formation of the stalk, or a hind-end cell and become a spore. If, on the other hand, the cells rearrange themselves as they organize into a slug, then it is conceiv-

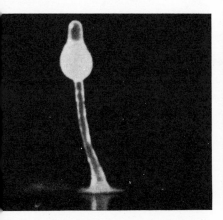
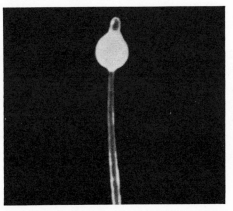
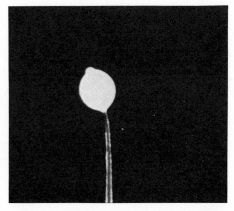

surface and is starting to lift the cell mass. In the fourth picture the spores have formed their cellulose coats, making the ball more opaque. In the last two pictures the spore mass moves up to the very top of the stalk, as the stalk itself becomes still longer.

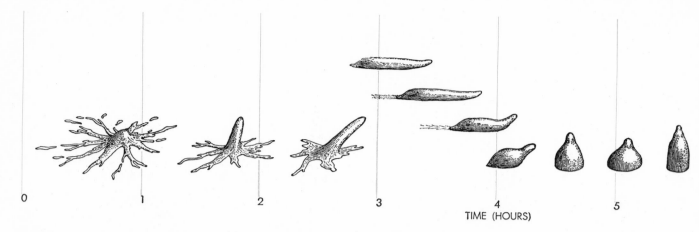

TIME (HOURS)

**LIFE CYCLE OF A SLIME MOLD,** typified by *Dictyostelium discoideum*, involves the aggregation of free-living amoebae into a unified mass (*first three drawings*), then the formation of a slug which moves about for a time (*next four drawings*) and finally

able that the front end might contain selected cells, differing in particular ways from those in the hind end. I am embarrassed to say that in 1944 I presented some evidence to support the idea that their chance position was the determining factor—evidence that, as will soon be clear, was inadequate. It is some comfort, however, that I was able to rectify the error myself.

The first faint hint that the cells do redistribute themselves in the slug stage came when we repeated some experiments first done by Kenneth B. Raper of the University of Wisconsin. We stained some slugs with harmless dyes and then grafted the hind half of a colored slug onto the front half of an unstained slug. The division line remained sharp for a

number of hours, just as Raper had previously observed. But later we noticed that a few stained cells were moving forward into the uncolored part of the slug. In the reverse graft, with the front end stained, a similar small group of colored cells gradually migrated toward the rear end of the slug. Still, the number of cells involved was so small that it could hardly be considered the sign of a major redistribution. Next we tried putting some colored front-end cells in the hind end of an intact slug. The result was a total surprise: now the colored cells rapidly moved to the front end, traveling as a band of color up the length of the slug.

Here was a clear demonstration that the cells do rearrange themselves in the

slug and that there is a difference between the cells at the front and hind ends. The difference between front-end and hind-end cells—whatever its nature—was confirmed in control experiments in which we grafted front-end cells to the front ends of the slugs and hind-end cells to the hind ends; in each case the cells maintained their positions.

It looked as if front-end cells were selected by their speed; the colored cells simply raced from the rear end to the front. When we placed hind-end cells in the front end, they traveled to the rear, outpaced by the faster-moving cells, which again assumed their forward positions. We tried to select fast cells and slow cells over a series of genera-

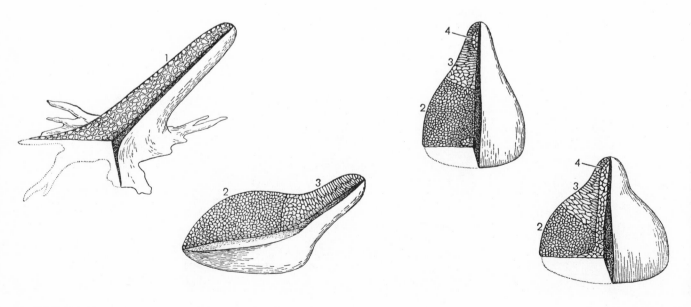

**CUTAWAY DRAWINGS** of five stages show how the cells change. At the end of aggregation all cells appear the same (1), but in the slug they are of two types (2 and 3). The cells near the tip (3) gradually turn into stalk cells (4) and move down inside the

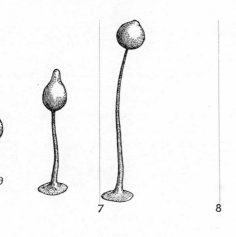

the development of a fruiting body (*last six drawings*). Times are only approximate.

tions to see if speed was a hereditary trait, but after selection the cultures showed no differences from one another or from the parent stock.

Quite by accident a new bit of evidence turned up in an experiment designed for totally independent reasons. Instead of using the fully formed slug we stained amoebae colonies in the process of aggregation and made grafts at this stage by removing the center of the stained group and replacing it with a colorless center, or vice versa. In either case the resulting slug was always uniformly colored, indicating a rapid reassortment of the cells during the formation of the slug.

The evidence for a rearrangement of

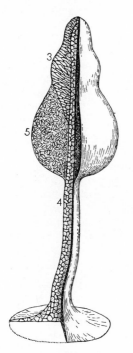

mass. The others (2) become spores (5) as the growing stalk lifts them into the air.

cells was becoming impressive, but I felt uneasy about the reliability of tests with dyes because such tests had led me into my earlier error. We needed to confirm our results by a different method.

At about this time M. F. Filosa, who was working in our laboratory on his doctoral dissertation, discovered that many of our amoeba cultures contained more than one genetic type. By isolating and cultivating single cells of each type he was able to obtain pure strains that displayed various recognizable abnormalities—in the way they aggregated, in the shape of their slugs or in the form of their spore masses [see illustration on page 162]. The discovery of these strains furnished natural "markers" for identifying and following cells.

Of course there remained one technical problem: How could the individual cells be identified? Fortunately Raper had shown some time earlier that each fragment of a slug that has been cut into pieces will form a midget fruiting body. Spores derived from the several fragments can then be cultured individually. The amoeba from each spore will give rise to many daughter amoebae which can be scored for mutant or normal characteristics as they proceed to form slugs and fruiting bodies.

In one experiment we started with a culture of cells in the free-living feeding stage, into which was mixed 10 to 15 per cent of mutant cells. If we were to find a higher concentration of one type of cell in one part of the resulting slug, then we could conclude that there had been a rearrangement. We allowed the cells to form a slug and cut it up into three parts. Upon culturing the individual spores produced by each part, we found that the hind third had 36 per cent mutant cells, the middle third 6 per cent and the front third 1 per cent. Nothing could be more clear-cut; obviously the cells sort themselves out in a way that brings the normal cells to the front end of the slug. In another experiment, with a larger percentage of mutant cells in the mixture, hind and middle fractions contained 91 per cent mutant cells, and the front end only 66 per cent. Further experiments, including some with other species of slime mold, all led to the same conclusion. During the process of slug formation some cells are more likely to reach the front end than others, and the position of a cell in the slug does not merely depend upon its chance position before aggregation.

One must assume that certain cells move to the front because they travel the fastest, while the other, slower cells are

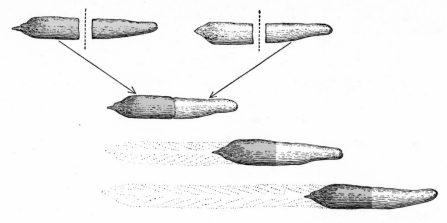

**GRAFTED SLUG** composed of the hind end of a stained slug and the front end of an unstained slug retains a sharp line of demarcation between the parts even after several hours.

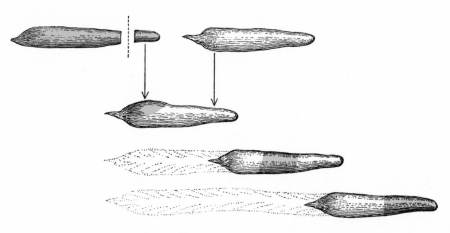

**COLORED TIP** taken from a stained slug can be inserted into the hind part of an intact slug. The colored cells then move forward as a band until they again are at the front tip.

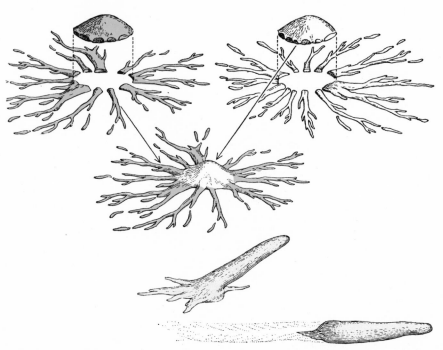

**COLORED AGGREGATE** in which the center has been replaced by a colorless center produces a uniformly colored slug, indicating that the cells are rearranged as the slug forms. The experiment illustrated in these drawings was originally performed by Kenneth B. Raper.

fastest, while the other, slower cells are left behind in the rear end of the slug. Considering the different fates of the front and rear cells, however, it is natural to wonder whether there are any other discernible differences between the front and hind cells. Size is one of the easiest qualities to measure, and comparison of spores from the front and rear portions showed that cells of the front segment are larger. From this it might be concluded that the fastest cells are the largest. But size is related to many other factors; some evidence indicates that cells in the front end divide less frequently than those in the hind regions, and this could affect their size. The possibility of a correlation between size and speed can only be settled by further experiment and observation.

But one fact is inescapable. The cells that tend to go forward are not identical with those that lag behind. Do the differences ultimately determine which cells become stalk cells and which will be spores? The most obvious deduction is that among feeding amoebae roughly a third are presumptive stalk cells, and the rest are predestined to be spores. This interpretation is clearly false, however, because then it would be impossible to explain how a single fragment of a cut-up slug can produce a perfect miniature fruiting body. The cells in the hind piece, which would normally yield spores, recover from the surgery that isolates them from the large slug, and one third of these presumptive spore cells proceed to form the midget stalk. This remarkable accommodation to a new situation is also exhibited by many types of cells in embryos and in animals capable of regenerating limbs and organs.

A more reasonable way to explain the relation between sorting-out and differentiation is to visualize the aggregating amoebae as having all shades of variation in characteristics between the extremes found at the ends of the slug. As they form a slug the cells place themselves in such an order that from the rear to the front they display a gradual increase in speed, in size and perhaps in other properties not yet measured. Thus each fragment of a cut-up slug retains a small gradient of these properties. It is conceivable that the gradient, set up in the process of cell rearrangement, actually controls the chain of events that leads the front cells to form a stalk and the hind cells to become

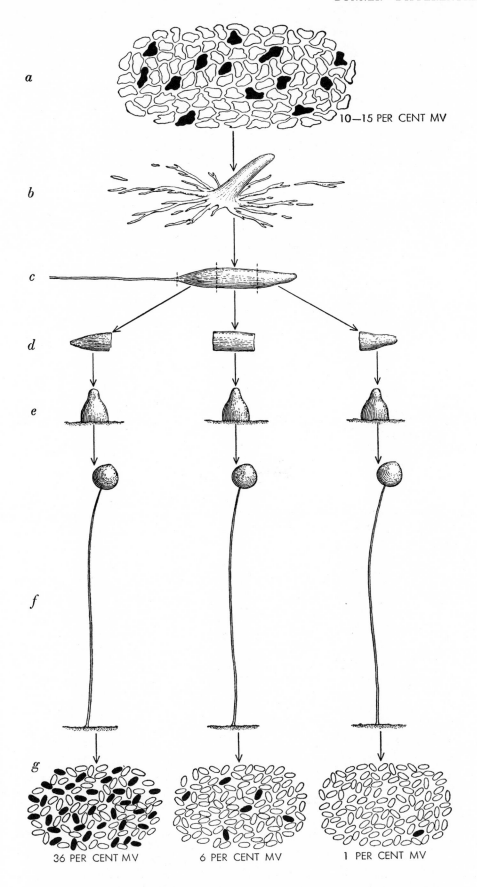

*a*

10—15 PER CENT MV

*b*

*c*

*d*

*e*

*f*

*g*

36 PER CENT MV    6 PER CENT MV    1 PER CENT MV

**REDISTRIBUTION OF CELLS** was proved in an experiment in which MV mutant cells (*black*) were randomly mixed with normal cells at feeding stage (*a*). The cells aggregated (*b*), and the resulting slug (*c*) was cut into three parts (*d*). Each part produced a fruiting body (*e* and *f*). Spores of each were then identified (*g*) by culturing them separately. The concentration of mutant cells was markedly higher in spores from the hind part of the slug.

spores. For the present, however, this is only conjecture.

At this point let me emphasize that the sorting-out process is not unique to slime molds. Recently A. A. Moscona of the University of Chicago and others have found that if the tissues of various embryos or simple animals are separated into individual cells, the cells can come together and sort themselves out [see "Tissues from Dissociated Cells," by A. A. Moscona; SCIENTIFIC AMERICAN, May, 1959]. For instance, if separate single pre-cartilage cells are mixed with pre-muscle cells, the cartilage cells will aggregate into a ball and ultimately form a central mass of cartilage surrounded by a layer of muscle. By marking the cells in a most ingenious way Moscona showed that there was no transformation of pre-cartilage cells into muscle cells or vice versa; each cell retained its original identity but moved to a characteristic location. In animals, then, sorting-out appears to be a general phenomenon when the cells are artificially dissociated. Since the movement in slime molds is part of their normal development, this raises the challenging question whether such sorting-out occurs in the normal development of animal embryos as well.

One must concede that slime-mold amoebae do profit by collectivization: the aggregate can do things the individuals cannot accomplish alone. In the amoebae's society, however, all are not created equal; some rise to the top and others lag behind. And then there is this distressing moral: Those that go forward with such zest to reach the fore are rewarded with sacrifice and destruction as stalk cells. It is the laggards that they lift into the air which survive to propagate the next generation.

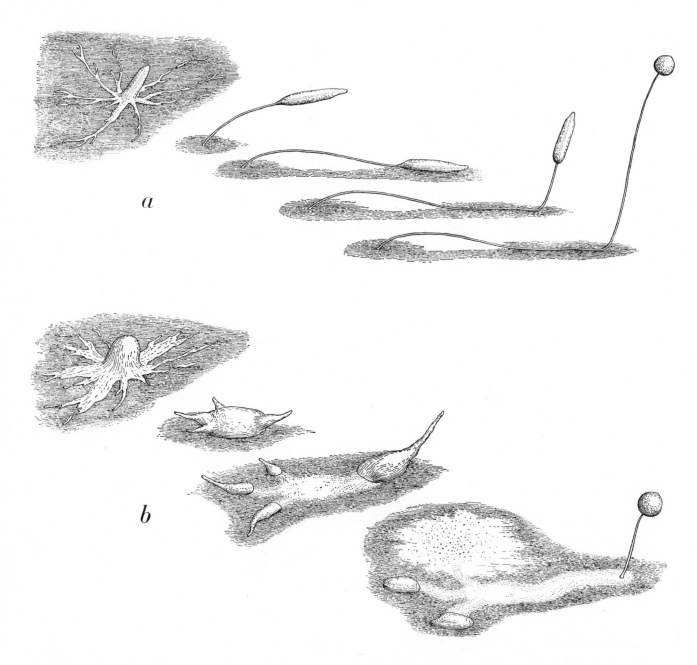

NORMAL AND MUTANT STRAINS of *Dictyostelium mucoroides* are contrasted in these drawings. The normal form (*a*) aggregates in thin streams, and its slug remains anchored by a thin stalk. The "MV" mutant (*b*) aggregates in broad streams and produces a starfish-like slug which then breaks up into smaller slugs. The stalk of the mutant is usually shorter than that of normal strain.

# 19 Pheromones

EDWARD O. WILSON · May 1963

It is conceivable that somewhere on other worlds civilizations exist that communicate entirely by the exchange of chemical substances that are smelled or tasted. Unlikely as this may seem, the theoretical possibility cannot be ruled out. It is not difficult to design, on paper at least, a chemical communication system that can transmit a large amount of information with rather good efficiency. The notion of such a communication system is of course strange because our outlook is shaped so strongly by our own peculiar auditory and visual conventions. This limitation of outlook is found even among students of animal behavior; they have favored species whose communication methods are similar to our own and therefore more accessible to analysis. It is becoming increasingly clear, however, that chemical systems provide the dominant means of communication in many animal species, perhaps even in most. In the past several years animal behaviorists and organic chemists, working together, have made a start at deciphering some of these systems and have discovered a number of surprising new biological phenomena.

In earlier literature on the subject, chemicals used in communication were usually referred to as "ectohormones." Since 1959 the less awkward and etymologically more accurate term "pheromones" has been widely adopted. It is used to describe substances exchanged among members of the same animal species. Unlike true hormones, which are secreted internally to regulate the organism's own physiology, or internal environment, pheromones are secreted externally and help to regulate the organism's external environment by influencing other animals. The mode of influence can take either of two general forms. If the pheromone produces a more or less immediate and reversible change

in the behavior of the recipient, it is said to have a "releaser" effect. In this case the chemical substance seems to act directly on the recipient's central nervous system. If the principal function of the pheromone is to trigger a chain of physiological events in the recipient, it has what we have recently labeled a "primer" effect. The physiological changes, in turn, equip the organism with a new behavioral repertory, the components of which are thenceforth evoked by appropriate stimuli. In termites, for example, the reproductive and soldier castes prevent other termites from developing into their own castes by secreting substances that are ingested and act through the *corpus allatum,* an endocrine gland controlling differentiation [see "The Termite and the Cell," by Martin Lüscher; SCIENTIFIC AMERICAN, May, 1953].

These indirect primer pheromones do not always act by physiological inhibition. They can have the opposite effect.

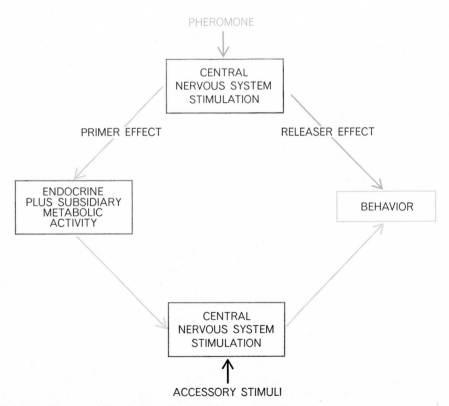

PHEROMONES INFLUENCE BEHAVIOR directly or indirectly, as shown in this schematic diagram. If a pheromone stimulates the recipient's central nervous system into producing an immediate change in behavior, it is said to have a "releaser" effect. If it alters a set of long-term physiological conditions so that the recipient's behavior can subsequently be influenced by specific accessory stimuli, the pheromone is said to have a "primer" effect.

Adult males of the migratory locust *Schistocerca gregaria* secrete a volatile substance from their skin surface that accelerates the growth of young locusts. When the nymphs detect this substance with their antennae, their hind legs, some of their mouth parts and the antennae themselves vibrate. The secretion, in conjunction with tactile and visual signals, plays an important role in the formation of migratory locust swarms.

A striking feature of some primer pheromones is that they cause important physiological change without an immediate accompanying behavioral response, at least none that can be said to be peculiar to the pheromone. Beginning in 1955 with the work of S. van der Lee and L. M. Boot in the Netherlands, mammalian endocrinologists have discovered several unexpected effects on the female mouse that are produced by odors of other members of the same species. These changes are not marked by any immediate distinctive behavioral patterns. In the "Lee-Boot effect" females placed in groups of four show an increase in the percentage of pseudopregnancies. A completely normal reproductive pattern can be restored by removing the olfactory bulbs of the mice or by housing the mice separately. When more and more female mice are forced to live together, their oestrous cycles become highly irregular and in most of the mice the cycle stops completely for long periods. Recently W. K. Whitten of the Australian National University has discovered that the odor of a male mouse can initiate and synchronize the oestrous cycles of female mice. The male odor also reduces the frequency of reproductive abnormalities arising when female mice are forced to live under crowded conditions.

A still more surprising primer effect has been found by Helen Bruce of the National Institute for Medical Research in London. She observed that the odor of a strange male mouse will block the pregnancy of a newly impregnated female mouse. The odor of the original stud male, of course, leaves pregnancy undisturbed. The mouse reproductive pheromones have not yet been identified chemically, and their mode of action is only partly understood. There is evidence that the odor of the strange male suppresses the secretion of the hormone prolactin, with the result that the *corpus luteum* (a ductless ovarian gland) fails to develop and normal oestrus is restored. The pheromones are probably part of the complex set of control mechanisms that regulate the population density of animals [see "Population Density and Social Pathology," by John B. Calhoun, beginning on page 269 in this book].

Pheromones that produce a simple releaser effect—a single specific response mediated directly by the central nervous system—are widespread in the animal kingdom and serve a great many functions. Sex attractants constitute a large and important category. The chemical structures of six attractants are shown on page 9. Although two of the six—the mammalian scents muskone and civetone—have been known for some 40 years and are generally assumed to serve a sexual function, their exact role has never been rigorously established by experiments with living animals. In fact, mammals seem to employ musklike compounds, alone or in combination with other substances, to serve several functions: to mark home ranges, to assist in territorial defense and to identify the sexes.

The nature and role of the four insect sex attractants are much better understood. The identification of each represents a technical feat of considerable magnitude. To obtain 12 milligrams of esters of bombykol, the sex attractant of the female silkworm moth, Adolf F. J. Butenandt and his associates at the Max Planck Institute of Biochemistry in Munich had to extract material from 250,000 moths. Martin Jacobson, Morton Beroza and William Jones of the U.S. Department of Agriculture processed 500,000 female gypsy moths to get 20 milligrams of the gypsy-moth attractant gyplure. Each moth yielded only about .01 microgram (millionth of a gram) of gyplure, or less than a millionth of its body weight. Bombykol and gyplure were obtained by killing the insects and subjecting crude extracts of material to chromatography, the separation technique in which compounds move at different rates through a column packed with a suitable adsorbent substance. Another technique has been more recently developed by Robert T. Yamamoto of the U.S. Department of Agriculture, in collaboration with Jacobson and Beroza, to harvest the equally elusive sex attractant of the American cockroach. Virgin females were housed in metal cans and air was continuously drawn through the cans and passed through chilled containers to condense any vaporized materials. In this manner the equivalent of 10,000 females were "milked" over a nine-month period to yield 12.2 milligrams of what was considered to be the pure attractant.

The power of the insect attractants is almost unbelievable. If some 10,000 molecules of the most active form of

**INVISIBLE ODOR TRAILS** guide fire ant workers to a source of food: a drop of sugar solution. The trails consist of a pheromone laid down by workers returning to their nest after finding a source of food. Sometimes the chemical message is reinforced by the touching of antennae if a returning worker meets a wandering fellow along the way. This is hap-

bombykol are allowed to diffuse from a source one centimeter from the antennae of a male silkworm moth, a characteristic sexual response is obtained in most cases. If volatility and diffusion rate are taken into account, it can be estimated that the threshold concentration is no more than a few hundred molecules per cubic centimeter, and the actual number required to stimulate the male is probably even smaller. From this one can calculate that .01 microgram of gyplure, the minimum average content of a single female moth, would be theoretically adequate, if distributed with maximum efficiency, to excite more than a billion male moths.

In nature the female uses her powerful pheromone to advertise her presence over a large area with a minimum expenditure of energy. With the aid of published data from field experiments and newly contrived mathematical models of the diffusion process, William H. Bossert, one of my associates in the Biological Laboratories at Harvard University, and I have deduced the shape and size of the ellipsoidal space within which male moths can be attracted under natural conditions [see bottom illustration on the next page]. When a moderate wind is blowing, the active space has a long axis of thousands of meters and a transverse axis parallel to

the ground of more than 200 meters at the widest point. The 19th-century French naturalist Jean Henri Fabre, speculating on sex attraction in insects, could not bring himself to believe that the female moth could communicate over such great distances by odor alone, since "one might as well expect to tint a lake with a drop of carmine." We now know that Fabre's conclusion was wrong but that his analogy was exact: to the male moth's powerful chemoreceptors the lake is indeed tinted.

One must now ask how the male moth, smelling the faintly tinted air, knows which way to fly to find the source of the tinting. He cannot simply fly in the direction of increasing scent; it can be shown mathematically that the attractant is distributed almost uniformly after it has drifted more than a few meters from the female. Recent experiments by Ilse Schwinck of the University of Munich have revealed what is probably the alternative procedure used. When male moths are activated by the pheromone, they simply fly upwind and thus inevitably move toward the female. If by accident they pass out of the active zone, they either abandon the search or fly about at random until they pick up the scent again. Eventually, as they approach the female, there is a slight increase in the concentration of the chemi-

cal attractant and this can serve as a guide for the remaining distance.

If one is looking for the most highly developed chemical communication systems in nature, it is reasonable to study the behavior of the social insects, particularly the social wasps, bees, termites and ants, all of which communicate mostly in the dark interiors of their nests and are known to have advanced chemoreceptive powers. In recent years experimental techniques have been developed to separate and identify the pheromones of these insects, and rapid progress has been made in deciphering the hitherto intractable codes, particularly those of the ants. The most successful procedure has been to dissect out single glandular reservoirs and see what effect their contents have on the behavior of the worker caste, which is the most numerous and presumably the most in need of continuing guidance. Other pheromones, not present in distinct reservoirs, are identified in chromatographic fractions of crude extracts.

Ants of all castes are constructed with an exceptionally well-developed exocrine glandular system. Many of the most prominent of these glands, whose function has long been a mystery to entomologists, have now been identified as the source of pheromones [see illustra-

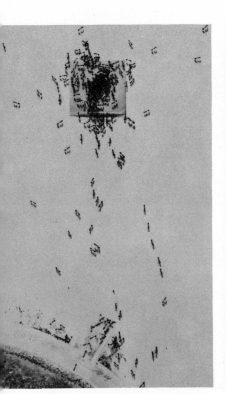
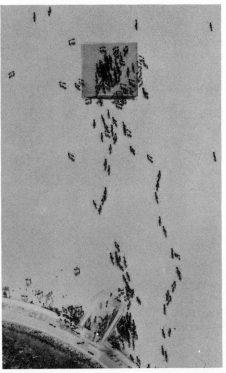

pening in the photograph at the far left. A few foraging workers have just found the sugar drop and a returning trail-layer is communicating the news to another ant. In the next two pictures the trail has been completed and workers stream from the nest in increasing numbers. In the fourth picture unrewarded workers return to the nest without laying trails and outward-bound traffic wanes. In the last picture most of the trails have evaporated completely and only a few stragglers remain at the site, eating the last bits of food.

*tion on page 168*]. The analysis of the gland-pheromone complex has led to the beginnings of a new and deeper understanding of how ant societies are organized.

Consider the chemical trail. According to the traditional view, trail secretions served as only a limited guide for worker ants and had to be augmented by other kinds of signals exchanged inside the nest. Now it is known that the trail substance is extraordinarily versatile. In the fire ant (*Solenopsis saevissima*), for instance, it functions both to activate and to guide foraging workers in search of food and new nest sites. It also contributes as one of the alarm signals emitted by workers in distress. The trail of the fire ant consists of a substance secreted in minute amounts by Dufour's gland; the substance leaves the ant's body by way of the extruded sting, which is touched intermittently to the ground much like a moving pen dispensing ink. The trail pheromone, which has not yet been chemically identified, acts primarily to attract the fire ant workers. Upon encountering the attractant the workers move automatically up the gradient to the source of emission. When the substance is drawn out in a line, the workers run along the direction of the line away from the nest. This simple response brings them to the food source or new nest site from which the trail is laid. In our laboratory we have extracted the pheromone from the Dufour's glands of freshly killed workers and have used it to create artificial trails. Groups of workers will follow these trails away from the nest and along arbitrary routes (including circles leading back to the nest) for considerable periods of time. When the pheromone is presented to whole colonies in massive doses, a large portion of the colony, including the queen, can be drawn out in a close simulation of the emigration process.

The trail substance is rather volatile, and a natural trail laid by one worker diffuses to below the threshold concentration within two minutes. Consequently outward-bound workers are able to follow it only for the distance they can travel in this time, which is about 40 centimeters. Although this strictly limits the distance over which the ants can communicate, it provides at least two important compensatory advantages. The more obvious advantage is that old, useless trails do not linger to confuse the hunting workers. In addition, the intensity of the trail laid by many workers provides a sensitive index of the amount of food at a given site and the rate of its depletion. As workers move to and from

ANTENNAE OF GYPSY MOTHS differ radically in structure according to their function. In the male (*left*) they are broad and finely divided to detect minute quantities of sex attractant released by the female (*right*). The antennae of the female are much less developed.

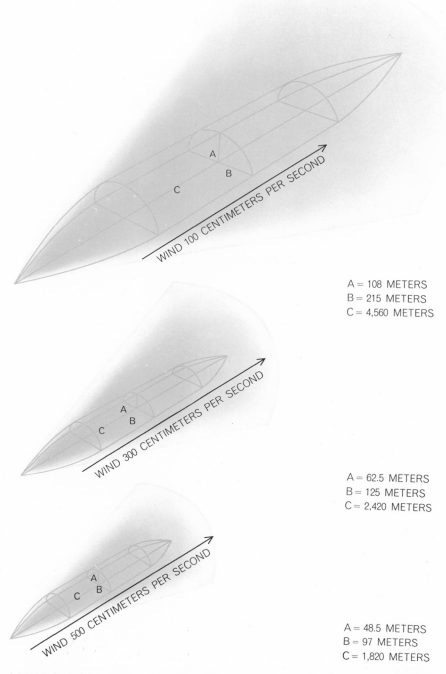

A = 108 METERS
B = 215 METERS
C = 4,560 METERS

A = 62.5 METERS
B = 125 METERS
C = 2,420 METERS

A = 48.5 METERS
B = 97 METERS
C = 1,820 METERS

ACTIVE SPACE of gyplure, the gypsy moth sex attractant, is the space within which this pheromone is sufficiently dense to attract males to a single, continuously emitting female. The actual dimensions, deduced from linear measurements and general gas-diffusion models, are given at right. Height (*A*) and width (*B*) are exaggerated in the drawing. As wind shifts from moderate to strong, increased turbulence contracts the active space.

**FIRE ANT WORKER** lays an odor trail by exuding a pheromone along its extended sting. The sting is touched to the ground periodically, breaking the trail into a series of streaks.

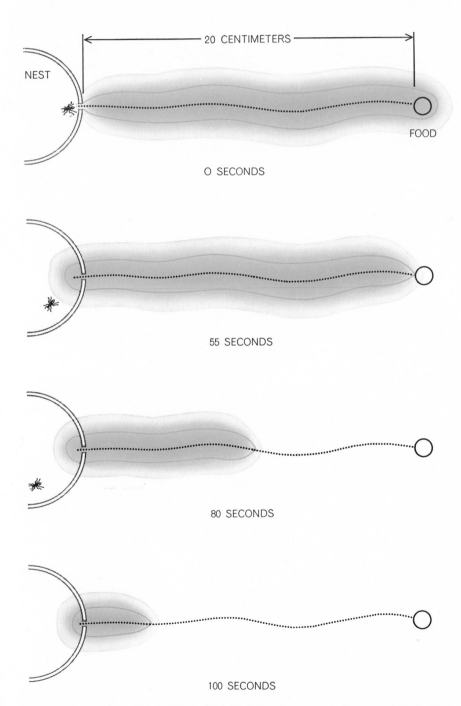

**ACTIVE SPACE OF ANT TRAIL,** within which the pheromone is dense enough to be perceived by other workers, is narrow and nearly constant in shape with the maximum gradient situated near its outer surface. The rapidity with which the trail evaporates is indicated.

the food finds (consisting mostly of dead insects and sugar sources) they continuously add their own secretions to the trail produced by the original discoverers of the food. Only if an ant is rewarded by food does it lay a trail on its trip back to the nest; therefore the more food encountered at the end of the trail, the more workers that can be rewarded and the heavier the trail. The heavier the trail, the more workers that are drawn from the nest and arrive at the end of the trail. As the food is consumed, the number of workers laying trail substance drops, and the old trail fades by evaporation and diffusion, gradually constricting the outward flow of workers.

The fire ant odor trail shows other evidences of being efficiently designed. The active space within which the pheromone is dense enough to be perceived by workers remains narrow and nearly constant in shape over most of the length of the trail. It has been further deduced from diffusion models that the maximum gradient must be situated near the outer surface of the active space. Thus workers are informed of the space boundary in a highly efficient way. Together these features ensure that the following workers keep in close formation with a minimum chance of losing the trail.

The fire ant trail is one of the few animal communication systems whose information content can be measured with fair precision. Unlike many communicating animals, the ants have a distinct goal in space—the food find or nest site—the direction and distance of which must both be communicated. It is possible by a simple technique to measure how close trail-followers come to the trail end, and, by making use of a standard equation from information theory, one can translate the accuracy of their response into the "bits" of information received. A similar procedure can be applied (as first suggested by the British biologist J. B. S. Haldane) to the "waggle dance" of the honeybee, a radically different form of communication system from the ant trail [see "Dialects in the Language of the Bees," by Karl von Frisch; SCIENTIFIC AMERICAN offprint 130]. Surprisingly, it turns out that the two systems, although of wholly different evolutionary origin, transmit about the same amount of information with reference to distance (two bits) and direction (four bits in the honeybee, and four or possibly five in the ant). Four bits of information will direct an ant or a bee into one of 16 equally probable sectors of a circle and two bits will identify one of four equally probable distances. It is conceivable that these information values represent the maximum that can be achieved with the insect brain and sensory apparatus.

Not all kinds of ants lay chemical trails. Among those that do, however, the pheromones are highly species-specific in their action. In experiments in which artificial trails extracted from one species were directed to living colonies of other species, the results have almost always been negative, even among related species. It is as if each species had its own private language. As a result there is little or no confusion when the trails of two or more species cross.

Another important class of ant pheromone is composed of alarm substances. A simple backyard experiment will show that if a worker ant is disturbed by a clean instrument, it will, for a short time, excite other workers with whom it comes in contact. Until recently most students of ant behavior thought that

the alarm was spread by touch, that one worker simply jostled another in its excitement or drummed on its neighbor with its antennae in some peculiar way. Now it is known that disturbed workers discharge chemicals, stored in special glandular reservoirs, that can produce all the characteristic alarm responses solely by themselves. The chemical structure of four alarm substances is shown on page 172. Nothing could illustrate more clearly the wide differences between the human perceptual world and that of chemically communicating animals. To the human nose the alarm substances are mild or even pleasant, but to the ant they represent an urgent tocsin that can propel a colony into violent and instant action.

As in the case of the trail substances, the employment of the alarm substances appears to be ideally designed for the purpose it serves. When the contents of the mandibular glands of a worker of the harvesting ant (*Pogonomyrmex badius*)

are discharged into still air, the volatile material forms a rapidly expanding sphere, which attains a radius of about six centimeters in 13 seconds. Then it contracts until the signal fades out completely some 35 seconds after the moment of discharge. The outer shell of the active space contains a low concentration of pheromone, which is actually attractive to harvester workers. This serves to draw them toward the point of disturbance. The central region of the active space, however, contains a concentration high enough to evoke the characteristic frenzy of alarm. The "alarm sphere" expands to a radius of about three centimeters in eight seconds and, as might be expected, fades out more quickly than the "attraction sphere."

The advantage to the ants of an alarm signal that is both local and short-lived becomes obvious when a *Pogonomyrmex* colony is observed under natural conditions. The ant nest is subject to almost innumerable minor disturbances. If the

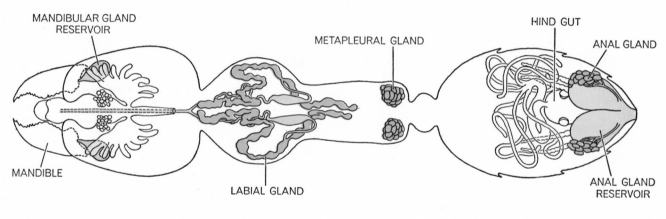

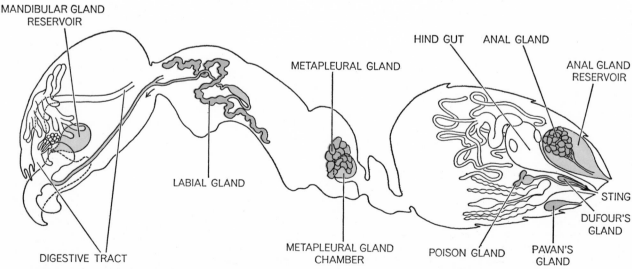

**EXOCRINE GLANDULAR SYSTEM** of a worker ant (*shown here in top and side cutaway views*) is specially adapted for the production of chemical communication substances. Some pheromones are stored in reservoirs and released in bursts only when needed; others are secreted continuously. Depending on the species, trail substances are produced by Dufour's gland, Pavan's gland or the poison glands; alarm substances are produced by the anal and mandibular glands. The glandular sources of other pheromones are unknown.

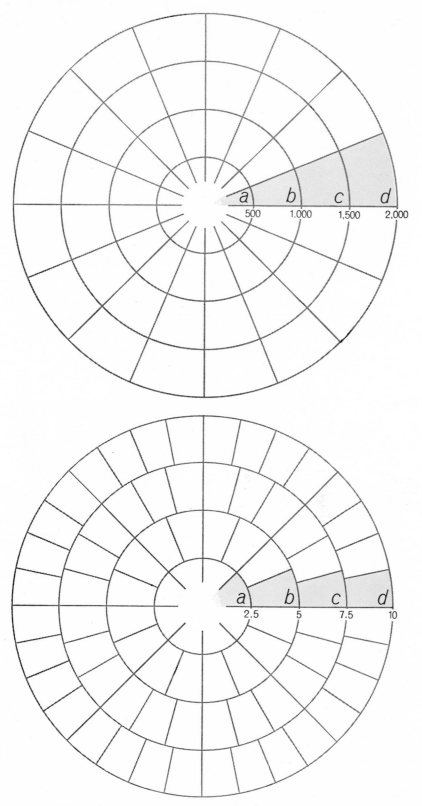

alarm spheres generated by individual ant workers were much wider and more durable, the colony would be kept in ceaseless and futile turmoil. As it is, local disturbances such as intrusions by foreign insects are dealt with quickly and efficiently by small groups of workers, and the excitement soon dies away.

The trail and alarm substances are only part of the ants' chemical vocabulary. There is evidence for the existence of other secretions that induce gathering and settling of workers, acts of grooming, food exchange, and other operations fundamental to the care of the queen and immature ants. Even dead ants produce a pheromone of sorts. An ant that has just died will be groomed by other workers as if it were still alive. Its complete immobility and crumpled posture by themselves cause no new response. But in a day or two chemical decomposition products accumulate and stimulate the workers to bear the corpse to the refuse pile outside the nest. Only a few decomposition products trigger this funereal response; they include certain long-chain fatty acids and their esters. When other objects, including living workers, are experimentally daubed with these substances, they are dutifully carried to the refuse pile. After being dumped on the refuse the "living dead" scramble to their feet and promptly return to the nest, only to be carried out again. The hapless creatures are thrown back on the refuse pile time and again until most of the scent of death has been worn off their bodies by the ritual.

Our observation of ant colonies over long periods has led us to believe that as few as 10 pheromones, transmitted singly or in simple combinations, might suffice for the total organization of ant society. The task of separating and characterizing these substances, as well as judging the roles of other kinds of stimuli such as sound, is a job largely for the future.

Even in animal species where other kinds of communication devices are prominently developed, deeper investigation usually reveals the existence of pheromonal communication as well. I have mentioned the auxiliary roles of primer pheromones in the lives of mice and migratory locusts. A more striking example is the communication system of the honeybee. The insect is celebrated for its employment of the "round" and "waggle" dances (augmented, perhaps, by auditory signals) to designate the location of food and new nest sites. It is not so widely known that chemical signals

**FORAGING INFORMATION** conveyed by two different insect communication systems can be represented on two similar "compass" diagrams. The honeybee "waggle dance" (*top*) transmits about four bits of information with respect to direction, enabling a honeybee worker to pinpoint a target within one of 16 equally probable angular sectors. The number of "bits" in this case remains independent of distance, given in meters. The pheromone system used by trail-laying fire ants (*bottom*) is superior in that the amount of directional information increases with distance, given in centimeters. At distances *c* and *d*, the probable sector in which the target lies is smaller for ants than for bees. (For ants, directional information actually increases gradually and not by jumps.) Both insects transmit two bits of distance information, specifying one of four equally probable distance ranges.

play equally important roles in other aspects of honeybee life. The mother queen regulates the reproductive cycle of the colony by secreting from her mandibular glands a substance recently identified as 9-ketodecanoic acid. When this pheromone is ingested by the worker bees, it inhibits development of their ovaries and also their ability to manufacture the royal cells in which new queens are reared. The same pheromone serves as a sex attractant in the queen's nuptial flights.

Under certain conditions, including the discovery of new food sources, worker bees release geraniol, a pleasant-smelling alcohol, from the abdominal Nassanoff glands. As the geraniol diffuses through the air it attracts other workers and so supplements information contained in the waggle dance. When a worker stings an intruder, it discharges, in addition to the venom, tiny amounts of a secretion from clusters of unicellular

glands located next to the basal plates of the sting. This secretion is responsible for the tendency, well known to bee-keepers, of angry swarms of workers to sting at the same spot. One component, which acts as a simple attractant, has been identified as isoamyl acetate, a compound that has a banana-like odor. It is possible that the stinging response is evoked by at least one unidentified alarm substance secreted along with the attractant.

Knowledge of pheromones has advanced to the point where one can make some tentative generalizations about their chemistry. In the first place, there appear to be good reasons why sex attractants should be compounds that contain between 10 and 17 carbon atoms and that have molecular weights between about 180 and 300—the range actually observed in attractants so far identified. (For comparison, the weight of a single

carbon atom is 12.) Only compounds of roughly this size or greater can meet the two known requirements of a sex attractant: narrow specificity, so that only members of one species will respond to it, and high potency. Compounds that contain fewer than five or so carbon atoms and that have a molecular weight of less than about 100 cannot be assembled in enough different ways to provide a distinctive molecule for all the insects that want to advertise their presence.

It also seems to be a rule, at least with insects, that attraction potency increases with molecular weight. In one series of esters tested on flies, for instance, a doubling of molecular weight resulted in as much as a thousandfold increase in efficiency. On the other hand, the molecule cannot be too large and complex or it will be prohibitively difficult for the insect to synthesize. An equally important limitation on size is

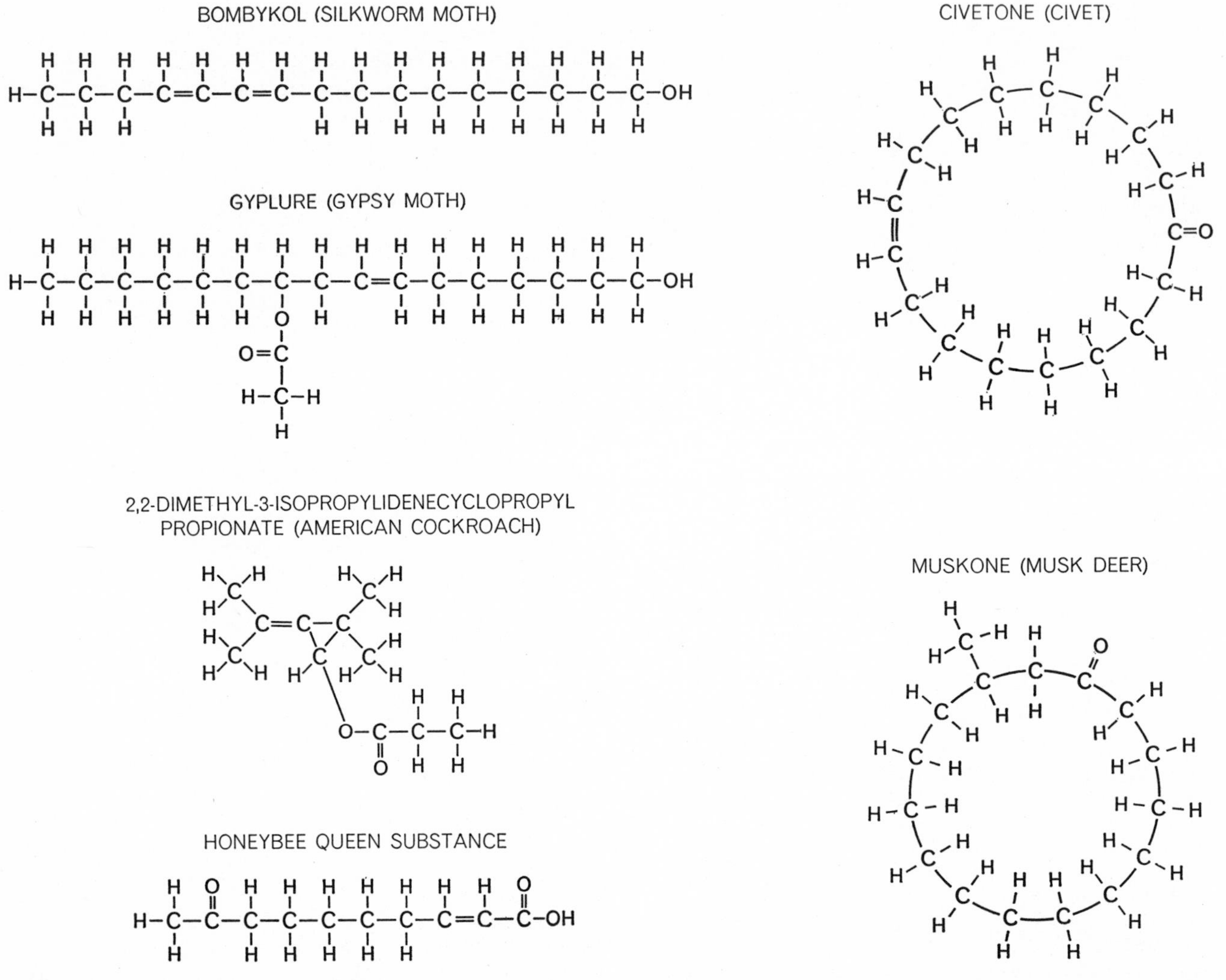

BOMBYKOL (SILKWORM MOTH)

GYPLURE (GYPSY MOTH)

2,2-DIMETHYL-3-ISOPROPYLIDENECYCLOPROPYL PROPIONATE (AMERICAN COCKROACH)

HONEYBEE QUEEN SUBSTANCE

CIVETONE (CIVET)

MUSKONE (MUSK DEER)

SIX SEX PHEROMONES include the identified sex attractants of four insect species as well as two mammalian musks generally believed to be sex attractants. The high molecular weight of most sex pheromones accounts for their narrow specificity and high potency.

the fact that volatility—and, as a result, diffusibility—declines with increasing molecular weight.

One can also predict from first principles that the molecular weight of alarm substances will tend to be less than those of the sex attractants. Among the ants there is little specificity; each species responds strongly to the alarm substances of other species. Furthermore, an alarm substance, which is used primarily within the confines of the nest, does not need the stimulative potency of a sex attractant, which must carry its message for long distances. For these reasons small molecules will suffice for alarm purposes. Of seven alarm substances known in the social insects, six have 10 or fewer carbon atoms and one (dendrolasin) has 15. It will be interesting to see if future discoveries bear out these early generalizations.

Do human pheromones exist? Primer pheromones might be difficult to detect, since they can affect the endocrine system without producing overt specific behavioral responses. About all that can be said at present is that striking sexual differences have been observed in the ability of humans to smell certain

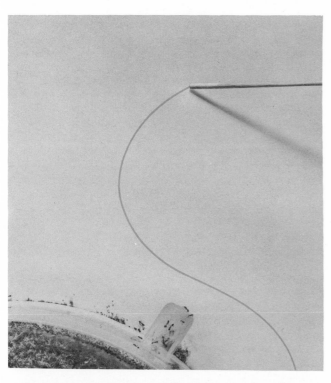

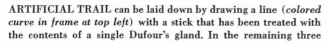

ARTIFICIAL TRAIL can be laid down by drawing a line (*colored curve in frame at top left*) with a stick that has been treated with the contents of a single Dufour's gland. In the remaining three frames, workers are attracted from the nest, follow the artificial route in close formation and mill about in confusion at its arbitrary terminus. Such a trail is not renewed by the unrewarded workers.

DENDROLASIN (*LASIUS FULIGINOSUS*)

CITRAL (*ATTA SEXDENS*)

CITRONELLAL (*ACANTHOMYOPS CLAVIGER*)

2-HEPTANONE (*IRIDOMYRMEX PRUINOSUS*)

**FOUR ALARM PHEROMONES, given off by the workers of the ant species indicated, have so far been identified. Disturbing stimuli trigger the release of these substances from various glandular reservoirs.**

substances. The French biologist J. Le-Magnen has reported that the odor of Exaltolide, the synthetic lactone of 14-hydroxytetradecanoic acid, is perceived clearly only by sexually mature females and is perceived most sharply at about the time of ovulation. Males and young girls were found to be relatively insensitive, but a male subject became more sensitive following an injection of estrogen. Exaltolide is used commercially as a perfume fixative. LeMagnen also reported that the ability of his subjects to detect the odor of certain steroids paralleled that of their ability to smell Exaltolide. These observations hardly represent a case for the existence of human pheromones, but they do suggest that the relation of odors to human physiology can bear further examination.

It is apparent that knowledge of chemical communication is still at an early stage. Students of the subject are in the position of linguists who have learned the meaning of a few words of a nearly indecipherable language. There is almost certainly a large chemical vocabulary still to be discovered. Conceiv-

ably some pheromone "languages" will be found to have a syntax. It may be found, in other words, that pheromones can be combined in mixtures to form new meanings for the animals employing them. One would also like to know if some animals can modulate the intensity or pulse frequency of pheromone emission to create new messages. The solution of these and other interesting problems will require new techniques in analytical organic chemistry combined with ever more perceptive studies of animal behavior.

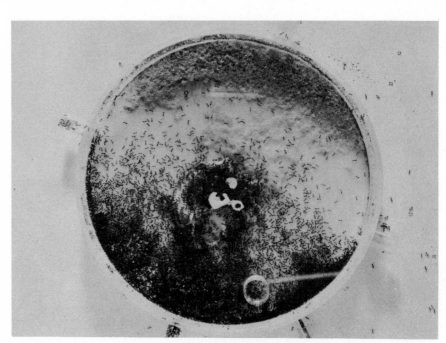

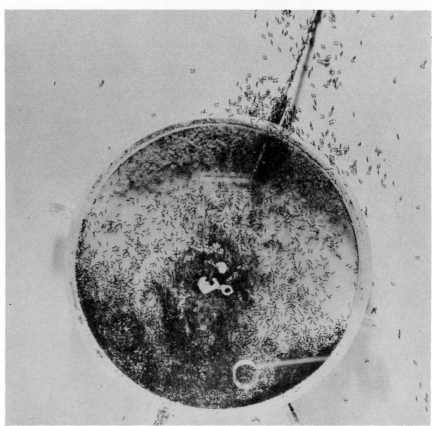

**MASSIVE DOSE of trail pheromone causes the migration of a large portion of a fire ant colony from one side of a nest to another. The pheromone is administered on a stick that has been dipped in a solution extracted from the Dufour's glands of freshly killed workers.**

# 20 Sound Communication in Honeybees

ADRIAN M. WENNER · April 1964

Can we ever fully understand how the members of another species communicate with one another? The question has been given a new implication by the recent proposals that we listen for messages from the planets of other stars. Whether we ever detect such messages or not, we can investigate the question here on earth. We now know of many forms of communication in other species. None is subtler or more interesting than the "language" of the honeybee.

It is no accident that Karl von Frisch of the University of Munich chose the bee for his now famous investigations of animal communication. A honeybee colony is a marvelously compact community of some 50,000 individuals; it takes care of itself and usually ignores its human investigator; its members are highly social and could not survive without constant intercommunication, and the more one looks into their methods of conversation, the more remarkable they are found to be.

The obvious features of honeybee communication have been reported widely and are now a familiar story. When a foraging bee finds a source of food, it flies back to the hive and conveys to its fellows the distance and direction of the source. In the course of doing so it performs on the vertical surface of the comb a waggling "dance" in which its abdomen traces a figure eight. The orientation and rate of the dance, it has been supposed, tells the location of the food source. This hypothesis runs into an awkward difficulty: the interior of most hives is so dark that the bees probably cannot see the dance. Investigators of the phenomenon have found, however, that the bees follow the dance by means of their antennae, which touch the dancer's body.

Robert C. King of Servomechanisms,

Inc., and I, working in my laboratory at the University of California at Santa Barbara, looked into the question further. The dancing bee traces the figure eight with the tip of its abdomen. That is not, however, the part of the body on which the observing bees usually concentrate their attention: their antennae tend to rest on the dancer's thorax. Does the thorax also describe a figure eight during the dance? We marked foraging bees with a spot of white paint on the thorax and later photographed its movement during the course of the dance in the hive by means of a series of rapid-flash exposures. The pictures showed that the thorax did not describe a figure-eight pattern [see lower illustration on page 175].

The dance pattern itself, then, can hardly convey an unequivocal message. What can? Using a tape recorder, I had discovered that during the dance the bee emitted a peculiar sound at the low frequency of 250 cycles per second. This sound was made while the bee was waggling along in the straight run of its dance. It suggested a surprising new outlook on the whole problem. Perhaps the honeybee communicated with its fellows not only by the dance movement but also by sound signals!

To test this possibility I made tape recordings of the sounds made by dancing bees after they had visited dishes of sugar syrup placed at different distances from the hive. Would the sound patterns show a relation to the distance traveled? In other words, did the foraging bee tell its hivemates the distance by means of a sound language?

Analyzed with the sound spectrograph, the sounds proved to be made up of trains, each train being further broken into pulses with a frequency of about 32 per second [see top illustration

on page 177]. The bee emitted a train of sound during each straight run of its waggling dance. A careful analysis showed that the average length of the sound trains during a given dance (and also the average number of pulses in a train) was directly proportional to the distance the bee had traveled to the food source [see bottom illustration on page 177]. The correlation was so good that it seems altogether likely—certainly as likely as any other proposed mechanism—that the bee reports the distance by means of this sound language.

How is the sound produced? The first and most obvious guess was that the bee might create the pulses of sound with the waggling of its abdomen. To resolve this question I attached a small piece of cellophane to a microphone and placed the microphone so that with each waggle the dancing bee would tap the cellophane. The sound pulses proved to be about two and a half times more frequent than the waggling taps, so it became clear that the sound could not be arising from the waggling. Harald Esch, now at the University of Munich, who independently had discovered the honeybee's dance sound at about the same time as I had, also demonstrated that it was not produced by the waggling. Instead of a cellophane-and-microphone device, he used the ingenious method of attaching a small magnet to the bee's abdomen; as the bee moved the magnet it generated a fluctuating electric voltage that was recorded simultaneously with the pulsed sound, so that the waggle and pulse rates could be compared.

The function of the sound train was illuminated by considering the question of whether or not the bee's judgment of distances is affected by the wind. Analysis of the sound-train records showed that it is to some extent. When

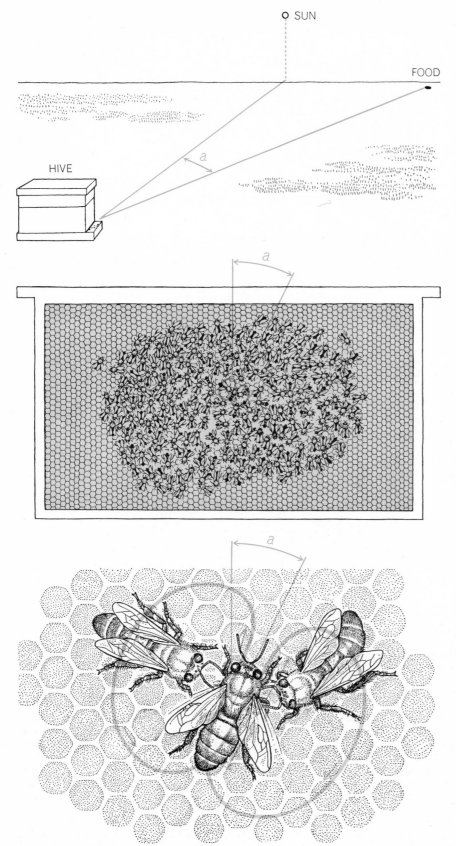

SUN

FOOD

HIVE

*a*

*a*

*a*

**FORAGING BEE** must transmit to its hivemates information about the distance from the hive to the food source (*top drawing*) and the angle (*a*) between the direction of the source and the direction of the sun. It does a dance on the honeycomb in which its abdomen describes a kind of figure eight (*middle*). The "straight run" (*A*) of the dance (*bottom*) has a duration proportional to the distance to the food, and it is oriented at an angle from the vertical equal to angle *a*. "Recruit" bees track the dancer's side with their antennae.

a bee flies to a source of food against the wind, the sound trains indicating the distance tend to be a little longer than when it does not buck a wind. The deviation from the true distance is not nearly so much, however, as one might expect on the basis of the wind velocity. A possible explanation is that the bee adjusts its flying efforts to the wind so that it always flies at about the same ground speed; thus, whatever the wind velocity, it can still use the elapsed time of travel to a goal as the measure of its distance. I measured the flight speed of bees under various wind conditions and found that they do tend to fly at a constant ground speed. For example, flying against a wind of five meters per second (about 11 miles per hour) bees are slowed by only about a fourth of that amount. They minimize the wind effect by flying closer to the ground. When the wind is too strong (more than 13 miles per hour), the bees simply stay in the hive.

We may conclude, then, that the foraging bee's communication to its fellows in the hive is made up of two elements: the dance and the accompanying sounds. The angle of the dance from the vertical is correlated with the angle between the food source and the overhead sun, and the length of the train of sound during the straight run of the dance tells the distance. This may not be the whole story, however. Some current experiments indicate, for instance, a strong correlation between the rate of pulse production and the strength of the sugar concentration in a food source. It may conceivably turn out that the foraging bee's entire message is carried by sound signals.

The sound spectrograph's indication of regularity and precision in the bee's dance sounds naturally drew attention to other forms of bee "talk." As everyone knows, the bee is a rather noisy animal. Even its buzz in flight, however, is not just noise. The buzz has modulations and variations. When bees begin to swarm, an experienced beekeeper can detect the event by the sound alone, even though he may be surrounded by other buzzing bees from hundreds of hives. When an individual bee is aroused to attack, its buzz rises in pitch and fluctuates in intensity. And recordings within the hive show that bees in the hive make at least 10 distinctly different sounds, some of which have already been related to specific activities.

Two of these sounds are particularly

noticeable. One, known as the characteristic hum of a beehive, is produced by the "ventilating" worker bees: bees that stand anchored on the comb or some other structure in the hive and create currents of air by beating their wings. This sound, varying in intensity, has a basic frequency of 250 cycles per second and often has strong overtones. It is usually much louder than the buzz of a flying bee, undoubtedly because the sound emitted by the ventilating bee is enhanced by the resonant vibra-

tion of the structure on which it is standing.

The other type of loud sound in the hive is heard when the hive is disturbed. When an intruder—for example an ant—approaches, the bees guarding the hive rock forward on their legs and issue a short burst of sound; they may go on repeating these warning bursts every two or three seconds for 10 minutes or more. When the hive is jarred, the collective reaction of hundreds of guarding bees is heard as a sharp, loud

buzz. This is followed shortly by a "piping" of workers throughout the hive, which consists of faint beeps at half-second intervals, the sound being a complex one with a fundamental frequency of 500 cycles per second. The piping goes on for several minutes. Apparently it serves to soothe the hive; it has been found that a recording of such piping, played to the hive, will quickly quiet the disturbed bees.

The most interesting of all the hive sounds, however, is the piping of the

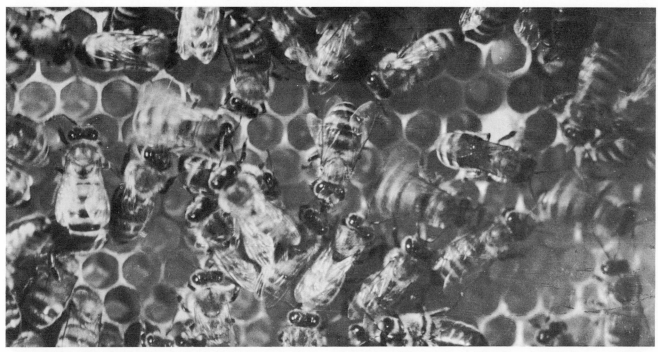

DANCING BEES and recruits are seen in this photograph. There are three dancers, or foragers (blurred images), heading to the right in a diagonal line starting near the upper left corner. The

dancer nearest the left has a recruit on each side, the center one has two recruits on its right and the bee at the right, apparently nearing the end of its straight run, has a recruit at its right rear.

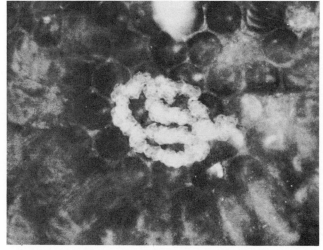

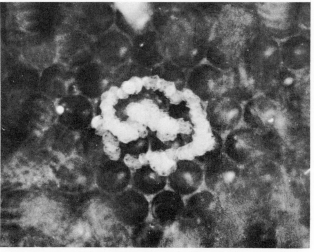

DANCE PATTERN described by the bee's thorax is not a well-defined figure eight with a distinctive straight run. This suggests that recruits would have difficulty gaining information by follow-

ing the dance movements alone. To make these pictures Robert C. King and the author put a spot of white paint on the thorax of foragers and then photographed their dances by repetitive flash.

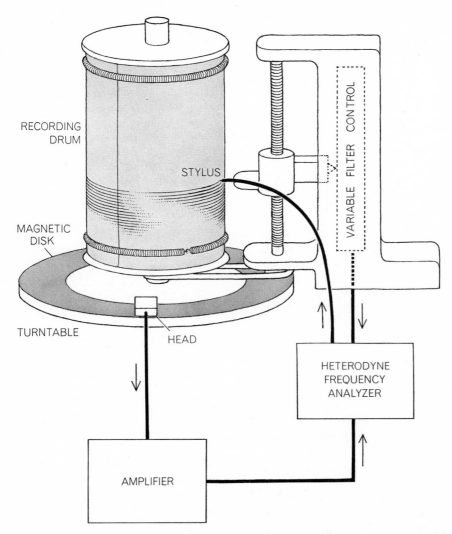

RECORDING
DRUM

STYLUS

VARIABLE FILTER CONTROL

MAGNETIC
DISK

TURNTABLE

HEAD

HETERODYNE
FREQUENCY
ANALYZER

AMPLIFIER

**BEE SOUNDS** are analyzed by a sound spectrograph. A short segment of a bee sound, recorded in the field, is transferred to the magnetic disk and then repeatedly sampled as the disk rotates with the recording drum. The stylus is a wire from which an electric spark passes to the drum, etching the recording paper. As the stylus rises, its position regulates the filter control so that the frequency analyzer extracts the proper frequency from the total sound, which is broken into a frequency "spectrum" changing with time.

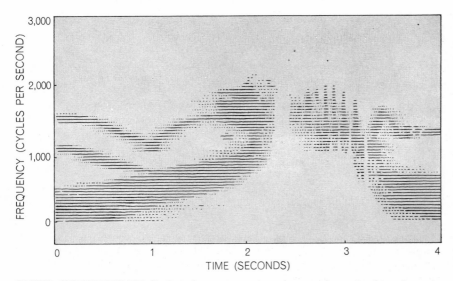

**SOUND SPECTROGRAM** displays frequency against time as shown in this schematic tracing. The amplitude of the signal components is indicated by the darkness of the trace.

queen. Naturalists have long known that queens inside the hive emit two kinds of sound, called "tooting" and "quacking." A close analysis of these sounds and the circumstances of their emission now provides the strongest evidence that bees use sound to convey specific messages.

Tooting is the regal identification of a virgin queen soon after she has emerged from the cell in which she developed. A hive cannot tolerate more than one queen at a time. In a hive that lacks a queen several queen-bearing cells develop simultaneously in a comb, but one matures earlier than the others. Once this queen has emerged, has hardened and has become steady on her legs, she proceeds to visit other queen cells, tear them open and sting to death their potential but not yet mature queens. Often, however, the worker bees do not allow her to dispose of all her potential rivals in this way; they bar her from some of the cells. She then begins to toot and continues to do so day and night, perhaps for a week or more. Her tooting rises in intensity and sometimes can be heard more than 10 feet from the hive.

Meanwhile the maturing queen bees still in cells try to get out their turn. The worker bees hold them back, however; as fast as one of them opens the cap of her cell the workers push it back in place and glue it shut. Thereupon the imprisoned queens also start to pipe, but in a different pattern and at a lower tone than the free queen. The workers let out some of these quackers, but only one at a time. The reigning queen and the newly released rival then battle until one is killed. Sometimes the series of fights between the survivor and the new rivals goes on until only one queen is left. This survivor, still a virgin, then flies away from the hive to mate successively with several drones (on the wing) and returns to begin laying eggs.

All this has been studied in hives set up for detailed observation. The tooting and the quacking have also been recorded and analyzed spectrographically. The pattern of the first turns out to be a long toot (lasting one second) followed by several shorter toots. Its fundamental frequency is 500 cycles per second, and this is overlaid with overtones that are varied considerably in emphasis, just as they are in human speech [see "Attention and the Perception of Speech," by Donald E. Broadbent; SCIENTIFIC AMERICAN offprint 467]. The quack differs from the toot in two ways: it has a lower fundamental frequency and it begins with short sounds instead of a drawn-out one.

Do the tooting and the quacking say different things to the bees? We investigated this question with a set of controlled experiments. First we recorded the tooting of a free, reigning queen in its hive. Analysis with the sound spectrograph showed that this tooting put the major emphasis on the third harmonic. We therefore mimicked this harmonic with an oscillator and played it in the same tooting pattern (a long toot followed by several short ones) in a second hive that contained a free queen and a caged one. To each sounding of the artificial toots the caged queen almost invariably responded by quacking [*see upper two illustrations on page 180*]. We then tried varying the frequency of the tone, while keeping the long-toot-short-toot pattern constant. Within a wide frequency range (600 to 2,000 cycles per second) the change in frequency seemed to make little difference: the queen still responded with quacks as long as the typical pattern of toots was the same. On the other hand, when we played the quacking pattern, the caged queen did not respond at all.

There is not much doubt that the tooting and the quacking represent certain messages. What do the messages say, and what functions do they serve? A reasonable working hypothesis is that (1) the tooting announces the presence of a free queen in the hive, (2) the quacking reports the presence of challengers ready and yearning to be freed from their cells and (3) all this information guides the worker bees. One queen tooting and others quacking means that there is just one free queen, and a quacker (but not more than one) may be released to challenge her. This procedure will result in the rapid killing off of all but one of the contenders, but that may be to the good; it will enable the hive to settle down quickly to a peaceful regime. Occasionally, however, particularly in the spring, a virgin queen or an older egg-laying queen may leave the hive permanently, taking along half of the adult bees, in the phenomenon called swarming. In the swarming season, therefore, it is essential to have a queen in reserve when the free queen departs; a quacking queen may represent survival for the hive and is not to be released until the swarm has left.

We must come back now to the important questions: How does the bee produce sounds, and how does it

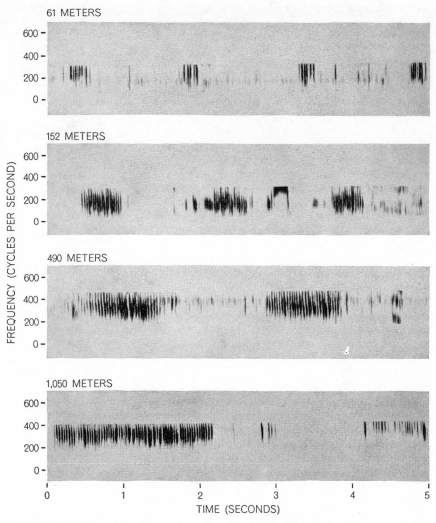

**SPECTROGRAMS** analyze the sound produced by forager bees during the dance. Sound trains are produced during the straight run; blank or light areas mark remainder of figure eight. The length of the sound train increases with the distance to the source of nectar.

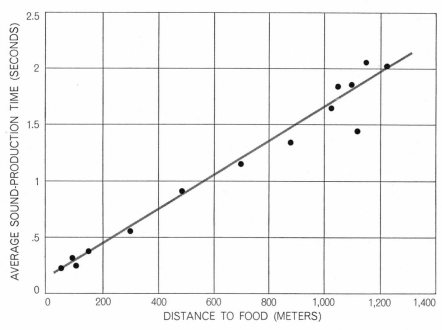

**DIRECT CORRELATION** is shown between the sound-production time and the distance the bee had just traveled to obtain food. Each point is an average for several dancing bees.

EFFECT OF SOUND on bees in a hive is illustrated by these photographs made by the author. Bees are normally in constant motion, but they quiet down at the sound of "piping," a beeping tone produced by workers. The normal motion is shown by the blurred images in the top photograph, which was made at a fifth of a second. When piping was simulated and transmitted to the hive wall by a vibrator, the bees became almost motionless, as shown by bottom photograph, made at the same aperture and speed.

perceive them? As to the production of sound, four hypotheses have been put forward, and the answer is still not clear.

The most interesting suggestion is that the bee makes its sounds by ejecting air through its spiracles: the breathing openings in the side of its body. On purely theoretical grounds it is quite plausible that the insect could produce the observed sounds by a whistling or a bagpipe effect. But recent experiments in our laboratory and also by other investigators generally negate this theory. For one thing, if helium is substituted for nitrogen in the air in which the bee produces its sounds, this does not change the frequency of the sound; if the spiracle theory is correct, it should, because the density of a gas affects the frequency of the sound produced by vibrating a column of the gas. For another thing, it has been found that the

sounds of a piping queen do not always coincide with accordion-like movements of its abdomen, so that its abdominal spiracles cannot be producing the sound. Finally, James Simpson of the Rothamsted Experimental Station in England has shown by delicate spiracle-blocking experiments that the bee's thoracic spiracles play no part in sound production.

The other possibilities are that the bee produces sound by vibrating its wings or the sclerites (hard plates) at the base of its wings or the entire surface of the upper part of its body. Simpson and I and others have been investigating these possibilities. At the moment the wing-vibration theory seems to be the most promising.

Until recently this idea was rejected on two grounds: that a bee's wings are too small to produce sounds of the fre-

quencies and intensities heard, and that experimenters who have clipped the wings have not found that this changed the intensity of the bee's piping. The second idea is simply wrong; careful experiments show that clipping the wings does affect the bee's sound-making. It raises the frequency and reduces the intensity of the sound, and the change is proportional to the amount of wing removed [*see bottom illustration on page 180*]. It appears, therefore, that wing vibration is responsible at least for amplification, and probably for production, of the bee's sounds. It is hoped that experiments now under way will answer the question more definitely.

Other recent studies have shed some light on how bees "hear" sound. In the experiments in which artificial tooting was played to a caged queen it was found that the queen responded only when the sound was transmitted via a vibrator attached to the hive; when it was transmitted through the air, even with the vibrator suspended close to the bee, she did not respond at all [*see second illustration from top on page 180*]. Similarly, worker bees show no reaction to piping when it is airborne. On the other hand, a disturbed hive can be quickly quieted by drawing a wet finger along the observation window, which causes a squeaking sound that arises from vibration of the glass. All these observations indicate that the bees receive sound through their legs from the vibrating structure on which they stand. Quite possibly they have receiving organs for sound on their legs below the knee.

There is also evidence that they receive sound through their antennae. Eleanor H. Slifer of the University of Iowa has found that each bee antenna has thousands of "plate organs" that are remarkably like the larger tympanic (eardrum-like) organs of other insects. She has established that these plate organs are not permeable to chemicals that might be used for communication. Although this finding does not eliminate the possibility that these organs are chemoreceptors, there is now good reason to entertain the notion that they do respond to mechanical stimuli. Charles Walcott of Harvard University has made some experimental findings that support this view: he discovered that vibrations transmitted to a bee's antennae caused electrical impulses to be generated in the antennal nerves.

Conceivably the honeybee receives sound both through its legs and through its antennae. Thus it may receive a

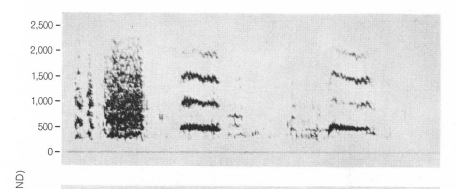
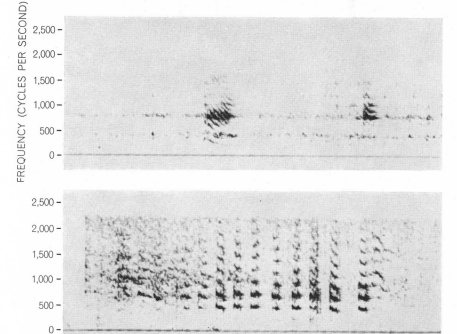

WORKER SOUNDS are shown in these spectrograms. The top tracing illustrates two sounds produced when a hive is disturbed: the sharp burst of a disturbed worker (*left*), followed by two faint beeps, or worker piping. The middle and bottom tracings show "croaking" and "bipping," two sounds that have yet to be related to any specific activity.

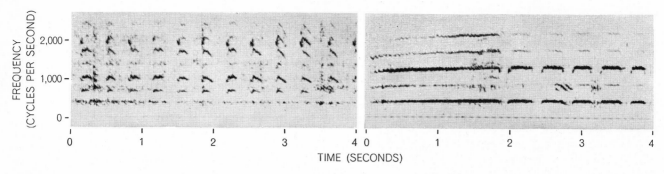

QUEEN PIPING includes "quacking" and "tooting." A queen in her cell produces quacking (*left*), a series of short pulses with emphasis on several harmonics. Once free in the hive a queen produces tooting (*right*), which begins with a long wail, has a somewhat higher fundamental frequency and usually emphasizes frequencies not simultaneously emphasized by quacking queens.

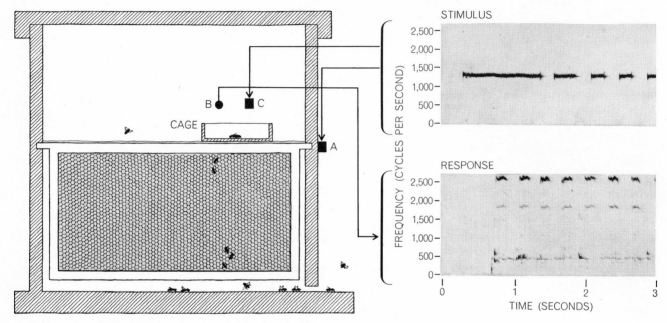

TOOTING was simulated (*upper tracing*) and played to a caged queen via a vibrator touching the hive (*A*). It elicited from the queen a response that was picked up by a microphone (*B*) and analyzed as quacking (*lower tracing*). When the tooting vibrator was suspended above the queen (*C*), there was no response, indicating that the queen perceived sound via the hive structure.

sound communication from another bee directly by touching the other bee's body with its antennae—as evidently occurs during the foraging bee's dance in the hive. The double receiving system would have a great advantage for bees in a noisy hive: in spite of the din of piping, which they apparently receive through their legs from the hive's vibrations, they would still be able to perceive the faint dance sounds by touching the dancer with their antennae.

Listening to the sounds of bees, recording them, analyzing them and designing experiments to explore their meaning, one cannot help feeling that much of this is akin to the problem of communicating with beings on another planet. With bees we have the advantage of being able to study them here and now.

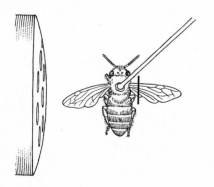

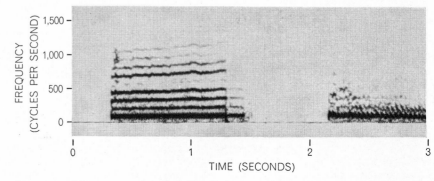

RELATION OF WING to sound production was demonstrated by severing most of two wings of a bee (*left*). Comparison with the sound produced by the intact animal (*center*) showed that loss of wing area reduced the intensity and changed the harmonics (*right*).

# 21 The Curious Behavior of the Stickleback

N. TINBERGEN · December 1952

WHEN I was a young lecturer in zoology at the University of Leyden 20 years ago, I was asked to organize a laboratory course in animal behavior for undergraduates. In my quest for animals that could be used for such a purpose, I remembered the sticklebacks I had been accustomed as a boy to catch in the ditches near my home and to raise in a backyard aquarium. It seemed that they might be ideal laboratory animals. They could be hauled in numbers out of almost every ditch; they were tame and hardy and small enough to thrive in a tank no larger than a hatbox.

I soon discovered that in choosing these former pets I had struck oil. They are so tame that they submit unfrightened to laboratory experiments, for the stickleback, like the hedgehog, depends on its spines for protection and is little disturbed by handling. Furthermore, the stickleback turned out to be an excellent subject for studying innate behavior, which it displays in some remarkably dramatic and intriguing ways. We found it to be the most reliable of various experimental animals that we worked with (including newts, bees, water insects and birds), and it became the focus of a program of research in which we now use hundreds of sticklebacks each year. The stickleback today is also a popular subject in various other zoological laboratories in Europe, notably at the universities in Groningen and Oxford. To us this little fish is what the rat is to many American psychologists.

My collaborator J. van Iersel and I have concentrated on the stickleback's courtship and reproductive behavior. The sex life of the three-spined stickleback (*Gasterosteus aculeatus*) is a complicated pattern, purely instinctive and automatic, which can be observed and manipulated almost at will.

In nature sticklebacks mate in early spring in shallow fresh waters. The mating cycle follows an unvarying ritual, which can be seen equally well in the natural habitat or in our tanks. First each male leaves the school of fish and stakes out a territory for itself, from which it will drive any intruder, male or female. Then it builds a nest. It digs a shallow pit in the sand bottom, carrying the sand away mouthful by mouthful. When this depression is about two inches square, it piles in a heap of weeds, preferably thread algae, coats the material with a sticky substance from its kidneys and shapes the weedy mass into a mound with its snout. It then bores a tunnel in the mound by wriggling through it. The tunnel, slightly shorter than an adult fish, is the nest.

Having finished the nest, the male suddenly changes color. Its normally inconspicuous gray coloring had already begun to show a faint pink blush on the chin and a greenish gloss on the back and in the eyes. Now the pink becomes a bright red and the back turns a bluish white.

IN THIS colorful, conspicuous dress the male at once begins to court females. They, in the meantime, have also become ready to mate: their bodies have grown shiny and bulky with 50 to 100 large eggs. Whenever a female enters the male's territory, he swims toward her in a series of zigzags—first a sideways turn away from her, then a quick movement toward her. After each advance the male stops for an instant and then performs another zigzag. This dance continues until the female takes notice and swims toward the male in a curious head-up posture. He then turns and swims rapidly toward the nest, and she follows. At the nest the male makes a series of rapid thrusts with his snout into the entrance. He turns on his side

as he does so and raises his dorsal spines toward his mate. Thereupon, with a few strong tail beats, she enters the nest and rests there, her head sticking out from one end and her tail from the other. The male now prods her tail base with rhythmic thrusts, and this causes her to lay her eggs. The whole courtship and egg-laying ritual takes only about one minute. As soon as she has laid her eggs, the female slips out of the nest. The male then glides in quickly to fertilize the clutch. After that he chases the female away and goes looking for another partner.

One male may escort three, four or even five females through the nest, fertilizing each patch of eggs in turn. Then his mating impulse subsides, his color darkens and he grows increasingly hostile to females. Now he guards the nest from predators and "fans" water over the eggs with his breast fins to enrich their supply of oxygen and help them to hatch. Each day the eggs need more oxygen and the fish spends more time ventilating them. The ventilating reaches a climax just before the eggs hatch. For a day or so after the young emerge the father keeps the brood together, pursuing each straggler and bringing it back in his mouth. Soon the young sticklebacks become independent and associate with the young of other broods.

TO GET light on the behavior of man, particularly his innate drives and conflicts, it is often helpful to study the elements of behavior in a simple animal. Here is a little fish that exhibits a complicated pattern of activities, all dependent on simple stimuli and drives. We have studied and analyzed its behavior by a large number of experiments, and have learned a good deal about why the stickleback behaves as it does.

Let us begin with the stimulus that

**IN FIRST STAGE** of courtship the male stickleback (*left*) zigzags toward the female (*right*). The female then swims toward him with her head up. The abdomen of the female bulges with from 50 to 100 eggs.

**IN SECOND STAGE,** seen from above, the male stickleback swims toward the nest he has built and makes a series of thrusts into it with his snout. He also turns on his side and raises his dorsal spines toward the female.

causes one stickleback to attack another. Early in our work we noticed that a male patrolling its territory would attack a red-colored intruder much more aggressively than a fish of some other color. Even a red mail van passing our windows at a distance of 100 yards could make the males in the tank charge its glass side in that direction. To investigate the reactions to colors we made a number of rough models of sticklebacks and painted some of the dummies red, some pale silver, some green. We rigged them up on thin wires and presented them one by one to the males in the tank. We found that the red models were always more provoking than the others, though even the silvery or green intruders caused some hostility.

In much the same way we tested the influence of shape, size, type of body movement and other stimuli, relating them to specific behavior in nest building, courting, attack, zigzag, fanning and so on. We discovered, for example, that a male swollen with food was courted as if it were a female.

As our work proceeded, we saw that the effective stimuli differed from one reaction to another, even when two reactions were caused by the same object. Thus a female will follow a red model wherever it leads; she will even make frantic efforts to enter a non-existent nest wherever the model is poked into the sand. Once she is in a real nest, she can be induced to spawn merely by prodding the base of her tail with a glass rod, even after she has seen the red fish that led her there removed. At one moment the male must give the visual signal of red; at the next, this stimulus is of no importance and only the tactile sensation counts. This observation led us to conclude that the stickleback responds simply to "sign stimuli," *i.e.*, to a few characteristics of an object rather than to the object as a whole. A red fish or a red mail truck, a thrusting snout or a glass rod—it is the signal, not the object, that counts. A similar dependence on sign stimuli, which indicates the existence of special central nervous mechanisms, has been found in other species. It seems to be typical of innate behavior, and many social relationships in animals apparently are based on a system of signs.

Sticklebacks will respond to our stimuli only when they are in breeding

**IN THIRD STAGE**, also seen from above, the female swims into the nest. The male then prods the base of her tail and causes her to lay her eggs. When the female leaves the nest, the male enters and fertilizes the eggs.

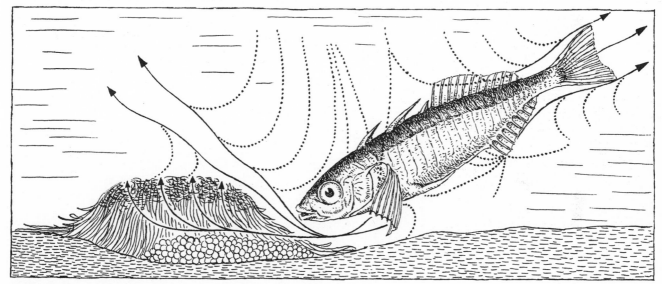

**IN FOURTH STAGE** the male "fans" water over the eggs to enrich their oxygen supply. The dotted lines show the movement of a colored solution placed in the tank; the solid lines, the direction of the water currents.

condition. At other seasons they ignore the signs. This fact led us to investigate the internal factors that govern the fish. The obvious way to study such fluctuations is to measure the frequency and intensity of a response under standard stimulation. For some of these tests we used either uniform models or live fish confined in glass tubes so that we could control their movement. To measure the parental drive we adopted the standard of the number of seconds spent in fanning a given number of eggs per time unit.

The stickleback's drives in the breeding sequence wax and wane in a series of cycles. Each drive runs its course in regular succession: first the male gets the urge to fight, then to build a nest, then to court a female, then to develop the brood. He will not start to build, even though material is available, until he has defended his territory for a while. Nor will he court until he has built the nest; females that approach him before the nest is finished are driven off or at best are greeted with a few zigzags. Within each cycle also there is a fixed rhythm and sequence; for example, if you fill up the pit the male has dug, he will dig one again before collecting nest material. After the pit has been filled several times, however, the fish will build the nest without completing the pit. The development of his inner drive overcomes outside interference.

It seems likely that the rise and fall of inner drives is controlled by hormonal changes, and we are now studying the effects on these drives of castrating and giving hormones to the males. One interesting finding so far is that castration abolishes the first phases of mating, but has no effect on the parental drive. A eunuch stickleback, when given a nest of eggs, ventilates it with abandon.

IN ANY animal the innate drives themselves are only the elementary forces of behavior. It is the interaction among those drives, giving rise to conflicts, that shapes the animal's actual behavior, and we have devoted a major part of our work with the stickleback to this subject. It struck us, as it has often struck observers of other animals, that the belligerent male sticklebacks spent little time in actual fighting. Much of their hostility consists of display. The threat display of male sticklebacks is of two types. When two males meet at the border of their territories, they begin a series of attacks and retreats. Each takes the offensive in his own territory, and the duel seesaws back and forth across the border. Neither fish touches the other; the two dart back and forth as though attached by an invisible thread. This behavior demonstrates that the tendency to attack and the tendency to retreat are both aroused in each fish.

When the fight grows in vigor, however, the seesaw maneuver may suddenly change into something quite different. Each fish adopts an almost vertical head-down posture, turns its side to its opponent, raises its ventral spines and makes jerky movements with the whole body. Under crowded conditions, when territories are small and the fighting tendency is intense, both fish begin to dig into the sand, as if they were starting to build a nest! This observation at first astonished us. Digging is so irrelevant to the fighting stimulus that it seemed to overthrow all our ideas about the specific connection between sign and response. But it became less mysterious when we considered similar instances of incongruous behavior by other animals. Fighting starlings always preen themselves between bouts; in the midst of a fight roosters often peck at the ground as though feeding, and wading-birds assume a sleeping posture. Even a man, in situations of embarrassment, conflict or stress, will scratch himself behind the ear.

So it appears that the stickleback does not start digging because its nest-building drive is suddenly activated. Rather, the fish is engaging in what a psychologist would call a "displacement activity." Alternating between the urge to attack and to escape, neither of which it can carry out, it finally is driven by its tension to find an outlet in an irrelevant action.

THE THEORY of displacement activity has been tested by the following experiment. We place a red model in a male's territory and, when the fish attacks, beat it as hard as we can with its supposed antagonist. This unexpected behavior causes the fish to flee and hide in the weeds. From that shelter it glares at the intruder. Its flight impulse gradually subsides and its attack drive rises. After a few minutes the fish emerges from shelter and cautiously approaches the model. Then, just at the moment when attack and retreat are evenly balanced, it suddenly adopts the head-down posture.

A similar interaction of drives seems to motivate the male when he is courting. In the zigzag dance the movement away from the female is the purely sexual movement of leading; the movement toward her is an incipient attack. This duality can be proved by measur-

**MALE STICKLEBACK** (*Gasterosteus aculeatus*) is photographed in full sexual markings. Its underside is a bright vermilion; its eyes, blue.

**MALE STICKLEBACK DIGS** in the sand after it has perceived its image in a mirror. This is one aspect of its behavior during a fight with another male.

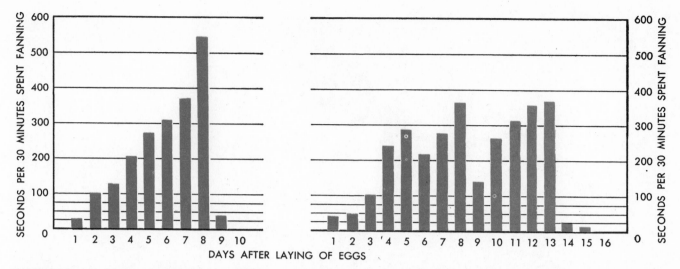

**FANNING OF EGGS** by the male stickleback follows a predictable pattern, as shown by the graph at the left. The fish spends more and more time fanning from the first day until the eighth. By the tenth day it has stopped fanning altogether. The graph at the right shows what happened when the eggs were removed on the sixth day and replaced with a fresh batch. The fanning pattern began anew, but the fanning time on the sixth day was still longer than that on the first. This suggested that fanning is controlled by internal as well as external factors.

ing the comparative intensity of the two drives in an individual male and relating it to his dance. Thus when the sex drive is strong (as measured by willingness to lead a standard female model) the zig component of the dance is pronounced and may shift to complete leading. When the fighting drive is strong (as measured by the number of bites aimed at a standard male model) the zag is more emphatic and may become a straightforward attack. A female evokes the double response because she provides sign stimuli for both aggression and sexuality. Every fish entering a male's territory evokes some degree of attack, and therefore even a big-bellied female must produce a hostile as well as a sexual response.

This complexity of drives continues when the fish have arrived at the nest. A close study of the movement by which the male indicates the entrance shows that it is very similar to fanning, at that moment an entirely irrelevant response. This fanning motion, we conclude, must be a displacement activity, caused by the fact that the male is not yet able to release his sex drive; he can ejaculate his sperm only after the female has laid her eggs. Even when the female has entered the nest, the male's drive is still frustrated. Before he can release it, he must stimulate her to spawn. The "quivering" motion with which he prods her is much like fanning. It, too, is a displacement activity and stops at the moment when the eggs are laid and the male can fertilize them. It is probable that the male's sex drive is frustrated not only by the absence of eggs but also by a strong conflict with the attack drive, which must be intense when a strange fish is so near the nest. This hostility is evident from the fact that the male raises his dorsal spines while exhibiting the nest to the female.

The ideas briefly outlined here seem to throw considerable light on the complicated and "irrelevant" activities typical of innate behavior in various animals. Of course these ideas have to be checked in more cases. This is now being done, particularly with fish and birds, and the results are encouraging.

I AM often asked whether it is worth while to stick to one animal species for so long a time as we have been studying the stickleback. The question has two answers. I believe that one should not confine one's work entirely to a single species. No one who does can wholly avoid thinking that his animal is The Animal, the perfect representative of the whole animal kingdom. Yet the many years of work on the stickleback, tedious as much of it has been, has been highly rewarding. Without such prolonged study we could not have gained a general understanding of its entire behavior pattern. That, in turn, is essential for an insight into a number of important problems. For instance, the aggressive component in courtship could never have been detected by a study of courtship alone, but only by the simultaneous study of fighting and courtship. Displacement activities are important for an understanding of an animal's motivation. To recognize them, one must have studied the parts of the behavior from which they are "borrowed" as well as the drives which, when blocked, use them as outlets. Furthermore, the mere observation and description of the stickleback's movements has benefited from our long study. Observation improves remarkably when the same thing is seen again and again.

Concentration on the stickleback has also been instructive to us because it meant turning away for a while from the traditional laboratory animals. A stickleback is different from a rat. Its behavior is much more purely innate and much more rigid. Because of its relative simplicity, it shows some phenomena more clearly than the behavior of any mammal can. The dependence on sign stimuli, the specificity of motivation, the interaction between two types of motivation with the resulting displacement activities are some of these phenomena.

Yet we also study other animals, because only by comparison can we find out what is of general significance and what is a special case. One result that is now beginning to emerge from the stickleback experiments is the realization that mammals are in many ways a rather exceptional group, specializing in "plastic" behavior. The simpler and more rigid behavior found in our fish seems to be the rule in most of the animal kingdom. Once one is aware of this, and aware also of the affinity of mammals to the lower vertebrates, one expects to find an innate base beneath the plastic behavior of mammals.

Thus the study of conflicting drives in so low an animal as the stickleback may throw light on human conflicts and the nature of neuroses. The part played by hostility in courtship, a phenomenon found not only in sticklebacks but in several birds, may well have a real bearing on human sex life. Even those who measure the value of a science by its immediate application to human affairs can learn some important lessons from the study of this insignificant little fish.

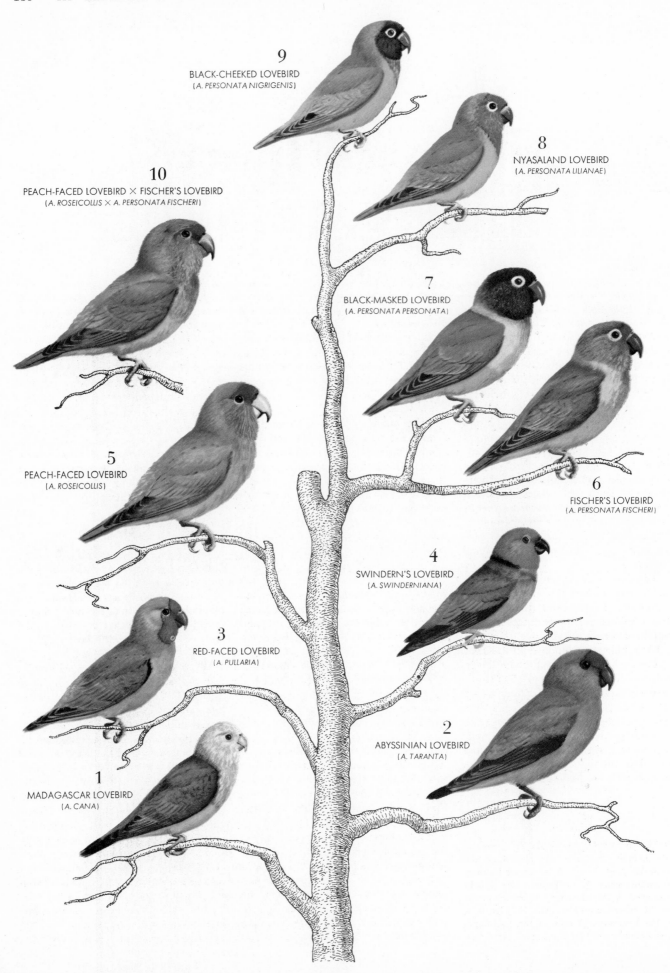

9
BLACK-CHEEKED LOVEBIRD
(A. PERSONATA NIGRIGENIS)

8
NYASALAND LOVEBIRD
(A. PERSONATA LILIANAE)

10
PEACH-FACED LOVEBIRD × FISCHER'S LOVEBIRD
(A. ROSEICOLLIS × A. PERSONATA FISCHERI)

7
BLACK-MASKED LOVEBIRD
(A. PERSONATA PERSONATA)

5
PEACH-FACED LOVEBIRD
(A. ROSEICOLLIS)

6
FISCHER'S LOVEBIRD
(A. PERSONATA FISCHERI)

3
RED-FACED LOVEBIRD
(A. PULLARIA)

4
SWINDERN'S LOVEBIRD
(A. SWINDERNIANA)

2
ABYSSINIAN LOVEBIRD
(A. TARANTA)

1
MADAGASCAR LOVEBIRD
(A. CANA)

# 22 The Behavior of Lovebirds

WILLIAM C. DILGER · January 1962

All lovebirds display the behavior that gives them their anthropomorphic common name. They pair early, and once pairs are formed they normally endure for life. The partners exhibit their mutual interest with great constancy and in a variety of beguiling activities. For the student of the evolution of animal behavior the lovebirds have special interest. The genus comprises nine forms (species or subspecies). They show a pattern of differentiation in their behavior that corresponds to their differentiation in color and morphology. By comparative study of their behavior, therefore, one can hope to reconstruct its evolution and to observe how natural selection has brought about progressive variations on the same fundamental scheme.

Together with my colleagues in the Laboratory of Ornithology at Cornell University, I have been studying both the constants and the variables in lovebird behavior for the past five years. It is not too difficult to duplicate in the laboratory the basic features of the lovebirds' natural African environment, so the birds thrive in captivity. Our work has covered all the lovebirds except Swindern's lovebird; we have not been able to obtain any specimens of this species. Our findings in two areas—sexual behavior and the defense and construction of the nest—have been particularly fruitful, be-

cause in these areas the evolutionary changes in lovebird behavior stand out in sharp relief.

Lovebirds constitute the genus *Agapornis,* and are members of the parrot family. Their closest living relatives are the hanging parakeets of Asia (the genus *Loriculus*). Three species of lovebird— the Madagascar lovebird, the Abyssinian lovebird and the red-faced lovebird—resemble the hanging parakeets and differ from all other lovebirds in two major respects. The males and females of these three species differ in color and are easily distinguishable from each other. The male and female of the other lovebirds are the same color. In these three species the primary social unit is the pair and its immature offspring. The other lovebirds are highly social and tend to nest in colonies. In these respects, then, the Madagascar lovebird, the Abyssinian lovebird and the red-faced lovebird most closely resemble the ancestral form, and the other lovebirds are more divergent.

Our study of interspecies differentiation of behavior has begun to reveal the order in which the other species arrived on the scene. Next after the three "primitive" species is Swindern's lovebird. Then comes the peach-faced lovebird and finally the four subspecies of *Agapornis personata,* commonly referred to as the white-eye-ringed forms: Fischer's lovebird, the black-masked lovebird, the Nyasaland lovebird and the black-cheeked lovebird. There are significant differences in behavior between the peach-faced lovebird and the four white-eye-ringed forms.

Perhaps the sharpest contrasts in behavior are those that distinguish the three primitive species from the species that evolved later. Even the common generic characteristic of pairing at an

early age shows changes between the two groups that must be related to their contrasting patterns of life—nesting in pairs as opposed to nesting in colonies. Among the primitive species pair formation takes place when the birds are about four months old. At that time they are entirely independent of their parents and have already developed adult plumage. In the more recently evolved species, the colonial nesting pattern of which offers them access to their contemporaries virtually from the moment of their birth, pair formation takes place even earlier: the birds are about two months old and still have their juvenile plumage.

Among all the lovebird species pair formation is a rather undramatic event. Unpaired birds seek out the company of other unpaired birds and test them, as it were, by attempting to preen them and otherwise engage their interest. Couples quickly discover if they are compatible, and generally it takes no more than a few hours to establish lifelong pairs.

When the paired birds reach sexual maturity, their behavior with respect to each other becomes much more elaborate. This behavior as a whole is common to all lovebirds, and some activities are performed in the same way by all. Other activities, however, are not, and they show a gradation from the most primitive forms to the most recently evolved ones. One constant among all species is the female's frequent indifference 'to, and even active aggression against, the male each time he begins to woo her. Another is the essential pattern of the male's response—a combination of fear, sexual appetite, aggression and consequent frustration. Primarily motivated by both fear and sexual appetite, the male makes his first approach to his mate by sidling toward and then away from

NINE FORMS OF LOVEBIRD, as well as one hybrid (*top left*), are shown on the opposite page. They are arranged in their apparent order of evolution. The hybrid was bred in the laboratory for experiments on the inheritance of behavior. The letter *A.* at the beginning of each of the Latin species names stands for the genus *Agapornis.*

her while turning about on his perch. This switch-sidling, as it is called, is common to all species.

Two forms of male behavior initially associated with frustration, on the other hand, show a distinct evolutionary progression. The first of these activities is called squeak-twittering. Among the three primitive species—the Madagascar lovebird, the Abyssinian lovebird and the red-faced lovebird—the male utters a series of high-pitched vocalizations when the female thwarts him by disappearing into the nest cavity. The sounds are quite variable in pitch and purity of tone and have no recognizable rhythm. In the more recently evolved species—the peach-faced and the four white-eye-ringed forms—squeak-twittering is rather different. The sound is rhythmic, purer in tone and less variable in pitch. Nor does it occur only when the female has turned her back on the male and entered the nest cavity. The male usually vocalizes even when the female is present and gives no indication whatever of thwarting him. Squeak-twittering has undergone a progressive change not only in its physical characteristics but also in the context in which it appears.

A similar evolution toward more highly ritualized behavior has occurred in another sexual activity, displacement

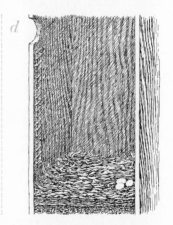

**BEHAVIOR OF MADAGASCAR LOVEBIRD** is outlined. Both sexes engage in courtship feeding (a). Accompanying head bobs are rapid and trace small arc (b). Nest materials, generally bark and leaves, are carried several pieces at a time and tucked among

**BEHAVIOR OF PEACH-FACED LOVEBIRD** suggests higher evolutionary stage. Only males perform courtship feeding; females fluff their feathers during this ritual (a). Slower head bobs trace wider arc (b). Nest materials, also bark and leaves, are

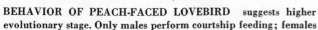

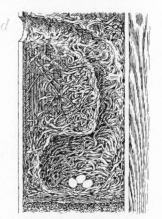

**BEHAVIOR OF FISCHER'S LOVEBIRD** indicates a further evolution. Courtship feeding (a), mobbing (e) and bill-fencing (f) are performed much as they are by the peach-faced lovebird. But other kinds of behavior are significantly different. Head bobs

scratching. This response derives from the habit, common to all species, of scratching the head with the foot when frustrated. Among the three primitive species displacement scratching is still close to its origins. Only two things distinguish it from ordinary head-scratching: its context and the fact that it is always performed with the foot nearest the female. Purely practical considerations govern this behavior: the male already has that foot raised preparatory to mounting his mate. In the more recently evolved species, displacement scratching has become primarily a form of display. Its progressive emancipation from the original motivation with which it is associated becomes more and more apparent as one observes it in the species from the peach-faced lovebird through the white-eye-ringed forms. Among all these the scratching is far more rapid and perfunctory than it is among the primitive species. Nor is it uniformly directed at the feathered portions of the head. In the peach-faced lovebird it is sometimes directed at the bill instead, and among the Nyasaland and black-cheeked lovebirds it is nearly always so directed. Moreover, these species use the far foot as well as the near one in displacement scratching; among the Nyasaland and black-cheeked lovebirds one is

all feathers of the body (c). Short strips are used to make an unshaped nest pad (d). **The young join the mother in cavity-**

defense display (e). In f birds show threat and appeasement display. It usually averts combat; if it fails, **the birds fight furiously.**

carried several at a time in back plumage (c); long strips are used to make a well-shaped nest (d). **Birds join in "mobbing" to**

protect nest (e). Bill-fencing (f) has a display function. It never leads to real harm; **the birds bite only their opponents' toes.**

(b) are still slower and trace an even wider arc. Nest materials are carried in the bill, one piece at a time (c); twigs as well

as strips of bark and leaf are used. This permits construction of an elaborate covered nest, entered through a tunnel (d).

used as often as the other. Finally, as in the case of squeak-twittering, which is often performed at the same time as displacement scratching among these species, the display occurs even when the female does not seem to be thwarting her mate.

All species engage in courtship feeding: the transfer of regurgitated food from one member of the pair to the other. In the three primitive species the female often offers food to her mate. This behavior has never been observed among the peach-faced and white-eye-ringed forms; here courtship feeding seems exclusively a male prerogative.

One can also discern an evolutionary progression in the manner in which the birds carry out the rather convulsive bobbing of the head associated with the act of regurgitation that immediately precedes courtship feeding. Among the primitive species these head-bobbings describe a small arc, are rapid and numerous and are usually followed by rather prolonged bill contacts while the food is being transferred. In the other forms the head-bobbings are slower, fewer in number and trace a wider arc; the bill contacts usually last for only a short time. Moreover, among the more recently evolved forms head-bobbing has become pure display; it is no longer accompanied by the feeding of the female. Unlike the females of the primitive lovebird species, which have no special display activity during courtship feeding, the females of the more recently evolved species play a distinctly ritualized role. They ruffle their plumage throughout the entire proceeding.

Females of all species indicate their fluctuating readiness to copulate by subtle adjustments of their plumage, particularly the feathers of the head. The more the female fluffs, the readier she is, and the more the male is encouraged. Finally she will solicit copulation by leaning forward and raising her head and tail. Females of the primitive species do not fluff their plumage during copulation; females of the more recently evolved species do. This is undoubtedly related to the morphological differences among the lovebirds. Since males and females of the more recently evolved species have the same coloring and patterning, the females must reinforce their mates' recognition of them, both in courtship and in copulation, by some behavioral means.

Although the forms of precopulatory behavior seem to be innate among all species, learning appears to play a major role in producing the changes that occur as the members of a pair become more familiar with each other. Newly formed pairs are rather awkward. The males make many mistakes and are frequently threatened and thwarted by their mates. After they have had a few broods, however, and have acquired experience, they become more expert and tend more and more to perform the right activity at the right time. As a result the female responds with aggression far less often, and the male engages more rarely in the displays that are associated with frustration and thwarting. Squeak-twittering and displacement scratching in particular become less frequent. Switch-sidling is still performed, but with a perceptibly diminished intensity. Altogether precopulatory bouts become less protracted. In spite of the male's reduced activity, the female seems to become receptive fairly quickly.

Disagreements among members of the same species are handled in quite different ways by those lovebirds that nest in pairs and those that nest colonially. Among the less social primitive species an elaborate pattern of threat and appeasement display has developed. For example, a formalized series of long, rapid strides toward an opponent signalizes aggression; a ruffling of the feathers, fear and the wish to escape. The loser in a bout of posturing may indicate submission by fleeing or by remaining quiet, turning its head away from its opponent and fluffing its plumage. By means of this code the birds can communicate rather exact items of information as to their readiness to attack or to flee. As a result actual fights seldom occur. When they do, however, the birds literally tear each other apart.

The peach-faced lovebird and the white-eye-ringed forms, which nest colonially, are thrown in contact with members of their own species much more often. This is undoubtedly related to the fact that they have developed a ritualized form of display fighting that goes far beyond a mere code of threat and appeasement and that replaces serious physical conflict. Display fighting among these more recently evolved species consists primarily of bill-fencing. The two birds parry and thrust with their bills and aim sharp nips at each other's toes.

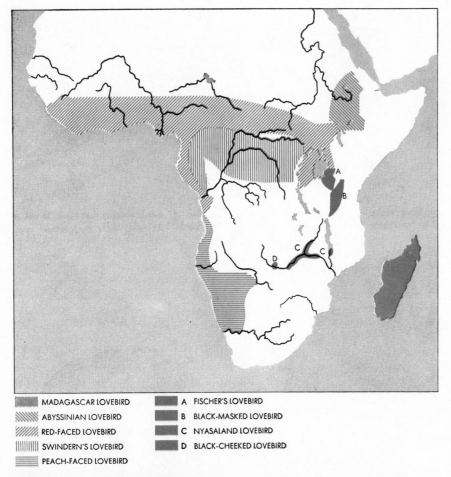

MADAGASCAR LOVEBIRD
ABYSSINIAN LOVEBIRD
RED-FACED LOVEBIRD
SWINDERN'S LOVEBIRD
PEACH-FACED LOVEBIRD

A  FISCHER'S LOVEBIRD
B  BLACK-MASKED LOVEBIRD
C  NYASALAND LOVEBIRD
D  BLACK-CHEEKED LOVEBIRD

**DISTRIBUTION OF LOVEBIRDS** is shown on this map of Africa and the island of Madagascar. All nine of the lovebird species and subspecies inhabit different areas.

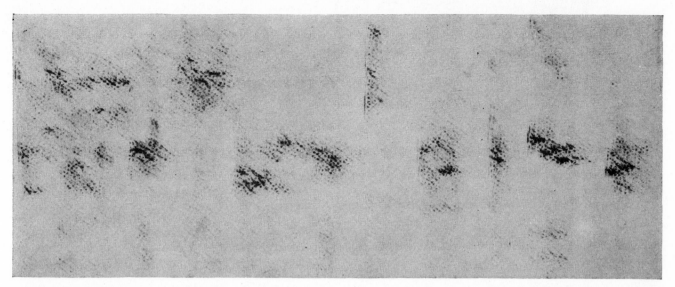

**SQUEAK-TWITTERING** in male Madagascar lovebird is seen on sound spectrogram. The horizontal axis represents time; the vertical axis, frequency. Uneven distribution of spots along both axes shows an arhythmic quality and a wide variation in pitch.

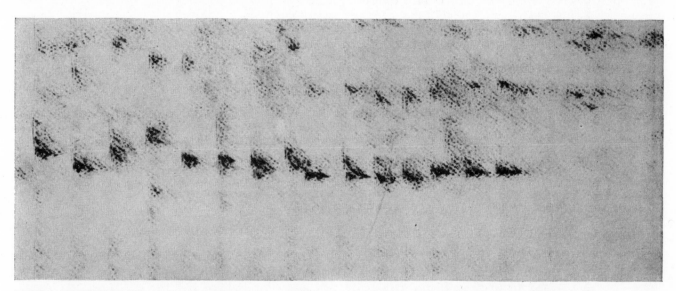

**SOUND SPECTROGRAM** of squeak-twittering in peach-faced lovebird shows greater rhythmicity and less variation in pitch. In Madagascar lovebird behavior is displayed only when female thwarts male. In peach-faced lovebird this is not always the case.

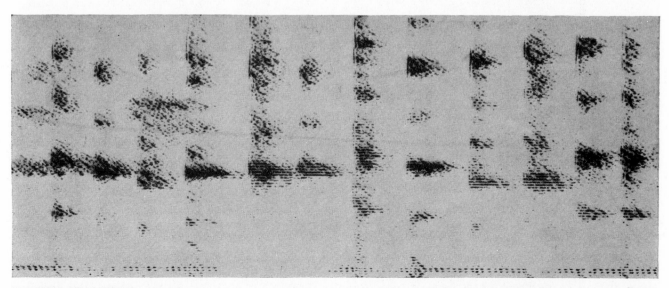

**FURTHER EVOLUTION** in squeak-twittering is seen in behavior of Nyasaland lovebird. Sounds are very rhythmic and show almost no variation in pitch; wide vertical distribution of spots reflects the large number of harmonics contained in the monotonous note.

The toe is the only part the birds ever bite, and the inhibition against biting a member of the same species in any other place seems to be, like bill-fencing itself, an innate pattern. Though bill-fencing appears to be innate, it must be perfected by learning. The colonial nesting pattern offers young birds considerable practice with their contemporaries, and they quickly become skilled.

If lovebirds have had experience in rearing their own young, they will not rear the young of those other forms that have a natal down of a different color. On the other hand, a female that is given the egg of such a form at the time of her first egg-laying will rear the bird that emerges. Indeed, if a peach-faced lovebird has her first experience of motherhood with a newly hatched Madagascar

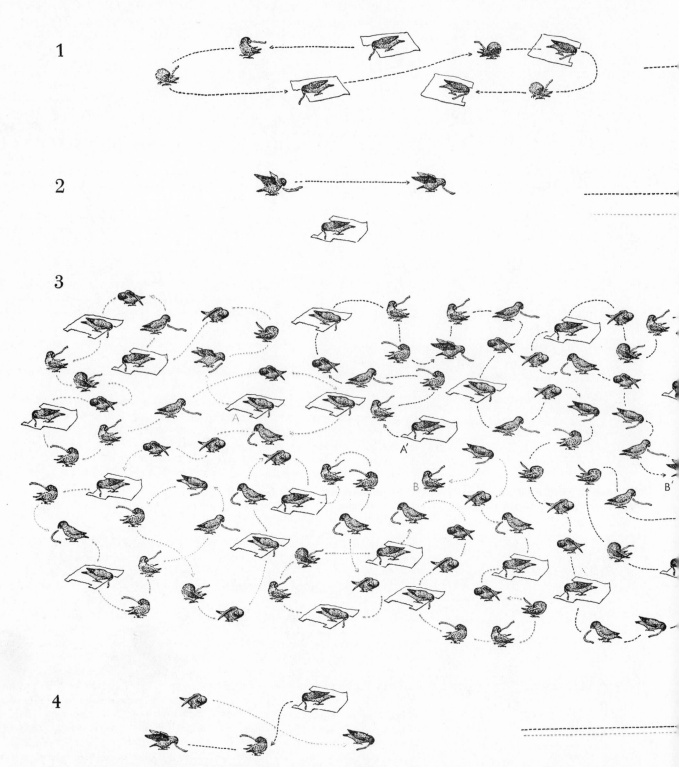

**HYBRID LOVEBIRD** inherits patterns for two different ways of carrying nest-building materials. From the peach-faced lovebird (1) it inherits patterns for carrying strips several at a time, in feathers. From Fischer's lovebird (2) it inherits patterns for carrying strips one at a time, in the bill. When the hybrid first begins to build a nest (3), it acts completely confused. Colored lines from *A* to *B* and black lines from *A′* to *B′* indicate the number of activities necessary for it to get two strips to the nest site, a feat achieved only when the strips are carried singly, in the bill. It takes three years before the bird perfects its bill-carrying behavior (4),

lovebird, she will thereafter refuse to raise her own offspring. The down of the peach-faced lovebird's newly hatched young (like the down of the white-eye-ringed forms) is red, and the down of newly hatched Madagascar, Abyssinian and red-faced lovebirds is white.

and even then it makes efforts to tuck its nest materials in its feathers. As the bird gains experience it becomes more and more proficient in this activity, which, however, never results in successful carrying.

Unlike most of the other members of the parrot family, which simply lay their eggs in empty cavities, all lovebird species make nests. The red-faced lovebird constructs its nest in a hole it digs in the hard, earthy nests certain ants make in trees. All other species, however, make their nests in pre-existing cavities, which are usually reached through small entrances. The nests of the Madagascar lovebird, the Abyssinian lovebird and the red-faced lovebird are quite simple, consisting essentially of deposits of soft material on the cavity floor. These three species have developed an elaborate cavity-defense display. The moment an intruder appears, the female ruffles her feathers, partly spreads her wings and tail and utters a rapid series of harsh, buzzing sounds. If the intruder persists, she will suddenly compress her plumage, utter a piercing yip and lunge toward it. She does not bite, but she gives every indication of being about to do so. Her older offspring may join her at this time, ruffling their feathers and making grating sounds.

The effect of this performance is quite startling; it can even give pause to an experienced investigator! The Madagascar lovebird, the most primitive of all the species, is the quickest to engage in the cavity-defense display and is the only species we have seen carry the display through both stages. A stronger stimulation is necessary before the Abyssinian lovebird engages in this behavior, and we have not seen the bird go any further than ruffling its body plumage and making the harsh, rasping sounds.

The white-eye-ringed lovebirds build rather elaborate nests, consisting of a roofed chamber at the end of a tunnel within the cavity. This fact and their strongly social nature combine to make their response to a threat to their nests different from the response of the primitive species. They have no cavity-defense displays at all. If a predator actually reaches the cavity, the birds within it will either cower or, if possible, flee through the entrance. But if the predator, encouraged by this show of fear, enters the cavity, it is likely to find that its troubles have just begun. It faces a journey down a narrow tunnel, defended at the end by a bird with a powerful and sharp bill. Moreover, a predator is seldom allowed to come close to the cavity. As soon as it is seen approaching, the entire colony engages in a form of behavior called mobbing: holding their bodies vertically, the birds beat their wings rapidly and utter loud, high-pitched squeaks. The sight and sound of a whole flock mobbing is quite impres-

sive and probably serves to deter many would-be predators.

All female lovebirds prepare their nest materials in much the same way: by punching a series of closely spaced holes in some pliable material such as paper, bark or leaf. The material is held between the upper and lower portions of the bill, which then works like a train conductor's ticket punch. The pieces cut out in this way vary in size and shape among the various lovebirds. So do the forms of behavior that now ensue.

The three primitive species and the peach-faced lovebird tuck the pieces they have cut into the feathers of their bodies and fly off with them. The Madagascar lovebird, the Abyssinian lovebird and the red-faced lovebird use very small bits of material. (This is one of the reasons their nests are so unstructured.) The entire plumage of the bird is erected as it inserts the six to eight bits of material in place and remains erect during the whole operation. The peach-faced lovebird cuts strips that are considerably longer. (This permits the more elaborate structuring of its cuplike nest.) Indeed, the strips are so long that they can be carried only in the feathers of the lower back. These are the feathers erected when the strips are tucked in, and the feathers are compressed after each strip is inserted. The peach-faced lovebird loses about half of its cargo before it gets to its nest site; either pieces fall out while others are being cut or tucked in, or they fall out while the bird is flying. The lovebirds that use smaller bits of nest material are more successful in carrying them.

Carrying nest material in the feathers is unique to these birds and the related hanging parakeets. What is more, speculation about its origin must begin with the fact that no other parrots (with one unrelated exception) build nests at all. It is almost certain that this behavior arose from fortuitous occurrences associated with two characteristic parrot activities: chewing on bits of wood, bark and leaf to keep the bill sharp and properly worn down; and preening, which serves to keep the plumage clean and properly arranged. Some parrots that do not build nests will accidentally leave bits of the material in their feathers when they proceed directly from chewing to preening. Such oversights almost certainly initiated the evolution of the habit of carrying nest materials in the feathers.

The four white-eye-ringed forms are completely emancipated from this ancestral pattern. Fischer's lovebird, the black-masked lovebird, the Nyasaland lovebird and the black-cheeked lovebird all carry their nest materials as do most birds—in their bills. They lose little material in the process of carrying, and they pick up twigs in addition to cutting strips of pliable material. With these materials, they can build their characteristically elaborate nests.

Although the peach-faced lovebird normally carries its nest-building material in its feathers, on about 3 per cent of its trips it carries material in its bill. This peculiarity suggested an experiment. We mated the peach-faced lovebird with Fischer's lovebird (the birds hybridize readily in captivity) to see what behavior would show up in the hybrids. In confirmation of the thesis that patterns of carrying nest materials are primarily innate, the hybrid displays a conflict in behavior between the tendency to carry material in its feathers (inherited from the peach-faced lovebird) and the tendency to carry material in its bill (inherited from Fischer's lovebird).

When our hybrids first began to build their nests, they acted as though they were completely confused. They had no difficulty in cutting strips, but they could not seem to determine whether to carry them in the feathers or in the bill. They got material to the nest sites only when they carried it in the bill, and in their first effort at nest building they did carry in their bills 6 per cent of the time. After they had cut each strip, however, they engaged in behavior associated with tucking. Even when they finally carried the material in the bill, they erected the feathers of the lower back and rump and attempted to tuck. But if they were able to press the strips into their plumage—and they were not always successful in the attempt—they could not carry it to the nest site in that fashion. Every strip dropped out.

Two months later, after they had become more experienced, the hybrids carried many more of their nest strips in their bills—41 per cent, to be exact. But they continued to make the movements associated with the intention to tuck: they erected their rump plumage and turned their heads to the rear, flying away with material in their bills only after attempting to tuck.

After two more months had passed they began to learn that strips could be picked up in the bill and carried off with a minimum of prior abortive tucking. But it took two years for them to learn to diminish actual tucking activity to any great extent, and even then they continued to perform many of the movements associated with tucking.

Today the hybrids are behaving, by and large, like Fischer's lovebird, the more recently evolved of their two parents. Only infrequently do they attempt to tuck strips into their plumage. But it has taken them three years to reach this stage—evidence of the difficulty they experience in learning to use one innate pattern at the expense of another, even though the latter is never successful. Moreover, when they do carry out the activities associated with tucking, they perform them far more efficiently than they did at first. Evidently this behavior need not achieve its normal objective in order to be improved.

So far our hybrids have proved to be sterile and therefore unable to pass on their behavior to a second generation. Even in the first generation, however, one can see the ways in which nature interweaves innate and learned elements to produce the behavior characteristic of a species. Further comparative studies can add much to our understanding not only of the behavior of lovebirds but also of the behavior of all vertebrates, including man.

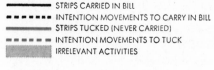

        STRIPS CARRIED IN BILL
        INTENTION MOVEMENTS TO CARRY IN BILL
        STRIPS TUCKED (NEVER CARRIED)
        INTENTION MOVEMENTS TO TUCK
        IRRELEVANT ACTIVITIES

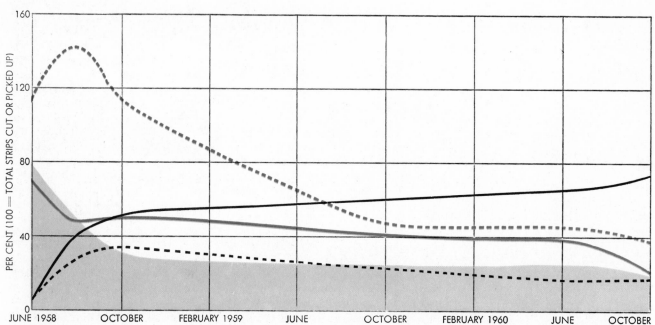

**CONFLICTING PATTERNS** of carrying nest-building materials are inherited by a hybrid lovebird, produced by mating the peach-faced and Fischer's lovebirds. The hybrid's behavior is charted here for a period of almost three years. As the bird progressively learns to carry nest materials as Fischer's lovebird does, the number of irrelevant movements and inappropriate activities decreases.

# $23$ "Imprinting" in Animals

ECKHARD H. HESS · March 1958

What is meant by "imprinting" in animals? The best answer is to describe an experiment performed on geese by the Austrian zoologist Konrad Lorenz. On an estate near Vienna Lorenz divided a clutch of eggs laid by a graylag goose into two groups. One group was hatched by the goose; the other group was hatched in an incubator. The goslings hatched by the goose immediately followed their mother around the estate. The goslings hatched in the incubator, however, did not see their mother; the first living thing they saw was Lorenz. They then followed Lorenz about the estate!

Lorenz now marked the two groups of goslings to distinguish them. He placed all the goslings under a large box, while the mother watched anxiously. When the box was lifted, the two groups of

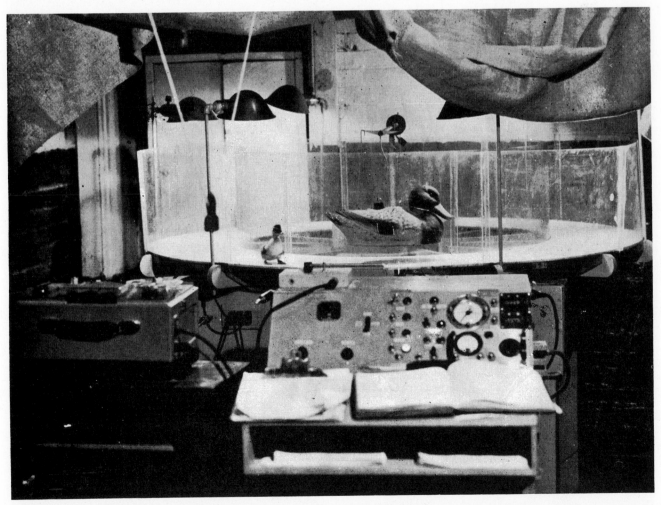

APPARATUS used by Hess and A. O. Ramsay in the study of imprinting consists primarily of a circular runway around which a decoy duck can be moved. In this photograph a duckling follows the decoy. In the foreground are the controls of the apparatus. At the top of the photograph is a cloth which is normally dropped so that movements of the experimenter will not distract the duckling.

**DUCKLING IS IMPRINTED** by placing it in the runway behind a model of a male duck which is wired for sound. Below the duckling is a trap door through which it is removed.

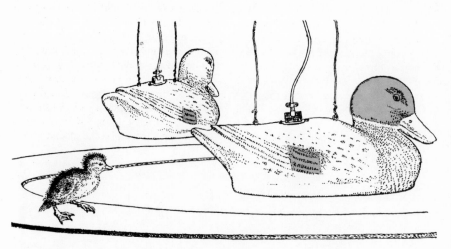

**DUCKLING IS TESTED** for imprinting by placing it between the male model and a female model which emits a different sound. If it follows the male, response is scored as positive.

**DUCKLING SCALES AN OBSTACLE** in the runway in an experiment to determine whether the effort it expends during imprinting is related to its score when it is tested.

goslings streamed to their respective "parents." Lorenz called this phenomenon, in which an early experience of the goslings determined their social behavior, "imprinting." Although earlier investigators had observed the effect, he was the first to name it and to point out that it appeared to occur at a critical period early in the life of an animal. He also postulated that the first object to elicit a social response later released not only that response but also related responses such as sexual behavior.

Students of behavior generally agree that the early experiences of animals (including man) have a profound effect on their adult behavior. D. O. Hebb of the University of Montreal goes so far as to state that the effect of early experience upon adult behavior is inversely correlated with age. This may be an oversimplification, but in general it appears to hold true. Thus the problem of the investigator is not so much to find out *whether* early experience determines adult behavior, but rather to discover *how* it determines adult behavior.

Three statements are usually made about the effects of early experience. The first is that early habits are very persistent and may prevent the formation of new ones. This, of course, refers not only to the study of experimental animals but also to the rearing of children. The second statement is that early perceptions deeply affect all future learning. This concept leads to the difficult question whether basic perceptions—the way we have of seeing the world around us—are inherited or acquired. The third statement is simply that early social contacts determine adult social behavior. This, of course, is imprinting.

Although imprinting has been studied mainly in birds, it also occurs in other animals. It has been observed in insects, in fishes and in some mammals. So far as mammals are concerned the phenomenon appears to be limited to those animals whose young are able to move about almost immediately after birth. For example, imprinting has been described in sheep, goats, deer and buffalo. For better or worse these observations have not been made under controlled laboratory conditions. One exception is a study begun in our laboratories at the University of Chicago. One of our students has observed that imprinting appears to occur in guinea pigs. Our work has dealt mainly, however, with imprinting in birds.

Lorenz and other European workers

have shown that a variety of birds are most easily imprinted during the first day after they are hatched, and that the birds will follow not only other animals but also inanimate objects. In this country A. O. Ramsay of the McDonogh School in McDonogh, Md., succeeded in making young Canada geese and mallard ducklings follow a small green box containing an alarm clock. Some ducklings and goslings responded to a football. In the early 1950s I met Ramsay and we decided to begin a cooperative study of imprinting under laboratory conditions. Among our goals were the following. What is the critical age at which imprinting occurs? How long must young birds be exposed to the imprinting object in order for them to discriminate between it and similar objects?

The subjects used in the experiments described here were mallard ducklings. We were fortunate in that our laboratory in Maryland had access to a small duck pond in which we could keep relatively wild mallards. The birds laid their eggs in nesting boxes, so the eggs could be regularly collected and hatched in laboratory incubators. Our experimental apparatus consisted of a circular runway about five feet in diameter and 12 inches wide, the walls of which were made of transparent plastic. Our imprinting object was a model of a male mallard duck, of the sort used by duck hunters as a decoy. The model was suspended from a motor-driven arm pivoted at the center of the apparatus; thus it could be moved around the runway at various speeds. Inside the model was a loudspeaker through which tape-recorded sounds could be played.

After the mallard eggs were collected, they were placed in a dark incubator. When the young birds were hatched, they were kept in individual cardboard boxes so that they would have no visual experience until they were put into the imprinting apparatus. The boxes were then kept in a brooder until we were ready to work with the birds. After each duckling was exposed to the imprinting object (the decoy duck) in the apparatus, it was automatically returned to its box by means of a trap door in the floor of the runway. The bird was then lodged in another brooder until it was to be tested for the imprinting effect.

The imprinting itself was accomplished first by placing the young mallard in the runway of the apparatus about a foot away from the decoy. As the bird was released, the loudspeaker inside the decoy was made to emit a human rendition of the sound "GOCK gock gock gock gock," and after a short interval the decoy was moved around the runway. The imprinting period, during which the duckling followed the decoy, usually lasted 10 minutes. We can also imprint ducklings with a silent object, or even with sound alone. In one experiment we tried to imprint ducklings with the "gock" sound while they were still in the egg. This effort was unsuccessful.

The bird was tested for imprinting by releasing it between two decoys four feet apart. One decoy was the male model with which the duckling had been imprinted; the other was a female model which differed from the male only in its coloration. One minute was allowed for the duckling to make a decisive response to the silent models. At the end of this time, regardless of the duckling's response, sound was turned on in both models. The male model made the "gock" call; the female emitted the sound of a mallard duck calling her young. This latter sound was a recording of a real female. Four test situations were run off in sequence: (1) both models stationary and silent; (2) both models stationary and calling; (3) male stationary and female moving, both calling; (4) male stationary and silent, female moving and calling. Each bird was scored according to the percentage of its positive responses, i.e., the number of times it moved toward the male model as opposed to doing something else.

To determine the age at which an imprinting experience was most effective we imprinted our ducklings at various ages after hatching. In this series of experiments the imprinting experience was standard: it consisted of having the duckling follow the model 150 to 200 feet around the runway during a period of 10 minutes. It appears that some imprinting occurs immediately after hatching; however, only those ducklings imprinted between 13 and 16 hours after hatching consistently made a maximum score [see chart below].

To answer the question how long the imprinting experience must last in order to be most effective we varied not only the time during which the duckling was exposed to the model but also the distance traveled by the duckling as it followed the model around the runway of our apparatus. We exposed groups of ducklings to the model for the same length of time (10 minutes), but during that time moved the model at different speeds so that the ducklings in each group moved a different distance (1,

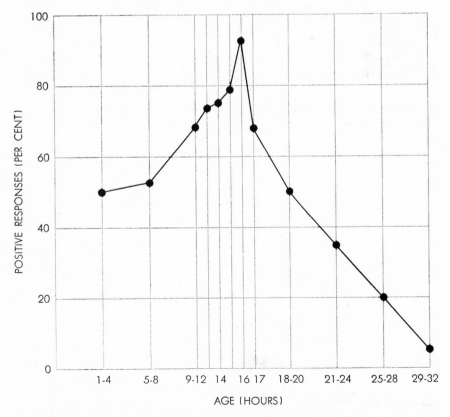

**CRITICAL AGE** at which ducklings are most strongly imprinted is reflected by this curve. Each black dot on the curve is the average test score of ducklings imprinted at that age.

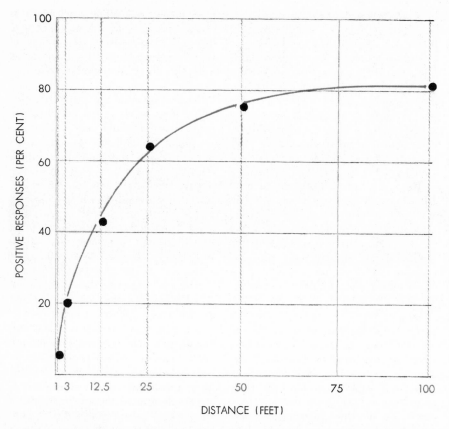

**DISTANCE TRAVELED** during imprinting affected the scores of ducklings as indicated by this curve. The farther the ducklings had traveled, the more strongly they were imprinted.

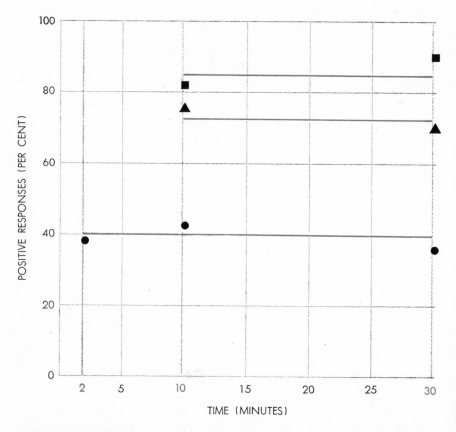

**TIME ELAPSED** during imprinting had little effect on the scores. The squares represent ducklings which had traveled 100 feet during imprinting; triangles, 50 feet; dots, 12.5 feet.

12½, 25, 50 and 100 feet). All the ducklings were imprinted between 12 and 17 hours after hatching. The results showed that at distances up to 50 feet the strength of imprinting increased with the distance traveled [*see chart at top of this page*].

We now allowed other groups of ducklings to travel the same distance, but over different periods of time. One turn around our runway is 12½ feet; a duckling can walk this distance in something less than two minutes. We moved the decoy so that groups of ducklings made one turn around the runway in 2, 10 and 30 minutes. The scores of these animals were essentially identical [*see chart at bottom of this page*]. Moreover, there was no significant difference between the scores of ducklings which followed the decoy 100 feet in 10 minutes and those which traveled the same distance in 30 minutes.

In other words, the strength of imprinting appeared to be dependent not on the duration of the imprinting period but on the effort exerted by the duckling in following the imprinting object. To confirm this notion we tried two supplementary experiments. In the first we placed four-inch hurdles in the runway so that the ducklings not only had to follow the model but also had to clear the obstacles. As we suspected, the birds which had to climb the hurdles, and thus expend more effort, made higher imprinting scores than those which traveled the same distance without obstacles. In the second experiment we allowed the duckling to follow the decoy up an inclined plane, with similar results. After further experiments we came to the conclusion that we could write a formula for imprinting: the strength of imprinting equals the logarithm of the effort expended by the animal during the imprinting period.

Now that we had this basic information, we began to explore other aspects of imprinting. We had been puzzled by the fact that the imprintability of ducklings rapidly declines soon after they are 16 hours old. We had noticed, as had other workers, that ducklings develop their first emotional response when they are 16 to 20 hours old. This response is an avoidance or fear of moving objects. Twenty-four hours after hatching almost 80 per cent of the ducklings exhibit this fear; the proportion increases to 100 per cent at about 32 hours. Does this fear response knock out imprinting?

At the time we were reflecting on this

question the tranquilizing drugs had just been introduced, and it occurred to us that these drugs which reduce fear and anxiety might solve our problem. We administered meprobamate (Miltown) to 24-hour-old ducklings; their fear response was indeed reduced. We then imprinted the drugged birds 26 hours after hatching. Ducklings 26 hours old are of course imprinted very weakly, but we were surprised that the imprinting scores of these animals were even lower than normal. In other words, eliminating fear did not improve imprintability. Later we found that the tranquilizer also interfered with the imprinting of young mallards at an age when they were normally most imprintable. So far our best conclusion is that meprobamate, being a muscle relaxant, nullifies the effectiveness of the imprinting experience by relaxing muscular tension. It is also possible that in the imprinting process some degree of anxiety is necessary. This anxiety, from an admittedly human viewpoint, may merely be the fear of being left alone; the duckling might thus tend to follow the imprinting object as it moved away. We are continuing our study of these drugs because we feel that it may not only shed some light on the mechanism of imprinting but also may give us valuable information about the action of the drugs themselves.

We have also considered the genetic side of imprinting. We have kept ducklings which were highly imprintable and bred them separately from ducklings which showed very little imprinting response. Significant differences appeared even in the first generation: the offspring of imprintable parents were easily imprinted; those of less imprintable par-

**REMOTE-CONTROLLED DECOY** was used by Hess and his colleagues in other imprinting experiments. Here both decoy and duckling move about freely rather than on a runway.

ents were difficult to imprint. We are also following up those animals which have had experimental imprinting experiences to determine what influence, if any, these experiences have on their adult behavior. So far the results are inconclusive, but they do suggest that experimental imprinting of mallards affects their adult behavior, particularly with respect to courtship patterns.

We have performed imprinting experiments not only with mallards and, as indicated earlier, guinea pigs, but also with other kinds of ducks, several varieties of geese, with sheep, turkeys, pheasants, quail and chickens. We have had some success in imprinting certain breeds of chicks (mainly Cochin bantams and Seabright bantams), but in general domestic fowl cannot be as clearly imprinted as wild birds.

What does all this have to do with human behavior? Of course it is not really necessary to relate our work to such behavior; it is interesting and important in its own right because it tells us something about the way an organism adapts itself to the world. We do feel, however, that the work has some implications which are relevant to humans. It has long been known, for example, that in order for a child to develop normally it must have a certain amount of attention and handling during a critical period of its infancy. This period is doubtless not as sharply defined as the imprinting period in birds, but it may lie within the first six months of life. Jere Wilson of our group is studying the smiling response of infants in an effort to get at some aspects of human behavior which may involve imprinting.

# 24 Love in Infant Monkeys

HARRY F. HARLOW · June 1959

The first love of the human infant is for his mother. The tender intimacy of this attachment is such that it is sometimes regarded as a sacred or mystical force, an instinct incapable of analysis. No doubt such compunctions, along with the obvious obstacles in the way of objective study, have hampered experimental observation of the bonds between child and mother.

Though the data are thin, the theoretical literature on the subject is rich. Psychologists, sociologists and anthropologists commonly hold that the infant's love is learned through the association of the mother's face, body and other physical characteristics with the alleviation of internal biological tensions, particularly hunger and thirst. Traditional psychoanalysts have tended to emphasize the role of attaining and sucking at the breast as the basis for affectional development. Recently a number of child psychiatrists have questioned such simple explanations. Some argue that affectionate handling in the act of nursing is a variable of importance, whereas a few workers suggest that the composite activities of nursing, contact, clinging and even seeing and hearing work together to elicit the infant's love for his mother.

Now it is difficult, if not impossible, to use human infants as subjects for the studies necessary to break through the present speculative impasse. At birth the infant is so immature that he has little or no control over any motor system other than that involved in sucking. Furthermore, his physical maturation is so slow that by the time he can achieve precise, coordinated, measurable responses of his head, hands, feet and body, the nature and sequence of development have been hopelessly confounded and obscured. Clearly research into

the infant-mother relationship has need of a more suitable laboratory animal. We believe we have found it in the infant monkey. For the past several years our group at the Primate Laboratory of the University of Wisconsin has been employing baby rhesus monkeys in a study that we believe has begun to yield significant insights into the origin of the infant's love for his mother.

Baby monkeys are far better coordinated at birth than human infants. Their responses can be observed and evaluated with confidence at an age of 10 days or even earlier. Though they mature much more rapidly than their human contemporaries, infants of both species follow much the same general pattern of development.

Our interest in infant-monkey love grew out of a research program that involved the separation of monkeys from their mothers a few hours after birth. Employing techniques developed by Gertrude van Wagenen of Yale University, we had been rearing infant monkeys on the bottle with a mortality far less than that among monkeys nursed by their mothers. We were particularly careful to provide the infant monkeys with a folded gauze diaper on the floor of their cages, in accord with Dr. van Wagenen's observation that they would tend to maintain intimate contact with such soft, pliant surfaces, especially during nursing. We were impressed by the deep personal attachments that the monkeys formed for these diaper pads, and by the distress that they exhibited when the pads were briefly removed once a day for purposes of sanitation. The behavior of the infant monkeys was reminiscent of the human infant's attachment to its blankets, pillows, rag dolls or cuddly teddy bears.

These observations suggested the series of experiments in which we have sought to compare the importance of nursing and all associated activities with that of simple bodily contact in engendering the infant monkey's attachment to its mother. For this purpose we contrived two surrogate mother monkeys. One is a bare welded-wire cylindrical form surmounted by a wooden head with a crude face. In the other the welded wire is cushioned by a sheathing of terry cloth. We placed eight newborn monkeys in individual cages, each with equal access to a cloth and a wire mother [see illustration on opposite page]. Four of the infants received their milk from one mother and four from the other, the milk being furnished in each case by a nursing bottle, with its nipple protruding from the mother's "breast."

The two mothers quickly proved to be physiologically equivalent. The monkeys in the two groups drank the same amount of milk and gained weight at the same rate. But the two mothers proved to be by no means psychologically equivalent. Records made automatically showed that both groups of infants spent far more time climbing and clinging on their cloth-covered mothers than they did on their wire mothers. During the infants' first 14 days of life the floors of the cages were warmed by an electric heating pad, but most of the infants left the pad as soon as they could climb on the unheated cloth mother. Moreover, as the monkeys grew older, they tended to spend an increasing amount of time clinging and cuddling on her pliant terrycloth surface. Those that secured their nourishment from the wire mother showed no tendency to spend more time on her than feeding required, contradicting the idea that affection is a response that is learned or derived in asso-

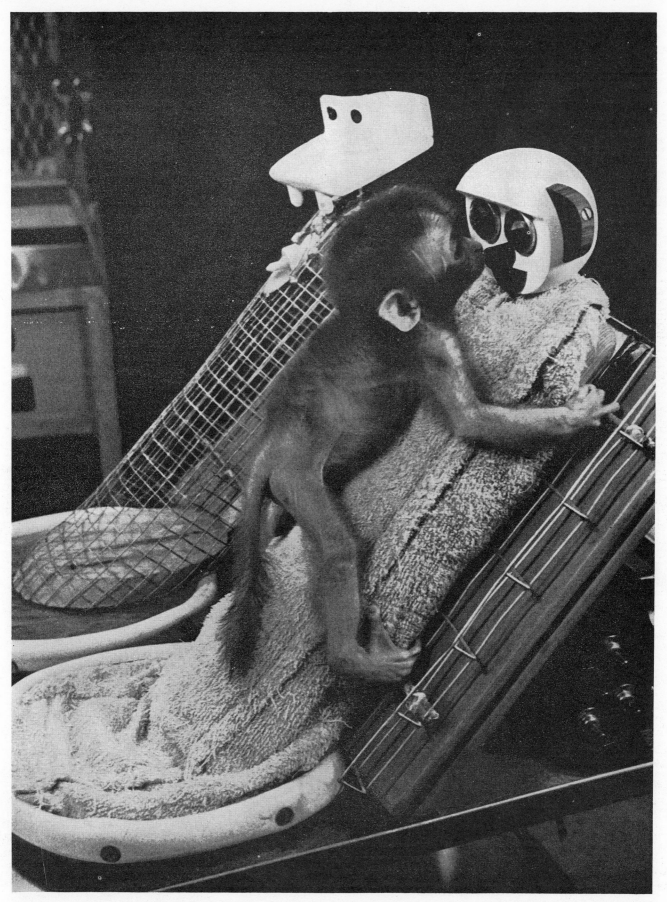

**CLOTH AND WIRE MOTHER-SURROGATES** were used to test the preferences of infant monkeys. The infants spent most of their time clinging to the soft cloth "mother," (*foreground*) even when nursing bottles were attached to the wire mother (*background*).

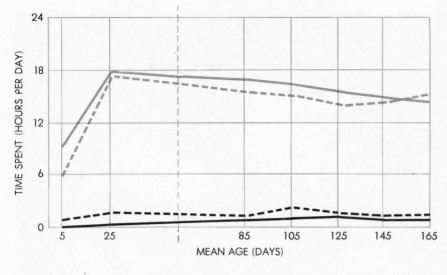

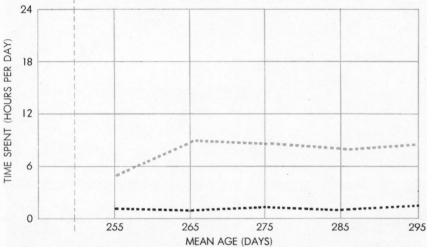

**STRONG PREFERENCE FOR CLOTH MOTHER** was shown by all infant monkeys. Infants reared with access to both mothers from birth (*top chart*) spent far more time on the cloth mother (*colored curves*) than on the wire mother (*black curves*). This was true regardless of whether they had been fed on the cloth (*solid lines*) or on the wire mother (*broken lines*). Infants that had known no mother during their first eight months (*bottom chart*) soon came to prefer cloth mother, but spent less time on her than the other infants.

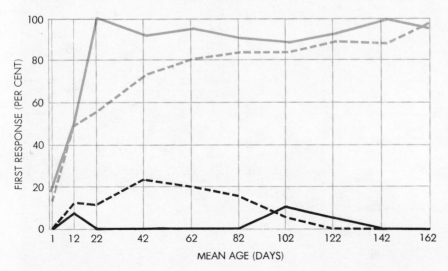

**RESULTS OF "FEAR TEST"** (*see photographs on opposite page*) showed that infants confronted by a strange object quickly learned to seek reassurance from the cloth mother (*colored curves*) rather than from the wire mother (*black curves*). Again infants fed on the wire mother (*broken lines*) behaved much like those fed on cloth mother (*solid lines*)

ciation with the reduction of hunger or thirst.

These results attest the importance—possibly the overwhelming importance—of bodily contact and the immediate comfort it supplies in forming the infant's attachment for its mother. All our experience, in fact, indicates that our cloth-covered mother surrogate is an eminently satisfactory mother. She is available 24 hours a day to satisfy her infant's overwhelming compulsion to seek bodily contact; she possesses infinite patience, never scolding her baby or biting it in anger. In these respects we regard her as superior to a living monkey mother, though monkey fathers would probably not endorse this opinion.

Of course this does not mean that nursing has no psychological importance. No act so effectively guarantees intimate bodily contact between mother and child. Furthermore, the mother who finds nursing a pleasant experience will probably be temperamentally inclined to give her infant plenty of handling and fondling. The real-life attachment of the infant to its mother is doubtless influenced by subtle multiple variables, contributed in part by the mother and in part by the child. We make no claim to having unraveled these in only two years of investigation. But no matter what evidence the future may disclose, our first experiments have shown that contact comfort is a decisive variable in this relationship.

Such generalization is powerfully supported by the results of the next phase of our investigation. The time that the infant monkeys spent cuddling on their surrogate mothers was a strong but perhaps not conclusive index of emotional attachment. Would they also seek the inanimate mother for comfort and security when they were subjected to emotional stress? With this question in mind we exposed our monkey infants to the stress of fear by presenting them with strange objects, for example a mechanical teddy bear which moved forward, beating a drum. Whether the infants had nursed from the wire or the cloth mother, they overwhelmingly sought succor from the cloth one; this differential in behavior was enhanced with the passage of time and the accrual of experience. Early in this series of experiments the terrified infant might rush blindly to the wire mother, but even if it did so it would soon abandon her for the cloth mother. The infant would cling to its cloth mother, rubbing its body against hers. Then, with its fears assuaged through intimate contact with the moth-

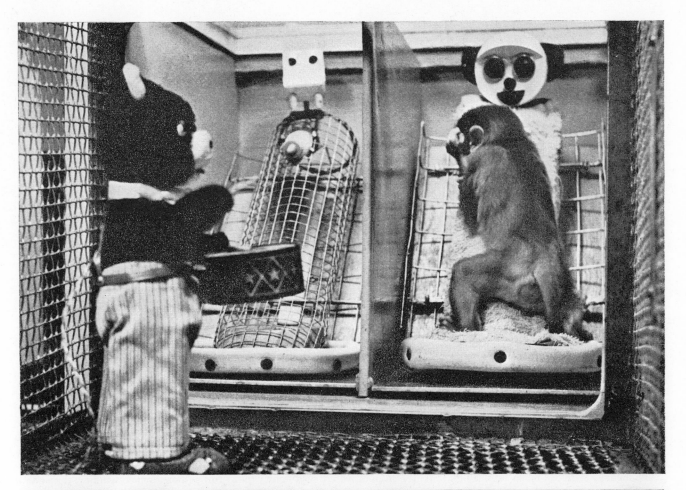

**FRIGHTENING OBJECTS** such as a mechanical teddy bear caused almost all infant monkeys to flee blindly to the cloth mother, as in the top photograph. Once reassured by pressing and rubbing against her, they would then look at the strange object (*bottom*).

"OPEN FIELD TEST" involved placing a monkey in a room far larger than its accustomed cage; unfamiliar objects added an addi-tional disturbing element. If no mother was present, the infant would typically huddle in a corner (*left*). The wire mother did

er, it would turn to look at the previously terrifying bear without the slightest sign of alarm. Indeed, the infant would some-times even leave the protection of the mother and approach the object that a few minutes before had reduced it to abject terror.

The analogy with the behavior of hu-man infants requires no elaboration. We found that the analogy extends even to less obviously stressful situations. When a child is taken to a strange place, he usually remains composed and happy so long as his mother is nearby. If the moth-er gets out of sight, however, the child is often seized with fear and distress. We developed the same response in our infant monkeys when we exposed them to a room that was far larger than the cages to which they were accustomed. In the room we had placed a number of unfamiliar objects such as a small arti-ficial tree, a crumpled piece of paper, a folded gauze diaper, a wooden block and a doorknob [*a similar experiment is depicted in the illustrations on these two pages*]. If the cloth mother was in the room, the infant would rush wildly to her, climb upon her, rub against her and cling to her tightly. As in the previous experiment, its fear then sharply di-minished or vanished. The infant would begin to climb over the mother's body and to explore and manipulate her face. Soon it would leave the mother to inves-tigate the new world, and the unfamiliar objects would become playthings. In a typical behavior sequence, the infant might manipulate the tree, return to the mother, crumple the wad-of paper, bring it to the mother, explore the block, ex-

plore the doorknob, play with the paper and return to the mother. So long as the mother provided a psychological "base of operations" the infants were unafraid and their behavior remained positive, exploratory and playful.

If the cloth mother was absent, how-ever, the infants would rush across the test room and throw themselves face-down on the floor, clutching their heads and bodies and screaming their distress. Records kept by two independent ob-servers—scoring for such "fear indices" as crying, crouching, rocking and thumb-and toe-sucking—showed that the emo-tionality scores of the infants nearly tripled. But no quantitative measure-ment can convey the contrast between the positive, outgoing activities in the presence of the cloth mother and the stereotyped withdrawn and disturbed behavior in the motherless situation.

The bare wire mother provided no more reassurance in this "open field" test than no mother at all. Control tests on monkeys that from birth had known only the wire mother revealed that even these infants showed no affection for her and obtained no comfort from her presence. Indeed, this group of animals exhibited the highest emotionality scores of all. Typically they would run to some wall or corner of the room, clasp their heads and bodies and rock convulsively back and forth. Such activities closely re-semble the autistic behavior seen fre-quently among neglected children in and out of institutions.

In a final comparison of the cloth and wire mothers, we adapted an experiment originally devised by Robert A. Butler

at the Primate Laboratory. Butler had found that monkeys enclosed in a dimly lighted box would press a lever to open and reopen a window for hours on end for no reward other than the chance to look out. The rate of lever-pressing de-pended on what the monkeys saw through the opened window; the sight of another monkey elicited far more activi-ty than that of a bowl of fruit or an emp-ty room [see "Curiosity in Monkeys," by Robert A. Butler; SCIENTIFIC AMERICAN offprint 426]. We now know that this "curiosity response" is innate. Three-day-old monkeys, barely able to walk, will crawl across the floor of the box to reach a lever which briefly opens the window; some press the lever hundreds of times within a few hours.

When we tested our monkey infants in the "Butler box," we found that those reared with both cloth and wire mothers showed as high a response to the cloth mother as to another monkey, but dis-played no more interest in the wire mother than in an empty room. In this test, as in all the others, the monkeys fed on the wire mother behaved the same as those fed on the cloth mother. A con-trol group raised with no mothers at all found the cloth mother no more inter-esting than the wire mother and neither as interesting as another monkey.

Thus all the objective tests we have been able to devise agree in showing that the infant monkey's relationship to its surrogate mother is a full one. Com-parison with the behavior of infant mon-keys raised by their real mothers con-firms this view. Like our experimental monkeys, these infants spend many

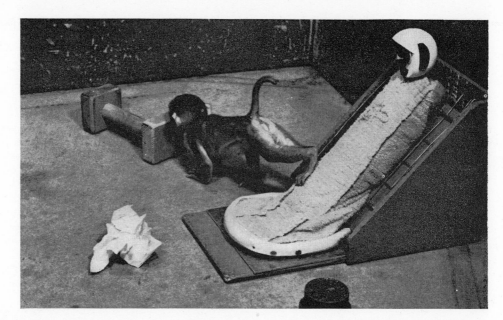

not alter this pattern of fearful behavior, but the cloth mother provided quick reassurance. The infant would first cling to her (*center*) and then set out to explore the room and play with the objects (*right*), returning from time to time for more reassurance.

hours a day clinging to their mothers, and run to them for comfort or reassurance when they are frightened. The deep and abiding bond between mother and child appears to be essentially the same, whether the mother is real or a cloth surrogate.

While bodily contact clearly plays the prime role in developing infantile affection, other types of stimulation presumably supplement its effects. We have therefore embarked on a search for these other factors. The activity of a live monkey mother, for example, provides her infant with frequent motion stimulation. In many human cultures mothers bind their babies to them when they go about their daily chores; in our own culture parents know very well that rocking a baby or walking with him somehow promotes his psychological and physiological well-being. Accordingly we compared the responsiveness of infant monkeys to two cloth mothers, one stationary and one rocking. All of them preferred the rocking mother, though the degree of preference varied considerably from day to day and from monkey to monkey. An experiment with a rocking crib and a stationary one gave similar results. Motion does appear to enhance affection, albeit far less significantly than simple contact.

The act of clinging, in itself, also seems to have a role in promoting psychological and physiological well-being. Even before we began our studies of affection, we noticed that a newborn monkey raised in a bare wire cage survived with difficulty unless we provided it with a cone to which it could cling. Re-

cently we have raised two groups of monkeys, one with a padded crib instead of a mother and the other with a cloth mother as well as a crib. Infants in the latter group actually spend more time on the crib than on the mother, probably because the steep incline of the mother's cloth surface makes her a less satisfactory sleeping platform. In the open-field test, the infants raised with a crib but no mother clearly derived some emotional support from the presence of the crib. But those raised with both showed an unequivocal preference for the mother they could cling to, and they evidenced the benefit of the superior emotional succor they gained from her.

Still other elements in the relationship remain to be investigated systematically. Common sense would suggest that the warmth of the mother's body plays its part in strengthening the infant's ties to her. Our own observations have not yet confirmed this hypothesis. Heating a cloth mother does not seem to increase her attractiveness to the infant monkey, and infants readily abandon a heating pad for an unheated mother surrogate. However, our laboratory is kept comfortably warm at all times; experiments in a chilly environment might well yield quite different results.

Visual stimulation may forge an additional link. When they are about three months old, the monkeys begin to observe and manipulate the head, face and eyes of their mother surrogates; human infants show the same sort of delayed responsiveness to visual stimuli. Such stimuli are known to have marked ef-

fects on the behavior of many young animals. The Austrian zoologist Konrad Lorenz has demonstrated a process called "imprinting"; he has shown that the young of some species of birds become attached to the first moving object they perceive, normally their mothers [see the preceding article, "'Imprinting' in Animals" by Eckhard H. Hess, page 195]. It is also possible that particular sounds and even odors may play some role in the normal development of responses or attention.

The depth and persistence of attachment to the mother depend not only on the kind of stimuli that the young animal receives but also on when it receives them. Experiments with ducks show that imprinting is most effective during a critical period soon after hatching; beyond a certain age it cannot take place at all. Clinical experience with human beings indicates that people who have been deprived of affection in infancy may have difficulty forming affectional ties in later life. From preliminary experiments with our monkeys we have found that their affectional responses develop, or fail to develop, according to a similar pattern.

Early in our investigation we had segregated four infant monkeys as a general control group, denying them physical contact either with a mother surrogate or with other monkeys. After about eight months we placed them in cages with access to both cloth and wire mothers. At first they were afraid of both surrogates, but within a few days they began to respond in much the same way as the other infants. Soon they were

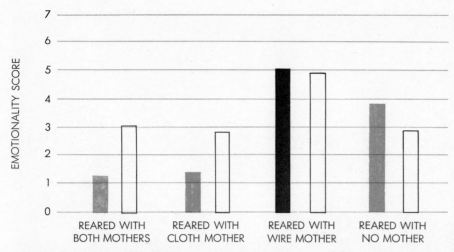

SCORES IN OPEN FIELD TEST show that all infant monkeys familiar with the cloth mother were much less disturbed when she was present (*color*) than when no mother was present (*white*); scores under 2 indicate unfrightened behavior. Infants that had known only the wire mother were greatly disturbed whether she was present (*black*) or not (*white*).

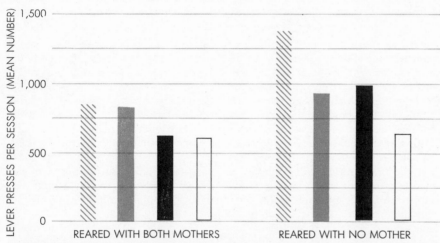

"CURIOSITY TEST" SHOWED THAT monkeys reared with both mothers displayed as much interest in the cloth mother (*solid color*) as in another monkey (*hatched color*); the wire mother (*black*) was no more interesting than an empty chamber (*white*). Monkeys reared with no mother found cloth and wire mother less interesting than another monkey.

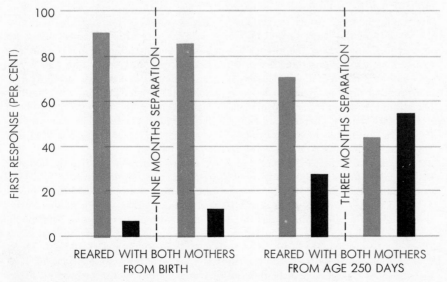

EARLY "MOTHERING" produced a strong and unchanging preference for the cloth mother (*color*) over the wire mother (*black*). Monkeys deprived of early mothering showed less marked preferences before separation and no significant preference subsequently.

spending less than an hour a day with the wire mother and eight to 10 hours with the cloth mother. Significantly, however, they spent little more than half as much time with the cloth mother as did infants raised with her from birth.

In the open-field test these "orphan" monkeys derived far less reassurance from the cloth mothers than did the other infants. The deprivation of physical contact during their first eight months had plainly affected the capacity of these infants to develop the full and normal pattern of affection. We found a further indication of the psychological damage wrought by early lack of mothering when we tested the degree to which infant monkeys retained their attachments to their mothers. Infants raised with a cloth mother from birth and separated from her at about five and a half months showed little or no loss of responsiveness even after 18 months of separation. In some cases it seemed that absence had made the heart grow fonder. The monkeys that had known a mother surrogate only after the age of eight months, however, rapidly lost whatever responsiveness they had acquired. The long period of maternal deprivation had evidently left them incapable of forming a lasting affectional tie.

The effects of maternal separation and deprivation in the human infant have scarcely been investigated, in spite of their implications concerning child-rearing practices. The long period of infant-maternal dependency in the monkey provides a real opportunity for investigating persisting disturbances produced by inconsistent or punishing mother surrogates.

Above and beyond demonstration of the surprising importance of contact comfort as a prime requisite in the formation of an infant's love for its mother —and the discovery of the unimportant or nonexistent role of the breast and act of nursing—our investigations have established a secure experimental approach to this realm of dramatic and subtle emotional relationships. The further exploitation of the broad field of research that now opens up depends merely upon the availability of infant monkeys. We expect to extend our researches by undertaking the study of the mother's (and even the father's!) love for the infant, using real monkey infants or infant surrogates. Finally, with such techniques established, there appears to be no reason why we cannot at some future time investigate the fundamental neurophysiological and biochemical variables underlying affection and love.

# 25 Attitude and Pupil Size

ECKHARD H. HESS · April 1965

One night about five years ago I was lying in bed leafing through a book of strikingly beautiful animal photographs. My wife happened to glance over at me and remarked that the light must be bad—my pupils were unusually large. It seemed to me that there was plenty of light coming from the bedside lamp and I said so, but she insisted that my pupils were dilated. As a psychologist who is interested in visual perception, I was puzzled by this little episode. Later, as I was trying to go to sleep, I recalled that someone had once reported a correlation between a person's pupil size and his emotional response to certain aspects of his environment. In this case it was difficult to see an emotional component. It seemed more a matter of intellectual interest, and no increase in pupil size had been reported for that.

The next morning I went to my laboratory at the University of Chicago. As soon as I got there I collected a number of pictures—all landscapes except for one seminude "pinup." When my assistant, James M. Polt, came in, I made him the subject of a quick experiment. I shuffled the pictures and, holding them above my eyes where I could not see them, showed them to Polt one at a time and watched his eyes as he looked at them. When I displayed the seventh picture, I noted a distinct increase in the size of his pupils; I checked the picture, and of course it was the pinup he had been looking at. Polt and I then embarked on an investigation of the relation between pupil size and mental activity.

The idea that the eyes are clues to emotions—"windows of the soul," as the French poet Guillaume de Salluste wrote—is almost commonplace in literature and everyday language. We say

"His eyes were like saucers" or "His eyes were pinpoints of hate"; we use such terms as "beady-eyed" or "bug-eyed" or "hard-eyed." In his *Expressions of Emotion in Man and Animals* Charles Darwin referred to the widening and narrowing of the eyes, accomplished by movements of the eyelids and eyebrows, as signs of human emotion; he apparently assumed that the pupil dilated and contracted only as a physiological mechanism responsive to changes in light intensity.

This light reflex is controlled by one of the two divisions of the autonomic nervous system: the parasympathetic system. Later investigators noted that pupil size is also governed by the other division of the autonomic system—the sympathetic system—in response to strong emotional states and that it can vary with the progress of mental activity. On a less sophisticated level some people to whom it is important to know what someone else is thinking appear to have been aware of the pupil-size phenomenon for a long time. It is said that magicians doing card tricks can identify the card a person is thinking about by watching his pupils enlarge when the card is turned up, and that Chinese jade dealers watch a buyer's pupils to know when he is impressed by a specimen and is likely to pay a high price. Polt and I have been able to study the pupil response in detail and to show what a remarkably sensitive indicator of certain mental activities it can be. We believe it can provide quantitative data on the effects of visual and other sensory stimulation, on cerebral processes and even on changes in fairly complex attitudes.

Most of our early experiments related pupil size to the interest value and "emotionality" of visual stimuli. Our

techniques for these studies are quite simple. The subject peers into a box, looking at a screen on which we project the stimulus picture. A mirror reflects the image of his eye into a motion-picture camera. First we show a control slide that is carefully matched in overall brightness to the stimulus slide that will follow it; this adapts the subject's eyes to the light intensity of the stimulus slide. At various points on the control slide are numbers that direct the subject's gaze to the center of the field. Meanwhile the camera, operating at the rate of two frames per second, records the size of his pupil. After 10 seconds the control slide is switched off and the stimulus slide is projected for 10 seconds; as the subject looks at it the camera continues to make two pictures of his eye per second. The sequence of control and stimulus is repeated about 10 or 12 times a sitting. To score the response to a stimulus we compare the average size of the pupil as photographed during the showing of the control slide with its average size during the stimulus period. Usually we simply project the negative image of the pupil, a bright spot of light, on a screen and measure the diameter with a ruler; alternatively we record the changes in size electronically by measuring the area of the pupil spot with a photocell.

In our first experiment, before we were able to control accurately for brightness, we tested four men and two women, reasoning that a significant difference in the reactions of subjects of different sex to the same picture would be evidence of a pupil response to something other than light intensity. The results confirmed our expectations: the men's pupils dilated more at the sight of a female pinup than the women's

SUBJECT in pupil-response studies peers into a box, looking at a rear-projection screen on which slides are flashed from the pro-jector at right. A motor-driven camera mounted on the box makes a continuous record of pupil size at the rate of two frames a second.

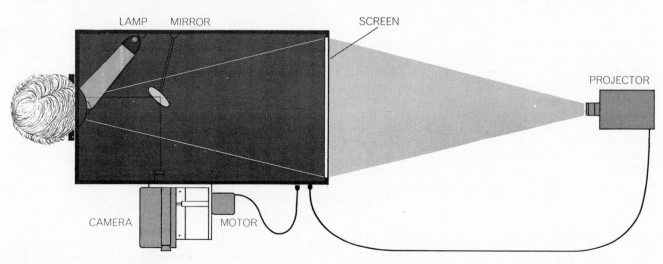

PUPIL-RESPONSE APPARATUS is simple. The lamp and the camera film work in the infrared. A timer advances the projector every 10 seconds, flashing a control slide and a stimulus slide alter-nately. The mirror is below eye level so that view of screen is clear.

did; the women showed a greater response than the men did to a picture of a baby or of a mother and baby and to a male pinup [*see illustration at right*]. We interpreted dilation in these cases as an indication of interest.

We then undertook another demonstration designed to eliminate the role of brightness. In this experiment we did not show a control slide; only the general room lighting illuminated the rear-projection screen of the apparatus during the control period. When the stimulus slide came on, every part of the screen was therefore at least somewhat brighter than it had been during the control period. If the eye responded only to changes in light intensity, then the response by all subjects to any stimulus ought to be negative; that is, the pupil should constrict slightly every time. This was not the case; we got positive responses in those subjects and for just those stimuli that would have been expected, on the basis of the results of the first study, to produce positive responses. We also got constriction, but only for stimuli that the person involved might be expected to find distasteful or unappealing.

These negative responses, exemplified by the reaction of most of our female subjects to pictures of sharks, were not isolated phenomena; constriction is as characteristic in the case of certain aversive stimuli as dilation is in the case of interesting or pleasant pictures. We observed a strong negative response, for example, when subjects were shown a picture of a cross-eyed or crippled child; as those being tested said, they simply did not like to look at such pictures. One woman went so far as to close her eyes when one of the pictures was on the screen, giving what might be considered the ultimate in negative responses. The negative response also turned up in a number of subjects presented with examples of modern paintings, particularly abstract ones. (We were interested to note that some people who insisted that they liked modern art showed strong negative responses to almost all the modern paintings we showed them.) The results are consistent with a finding by the Soviet psychologist A. R. Shachnowich that a person's pupils may constrict when he looks at unfamiliar geometric patterns.

We have come on one special category of stimuli, examples of which are pictures of dead soldiers on a battlefield, piles of corpses in a concentration camp and the body of a murdered gang-

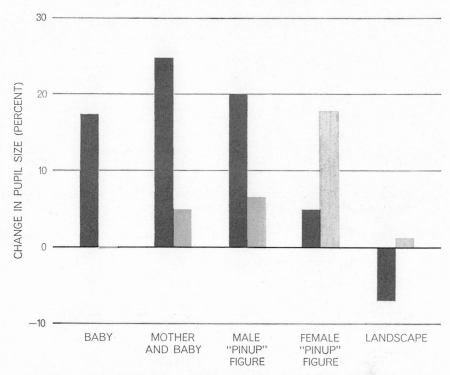

DIFFERENT RESPONSES to the same picture by female subjects (*gray bars*) and male (*colored bars*) established that the pupil response was independent of light intensity. The bars show changes in average area of pupils from the control period to the stimulus period.

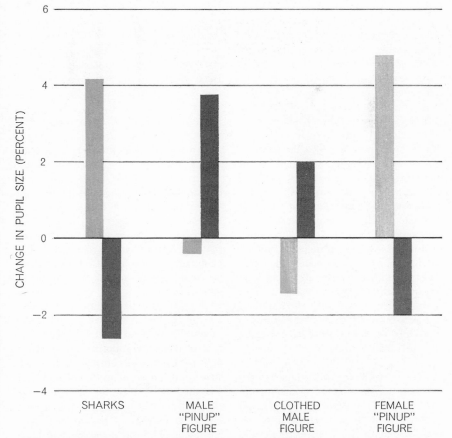

ROLE OF BRIGHTNESS was also eliminated in an experiment in which the screen was unlighted before the stimulus appeared. Whereas responses to light alone would therefore have resulted in constriction, some pictures caused dilation in men (*colored bars*) and women (*gray*). In this experiment pupil diameter was tabulated rather than area.

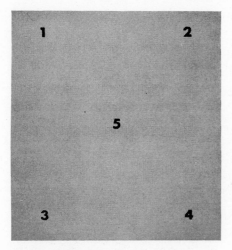

CONTROL SLIDE provides calibration for experiments involving direction of gaze (*opposite page*). The subject looks at the five numbers in sequence and the camera records the resulting movements of his pupil.

ster. One might expect these to be "negative," and indeed they do produce extreme pupil constriction in some subjects, but they elicit a very different pattern of responses in others. On initial exposure the subject often responds with a large increase, rather than a decrease, in pupil size. Then, with repeated presentations, there is a shift to a negative response; the shift is usually accomplished after three to five exposures, and the time interval between those exposures seems to make little difference. Our impression was that these were negative stimuli with an additional "shock" content that prompted a strong emotional reaction. To check this hypothesis we attached electrodes to the hands of some of our volunteers and recorded their galvanic skin response, a measure of the electrical resistance of the skin that has been correlated with emotional level and is a component of most so-called lie-detector tests. As we had anticipated, stimuli we had classified as "shocking" got a high galvanic skin response along with the initial high pupil response in most subjects. After repeated presentations the skin response decreased rapidly as the pupil response shifted from dilation to constriction.

Although we have dealt primarily with positive stimuli, the evidence suggests that at least with respect to visual material there is a continuum of responses that ranges from extreme dilation for interesting or pleasing stimuli to extreme constriction for material that is unpleasant or distasteful to the viewer. In the presence of uninteresting or boring pictures we find only slight random variations in pupil size.

One of the most interesting things about the changes in pupil size is that they are extremely sensitive, sometimes revealing different responses to stimuli that at the verbal level seem to the person being tested quite similar. We once demonstrated this effect with a pair of stimulus photographs that in themselves provided an interesting illustration of the relation between pupil size and personality. In a series of pictures shown to a group of 20 men we included two photographs of an attractive young woman. These two slides were identical except for the fact that one had been retouched to make the woman's pupils extra large and the other to make them very small. The average response to the picture with the large pupils was more than twice as strong as the response to the one with small pupils; nevertheless, when the men were questioned after the experimental session, most of them reported that the two pictures were identical. Some did say that one was "more feminine" or "prettier" or "softer." None noticed that one had larger pupils than the other. In fact, they had to be shown the difference. As long ago as the Middle Ages women dilated their pupils with the drug belladonna (which means "beautiful woman" in Italian). Clearly large pupils are attractive to men, but the response to them—at least in our subjects—is apparently at a nonverbal level. One might hazard a guess that what is appealing about large pupils in a woman is that they imply extraordinary interest in the man she is with!

Pupillary activity can serve as a measure of motivation. We have investigated the effect of hunger, which is a standard approach in psychological studies of motivation. It occurred to us that a person's physiological state might be a factor in the pupil response when we analyzed the results of a study in which several of the stimulus slides were pictures of food—rather attractive pictures to which we had expected the subjects to respond positively. The general response was positive, but about half of the people tested had much stronger responses than the others. After puzzling over this for a while we checked our logbook and found that about 90 percent of the subjects who had evinced strong responses had been tested in the late morning or late afternoon—when, it seemed obvious, they should have been hungrier than the people tested soon after breakfast or lunch.

To be sure, not everyone is equally hungry a given number of hours after eating, but when we tested two groups controlled for length of time without food, our results were unequivocal: the pupil responses of 10 subjects who were "deprived" for four or five hours were more than two and a half times larger than those of 10 subjects who had eaten a meal within an hour before being tested. The mean responses of the two groups were 11.3 percent and 4.4 percent respectively.

Interestingly enough the pupils respond not only to visual stimuli but also to stimuli affecting other senses. So far our most systematic research on nonvisual stimuli has dealt with the sense of taste. The subject places his head in a modified apparatus that leaves his mouth free; he holds a flexible straw to which the experimenter can raise a cup of the liquid to be tasted. During the test the taster keeps his eyes on an X projected on the screen, and the camera records any changes in pupil size.

Our first study involved a variety of presumably pleasant-tasting liquids—carbonated drinks, chocolate drinks and milk—and some unpleasant-tasting ones, including concentrated lemon juice and a solution of quinine. We were surprised to find that both the pleasant and the unpleasant liquids brought an increase in pupil size compared with a "control" of water. Then we decided to test a series of similar liquids, all presumably on the positive side of the "pleasant-unpleasant" continuum, to see if, as in the case of visual material, some of the stimuli would elicit greater responses than others. We selected five "orange" beverages and had each subject alternate sips of water with sips of a beverage. One of the five orange beverages caused a significantly larger average increase in pupil size than the others did; the same drink also won on the basis of verbal preferences expressed by the subjects after they had been through the pupil-size test. Although we still have a good deal of work to do on taste, particularly with regard to the response to unpleasant stimuli, we are encouraged by the results so far. The essential sensitivity of the pupil response suggests that it can reveal preferences in some cases in which the actual taste differences are so slight that the subject cannot even articulate them—a possibility with interesting implications for market research.

We have also had our volunteers listen to taped excerpts of music while

DIRECTIONAL ANALYSIS reveals where a subject was looking when each frame of film was made as well as how large his pupil was. Superposed on the upper reproduction of Leon Kroll's "Morning on the Cape" are symbols showing the sequence of fixations by a female subject looking at the painting; a man's responses are shown below. The light-color symbols indicate a pupil size about the same as during the preceding control period; open symbols denote smaller responses and dark-color symbols larger responses. The experimenters determine the direction of gaze by shining light through the film negative; the beam that passes through the image of the pupil is projected on a photograph of the stimulus (in this case the painting) and its position is recorded.

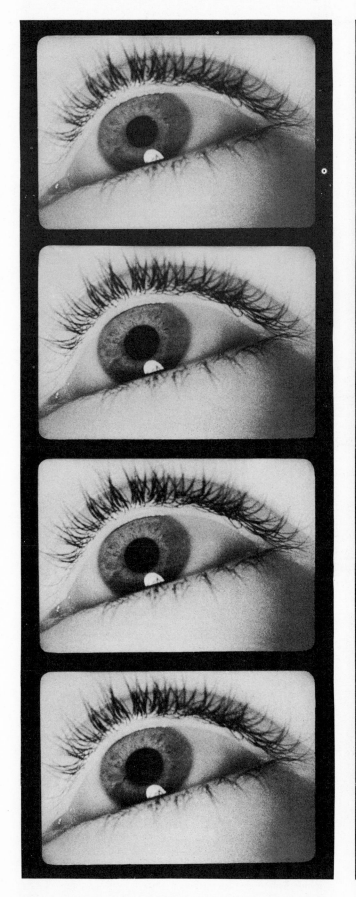

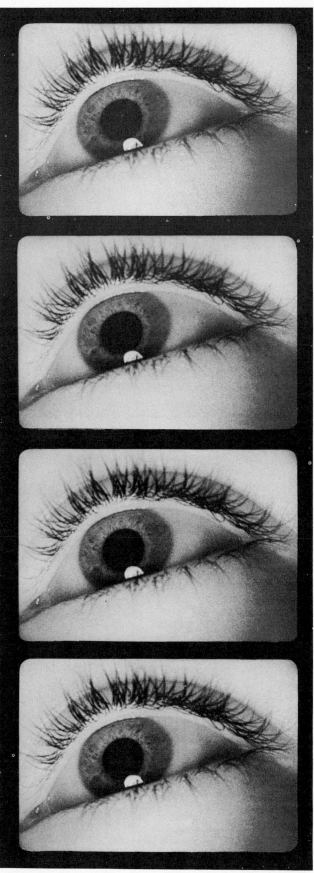

PUPIL SIZE varies with the interest value of a visual stimulus. In the author's laboratory a subject's eye is filmed as he looks at slides flashed on a screen. These consecutive frames (*top to bottom at left and top to bottom at right*) show the eye of a male subject during the first four seconds after a photograph of a woman's face appeared. His pupil increased in diameter 30 percent.

the camera monitors their pupil size. We find different responses to different compositions, apparently depending on individual preference. As in the case of the taste stimuli, however, the response to music seems always to be in a positive direction: the pupil becomes larger when music of any kind is being played. We have begun to test for the effect of taped verbal statements and individual words, which also seem to elicit different pupil responses. Research in these areas, together with some preliminary

work concerning the sense of smell, supports the hypothesis that the pupil is closely associated not only with visual centers in the brain but also with other brain centers. In general it strongly suggests that pupillary changes reflect ongoing activity in the brain.

It is not surprising that the response of the pupil should be intimately associated with mental activity. Embryologically and anatomically the eye is an extension of the brain; it is almost

as though a portion of the brain were in plain sight for the psychologist to peer at. Once it is, so to speak, "calibrated" the pupil response should make it possible to observe ongoing mental behavior directly and without requiring the investigator to attach to his subject electrodes or other equipment that may affect the very behavior he seeks to observe.

More than 50 years ago German psychologists noted that mental activity (solving arithmetical problems, for ex-

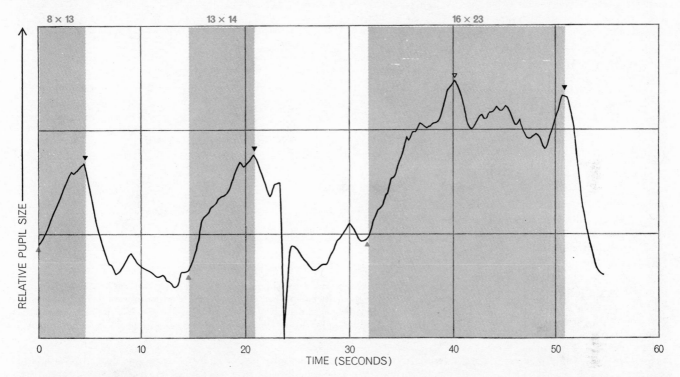

**CHANGES IN PUPIL SIZE** are traced in a subject doing the three mental-arithmetic problems shown at the top. Beginning when the problem is posed (*colored triangles*), the pupil dilates until the answer is given (*solid black triangles*). This subject appears to have reached a solution of the third problem (*open triangle*) and then to have reconsidered, checking his answer before giving it.

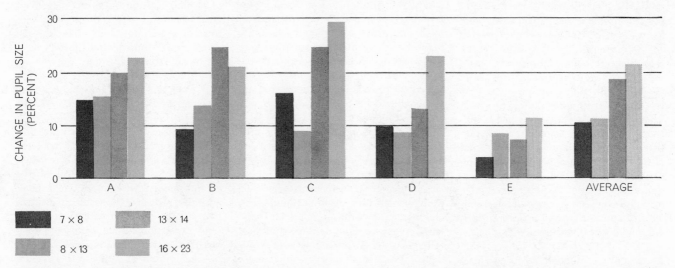

**INDIVIDUAL DIFFERENCES** in pupil response while solving multiplication problems reflect the fact that two of the five subjects, *D* and *E*, could do mental arithmetic with less effort than the others. The change in pupil size was computed by comparing the average size in the five frames before the problem was posed with the average in the five frames just before the answer was given.

ample) caused a gross increase in pupil size. We decided this would be a good area for detailed study in an effort to see how precise and differentiated an indicator the response could be. We present mental-arithmetic problems of varying difficulty to volunteers and then obtain a continuous trace of their pupil response by measuring the filmed images of the pupil with a photocell [*see upper illustration on preceding page*]. As soon as the problem is presented the size of the pupil begins to increase. It reaches a maximum as the subject arrives at his solution and then immediately starts to decrease, returning to its base level as soon as the answer is verbalized. If the subject is told to solve the problem but not give the answer, there is some decrease at the instant of solution but the pupil remains abnormally large; then, when the experimenter asks for the solution, the pupil returns to its base level as the subject verbalizes the answer.

In one study we tested five people, two who seemed to be able to do mental arithmetic easily and three for whom even simple multiplication required a lot of effort. The pupil-response results reflect these individual differences [*see lower illustration on preceding page*] and also show a fairly consistent increase in dilation as the problems increase in difficulty. Individual differences of another kind are revealed by the trace of a subject's pupil size. Most subjects do have a response that drops to normal as soon as they give the answer. In some people, however, the size of the pupil decreases momentarily after the answer is given and then goes up again, sometimes as high as the original peak, suggesting that the worried subject is working the problem over again to be sure he was correct. Other people, judging by the response record, tend to recheck their answers before announcing them.

We have found a similar response in spelling, with the maximum pupil size correlated to the difficulty of the word. The response also appears when a subject is working an anagram, a situation that is not very different from the kind of mental activity associated with decision-making. We believe the pupil-response technique should be valuable for studying the course of decision-making and perhaps for assessing decision-making abilities in an individual.

It is always difficult to elicit from someone information that involves his private attitudes toward some person or concept or thing. The pupil-

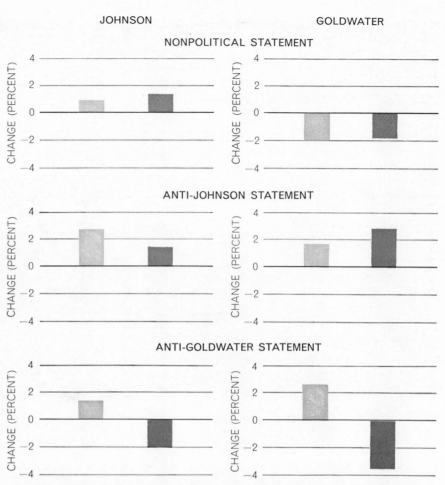

ATTITUDE CHANGES are revealed by responses to Johnson (*left*) and Goldwater (*right*) before (*light bars*) and after (*dark bars*) subjects read a statement supplied by the experimenter. Nonpolitical material had no appreciable effect. The anti-Johnson material had the expected effect. Bitter anti-Goldwater material made response to both candidates negative.

response technique can measure just such attitudes. We have established that the correlation between a person's expressed attitude and his "measured pupil" attitude can vary widely, depending on the topic. For example, we tested 64 people with five pictures of foods and also asked them to rank the foods from favorite to least preferred. When we matched each person's verbal report with his pupil response, we obtained 61 positive correlations—a result one could expect to get by chance only once in a million times.

The correlation is poor in an area that involves social values or pressures, however. For example, we do not get such good agreement between pupillary and verbal responses when we show women pictures of seminude men and women. Nor did we get good correlation when we did a political study last fall. We showed photographs of President Johnson and Barry Goldwater to 34 University of Chicago students, faculty members and employees. Everyone professed to be in favor of Johnson and

against Goldwater. The pupil-response test, however, had indicated that about a third of these people actually had a slightly more positive attitude toward Goldwater than toward Johnson.

To be sure, the pupil test may overemphasize the effect of physical appearance; certainly our data do not prove that a third of the subjects went on to vote for Goldwater. But the results do raise the interesting possibility that at least some of them did, and that in the liberal atmosphere of the university these people found it difficult to utter any pro-Goldwater sentiment. The results suggest that our technique, by which we measure a response that is not under the control of the person being tested, may yield more accurate representations of an attitude than can be obtained with even a well-drawn questionnaire or with some devious "projective" technique in which a person's verbal or motor responses are recorded in an effort to uncover his real feelings.

For me the most interesting aspect

**TWO PHOTOGRAPHS,** almost identical, elicited very different responses from a group of male subjects. One in which a girl's eyes were retouched, as at left, to make the pupils large got a greater response than one in which the pupils were made small (*right*).

of our work has been the measurement of changes in attitude. We begin by determining the pupil response of one of our volunteers to someone's picture. Then we have the subject read some kind of informative material, we retest for the response and compare the "before" and "after" scores. In one case the reading material consisted of a passage indicating that the man whose picture had been displayed was the former commandant of the concentration camp at Auschwitz. When we then remeasured the subject's pupil response to the man in question, we found that a more negative attitude had clearly developed as a result of the intervening reading.

Take another and more hypothetical example: Suppose a patient seeking psychotherapy has a fear of people with beards. We ought to be able to get a pupillary measure of his attitude by showing him photographs of bearded men, among others, and then be able to check on the course of treatment by repeating the test later. Regardless of whether what intervenes is straightforward information, psychotherapy, political propaganda, advertising or any other material intended to change attitudes, it should be possible to monitor the effectiveness of that material by measuring changes in pupil size, and to

do this with a number of people at any desired interval.

One recent study along these lines will illustrate the possibilities. We showed five different photographs of President Johnson and five of Goldwater, along with a single photograph of former presidents Kennedy and Eisenhower, to three groups of people. One group thereupon read anti-Johnson material, another read anti-Goldwater material and the third read some excerpts from a psychology journal that had no political content. Then each group was retested.

Now the people who had read the anti-Johnson material showed a slightly smaller response than before to Johnson and a slightly larger response than before to Goldwater. Some extremely negative anti-Goldwater material, which one of my assistants apparently found very easy to write, had a different kind of effect. It did cause the expected decrease in the response to Goldwater, but it also caused a large drop in the response to Johnson and even to Eisenhower! The only person who was unaffected was Kennedy. This may indicate that bitter campaign propaganda can lower a person's attitude toward politicians in general, Kennedy alone being spared for obvious reasons.

The pupil response promises to be

a new tool with which to probe the mind. We are applying it now in a variety of studies. One deals with the development in young people of sexual interest and of identification with parents from preschool age to high school age. In an attempt to establish personality differences, we are tabulating the responses of a number of subjects to pictures of people under stress and pictures of the same people after they have been released from the stressful situation. Our other current study deals with volunteers who are experiencing changes in perception as the result of hypnotic suggestion. In the perception laboratory of Marplan, a communications-research organization that has supported much of our work, Paula Drillman is studying responses to packages, products and advertising on television and in other media. Several laboratories at Chicago and elsewhere are employing our techniques to study such diverse problems as the process of decision-making, the effect of certain kinds of experience on the attitudes of white people toward Negroes and the efficacy of different methods of problem-solving. Those of us engaged in this work have the feeling that we have only begun to understand and exploit the information implicit in the dilations and constrictions of the pupil.

# 26 Ulcers in "Executive" Monkeys

JOSEPH V. BRADY · October 1958

Physicians and laymen alike have long recognized that emotional stress can produce bodily disease. Psychic disturbances can induce certain skin and respiratory disorders, can set off attacks of allergic asthma and may even play a part in some forms of heart disease. Of all the body's systems, however, the gastrointestinal tract is perhaps the most vulnerable to emotional stress. The worries, fears, conflicts and anxieties of daily life can produce gastrointestinal disorders ranging from the "nervous stomach," which most of us know at first hand, to the painful and often disabling ulcers which are the traditional occupational disease of business executives.

Emotional stress appears to produce ulcers by increasing the flow of the stomach's acid juices. The connection between emotional disturbance, stomach secretion and ulcers is well documented. A recent study of 2,000 Army draftees, for example, found that those who showed emotional disturbance and excessive gastric secretion during their initial physical examination developed

**CONDITIONING EXPERIMENT** involves training monkeys in "restraining chairs." Both animals receive brief electric shocks at regular intervals. The "executive" monkey (*left*) has learned to press the lever in its left hand, which prevents shocks to both animals. The control monkey (*right*) has lost interest in its lever, which is a dummy. Only executive monkeys developed ulcers.

ulcers later on under the strains of military life.

But not every kind of emotional stress produces ulcers, and the same kind of stress will do so in one person and not in another. Experimental investigation of the problem is difficult. Animals obviously cannot provide wholly satisfactory experimental models of human mind-body interactions. They can, however, be studied under controlled conditions, and it is through animal experiments that we are finding leads to the cause of ulcers as well as to the effect of emotional stress on the organism in general.

Various investigators have succeeded in inducing ulcers in experimental animals by subjecting them to physical stress. But the role of the emotional processes in such experiments has been uncertain. Experiments on dogs by George F. Mahl of Yale University Medical School indicate that a "fear producing" situation lasting many hours increases the animals' gastric secretions, but these animals do not develop ulcers. William L. Sawrey and John D. Weisz of the University of Colorado produced ulcers in rats by subjecting them to a conflict situation: keeping them in a box where they could obtain food and water only by standing on a grid which gave them a mild electric shock. But this experiment, as Sawrey and Weisz themselves pointed out, did not prove conclusively that emotional stress was the crucial factor in producing the ulcers.

Our studies of ulcers in monkeys at the Walter Reed Army Institute of Research developed somewhat fortuitously. For several years we had been investigating the emotional behavior of these animals. In some of our experiments we had been keeping monkeys in "restraining chairs" (in which they could move their heads and limbs but not their bodies) while we conditioned them in various ways. Since these procedures seemed to impose considerable emotional stress on the animals, we decided that we ought to know something about their physiological reactions. Preliminary investigation showed that stress brought about dramatic alterations in the hormone content of the animals' blood, but a more extensive study of 19 monkeys was brought to a halt when many of them died.

At first we considered this merely a stroke of bad luck, but the post-mortem findings showed that more than bad luck was involved. Many of the dead monkeys had developed ulcers as well as other extensive gastrointestinal damage. Such pathological conditions are normally rare in laboratory animals, and previous experiments with monkeys kept in restraining chairs up to six months convinced us that restraint alone did not produce the ulcers. Evidently the conditioning procedures were to blame.

One of the procedures which showed a high correlation with ulcers involved training the monkey to avoid an electric shock by pressing a lever. The animal received a brief shock on the feet at regular intervals, say, every 20 seconds. It could avoid the shock if it learned to press the lever at least once in every 20-second interval. It does not take a monkey very long to master this problem; within a short time it is pressing the lever far oftener than once in 20 seconds. Only occasionally does it slow down enough to receive a shock as a reminder.

One possibility, of course, was that the monkeys which had developed ulcers under this procedure had done so not because of the psychological stress in-

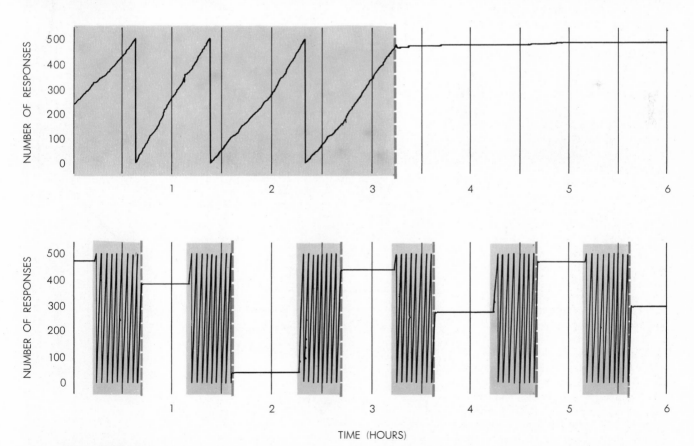

TIME (HOURS)

**RESPONSES OF MONKEYS** were recorded automatically. Slope of the lines shows the rate of lever-pressing (*vertical lines indicate resetting of stylus*). Upper chart shows responses of an executive monkey during the last half of a six-hour avoidance session (*colored area*) and the first half of a six-hour rest period; shocks were programmed every 20 seconds. Monkeys kept on this schedule developed ulcers. Lower chart shows responses during a 30-minutes-on, 30-minutes-off schedule with shocks programmed every two seconds. Monkeys on this schedule failed to develop ulcers, despite more intense activity and presumably greater psychic stress.

volved but rather as a cumulative result of the shocks. To test this possibility we set up a controlled experiment, using two monkeys in "yoked chairs" in which both monkeys received shocks but only one monkey could prevent them. The experimental or "executive" monkey could prevent shocks to himself and his partner by pressing the lever; the control monkey's lever was a dummy. Thus both animals were subjected to the same physical stress (*i.e.*, both received the same number of shocks at the same time), but only the "executive" monkey was under the psychological stress of having to press the lever.

We placed the monkeys on a continuous schedule of alternate periods of shock-avoidance and rest, arbitrarily choosing an interval of six hours for each period. As a cue for the executive monkey we provided a red light which was turned on during the avoidance periods and turned off during the "off" hours. The animal soon learned to press its lever at a rate averaging between 15 and 20 times a minute during the avoidance periods, and to stop pressing the lever when the red light was turned off. These responses showed no change throughout the experiment. The control monkey at first pressed the lever sporadically during both the avoidance and rest sessions, but lost interest in the lever within a few days.

After 23 days of a continuous six-hours-on, six-hours-off schedule the executive monkey died during one of the avoidance sessions. Our only advance warning had been the animal's failure to eat on the preceding day. It had lost no weight during the experiment, and it pressed the lever at an unflagging rate through the first two hours of its last avoidance session. Then it suddenly collapsed and had to be sacrificed. An autopsy revealed a large perforation in the wall of the duodenum—the upper part of the small intestine near its junction with the stomach, and a common site of ulcers in man. Microscopic analysis revealed both acute and chronic inflammation around this lesion. The control monkey, sacrificed in good health a few hours later, showed no gastrointestinal abnormalities. A second experiment using precisely the same procedure produced much the same results. This time the executive monkey developed ulcers in both the stomach and the duodenum; the control animal was again unaffected.

In a series of follow-up experiments which is still in progress we have tried to isolate the physiological and

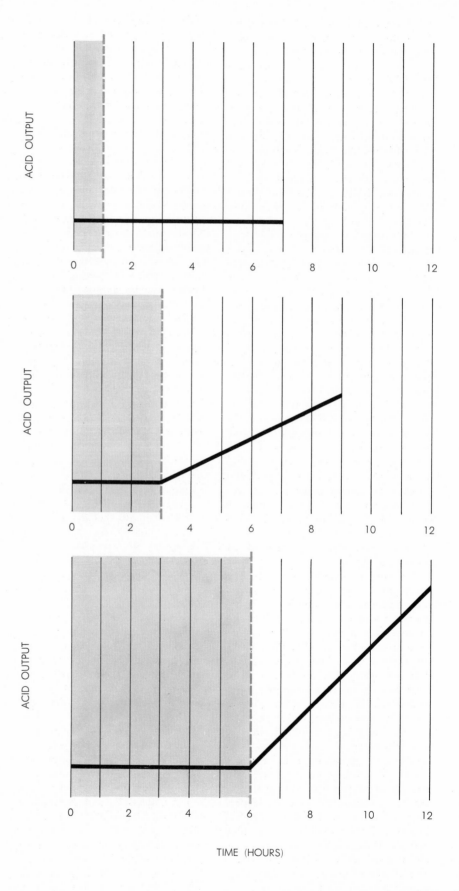

**STOMACH ACIDITY** of executive monkeys, as shown in these highly simplified charts, did not increase during avoidance sessions (*color*) but rather during the subsequent rest periods. The greatest increase followed a six-hour session; no rise followed a one-hour session.

psychological factors which produce the "laboratory ulcers." For example, one of our groups suggested that the "social" interaction between the two monkeys might be important. Certainly the most casual observation showed that considerable "communication" was going on between the two animals, who were seated within easy chattering distance of each other. We therefore studied several pairs of animals isolated from each other in soundproof "telephone booths." Unfortunately isolation failed to protect the executive monkeys, for they continued to develop ulcers.

More recently, however, we have found a factor or group of factors which does seem to be critical in producing ulcers. What we have learned seems to pivot on our chance selection of six hours as the interval for shock-avoidance and for rest in the conditioning procedure. We made this discovery when we sought to improve on the results of our experiments. Though laboratory animals can rarely be made to develop ulcers, we had come upon a procedure that seemed to produce ulcers "to order." The only uncertainty was the length of exposure required. This varied greatly among individual monkeys; some came down with ulcers in 18 days, others took as long as six weeks. If we could develop a technique guaranteed to produce ulcers in, say, 10 days, we could stop the shock-avoidance sessions on the eighth or ninth day, apply various therapeutic measures and study the monkey's response to them.

It seemed reasonable to assume that we might induce ulcers more rapidly and dependably by simply increasing the stress on the animals. We therefore put several monkeys on an 18-hours-on, six-hours-off schedule. After a few weeks one of the animals died, but of tuberculosis, not ulcers. The rest continued to press their levers week after week with no apparent ill effects. Finally, when it began to seem as if we might have to wait for the animals to die of old age, we sacrificed them—and found no gastrointestinal abnormalities whatever!

We put another group on an even more strenuous schedule: 30 minutes on and 30 minutes off, with the shocks programmed for every two seconds rather than every 20. Again one of the animals died, this time of a generalized virus infection unrelated to ulcers. The others, after weeks of frantic lever pressing, showed no gastrointestinal changes.

We had to conclude that the crucial factor was not the degree or even the frequency of stress but was to be sought in the relationship between the length of the stress period and that of the rest period. The six-hours-on, six-hours-off schedule had produced ulcers (and occasionally other somatic disorders) despite individual differences in monkeys, variations in diet and maintenance routines and gross alterations in preliminary physiological tests. No other schedule we had tried produced ulcers at all.

This unexpected finding suggested that we should investigate what was going on in the monkeys' stomachs during the conditioning procedure. A standard technique for investigating gastric processes in experimental animals makes use of an artificial opening, or fistula, in the animal's abdominal and stomach walls through which the contents of its stomach can be sampled. Such fistulas have played an important role in expanding our knowledge of the gastrointestinal system. In the early 19th century the famous U. S. Army surgeon William Beaumont made the first systematic study of the digestive process with the cooperation of a young Canadian who had a fistula due to an imperfectly healed gunshot wound. More than a century later Stewart G. Wolf, Jr., and Harold G. Wolff at the Cornell University Medical College, with the help of a man who had a similar injury, conducted a pioneer investigation of the relationship between emotional stress and ulcers. They found that situations which produced feelings of anxiety or aggression in their subject stepped up his gastric secretions and engorged his stomach wall with blood. Physiological changes of this sort, they believed, are the precursors of ulcers.

Edwin Polish of our department of neuroendocrinology has been studying the stomach acidity of some of our executive monkeys by means of artificial fistulas. His measurements, though far from complete, seem to provide one possible explanation of the results of our experiments.

The stomach secretions of the executive monkeys do indeed become considerably more acid, but not (as one might expect) during the avoidance periods. When the animals are actually pressing the levers the acidity of their stomachs rises little. The significant increase in acidity begins at the end of the avoidance session and reaches a peak several hours later, while the animal is presumably resting. This finding suggests a close relationship between the formation of ulcers and the cyclic character of the six-hours-on, six-hours-off procedure. Emotional stress, it appears, must be intermittent—turning the animal's system on and off, so to speak—if it is to cause ulcers. Continuous emotional stress seems to permit a stable adjustment (at least for a while) under which ulcers do not develop. It is tempting to consider the analogy of the vacuum tube or light bulb which seems to last much longer under conditions of continuous current than when it is subjected to frequent heating and cooling.

Like most analogies, this one limps badly and has its limitations. For example, our experiments show that periodic stress does not always bring on ulcers, and Polish's findings are consistent with this. His measurements indicate that the greatest increase in acidity occurs after a six-hour avoidance session. After a three-hour session acidity rises, but less sharply; after a one-hour session it does not rise at all [see illustration on page 218]. Periodic emotional stress apparently causes ulcers only if its period coincides with that of some natural rhythm of the gastrointestinal system.

Obviously our knowledge of the physiological and psychological processes which produce ulcers is far from complete. Our understanding of even the relatively well-controlled experiments I have described is just beginning to progress beyond the primitive level. We have yet to discover why emotional stress steps up the stomach's acidity later rather than immediately. We are still looking for a method of producing ulcers at will, in days rather than weeks. Eventually we hope to learn to detect an incipient ulcer before the animal collapses, by examining the subject's blood, urine and other secretions, thus making post-mortem examinations unnecessary.

There are many other questions about the effects of emotional stress which we have not yet begun to investigate. Really thorough examination of the experimental animals might well show other types of damage of which we are at present unaware. The two monkeys which died of causes unrelated to ulcers, for example, may have succumbed because their resistance had been lowered in some way by psychological stress. It would be surprising to find physical processes wholly unimpaired in monkeys who have been on a 30-minutes-on, 30-minutes-off schedule for several weeks. The opportunity to bring psychosomatic relationships under experimental scrutiny in the laboratory seems to open broad horizons for research into the causes and alleviation of this poorly understood class of ills.

*Ecological Approaches to Population Problems*

# Ecological Approaches to Population Problems

## INTRODUCTION

In the first chapter of Genesis we are told that God, after creating Adam and Eve, said to the primal pair: "Be fruitful, and multiply, and replenish the earth, and subdue it: and have dominion over the fish of the sea, and over the fowl of the air, and over every living thing that moveth upon the earth." In the opinion of many biologists this advice to "have dominion" over the living world has, by Western man, been taken too literally for his own good. We habitually speak of "conquering Nature," instead of living in harmony with her, as Eastern philosophers recommend. Because of greed and our imperfect knowledge of the subtleties of the living world our attempts to dominate nature often backfire.

LaMont C. Cole, in "The Ecosphere," has given us a broad scientific background against which all population problems can be oriented. In "The Human Population," Edward S. Deevey, Jr., has placed man's present population problems in an all-inclusive historical setting. From this orientation it is crystal clear that the rapid growth of population during the past century is an absolutely unique event. Such a growth rate has never occurred before; and it must soon come to an end. There is a natural tendency in human affairs to think that whatever has been true for the past three generations will continue forever. When we come to realize how mistaken is this expectation we may then be able to get on with the hard intellectual and emotional labor of preparing to live in a world we have never known—a world in which the rate of growth of the population is *zero*.

Even when we understand a problem completely at the intellectual level we may have great trouble carrying out the measures that are called for. Scott McVay tells the story of "The Last of the Great Whales," a story that is now unfolding before our eyes, while we stand wringing our hands helplessly. We know what is wrong, of course: the oceans are still treated as a "commons." The nation that shows restraint in harvesting them benefits all nations (including itself), but only slightly; whereas the nation that acts greedily benefits itself a great deal—in the short run. Selection favors gluttony and produces destruction. The answer to this type of problem was worked out in England in the eighteenth century when terrestrial commons were enclosed and converted to private property or private privilege. A field that is common property puts pressure on everyone to over-harvest in order to survive; when it is private property it is in the interest of its owner to harvest it at that rate which produces the highest sustainable yield. We cannot very well put fences in the ocean or restrict migrating species; but we must find some sort of logical equivalent of the Enclosure Acts of eighteenth-century England. Conscience is *not* such an equivalent. To try to control the harvesting of a commons by an appeal to conscience is to ensure a competitive advantage to the conscienceless.

In our efforts to achieve maximum harvests we must frequently resort to coercion by the law or community opinion. This has its unfortunate aspect. Scientific knowledge progresses much more rapidly than legal or cultural change. It not infrequently happens that by the time scientists succeed in getting the community to specify a particular practice, new scientific knowledge shows that it is not the best. In the management of forests, for example, "everyone knows" that fire is to be avoided at all cost (Smokey the Bear says so). Now come the ecologists to point out that sometimes fire actually increases the harvest. Charles F. Cooper tells this story in "The Ecology of Fire."

But increasing the productivity of fishing or forestry does not really get at the root of our problem, which is the control of human populations. Many demographers are now of the opinion that we stand on the threshold of a new time of famines, a time when people will die by the tens of millions, perhaps by the hundreds of millions. If their predictions are correct, the loss of human life will be, in absolute terms, unprecedented. In relative terms, we can see its equal in "The Black Death" in Europe six centuries ago, as recounted by the historian William L. Langer. In preparing ourselves emotionally for the catastrophe ahead can we learn from the past?

Population "crashes" are comparatively rare in the living world, being confined mostly to ecologically simple environments like the arctic, where the lemmings live. In most species of animals overpopulation is prevented by the nonhuman equivalent of private property: territory and its selfish defence. V. C. Wynne-Edwards says that this is how "Population Control in Animals" takes place. Are there political lessons here for *Homo sapiens?*

If we dispense with territory entirely, or if the territories of individual human beings are too small, the consequences may be devastating. Deliberately, John B. Calhoun diminished the area available to rats as he investigated "Population Density and Social Pathology." It is impossible to read his account and not suspect that the findings have some applicability to human beings. Those who stand to benefit by the sale of fertilizers or insecticides frequently say that "the world needs more food." Many biologists suspect it is closer to the truth to say that the world needs fewer people. The intellectual solution to this problem will be emotionally and politically hard to accept because it will require not merely man's "dominion over the fish of the sea, and over the fowl of the air, and over every living thing," but dominion over man himself—which the first chapter of Genesis fails to mention.

# 27 The Ecosphere

LaMONT C. COLE · April 1958

Probably I should apologize for using a coined word like "ecosphere," but it seems nicely to describe just what I want to discuss. It is intended to combine two concepts: the "biosphere" and the "ecosystem."

The great 19th-century French naturalist Jean Lamarck first conceived the idea of the biosphere as the collective totality of living creatures on the earth, and the concept has been taken up and developed in recent years by the Russian geochemist V. I. Vernadsky. The word "ecosystem" means a self-sustaining community of organisms—plants as well as animals—taken together with its inorganic environment.

Now all these are interdependent. Animal life could not exist without plants nor plants without animals, which supply them with carbon dioxide. Even the composition of the inorganic environment depends upon the cyclic activity of life. Photosynthesis by the earth's plants would remove all of the carbon dioxide from the atmosphere within a year or so if it were not returned by fires and by the respiration of animals and other consumers of plants. Similarly nitrogen-fixing organisms would exhaust all of the nitrogen in the air in less than a million years. And so on. The conclusion is that a self-sustaining community must contain not just plants, animals and nitrogen-fixers but also decomposers which can free the chemicals bound in proto-

THE AMAZON, one of whose mouths is shown in this aerial photograph, plays an important role in the earth's circulation of water. Together with the Congo it carries more than 10 per cent of the 9,000 cubic miles of water that flow into the sea every year.

plasm. It is very fortunate from our standpoint that some microorganisms have solved the biochemical trick of decomposing chitin, lignins and other inert organic compounds that tie up carbon.

A community must consist of producers or accumulators of energy (green plants), primary consumers (fungi, microorganisms and herbivores), higher-order consumers (carnivorous predators, parasites and scavengers), and decomposers that regenerate the raw materials.

Communities vary, of course, all over the world, and each ecosystem is a composite of the community and the features of the inorganic environment that govern the availability of energy and essential chemicals and the conditions that the community members must tolerate. But the system that I wish to consider here is not a local one but the largest possible ecosystem: namely, the sum total of life on earth together with the global environment and the earth's total resources. This is what I call the ecosphere. My purpose is to reach some conclusions on such questions as how much life the earth can support.

Organisms living on the face of the earth as it floats around in space can receive energy from several sources. Energy from outside comes to us as sunlight and starlight, is reflected to us as moonlight, and is brought to earth by cosmic radiation and meteors. Internally the earth is heated by radioactivity, and it is also gaining heat energy from the tidal friction that is gradually slowing our rotation. On top of this man is tapping enormous amounts of stored energy by burning fossil fuels. But all these secondary sources of energy are infinitesimal compared to our daily sunshine, which accounts for 99.9998 per cent of our total energy income.

This supply of solar energy amounts to $13 \times 10^{23}$ gram-calories per year, or, if you prefer, it represents a continuous power supply at the rate of 2.5 billion billion horsepower. About one third of the incoming energy is lost at once by being reflected back to space, chiefly by clouds. The rest is absorbed by the atmosphere and the earth itself, to remain here temporarily until it is re-radiated to space as heat. During its residence on earth this energy serves to melt ice, to warm the land and oceans, to evaporate water, to generate winds and waves and currents. In addition to these activities, a ridiculously small proportion—about four hundredths of 1 per cent—of the solar energy goes to feed the metabolism of the biosphere.

Practically all of this energy enters the biosphere by means of photosynthesis. The plants use one sixth of the energy they take up from sunlight for their own metabolism, making the other five sixths available for animals and other consumers. About 5 per cent of this net energy is dissipated by forest and grass fires and by man's burning of plant products as fuel.

When an animal or other consumer eats plant protoplasm, it uses some of the substance for energy to fuel its metabolism and some as raw materials for growth. Some it discharges in broken-down form as metabolic waste products: for example, animals excrete urea, and yeast releases ethyl alcohol. And a large part of the plant material it ingests is simply indigestible and passes through the body unused. Herbivores, whether they are insects, rabbits, geese or cattle, succeed in extracting only about 50 per cent of the calories stored in the plant protoplasm. (The lost calories are, however, extractable by other consumers: flies may feed on the excretions or man himself may burn cattle dung for fuel.)

Of the plant calories consumed by an animal that eats the plant, only 20 to 30 per cent is actually built into protoplasm. Thus, since half of its consumption is lost as waste, the net efficiency of a herbivore in converting plant protoplasm into meat is about 10 to 15 per cent. The secondary consumers—i.e., meat-eaters feeding on the herbivores—do a little better. Because animal protoplasm has a smaller proportion of indigestible matter than plants have, a carnivore can use 70 per cent of the meat for its internal chemistry. But again only 30 per cent at most goes into building tissue. So the maximum efficiency of carnivores in converting one kind of meat into another is 20 per cent.

Some of the consequences of these relationships are of general interest and are fairly well known. For example, 1,000 calories stored up by the algae in Cayuga Lake can be converted into protoplasm amounting to 150 calories by small aquatic animals. In turn, smelt eating these animals produce 30 calories of protoplasm from the 150. If a man then eats the smelt, he can synthesize six calories worth of fat or muscle from the 30; if he waits for the smelt to be eaten by a trout and then eats the trout, the yield shrinks to 1.2 calories. If we were really dependent on the lake for food, we would do well to exterminate the trout and eat the smelt ourselves, or, better yet, to exterminate the smelt and live on planktonburgers. The same principles, of course, apply on land. If man is really determined to support the largest possible populations of his kind, he will have to shorten the food chains leading to himself and, so far as practicable, turn to a vegetarian diet.

The rapid shrinkage of stored energy as it passes from one organism to another serves to make the study of natural communities a trifle more simple for the ecologist than it would otherwise be. It explains why food chains in nature rarely contain more than four or five links. Thus in our Cayuga Lake chain the trout was the third animal link and man the fourth. Chains of the same sort occur in the ocean, with, for example, a tuna or cod as the third link and perhaps a shark or a seal replacing man as the fourth link. Now if we look for the fifth link in the chain we find that it takes something like a killer whale or a polar bear to be able to subsist on seals. As to a sixth link—it would take quite a predator to make its living by devouring killer whales or polar bears.

We could, of course, trace food chains in other directions. Each species has its parasites that extort their cut of the stored energy, and these in turn support other parasites down to the point where there is not enough energy available to support another organism. Also, we should not forget the unused energy contained in the feces and urine of each animal. The organic matter in feces is often the basic resource of a food chain in which the next link may be a dung beetle or the larva of a fly.

I estimate that the maximum amount of protoplasm of all types that can be produced on earth each year amounts to 410 billion tons, of which 290 billion represent plant growth and the other 120 billion all of the consumer organisms. We see, then, that the availability of energy sets a limit to the amount of life on earth—that is, to the size of the biosphere. This energy also keeps the nonliving part of the ecosphere animated, largely through the agency of moving water, which is the single most important chemical substance in the physiology of the ecosphere.

Each year the oceans evaporate a quantity of water equivalent to an average depth of one meter. The total evaporation from land and bodies of fresh water is one sixth of the evaporation from the sea, and at least one fifth of this evaporation is from the transpiration of plants growing on land. The grand total of water evaporated annually is roughly 100,000 cubic miles, and this must be roughly the annual precipitation. The precipitation on land exceeds the evaporation by slightly over 9,000 cubic

**ENERGY CYCLES** of the ecosphere are powered by the sun. Land plants bind solar energy into organic compounds utilized successively (*gray arrows*) by herbivore, carnivore and scavenger; residual compounds are decomposed by bacteria. Energy fixed by micro-scopic sea plants through a similar "food chain" (*color arrows*). In the water cycle (*broken gray arrows*) water evaporated from the sea is precipitated on land and used by living organisms, eventually returning to the sea bearing minerals and organic matter.

miles, which therefore represents the annual runoff of water from land to sea. It is astonishing to me to note that more than one tenth of this total runoff is carried to the sea by just two rivers—the Amazon and the Congo.

Precipitation supplies nonmarine organisms with the water which they require in large quantities. Protoplasm averages at least 75 per cent water, and plants require something like 450 grams of water to produce one gram of dry organic matter. The water moving from land to sea also erodes the land surface and dissolves soluble mineral matter. It brings to the plants the chemical nutrients that they require and it tends to level the land surface and deposit the minerals in the sea. At present the continents are being worn down at an average world-wide rate of one centimeter per century. The leveling process, however, apparently has never gone on to completion on the earth. Geological uplift of the land always intervenes and brings marine sediments above sea level, where the cycle can begin again.

The rivers of the world are now washing into the seas some four billion tons of dissolved inorganic matter a year, about 400 million tons of dissolved organic matter and about five times as much undissolved matter. The undissolved matter represents destruction of the land where organisms live, but the dissolved material is of greater interest, because it includes such important chemicals as 3.5 million tons of phosphorus, 100 million tons of potassium and 10 million tons of fixed nitrogen. In order to say what these losses may mean to the biosphere we must review a few facts about the chemical composition of the earth and of organisms.

Every organism seems to require at least 20 chemical elements and probably several others in trace amounts. Some of the organisms' requirements are rather surprising. *Penicillium* is said to need traces of tungsten, and the common duckweed demands manganese and the rare earth gallium. There is a European pansy which needs high concentrations of zinc in the soil, and several plants in different parts of the world are so hungry for copper that they help prospectors to find the mineral. Many organisms have fantastic abilities to concentrate the necessary elements from dilute media. The sea-squirts have vanadium in their blood, and the liver of the edible scallop contains on a dry-weight basis one tenth of 1 per cent of cadmium, although the amount of this element in sea water is so small that it cannot be detected by chemical tests.

But the exotic chemical tastes of organisms are comparatively unimportant. Their main needs can be summed up in just five words—oxygen, carbon, hydrogen, nitrogen and phosphorus, which account for more than 95 per cent of the mass of all protoplasm. Oxygen is the most abundant chemical element on earth, so we probably do not need to be concerned about any absolute deficiency of oxygen. But nitrogen is a different matter. Whereas protein, the main stuff of life, is 18 per cent nitrogen, the relative abundance of this element on the earth is only one 10,000th of the earth's mass. It is apparent that our land forms of life could not long tolerate a net annual loss of 10 million tons of fixed nitrogen to the sea. Fortunately this nitrogen loss from land is reversible, so that we can speak of a "nitrogen cycle." Organisms in the sea convert the fixed nitrogen into ammonia, a gas which can return to land via the atmosphere.

Carbon also is not in too abundant supply, for it amounts to less than three parts in 10,000 of the total mass of the earth's matter. But once again the biosphere profits from the fact that carbon can escape from the oceans as a gas—carbon dioxide. This gas goes through a complex circulation in the atmosphere, being released from the oceans in tropical regions and absorbed by the ocean waters in polar regions. Because some carbon is deposited in ocean sediments as carbonates, there is a net loss of carbon from the ecosphere. But there seems to be no danger that a shortage of this element will restrict life. The atmosphere contains 2,400 billion tons of carbon dioxide, and at least 30 times that much is dissolved in the oceans, waiting to be released if the atmosphere should become depleted. Volcanoes discharge carbon dioxide, and man is burning fossil fuels at such a rate that he has been accused of increasing the average carbon dioxide content of the atmosphere by some 10 per cent in the last 50 years. In addition, lots of limestone, which is more than 4 per cent carbon dioxide, has been pushed up from ancient seas by uplifts of the earth.

The story of phosphorus appears somewhat more alarming. This element accounts for a bit more than one tenth of 1 per cent of the mass of terrestrial matter, is enriched to about twice this level in plant protoplasm and is greatly enriched in animals, accounting for more than 1 per cent of the weight of the human body. As a constituent of nucleic

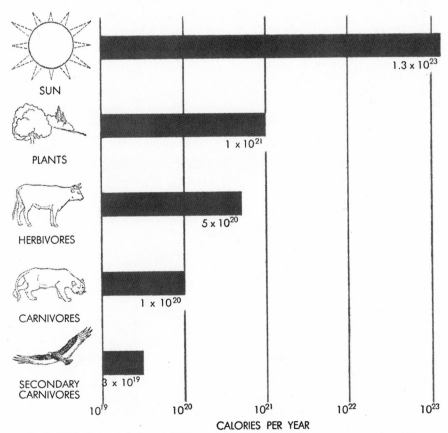

UTILIZATION OF SOLAR ENERGY decreases with each step along the food chain. These bars (on a logarithmic scale) show that plants use only .08 per cent of energy reaching the atmosphere; plant-eaters use only part of this fraction and flesh-eaters even less.

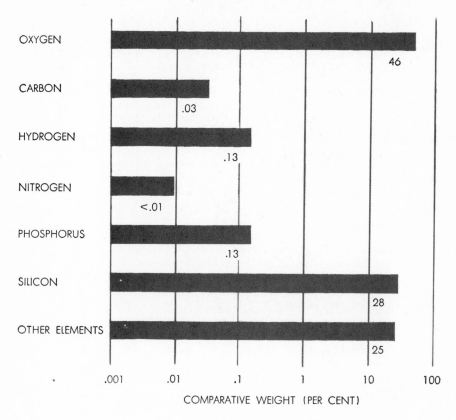

ESTIMATED RELATIVE ABUNDANCE of elements in the earth and its atmosphere (*above*) and in living matter (*below*) is compared in these charts; the scale is logarithmic. Silicon, with many stable compounds, is abundant on earth but rare in living organisms. Nitrogen, rare on earth, is important to life, making up as much as 18 per cent of proteins.

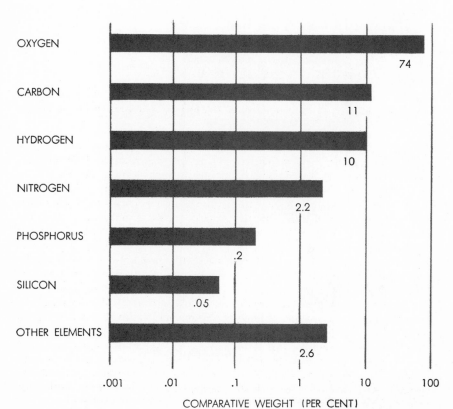

acids it is indispensable for all types of life known to us. But many agricultural lands already suffer a deficiency of phosphorus, and a corn crop of 60 bushels per acre removes 10 per cent of the phosphorus in the upper six inches of fertile soil. Each year 3.5 million tons of phosphorus are washed from the land and precipitated in the seas. And unfortunately phosphorus does not escape from the sea as a gas. Its only important recovery from the sea is in the guano produced by sea birds, but less than 3 per cent of the phosphorus annually lost from the land is returned in this way.

I must agree with agriculturalists who say that phosphorus is the critical limiting resource for the functioning of the ecosphere. The supply is at least shrinking (if dwindling is too strong a word) and there seems to be no practical way of improving the situation short of waiting for the next geological cycle of uplift to bring phosphate rock above sea level. Perhaps we should also worry about other essential elements, such as calcium, potassium, magnesium and iron, which behave much like phosphorus in the metabolism of the ecosphere, but the evidence clearly indicates that if present trends continue phosphorus will be the first to run out.

This brings me to the close of a very superficial summary of some of the physiological processes of the ecosphere. There are drastic oversimplifications in this treatment; the importance of some processes may be overestimated, and others (*e.g.*, dumping sewage in rivers and oceans) may not have received enough attention. The figures for the total quantity of energy received by the earth, for total annual precipitation and for the total supply of some chemical elements may overlook the very irregular distribution of these resources in time and space. Much solar energy falls on deserts and fields of snow and ice where it cannot be used by plants, and much precipitation arrives at unfavorable seasons or in such torrents that it does more harm than good to organisms. Yet I believe that there may be some merit, both intellectual and practical, in attempting to scan the entire picture.

Our survey suggests that man may be justified in feeling some real concern about the problem of erosion. It should also make us aware of the important role played by organisms that we might otherwise ignore or even regard as pests. The dung beetles, the various scavengers and the termites and other decomposers all play important bit parts in this great production. At least six diverse groups

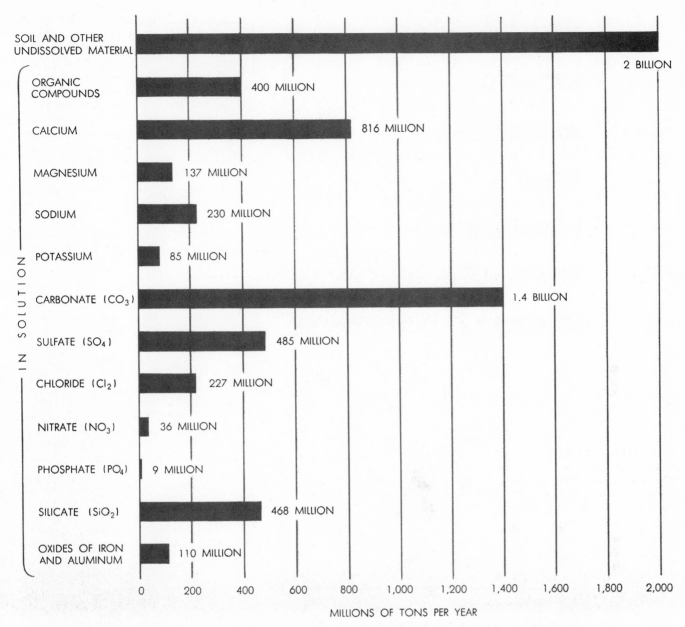

ANNUAL LOSS of minerals and organic matter washed into the sea amounts to billions of tons. Much nitrogen and carbon even-tually return to the land via the atmosphere; the loss of phos-phate is more serious since almost all of it remains in the oceans.

of bacteria are absolutely essential for the proper physiological functioning of the nitrogen cycle alone. Man in his care-lessness would probably neither notice nor care if by some unlikely chance his radioactive fallout or one of his chemi-cal sprays or fumes should exterminate all of the microorganisms that are cap-able of decomposing chitin. Yet, as we have seen, such a tragedy would even-tually mean an end to life on earth.

Finally, it is interesting to ask how large a role man plays in the physiology of the ecosphere. The Statistical Office of the United Nations estimates the present human population of the earth at 2.7 billion persons. Each of these is supposed to consume at least 2,200 metabolizable kilocalories per day. This

makes a total food requirement of $22 \times 10^{14}$ kilocalories per year. I have estimated that all of the plant growth in the world amounts to an annual net of $5 \times 10^{17}$ kilocalories, of which not more than 50 per cent is metabolizable by any primary consumer. Thus if man were to feed exclusively on plants he would require almost exactly 1 per cent of the total productivity of the earth.

To me this is a very impressive figure. There are more than one million species of animals, and when just one of these million species can corner 1 per cent of the total food resources, this form is truly in a position of overwhelming dominance. The figure becomes even more impressive when we reflect that 70 per cent of the total plant production

takes place in the oceans, and that our figure for productivity includes inedible materials such as straw and lumber.

If human beings were to eat meat ex-clusively, the present world population would require 4 per cent of all of the flesh of primary consumers of all types that the earth could support—and this means that much of our meat would be insects and tiny crustaceans. I suspect that the human population is already so large that no conceivable technical ad-vances could make it possible for all mankind to live on a meat diet. Speaking as one who would like to live on a meat diet, I can't see very much to be opti-mistic about for the future. This opinion, however, cannot be expected to alter the physiology of the ecosphere.

**ROMAN TOMBSTONE** from the first century A.D. records the death of Cominia Tyche, aged 27 years, 11 months, 28 days. Tombstones are a source of information on life expectancy in the ancient world. Stone is in the Metropolitan Museum of Art in New York.

# 28 The Human Population

EDWARD S. DEEVEY, JR. · September 1960

Almost until the present turn in human affairs an expanding population has been equated with progress. "Increase and multiply" is the Scriptural injunction. The number of surviving offspring is the measure of fitness in natural selection. If number is the criterion, the human species is making great progress. The population, now passing 2.7 billion, is doubling itself every 50 years or so. To some horrified observers, however, the population increase has become a "population explosion." The present rate of increase, they point out, is itself increasing. At 1 per cent per year it is double that of the past few centuries. By A.D. 2000, even according to the "medium" estimate of the careful demographers of the United Nations, the rate of increase will have accelerated to 3 per cent per year, and the total population will have reached 6.267 billion. If Thomas Malthus's assumption of a uniform rate of doubling is naive, because it so quickly leads to impossible numbers, how long can an accelerating annual increase, say from 1 to 3 per cent in 40 years, be maintained? The demographers confronted with this question lower their eyes: "It would be absurd," they say, "to carry detailed calculations forward into a more remote future. It is most debatable whether the trends in mortality and fertility can continue much longer. Other factors may eventually bring population growth to a halt."

So they may, and must. It comes to this: Explosions are not made by force alone, but by force that exceeds restraint. Before accepting the implications of the population explosion, it is well to set the present in the context of the record of earlier human populations. As will be seen, the population curve has moved upward stepwise in response to the three major revolutions that have marked the evolution of culture [see bottom illustration on page 234]. The tool-using and toolmaking revolution that started the growth of the human stem from the primate line gave the food-gatherer and hunter access to the widest range of environments. Nowhere was the population large, but over the earth as a whole it reached the not insignificant total of five million, an average of .04 person per square kilometer (.1 person per square mile) of land. With the agricultural revolution the population moved up two orders of magnitude to a new plateau, multiplying 100 times in the short span of 8,000 years, to an average of one person per square kilometer. The increase over the last 300 years, a multiplication by five, plainly reflects the first repercussions of the scientific-industrial revolution. There are now 16.4 persons per square kilometer of the earth's land area. It is thus the release of restraint that the curve portrays at three epochal points in cultural history.

But the evolution of the population size also indicates the approach to equilibrium in the two interrevolutionary periods of the past. At what level will the present surge of numbers reach equilibrium? That is again a question of restraint, whether it is to be imposed by the limitations of man's new command over his environment or by his command over his own nature.

The human generative force is neither new nor metabiological, nor is it especially strong in man as compared to other animals. Under conditions of maximal increase in a suitable environment empty of competitors, with births at maximum and deaths negligible, rats can multiply their numbers 25 times in an average generation-time of 31 weeks. For the water flea *Daphnia,* beloved by ecologists for the speedy answers it gives, the figures are 221 times in a generation of 6.8 days. Mankind's best efforts seem puny by contrast: multiplication by about 1.4 times in a generation of 28 years. Yet neither in human nor in experimental populations do such rates continue unchecked. Sooner or later the births slow down and the deaths increase, until—in experiments, at any rate —the growth tapers off, and the population effectively saturates its space. Ecologists define this state (of zero rate of change) as equilibrium, without denying the possibility of oscillations that average out to zero, and without forgetting the continuous input of energy (food, for instance) that is needed to maintain the system.

Two kinds of check, then, operate to limit the size of a population, or of any living thing that grows. Obviously the environment (amount of space, food or other needed resources) sets the upper limit; sometimes this is manipulatable, even by the population itself, as when it exploits a new kind of food in the same old space, and reaches a new, higher limit. More subtly, populations can be said to limit their own rates of increase. As the numbers rise, female fruit-flies, for example, lay fewer eggs when jostled by their sisters; some microorganisms battle each other with antibiotics; flour beetles accidentally eat their own defenseless eggs and pupae; infectious diseases spread faster, or become more virulent, as their hosts become more numerous. For human populations pestilence and warfare, Malthus's "natural restraints," belong among these devices for self-limitation. So, too, does his "moral restraint," or voluntary birth control. Nowadays a good deal of attention is being given, not only to voluntary methods,

| YEARS AGO | CULTURAL STAGE | AREA POPULATED | ASSUMED DENSITY PER SQUARE KILOMETER | TOTAL POPULATION (MILLIONS) |
|---|---|---|---|---|
| 1,000,000 | LOWER PALEOLITHIC | | .00425 | .125 |
| 300,000 | MIDDLE PALEOLITHIC | | .012 | 1 |
| 25,000 | UPPER PALEOLITHIC | | .04 | 3.34 |
| 10,000 | MESOLITHIC | | .04 | 5.32 |
| 6,000 | VILLAGE FARMING AND EARLY URBAN | | 1.0 / .04 | 86.5 |
| 2,000 | VILLAGE FARMING AND URBAN | | 1.0 | 133 |
| 310 | FARMING AND INDUSTRIAL | | 3.7 | 545 |
| 210 | FARMING AND INDUSTRIAL | | 4.9 | 728 |
| 160 | FARMING AND INDUSTRIAL | | 6.2 | 906 |
| 60 | FARMING AND INDUSTRIAL | | 11.0 | 1,610 |
| 10 | FARMING AND INDUSTRIAL | | 16.4 | 2,400 |
| A.D. 2000 | FARMING AND INDUSTRIAL | | 46.0 | 6,270 |

but also to a fascinating new possibility: mental stress.

Population control by means of personality derangement is probably a vertebrate patent; at least it seems a luxury beyond the reach of a water flea. The general idea, as current among students of small mammals, is that of hormonal imbalance (or stress, as defined by Hans Selye of the University of Montreal); psychic tension, resulting from overcrowding, disturbs the pituitary-adrenal system and diverts or suppresses the hormones governing sexuality and parental care. Most of the evidence comes from somewhat artificial experiments with caged rodents. It is possible, though the case is far from proved, that the lemming's famous mechanism for restoring equilibrium is the product of stress; in experimental populations of rats and mice, at least, anxiety has been observed to increase the death rate through fighting or merely from shock.

From this viewpoint there emerges an interesting distinction between crowding and overcrowding among vertebrates; overcrowding is what is perceived as such by members of the population. Since the human rate of increase is holding its own and even accelerating, however, it is plain that the mass of men, although increasingly afflicted with mental discomfort, do not yet see themselves as overcrowded. What will happen in the future brings other questions. For the present it may be noted that some kind of check has always operated, up to now, to prevent populations from ex-

**POPULATION GROWTH, from inception of the hominid line one million years ago through the different stages of cultural evolution to A.D. 2000, is shown in the chart on the opposite page. In Lower Paleolithic stage, population was restricted to Africa (*colored area on world map in third column*), with a density of only .00425 person per square kilometer (*fourth column*) and a total population of only 125,000 (*column at right*). By the Mesolithic stage, 10,000 years ago, hunting and food gathering techniques had spread the population over most of the earth and brought the total to 5,320,-000. In the village farming and early urban stage, population increased to a total of 86,500,000 and a density of one person per square kilometer in the Old World and .04 per square kilometer in the New World. Today the population density exceeds 16 persons per square kilometer, and pioneering of the antarctic continent has begun.**

ceeding the space that contains them. Of course space may be non-Euclidean, and man may be exempt from this law.

The commonly accepted picture of the growth of the population out of the long past takes the form of the top graph on the next page. Two things are wrong with this picture. In the first place the basis of estimates, back of about A.D. 1650, is rarely stated. One suspects that writers have been copying each other's guesses. The second defect is that the scales of the graph have been chosen so as to make the first defect seem unimportant. The missile has left the pad and is heading out of sight—so it is said; who cares whether there were a million or a hundred million people around when Babylon was founded? The difference is nearly lost in the thickness of the draftsman's line.

I cannot think it unimportant that (as I calculate) there were 36 billion Paleolithic hunters and gatherers, including the first tool-using hominids. One begins to see why stone tools are among the commonest Pleistocene fossils. Another 30 billion may have walked the earth before the invention of agriculture. A cumulative total of about 110 billion individuals seem to have passed their days, and left their bones, if not their marks, on this crowded planet. Neither for our understanding of culture nor in terms of man's impact upon the land is it a negligible consideration that the patch of ground allotted to every person now alive may have been the lifetime habitat of 40 predecessors.

These calculations exaggerate the truth in a different way: by condensing into single sums the enormous length of prehistoric time. To arrive at the total of 36 billion Paleolithic hunters and gatherers I have assumed mean standing populations of half a million for the Lower Paleolithic, and two million for the Middle and Upper Paleolithic to 25,000 years ago. For Paleolithic times there are no archeological records worth considering in such calculations. I have used some figures for modern hunting tribes, quoted by Robert J. Braidwood and Charles A. Reed, though they are not guilty of my extrapolations. The assumed densities per square kilometer range from a tenth to a third of those estimated for eastern North America before Columbus came, when an observer would hardly have described the woods as full of Indians. (Of course I have excluded any New World population from my estimates prior to the Mesolithic climax of the food-gathering and hunting phase of cultural evolution.) It is only

because average generations of 25 years succeeded each other 39,000 times that the total looms so large.

For my estimates as of the opening of the agricultural revolution, I have also depended upon Braidwood and Reed. In their work in Mesopotamia they have counted the number of rooms in buried houses, allowing for the areas of town sites and of cultivated land, and have compared the populations so computed with modern counterparts. For early village-farmers, like those at Jarmo, and for the urban citizens of Sumer, about 2500 B.C., their estimates (9.7 and 15.4 persons per square kilometer) are probably fairly close. They are intended to apply to large tracts of inhabited country, not to pavement-bound clusters of artisans and priests. Nevertheless, in extending these estimates to continent-wide areas, I have divided the lower figure by 10, making it one per square kilometer. So much of Asia is unirrigated and nonurban even today that the figure may still be too high. But the Maya, at about the same level of culture (3,000 or 4,000 years later), provide a useful standard of comparison. The present population of their classic homeland averages .6 per square kilometer, but the land can support a population about a hundred times as large, and probably did at the time of the classic climax. The rest of the New World, outside Middle America, was (and is) more thinly settled, but a world-wide average of one per square kilometer seems reasonable for agricultural, pre-industrial society.

For modern populations, from A.D. 1650 on, I have taken the estimates of economic historians, given in such books as the treatise *World Population and Production,* by Wladimir S. and Emma S. Woytinsky. All these estimates are included in the bottom graph on the next page. Logarithmic scales are used in order to compress so many people and millennia onto a single page. Foreshortening time in this way is convenient, if not particularly logical, and back of 50,000 years ago the time-scale is pretty arbitrary anyway. No attempt is made to show the oscillations that probably occurred, in glacial and interglacial ages, for example.

The stepwise evolution of population size, entirely concealed in graphs with arithmetic scales, is the most noticeable feature of this diagram. For most of the million-year period the number of hominids, including man, was about what would be expected of any large Pleistocene mammal—scarcer than horses, say, but commoner than elephants. Intellectual superiority was simply a successful adaptation, like longer legs; essential to stay in the running, of course, but making man at best the first among equals. Then the food-gatherers and hunters became plowmen and herdsmen, and the population was boosted by about 16 times, between 10,000 and 6,000 years ago. The scientific-industrial revolution, beginning some 300 years ago, has spread its effects much faster, but it has not yet taken the number as far above the earlier base line.

The long-term population equilibrium implied by such base lines suggests

something else. Some kind of restraint kept the number fairly stable. "Food supply" offers a quick answer, but not, I think, the correct one. At any rate, a forest is full of game for an expert mouse-hunter, and a Paleolithic man who stuck to business should have found enough food on two square kilometers, instead of 20 or 200. Social forces were probably more powerful than mere starvation in causing men to huddle in small bands. Besides, the number was presumably adjusted to conditions in the poorest years, and not to average environments.

The main point is that there were ad-

justments. They can only have come about because the average female bore two children who survived to reproduce. If the average life span is 25 years, the "number of children ever born" is about four (because about 50 per cent die before breeding), whereas a population that is really trying can average close to eight. Looking back on former times, then, from our modern point of view, we might say that about two births out of four were surplus, though they were needed to counterbalance the juvenile death toll. But what about the other four, which evidently did not occur? Unless the life expectancy was very much less

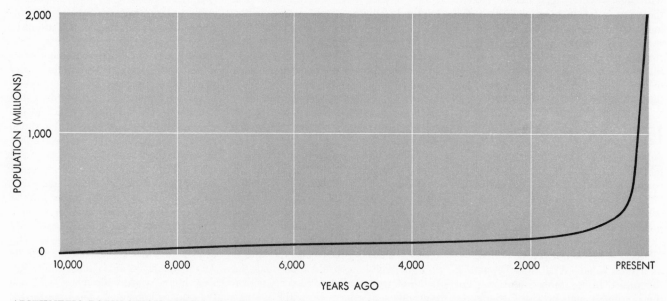

ARITHMETIC POPULATION CURVE plots the growth of human population from 10,000 years ago to the present. Such a curve suggests that the population figure remained close to the base line for an indefinite period from the remote past to about 500 years ago, and that it has surged abruptly during the last 500 years as a result of the scientific-industrial revolution.

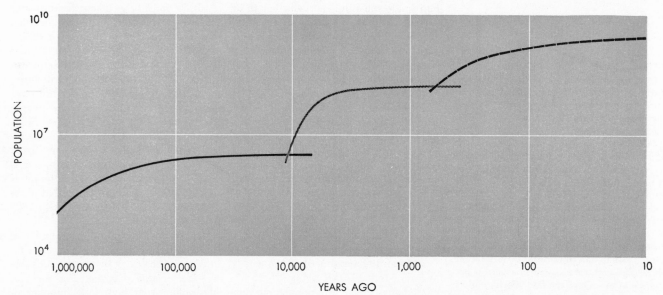

LOGARITHMIC POPULATION CURVE makes it possible to plot, in a small space, the growth of population over a longer period of time and over a wider range (from $10^4$, or 10,000, to $10^{10}$, or 10 billion, persons). Curve, based on assumptions concerning relationship of technology and population as shown in chart on page 232, reveals three population surges reflecting toolmaking or cultural revolution (solid line), agricultural revolution (gray line) and scientific-industrial revolution (broken line).

than I have assumed (and will presently justify), some degree of voluntary birth control has always prevailed.

Our 40 predecessors on earth make an impressive total, but somehow it sounds different to say that nearly 3 per cent of the people who have ever lived are still around. When we realize that they are living twice as long as their parents did, we are less inclined to discount the revolution in which we are living. One of its effects has just begun to be felt: The mean age of the population is increasing all over the world. Among the more forgivable results of Western culture, when introduced into simpler societies, is a steep drop in the death rate. Public-health authorities are fond of citing Ceylon in this connection. In a period of a year during 1946 and 1947 a campaign against malaria reduced the death rate there from 20 to 14 per 1,000. Eventually the birth rate falls too, but not so fast, nor has it yet fallen so far as a bare replacement value. The natural outcome of this imbalance is that acceleration of annual increase which so bemuses demographers. In the long run it must prove to be temporary, unless the birth rate accelerates, for the deaths that are being systematically prevented are premature ones. That is, the infants who now survive diphtheria and measles are certain to die of something else later on, and while the mean lifespan is approaching the maximum, for the first time in history, there is no reason to think that the maximum itself has been stretched. Meanwhile the expectation of life at birth is rising daily in most countries, so that it has already surpassed 70 years in some, including the U. S., and probably averages between 40 and 50.

It is hard to be certain of any such world-wide figure. The countries where mortality is heaviest are those with the least accurate records. In principle, however, mean age at death is easier to find out than the number of children born, the frequency or mean age at marriage, or any other component of a birth rate. The dead bones, the court and parish records and the tombstones that archeology deals with have something to say about death, of populations as well as of people. Their testimony confirms the impression that threescore years and ten, if taken as an average and not as a maximum lifetime, is something decidedly new. Of course the possibilities of bias in such evidence are almost endless. For instance, military cemeteries tend to be full of young adult males. The hardest bias to allow for is the deficiency of in-

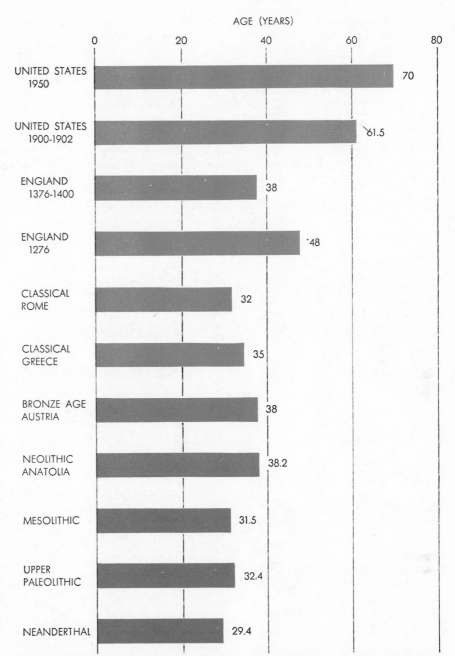

AGE (YEARS)

LONGEVITY in ancient and modern times is charted. From time of Neanderthal man to 14th century A.D., life span appears to have hovered around 35 years. An exception is 13th-century England. Increase in longevity partly responsible for current population increase has come in modern era. In U.S. longevity increased about 10 years in last half-century.

fants and children; juvenile bones are less durable than those of adults, and are often treated less respectfully. Probably we shall never know the true expectation of life at birth for any ancient people. Bypassing this difficulty, we can look at the mean age at death among the fraction surviving to adolescence.

The "nasty, brutish and short" lives of Neanderthal people have been rather elaborately guessed at 29.4 years. The record, beyond them, is not one of steady improvement. For example, Neolithic farmers in Anatolia and Bronze Age Austrians averaged 38 years, and even the

Mesolithic savages managed more than 30. But in the golden ages of Greece and Rome the life span was 35 years or less. During the Middle Ages the chances of long life were probably no better. The important thing about these averages is not the differences among them, but their similarity. Remembering the crudeness of the estimates, and the fact that juvenile mortality is omitted, it is fair to guess that human life-expectancy at birth has never been far from 25 years— 25 plus or minus five, say—from Neanderthal times up to the present century. It follows, as I have said, that about half

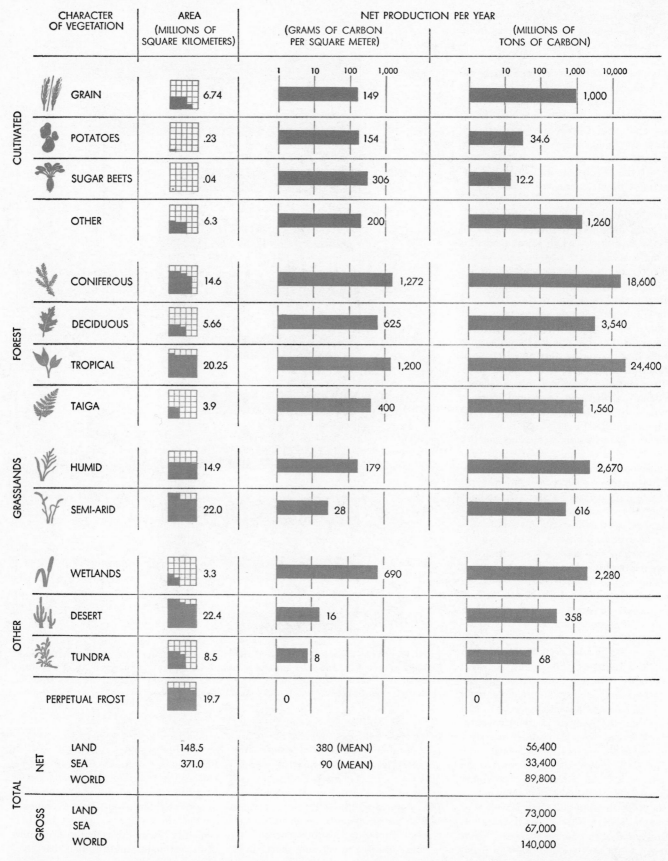

| CHARACTER OF VEGETATION | | AREA (MILLIONS OF SQUARE KILOMETERS) | NET PRODUCTION PER YEAR | |
|---|---|---|---|---|
| | | | (GRAMS OF CARBON PER SQUARE METER) | (MILLIONS OF TONS OF CARBON) |
| **CULTIVATED** | GRAIN | 6.74 | 149 | 1,000 |
| | POTATOES | .23 | 154 | 34.6 |
| | SUGAR BEETS | .04 | 306 | 12.2 |
| | OTHER | 6.3 | 200 | 1,260 |
| **FOREST** | CONIFEROUS | 14.6 | 1,272 | 18,600 |
| | DECIDUOUS | 5.66 | 625 | 3,540 |
| | TROPICAL | 20.25 | 1,200 | 24,400 |
| | TAIGA | 3.9 | 400 | 1,560 |
| **GRASSLANDS** | HUMID | 14.9 | 179 | 2,670 |
| | SEMI-ARID | 22.0 | 28 | 616 |
| **OTHER** | WETLANDS | 3.3 | 690 | 2,280 |
| | DESERT | 22.4 | 16 | 358 |
| | TUNDRA | 8.5 | 8 | 68 |
| | PERPETUAL FROST | 19.7 | 0 | 0 |
| **TOTAL NET** | LAND | 148.5 | 380 (MEAN) | 56,400 |
| | SEA | 371.0 | 90 (MEAN) | 33,400 |
| | WORLD | | | 89,800 |
| **TOTAL GROSS** | LAND | | | 73,000 |
| | SEA | | | 67,000 |
| | WORLD | | | 140,000 |

**PRODUCTION OF ORGANIC MATTER** per year by the land vegetation of the world—and thus its ultimate food-producing capacity—is charted in terms of the amount of carbon incorporated in organic compounds. Cultivated vegetation (*top left*) is less efficient than forest and wetlands vegetation, as indicated by the uptake of carbon per square meter (*third column*), and it yields a smaller over-all output than forest, humid grasslands and wetlands vegetation (*fourth column*). The scales at top of third and fourth columns are logarithmic. Land vegetation leads sea vegetation in efficiency and in net and gross tonnage (*bottom*). The difference between the net production and gross production is accounted for by the consumption of carbon in plant respiration.

the children ever born have lived to become sexually mature. It is not hard to see why an average family size of four or more, or twice the minimum replacement rate, has come to seem part of a God-given scheme of things.

The 25-fold upsurge in the number of men between 10,000 and 2,000 years ago was sparked by a genuine increase in the means of subsistence. A shift from animal to plant food, even without agricultural labor and ingenuity, would practically guarantee a 10-fold increase, for a given area can usually produce about 10 times as much plant as animal substance. The scientific-industrial revolution has increased the efficiency of growing these foods, but hardly, as yet, beyond the point needed to support another 10 times as many people, fewer of whom are farmers. At the present rate of multiplication, without acceleration, another 10-fold rise is due within 230 years. Disregarding the fact that developed societies spend 30 to 60 times as much energy for other purposes as they need for food, one is made a little nervous by the thought of so many hungry mouths. Can the increase of efficiency keep pace? Can some of the apparently ample energy be converted to food as needed, perhaps at the cost of reducing the size of Sunday newspapers? Or is man now pressing so hard on his food supply that another 10-fold increase of numbers is impossible?

The answers to these questions are not easy to find, and students with different viewpoints disagree about them. Richard L. Meier of the University of Michigan estimates that a total of 50 billion people (a 20-fold increase, that is) can be supported on earth, and the geochemist Harrison Brown of the California Institute of Technology will allow (reluctantly) twice or four times as many. Some economists are even more optimistic; Arnold C. Harberger of the University of Chicago presents the interesting notion that a larger crop of people will contain more geniuses, whose intellects will find a solution to the problem of feeding *still* more people. And the British economist Colin Clark points out that competition for resources will sharpen everyone's wits, as it always has, even if the level of innate intelligence is not raised.

An ecologist's answer is bound to be cast in terms of solar energy, chlorophyll and the amount of land on which the two can interact to produce organic carbon. Sources of energy other than the sun are either too expensive, or nonrenewable or both. Land areas will continue for a very long time to be the places where food is grown, for the sea is not so productive as the land, on the average. One reason, sometimes forgotten, is that the plants of the sea are microscopic algae, which, being smaller than land plants, respire away a larger fraction of the carbon they fix. The culture of the fresh-water alga *Chlorella* has undeniable promise as a source of human food. But the high efficiencies quoted for its photosynthesis, as compared with agricultural plants, are not sustained outdoors under field conditions. Even if Chlorella (or another exceptionally efficient producer, such as the water hyacinth) is the food plant of the future, flat areas exposed to sunlight will be needed. The 148.5 million square kilometers of land will have to be used with thoughtful care if the human population is to increase 20-fold. With a population of 400 per square kilometer (50 billion total) it would seem that men's bodies, if not their artifacts, will stand in the way of vital sunshine.

Plants capture the solar energy impinging on a given area with an efficiency of about .1 per cent. (Higher values often quoted are based on some fraction of the total radiation, such as visible light.) Herbivores capture about a 10th of the plants' energy, and carnivores convert about 10 per cent of the energy captured by herbivores (or other carnivores). This means, of course, that carnivores, feeding on plants at second hand, can scarcely do so with better than 1 per cent efficiency ($1/10 \times 1/10$ equals $1/100$). Eugene I. Rabinowitch of the University of Illinois has calculated that the current crop of men represents an ultimate conversion of about 1 per cent of the energy trapped by land vegetation. Recently, however, I have re-examined the base figure—the efficiency of the land-plant production—and believe it should be raised by a factor of three or four. The old value came from estimates made in 1919 and in 1937. A good deal has been learned since those days. The biggest surprise is the high productivity of forests, especially the forests of the Temperate Zone.

If my new figures are correct, the population could theoretically increase by 30 or 40 times. But man would have to displace all other herbivores and utilize all the vegetation with the 10 per cent efficiency established by the ecological rule of tithes. No land that now supports greenery could be spared for nonagricultural purposes; the populace would have to reside in the polar regions, or on artificial "green isles in the sea, love"—scummed over, of course, by 10 inches of Chlorella culture.

The picture is doubtless overdrawn. There is plenty of room for improvement in present farming practice. More land could be brought under cultivation if a better distribution of water could be arranged. More efficient basic crops can be grown and used less wastefully. Other sources of energy, notably atomic energy, can be fed back into food production to supplement the sun's rays. None of these measures is more than palliative, however; none promises so much as a 10-fold increase in efficiency; worse, none is likely to be achieved at a pace equivalent to the present rate of doubling of the world's population. A 10-fold, even a 20-fold, increase can be tolerated, perhaps, but the standard of living seems certain to be lower than today's. What happens then, when men perceive themselves to be overcrowded?

The idea of population equilibrium will take some getting used to. A population that is kept stable by emigration, like that of the Western Islands of Scotland, is widely regarded as sick—a shining example of a self-fulfilling diagnosis. Since the fall of the death rate is temporary, it is those two or more extra births per female that demand attention. The experiments with crowded rodents point to one way they might be corrected, through the effect of anxiety in suppressing ovulation and spermatogenesis and inducing fetal resorption. Some of the most dramatic results are delayed until after birth: litters are carelessly nursed, deserted or even eaten. Since fetuses, too, have endocrine glands, the specter of maternal transmission of anxiety now looms: W. R. Thompson of Wesleyan University has shown that the offspring of frustrated mother mice are more "emotional" throughout their own lives, and my student Kim Keeley has confirmed this.

Considered abstractly, these devices for self-regulation compel admiration for their elegance. But there is a neater device that men can use: rational, voluntary control over numbers. In mentioning the dire effects of psychic stress I am not implying that the population explosion will be contained by cannibalism or fetal resorption, or any power so naked. I simply suggest that vertebrates have that power, whether they want it or not, as part of the benefit—and the price —of being vertebrates. And if the human method of adjusting numbers to resources fails to work in the next 1,000 years as it has in the last million, subhuman methods are ready to take over.

# 29 The Last of the Great Whales

SCOTT McVAY · August 1966

The order Cetacea—the whales—consists of more than 100 species. The 12 largest either were in the past or are now commercially important to man. At one time their oil was valued as a lamp fuel and a high-grade lubricant. Today most whale oil is made into margarine and soap, some whale meat is eaten and the rest of the animal is utilized as feed for domestic animals and fertilizer. Whale hunting is profitable, and as a result a majority of the 12 commercially hunted species have been all but exterminated. In the 18th and 19th centuries the whaling vessels of a dozen nations sailed all the oceans in pursuit of five species of whales. In that period four of the five were hunted almost to the point of extinction; the complete disappearance of these whales during the age of sail was probably prevented only by a slump in the demand for whale oil late in the 19th century. With the age of steam another seven species (which were unsuitable as quarry in the previous era) became the hunted. These species are now also in danger of extinction. It is the purpose of this article to trace the circumstances that have allowed this sorry episode to be repeated in so short a time.

The ultimate fate of the great whales has been a question for more than a century. Herman Melville included such a query among the observations that make his *Moby Dick* an encyclopedia of whales and whaling: "Owing to the almost omniscient look-outs at the mastheads of the whale-ships, now penetrating even through Behring's straits, and into the remotest secret drawers and lockers of the world; and the thousand harpoons and lances darting along all the continental coasts; the moot point is, whether Leviathan can long endure so wide a chase, and so remorseless a

havoc; whether he must not at last be exterminated from the waters." Melville's conclusion was that Leviathan could endure. This was not unreasonable at the time (1851), when whalers pursued whales in open boats and killed them with lances. The five species of whales that were hunted then included only one from the suborder Odontoceti, or toothed whales; this was the sperm whale (*Physeter catodon*). The other four were baleen whales, of the suborder Mysticeti. These were the bowhead (*Balaena mysticetus*), the two right whales (*Eubalaena glacialis* and *E. australis*) and a lesser cousin, the gray whale (*Eschrichtius glaucus*). All five were hunted because they do not swim too fast to be overtaken by oarsmen and because they float when they are dead.

The bowhead whale and the right whales suffered near extinction. Very few of these once abundant animals have been seen in the past decade. In May, 1963, for example, the Norwegian ship *Rossfjord* was steaming west of the Russian island Novaya Zemlya when a whale with "jaws [that] were extremely curved" was sighted. The event was duly noted in the *Norwegian Whaling Gazette* with the observation that the whale—clearly a right whale—belonged to "a species that the crew had not previously seen."

Today all four of these baleen whales (the gray, the bowhead and both right whales) are nominally protected by international agreement, although three right whales that were sighted in the Antarctic in the early 1960's were promptly killed and processed. Perhaps because of its gregarious way of life, the gray whale has managed a slow recovery from the pressure of hunting. An estimated 6,000 gray whales now migrate annually from the Arctic Ocean

to their breeding grounds off the coast of Lower California [see "The Return of the Gray Whale," by Raymond M. Gilmore; SCIENTIFIC AMERICAN, January, 1955]. No one knows today how many (or how few) bowhead and right whales are still alive.

Of the eight great whales that are the quarry of modern whaling fleets, seven belong to the suborder of baleen whales and six of these to the genus *Balaenoptera* [see illustration on pages 240–241]. The largest of the six is the largest animal known to evolutionary history: the blue whale (*Balaenoptera musculus*). Weighing as much as 25 elephants and attaining a length of as much as 85 feet, this is the true Leviathan. It was known to Melville, who remarked that blue whales (he called them sulfur-bottoms) are seldom seen except in the remoter southern seas and are never chased because they can "run away with rope-walks of line." The modern catcher ship, armed with cannon-launched explosive harpoons, proved to be the blue whale's nemesis. Over the past 60 years antarctic waters have yielded more than 325,000 blue whales, with an aggregate weight in excess of 26 million tons [see "The Blue Whale," by Johan T. Ruud; SCIENTIFIC AMERICAN, December, 1956]. Even though the blue whale is now a rare animal, many of the statistics concerning baleen whales caught in the Antarctic continue to be reckoned in terms of "blue-whale units," as are the whaling nations' annual antarctic quotas.

Five other baleen whales of commercial significance are the finback whale (*Balaenoptera physalus*), the sei whale (*B. borealis*) and three smaller whales: Bryde's whale (*B. edeni*) and the two minke whales (*B. acutorostrata* and *B.*

CATCHER VESSEL pitches in a heavy antarctic swell. The stubby device seen silhouetted on the bow platform is the cannon that fires harpoons loaded with explosives. A dead whale, probably a finback, has had its flukes bobbed and is chained by its tail to the ship's side.

bulls, cows and calves. Once a year the mature bulls leave the pack and travel to antarctic waters for the summer months. As a result the whaling fleets have an opportunity to kill sperm bulls in the Antarctic and bulls and cows alike during the voyage to and from the fishery.

As the population of baleen whales in antarctic waters has dwindled, the whaling fleets have begun to spend more time in the North Pacific, where the primary quarry is the sperm whale. Every year since 1962 the industry has killed more sperm whales than whales of any other single species; the peak catch (in 1964) was more than 29,000. Sperm whales are not counted in terms of blue-whale units, and as yet there is no limit on the number that may be taken in any year. The only limitation is on the minimum size of sperm cow that may be killed. The bowhead and the right whales, on the other hand, are supposedly protected everywhere in the world, as are the humpback and the blue whales throughout the Pacific and the humpback south of the Equator around the world.

Before World War II whaling was a *laissez faire* enterprise. Then in the postwar epoch of international cooperation 17 interested nations entered into a convention designed to regulate the whaling industry. In December, 1946, the International Whaling Commission was established as an executive body to oversee the conservation and sensible utilization of the world's whale resources. The participating nations in the Western Hemisphere were Argentina, Brazil, Canada, Mexico, Panama and the U.S., although only Argentina and Panama were then active in the industry. (Both have since abandoned whaling.) Among the nations of Europe, Denmark, France, Britain, the Netherlands, Norway and the U.S.S.R. were signatories. So were Iceland, South Africa, Australia, New Zealand and Japan. At that time five nations operated factory ships and catcher fleets; today only Japan, Norway and the U.S.S.R. are major whaling nations. The Netherlands and Britain have abandoned their fleets, although the British continue their shore-based antarctic whaling enterprise (which is now conducted jointly with the Japanese) on the subantarctic island of South Georgia.

Since its activation in the fall of 1948 the International Whaling Commission has been charged with such tasks as protecting overexploited whale species,

*bonaerensis*). The finback averages little more than 65 feet in length and yields only 10 tons of oil, compared with the blue whale's 20 tons. Accordingly in terms of blue-whale units it takes two finbacks to equal one blue. The sei is slighter, averaging 55 feet in length. It is comparatively blubber-poor and meat-rich; six sei whales equal one blue-whale unit. Bryde's whale and the minkes, the first averaging 45 feet and the other two 30 feet, are not separately identified in whaling statistics. When taken, they are probably counted as sei whales; they will receive no further mention here.

The remaining baleen whale to be taken commercially is the small but oil-rich humpback whale (*Megaptera novaeangliae*). This animal is shorter than the sei, averaging about 45 feet, but it is so stocky that it yields some eight tons of oil. Two and a half humpbacks thus equal one blue-whale unit. The humpback has evidently never existed in large enough numbers to constitute a major whaling resource. Nonetheless, until recently some 1,000 humpbacks were taken each year.

The eighth and last whale that is hunted today, surprisingly enough, is one that somehow escaped the near extermination that was the lot of the gray, bowhead and right whales in the days of sail. This is the sperm whale, which dives deep to hunt for squid along the ocean floor (its deepest-known dive is about 3,500 feet) and can remain submerged as long as 90 minutes. The sperm's huge square head contains the largest brain in the animal kingdom: it weighs more than 20 pounds. Sperm whales roam the mid-latitude oceans in groups that whalers call pods, including

setting minimum-size limits below which various species may not be taken, setting maximum annual catch quotas for the antarctic fishery and designating areas closed to hunting. Although each commissioner is in principle responsible for his nation's observance of the commission's regulations, the commission itself unfortunately has neither inspection nor enforcement powers; any member nation can repudiate or simply ignore the commission's actions. Nonmember nations, of course, are equally unrestricted in their whaling activities. It calls for little political insight to forecast that recommendations made by the nonwhaling members of such a body will be ignored by the whaling members. What comes as a surprise is the fact that both the whaling and the nonwhaling nations on the commission were unresponsive to the significance of the whaling statistics that were presented to them each year during the 1950's.

In the years after World War II the waters of the Antarctic constituted the world's last great whaling ground. Record catches such as the one of 1930–1931 were never repeated, but up to 1950–1951 the whalers killed some 7,000 blue whales each season. The commission's annual quota for the antarctic fishery was 16,000 blue-whale units; the catch of finbacks (at the rate of two for each blue) helped to fulfill the quota. During this period about 18,000 finbacks were killed each season [*see bottom illustration on page 243*].

As the 1950's progressed, however, an ominous trend was evident. The blue whales were becoming scarce. The blue-whale kill, which totaled only about 5,000 in 1951–1952, fell below 2,000 in 1955–1956 and was down to 1,200 by 1958–1959. To counterbalance the declining catch of blues, the whalers pursued the finbacks more vigorously. By the end of the 1950's, 25,000 or more finbacks were being taken each season. Those familiar with patterns of predation could see that the blue whales were being fished out and were in need of immediate full protection. The finbacks in turn probably could not survive another decade like the preceding one, during which some 240,000 animals had been subtracted from the stock.

By 1960, in spite of continued indifference on the part of the whaling nations, the commission finally decided to undertake some fact-finding. A special three-man committee was assigned the task of assessing the antarctic whale populations, even though an expert as

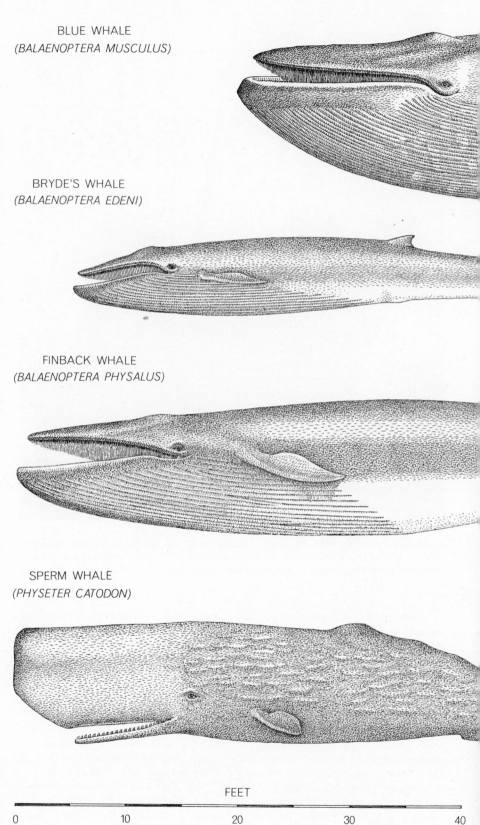

BLUE WHALE
(*BALAENOPTERA MUSCULUS*)

BRYDE'S WHALE
(*BALAENOPTERA EDENI*)

FINBACK WHALE
(*BALAENOPTERA PHYSALUS*)

SPERM WHALE
(*PHYSETER CATODON*)

FEET

0          10          20          30          40

**WHALERS' QUARRY TODAY** consists mainly of animals of the baleen suborder; six of the seven species are illustrated above. The blue whale, the world's largest animal, is on the verge of extinction, as is the oil-rich humpback. The finback is seriously overhunted and the same fate is befalling the sei whale. Kills of Bryde's whale and two minke whale

SEI WHALE
(BALAENOPTERA BOREALIS)

MINKE WHALE
(BALAENOPTERA ACUTOROSTRATA)

WHITE WHALE
(DELPHINAPTERUS LEUCAS)

NARWHAL
(MONODON MONOCEROS)

HUMPBACK WHALE
(MEGAPTERA NOVAEANGLIAE)

species (one of which is not illustrated) are not reported by name in the whaling statistics; they are probably counted as sei. As a result their present numbers are unknown. The toothed suborder of whales includes such familiar animals as the porpoises, the dolphins, the grampus, pothead and the true and false killer whales. Three of the toothed whales are illustrated. Only the largest, the sperm whale, is commercially valued and endangered by overhunting, although the narwhal and white whale are hunted occasionally.

well-regarded as the Dutch cetologist E. J. Slijper declared that the danger of their extinction was "surely remote." The committee was also to recommend any actions necessary to maintain the fishery as a continuing resource. It was agreed that, to avoid bias, the three men should be neither citizens of any nation active in antarctic whaling nor experts on whales. Three specialists in the field of population dynamics were chosen: K. Radway Allen of New Zealand, Douglas G. Chapman of the U.S. and Sidney J. Holt. Although Holt is a British subject, he has the status of an international civil servant by virtue of his employment with the Food and Agriculture Organization of the United Nations. The three men were asked to report their findings to the commission at its annual meeting in 1963.

As the special committee set about its three-year job, the world's whaling fleets continued to kill whales indiscriminately in the antarctic fishery. For the first season following the appointment of the committee the International Whaling Commission failed to set any quota for the antarctic catch. The whaling industry took more than 16,000 units that season, as well as some 4,500 nonquota sperm whales. Within the 16,000 units the catch consisted of 1,740 blue whales (510 more than the previous season) and 27,374 finbacks (a record number for kills of that species). The industry also took 4,310 sei whales, 718 humpbacks and even two protected right whales that surfaced within range of the gunners.

During the second year of the committee's work the whaling industry did less well in the antarctic fishery. Once again the commission set no quota; the industry only managed to process 15,-229 units. A few more sei and sperm whales were killed than during the previous season and another right whale was illegally shot. Among the whales that counted most—the blues and the finbacks—a larger number were immature and the numbers of both were diminishing.

The final season before the committee's report was due (1962–1963) produced a similar record. The commission set a quota of 15,000 blue-whale units. There was a modest increase in the sei and sperm kill but a sharp decline in blue and finback kills. For the first time since World War II the kill of blues fell below 1,000.

In July, 1963, the commission met in London and the special committee presented its report. The committee stated that in the antarctic fishery both the blue whale and the humpback were in serious danger of extermination. It was estimated that no more than 1,950 blue whales—possibly as few as 650—still survived in antarctic waters. The committee also noted that overfishing had reduced the stock of finbacks to approximately 40,000, far below the population level required for a maximum yield. It was recommended that the taking of blues and humpbacks be immediately prohibited and that the annual kill of finbacks be limited to 5,000 or fewer. Elimination of the blue-whale-unit system of accounting and substitution of separate quotas for each whale species was also strongly recommended.

Finally the committee's three members gave the whaling industry a prediction with a clear practical meaning. They forecast that, if unrestricted whaling were permitted in the 1963–1964 season, the industry would not be able to harvest more than 8,500 blue-whale units and would slaughter 14,000 finbacks—nearly three times the recommended number—in the process.

The prediction was disregarded. The commission voted a 1963–1964 quota of 10,000 blue-whale units for the antarctic fishery on a motion by the Japanese commissioner that was seconded by the Russian commissioner. In view of the committee's predicted maximum catch this was in effect no quota at all.

As for the committee's other findings, the commission failed to act on some and was lukewarm toward others. In the case of the now economically insignificant humpback the commission could afford to be forthright; that whale was declared protected anywhere in the world south of the Equator. In the case of the blue whale a partial sanctuary was established in all waters south of 40 degrees south latitude except some 3.3 million square miles from 40 to 55 degrees south latitude and from the Greenwich meridian to 80 degrees east

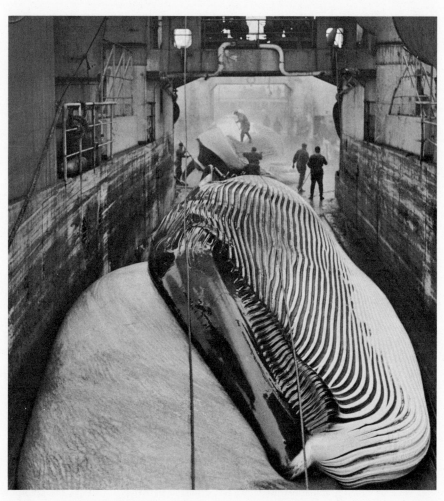

FINBACK WHALE is winched from the sea up the ramp of a factory ship. Its tongue is grotesquely expanded by the action of air that was pumped into the corpse to keep it afloat. On the flensing deck *(rear)* another whale is having its blubber stripped off for trying out.

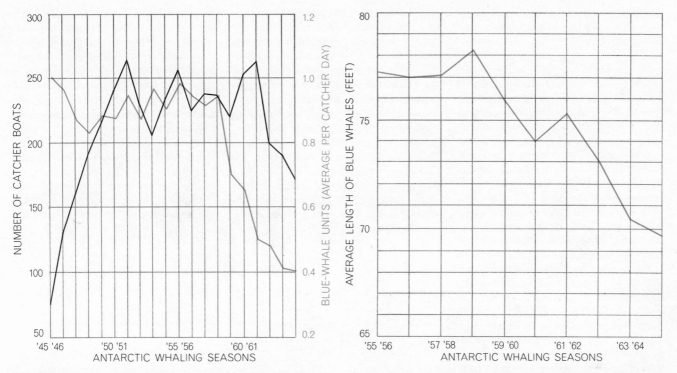

**PRODUCTIVITY** of the antarctic fishery began a sharp decline in the late 1950's (*color*). The decline, measured in terms of the catch per catcher-day, continued unchecked into the early 1960's although the number of catcher vessels (*black*) remained well above 200.

**NINE-SEASON RECORD** of the average length of blue whales killed in the Antarctic shows a decline that began in the 1959–1960 season. The average mature female is 77 feet long and a mature male 74 feet. Evidently recent catches have included immature whales.

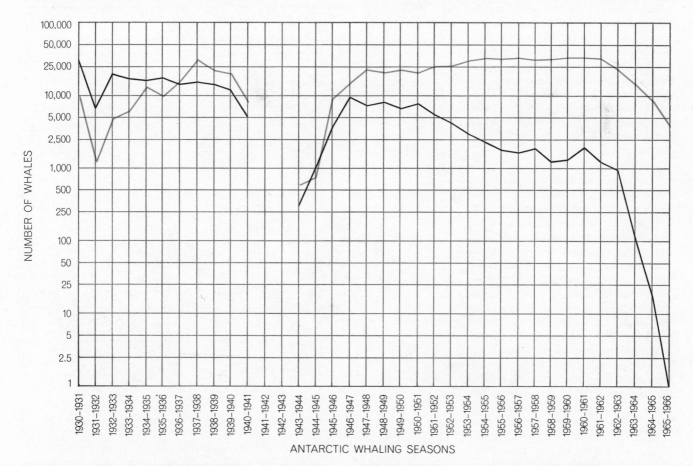

**RISE AND FALL** in the numbers of blue and finback whales that have been killed in the Antarctic during the past 36 years shows a correlation between the steadily diminishing blue-whale catch dur-

ing the 1950's and an increase in the catch of finbacks (*color*). Just as the blue-whale stock dwindled away under the pressure of overhunting, the finback stock is now showing a severe decline.

longitude. Japanese whalers had taken some 700 small blue whales in this zone during the 1962–1963 season; they considered it too good a hunting ground to be put out of bounds. The suggested elimination of the blue-whale unit and the establishment of species quotas were ignored. The commission added a fourth man (John A. Gulland of Great Britain) to the special committee and asked that a further report be presented in 1964. At that time it was intended to set the antarctic quota at a level in line with the committee's findings.

In 1963 a few members of the commission may have viewed with skepticism the ability of the three committee members to make accurate forecasts of a phenomenon as full of variables and unknowns as the effects of harvesting the antarctic whale stock. If so, the results of the 1963–1964 season settled their doubts. Sixteen factory ships and their catcher fleets worked the fishery; the industry's statistics, weighing such factors as the number of days each catcher was able to spend in hunting, showed that the total effort of the catchers was 91 percent of that during the season of 1962–1963. The number of blue whales killed, however, was the lowest of any season in the industry's history: a mere 112. The committee had predicted a total catch of 8,500 blue-whale units; the fleet managed to process 8,429 units. The committee had predicted that 14,000 finbacks would be killed; the finback toll came to 13,870. The committee's forecasts thus proved to be highly accurate.

At the commission's 1964 meeting the enlarged committee added the sei whale, formerly the least prized of any in the antarctic fishery, to the list of the overhunted. The committee pointed out that the total sei population had probably never exceeded 60,000, yet more than 20,000 sei had been killed in the course of the four previous seasons. With a whale stock of reasonable size it is a rule of thumb that 10 to 15 percent of the population can be harvested annually without causing a decline. With the expectation that more and more sei whales would be killed each season as the finback population thinned out, the committee anticipated sei kills above the sustainable level in the immediate future. In line with the commission's declared intention of setting quotas according to the committee's findings, it was proposed that the antarctic quota be drastically reduced in three annual steps. A limit of 4,000 units was sought for the 1964–1965 season, a lim-

it of 3,000 units for 1965–1966 and one of 2,000 units for 1966–1967. This degree of restraint, the population experts declared, was necessary merely to hold the number of whales in the Antarctic at the present level. They once more appealed—once more unsuccessfully—for the establishment of species quotas in place of the blue-whale-unit system.

Finally, a new gloomy statistic came before the commission: in 1963, for the first time since modern whaling had begun in the Antarctic, the larger part of the world catch had been taken in other waters. The most heavily fished

area had been the North Pacific; most of the whales taken there had been sperm, which continued to be free of quota restrictions. The committee pointed out that this diversion of the industry's effort from the dwindling antarctic whale resource to the North Pacific could have ominous consequences for the sperm-whale stock.

The proposal for a reduced antarctic quota came to a vote in the commission. Japan, the U.S.S.R., Norway and the Netherlands all voted against it; in spite of the commission's declared intent to give substance to the committee's find-

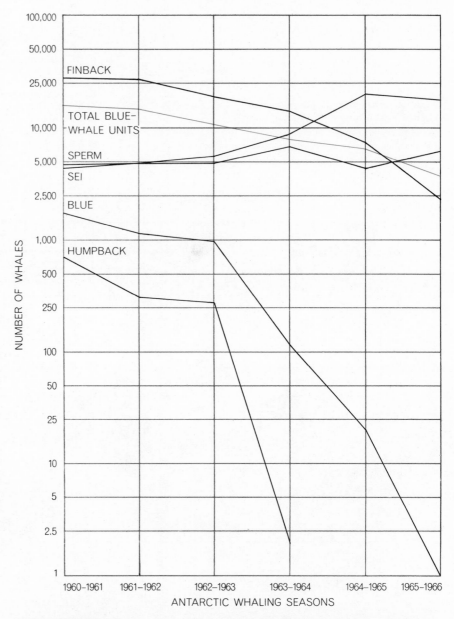

**CATCH RECORDS** for five species of whales killed in the Antarctic during the past six seasons show that increasing catches of sperm and sei whales have failed to counterbalance the decline in the fishery's productivity. The yield, calculated in blue-whale units (*color*), has dropped from 16,375 units in 1960–1961 to one-quarter of that amount in 1965–1966.

ings, the 1964 meeting adjourned with no commission quota set for the next antarctic season. The four whaling nations subsequently agreed in private that they would limit themselves to 8,000 blue-whale units in the 1964–

1965 season, a figure twice the one recommended by the committee.

The 1964–1965 season was disastrous. The industry processed only 7,052 units, more than 10 percent short of its self-established quota. Only 20 blue

whales were killed. The finback kill, declining for the fourth successive year, was 7,308 animals, or only a quarter of the 1960–1961 peak. As the committee had anticipated, the industry made up the difference by overkilling sei whales —almost 20,000 of them. In spite of this slaughter and a fairly large nonquota sperm-whale catch, the antarctic fishery for a second year supplied the industry with fewer whales than were taken in other waters.

For the first time since the beginning of the crisis the International Whaling Commission convened a special meeting. At this meeting (in May, 1965) the commission established a quota for the 1965–1966 antarctic season that reflected, at least in part, the committee's concern. The catch, even the whaling nations agreed, should not exceed 4,500 blue-whale units. At the regular June meeting that followed, the reduced quota was approved, and the commission agreed on a plan for further successive reductions of the antarctic fishery's quotas in the seasons to come.

The commission also attempted a first step toward partial protection of the world's sperm-whale stock. Up to that time the only restriction governing sperm kills was that cows less than 38 feet in length should not be taken. In 1964 the worldwide sperm catch had risen to a high of more than 29,000. The fleets en route to and from the Antarctic had killed 4,316 sperm whales. Once they were in the antarctic fishery they had taken 4,211 more; most of the rest had been killed in the North Pacific. In the hope of protecting sperm cows in Temperate Zone waters the commission ordered a worldwide hunting ban in the area between 40 degrees north latitude and 40 degrees south latitude. All three whaling nations, however, objected to the commission's order; the ban has simply been ignored. The worldwide sperm catch in 1965 was somewhat lower than in 1964: future catch records will reveal whether or not this drop reflects overkilling.

The imperative need for a reduced antarctic quota was demonstrated clearly enough by the results of the 1965–1966 season. With a quota of 4,500 blue-whale units the antarctic fleets could process only 4,089 units. The finback kill reached a new low, less than 10 percent of the 1960–1961 peak; in spite of protection, one blue whale and one humpback were taken. Again it was the sei whales that bore the brunt of the slaughter, and even their numbers were less than in the previous

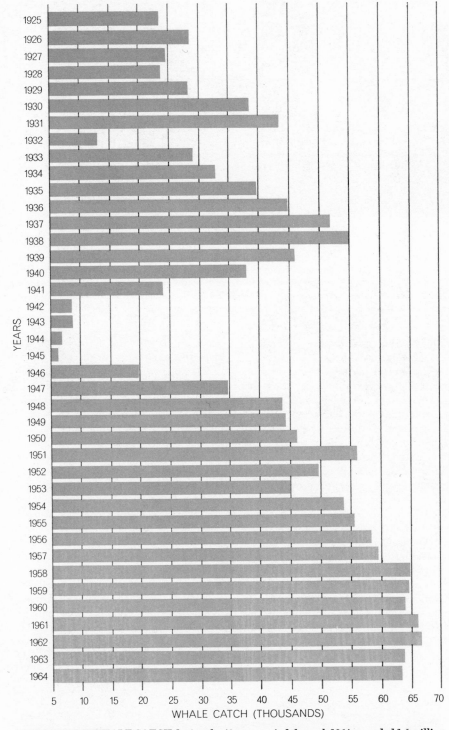

**WORLDWIDE WHALE CATCH** during the 40-year period through 1964 exceeded 1.6 million animals. The increase in numbers of whales taken from the 1950's on reflects the antarctic fishery's growing dependence first on finbacks in lieu of blue whales and next on sei whales in lieu of finbacks. From 1963 on the antarctic fishery has provided less than half of the world's whale catch. Figures are from Norway's Bureau of International Whaling Statistics.

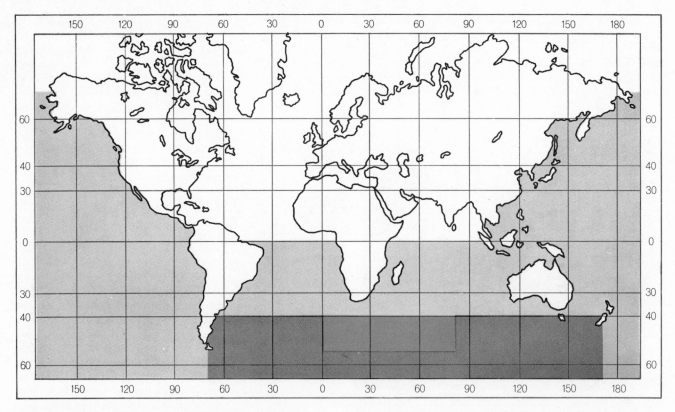

**REFUGE AREAS** within which designated species of whales are safe from hunting by member nations of the International Whaling Commission have been expanded in recent years. The nearly extinct bowhead and right whales enjoy worldwide protection. The blue and humpback whales are protected throughout the Pacific. The humpback is also protected south of the Equator elsewhere in the world, but the blue whale's protection elsewhere is limited to a zone south of 40 degrees south latitude (*gray area*). Even within this zone of protection 3.3 million square miles of ocean were kept open for blue-whale hunting at the request of Japan until a year ago.

season. The conclusion was inescapable: The antarctic fishery, with its seasonal yield down to less than 100,000 tons of oil, was no longer economically significant.

Can the antarctic whale fishery ever be restored? Even with the progressively reduced quotas now envisioned it may take 100 years before this resource recovers to the level of the middle 1950's. Recovery to the levels before World War II, which depended almost exclusively on the blue whale, is improbable. This giant mammal—one of the most remarkable ever to appear on the earth—has probably been reduced in numbers below the level that allows a species to survive; its worldwide population today may well be less than 1,000. Certainly there are 594 fewer blue whales this year than last. Whaling from land stations in Peru and Chile—two nations that are not parties to the international convention—accounted for 449 of these casualties in 1965.

The crucial question today does not concern the antarctic fishery but rather the future of all whaling. Continued overhunting of the finback whale can be expected to do to that species what has already been done to the blue whale. Last year, in addition to the antarctic season's kill of 2,314 finbacks, roughly 4,500 more of these animals were taken in other waters. Throughout the world's oceans today the only great whale that survives in economically significant numbers is the sperm. Yet a measure of the industry's lack of concern for its dwindling resources may be gained from recent efforts to establish quotas in the North Pacific, where the absence of quotas or restrictions allows hunting all year long. In spite of efforts by Canada and the U.S. the two whaling nations with fleets in the North Pacific— the U.S.S.R. and Japan—could not even agree to restrict the finback kill, let alone that of either sei or sperm.

Each of two past eras of whaling has virtually eradicated its own most highly prized whale species. The bowhead whale and the right whales are monuments to man's thoughtlessness in the days of sail. The blue whale and humpback—and possibly the finback and sei as well—are monuments to an industry's lack of foresight in the days of steam. The whaling nations today face a third and almost certainly a final decision. If essentially unrestricted whaling continues, the only surviving stock of any economic importance—the sperm whale, of whose numbers more than 250,000 have been killed in the past 12 years—is doomed to become a monument to international folly. Only sharply reduced annual harvests and protective regulations that are both enforceable and enforced offer the possibility that the last of the great whales will survive.

# 30 The Ecology of Fire

CHARLES F. COOPER · April 1961

Before Europeans came to North America, fires periodically swept over virtually every acre on the continent that had anything to burn. Along with climate, soil, topography and animal life, these conflagrations helped shape the pattern of vegetation that covered the land.

Civilization brought a tendency to regard fire as pure disaster, together with massive efforts to exclude fire completely from forest and grassland. The attempts frequently succeeded all too well. Over wide regions the pattern of plant life has changed, but not always in a way that users of the land could wish. Paradoxically, in some forest areas fire prevention has greatly increased the destructiveness of subsequent fires.

There is evidence that natural fires have occurred over most of the earth for thousands of years. Buried layers of charcoal testify to prehistoric fires. Historical writings mention great conflagrations witnessed by men. In the narratives of the explorers of North America are numerous accounts of traveling for days through smoke from distant fires, and of passing through burned-over prairies and woodlands.

Tree trunks in forested areas contain a record of past fires. A moderately intense fire often kills an area on one side of a tree, leaving the rest of the tree unharmed. As new layers of tissue grow over the dead spot, they count off the years since the fire. Examining freshly cut stumps of large redwoods, the California forester Emanuel Fritz found evidence of about four fires a century during the 1,100-year history of the stand. The figure is probably conservative, because there must have been many fires not severe enough to leave scars. In the ponderosa pine forests of California and Arizona, fire scars indicate an average of one burning every eight years.

Many forest fires are started by lightning; on the prairies rain immediately extinguishes lightning-set grass fires. Most prehistoric fires were undoubtedly the work of man.

Notwithstanding the popular conception, American Indians were not cautious in using fire. They did not conscientiously put out camp fires nor, unless their villages were threatened, did they try to keep fires from spreading. Often they burned intentionally—to drive game in hunting, as an offensive or defensive measure in warfare, or merely to keep the forest open to travel. A contemporary history of the Massachusetts Bay Colony, dated 1632, relates that "the Salvages are accustomed to set fire of the country in all places where they come; and to burn it twize a year, vixe, at the Spring, and at the fall of the leafe. The reason that moves them to do so, is because it would be otherwise so overgrown with underweedes that it would all be a copice wood, and the people could not be able in any wise to passe through the country out of a beaten path."

In open country fire favors grass over shrubs. Grasses are better adapted to withstand fire than are woody plants. The growing point of dormant grasses, from which issues the following year's growth, lies near or beneath the ground, protected from all but the severest heat. A grass fire removes only one year's growth, and usually much of this is dried and dead. The living tissue of shrubs, on the other hand, stands well above the ground, fully exposed to fire. When it is burned, the growth of several years is destroyed. Even though many shrubs sprout vigorously after burning, repeated loss of their top growth keeps them small. Perennial grasses, moreover, produce seeds in abundance one or two years after germination; most woody plants require several years to reach seed-bearing age. Fires that are frequent enough to inhibit seed production in woody plants usually restrict the shrubs to a relatively minor part of the grassland area.

Most ecologists believe that a substantial portion of North American grasslands owe their origin and maintenance to fire. Some disagree, arguing that climate is the deciding factor and fire has had little influence. To be sure, some areas, such as the Great Plains of North America, are too dry for most woody plants, and grasses persist there without fire. In other places, for example the grass-covered Palouse Hills of the southeastern part of the state of Washington, the soil is apparently unsuited to shrub growth, although the climate is favorable. But elsewhere—in the desert grasslands of the Southwest and the prairies of the Midwest—periodic fires must have tipped the vegetation equilibrium toward grasses.

Large parts of these grasslands are now being usurped by such shrubs as mesquite, juniper, sagebrush and scrub oak. Mesquite alone has spread from its former place along stream channels and on a few upland areas until now it occupies about 70 million acres of former grassland. Many ecologists and land managers blame the shrub invasion entirely on domestic livestock; they argue that overgrazing has selectively weakened the grasses and allowed the less palatable shrubs to increase. These explanations do not suffice; even on plots fenced off from animals shrubs continue to increase. A decrease in the frequency of fires is almost surely an essential part of the answer.

Fire has played an equally decisive role in many forests. A good example is found in the forests of jack pine that now spread in a broad band across Michigan, Wisconsin and Minnesota. When lumbermen first entered this region, they found little jack pine; the forests consisted chiefly of hardwood trees and white pines that towered above the general forest canopy. The loggers singled out the white pines for cutting, considering the other species worthless. Their activities were usually followed by fires, accidental or intentional. Supported by the dry debris of logging, the fires became holocausts that killed practically all the remaining vegetation. The mixed forest had little chance to regenerate; even the seeds of most trees were destroyed. But those of the jack pine survived. Unlike most pine cones, which drop off and release their seeds in the fall, jack pine cones stay closed and remain attached to the tree, sometimes so firmly that

FIRE MAINTAINS GRASSLAND by holding back the spread of mesquite *(shown here)* and other shrubs, which originally constitute a small part of the vegetation *(a)* but which soon proliferate and reduce areas that are available to grass *(b)*. Fire *(c)* reduces grasses and shrubs alike, but while the growing point of grass lies near or beneath the ground *(root system at right in "c")* and is left unharmed, the buds and growing tissue of shrub stand fully exposed and are destroyed. The balance is further tipped toward grasses *(d)* because they produce abundant seed a year or two after germination; as a result of this they lose only one or two years' growth in fire. Shrubs lose several years' growth.

branches grow right around them. Inside the cones the seeds remain viable for years. When the cones are heated, as in a forest fire, they slowly open and release their seeds. Thus the fires simultaneously eliminated the seeds of competing species and provided an abundant supply of jack pine seed together with a bed of ash that is ideal for germination. The result of the process is a pure stand of jack pine.

The valuable Douglas fir forests of the Pacific Northwest also owe their origin to fire. This species requires full sunlight; it cannot grow in the dense shade cast by a mature fir forest. When old Douglas firs die, their place is taken not by new Douglas firs but by cedars and hemlocks, more tolerant of shade, which therefore constitute the "climax" vegetation of the region. Forest fires, however, arrest the succession by creating openings in the forest into which the light, winged seeds of Douglas firs can fly from adjacent stands. The seedlings take advantage of the sunlight in the openings: they flourish and top competing vegetation; ultimately they grow into pure stands of uniform age.

Jack pine and Douglas fir are dependent on fire for their establishment but cannot endure frequent burning thereafter. In other forests fire is a normal part of the environment during the whole life of the stand. The longleaf pine of the southeastern U. S. is a striking example. This species is almost ideally adapted to recurring fires.

Unlike most pines, the young longleaf does not grow uniformly after germination. The seedling reaches a height of a few inches in a few weeks. Then it stops growing upward and sprouts a grasslike ring of long drooping needles that surrounds the stem and terminal bud. During this so-called grass stage, which usually lasts from three to seven years, the plant's growth processes are concentrated in forming a deep and extensive root system and in storing food reserves.

Longleaf pine is easily shaded out by competing hardwoods and is susceptible to a serious blight known as brown spot. The brown spot fungus multiplies during the dry summer, and the autumn rains splash its spores onto the needles of the low seedlings. Unless overtopping vegetation is cleared away and brown spot is controlled, the young pines may remain in the grass stage indefinitely.

One of America's first professional foresters, H. H. Chapman of Yale University, perceived in the early 1920's that periodic fires were essential to the life of longleaf pine. Protected by its canopy of needles, the longleaf seedling can withstand heat that kills the aboveground portions of competing hardwoods and grasses. At the same time the flames consume dry needles infected with brown spot, destroying the principal source of fungus spores. After the young pine emerges from the grass stage, its phenomenal growth—often four to six feet a year for the first two or three years—quickly carries the buds beyond the reach of surface fires. The thick, corky bark of the sapling protects its sensitive growing tissue. As the tree

**SEROTINOUS JACK PINE CONES** resist fire (*top*). Unlike other pine cones, which open and release their seeds in the fall, jack pine cones open after being heated (*bottom*).

ORIGINAL FORESTS of Great Lakes region were of mixed hardwoods, some jack pines (*at right in "a"*) and white pines (*middle distance and background*). Early loggers cut white pines and left other species standing (*jack pine cone is in foreground of*

grows and the bark thickens, it becomes resistant to any but the most intense fires.

Largely at Chapman's urging, prescribed fire has become an accepted management tool in the southeastern longleaf pine forests. Before a stand is harvested a fire is run through during the dry summer, when it will burn fairly hot. This clears out most of the undergrowth without killing the trees and prepares a good seedbed. The old trees are cut during the following winter, after the seeds have fallen. About three winters later, when burning conditions permit only a relatively cool fire and the seedlings have entered the grass stage, the area is burned again. Fires at regular three-year intervals thereafter keep down the worthless scrub oaks and help control brown spot. They hold back the normal succession, which would lead to a climax oak-hickory forest. Moreover, a regime of periodic fires reduces the accumulation of dry fuel on the ground that might otherwise lead to an uncontrollable holocaust.

FIRE-RESISTANT FORESTS of longleaf pine in southeastern U. S. are well adapted to recurrent fires. Long, green needles of seedling longleaf (*lower right in "a"*) protect central stem and bud against surface fires that burn out forest debris and saplings of competing hardwoods (*middle distance and background in "b"*). Rapid vertical growth of tree after seedling stage carries

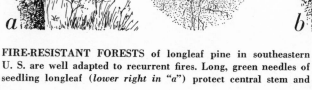

"b"). Debris of logging supported holocausts that consumed remaining vegetation. Although jack pines were destroyed, their cones survived and released seeds (c). Seedling jack pines (d) grew in fertile ashes, giving rise to pure jack pine stands today (e).

My own work has dealt with the ponderosa pine forests of the Southwest. As 19th-century chronicles attest, they used to be open, parklike forests arranged in a mosaic of discrete groups, each containing 10 to 30 trees of a common age. Small numbers of saplings were dispersed among the mature pines, and luxuriant grasses carpeted the forest floor. Fires, when they occurred, were easily controlled and seldom killed a whole stand. Foresters in other regions envied the men assigned to the "asbestos forests" of the Southwest.

Today dense thickets of young trees have sprung up everywhere in the forests. The grass has been reduced, and dry branches and needles have accumulated to such an extent that any fire is likely to blow up into an inferno that will destroy everything in its path. Foresters have generally blamed the overproduction of trees on a period of unusually favorable weather conditions, or on removal of competing grasses and exposure of bare soil through past

vulnerable bud beyond reach of bigger fires (c); thickening bark affords increasing insulation for delicate cambium against hotter fires. At the same time the tree drops more needles, supporting hotter fires that clear out larger saplings (d). Self-governing mechanism keeps forest open (e). Illustrations follow single tree from seedling ("a" and "b") to sapling ("c" and "d") to maturity (e).

trampling and grazing by domestic animals. But it is becoming increasingly apparent that a vigorous policy of fire
exclusion, too long followed, is at least
partly responsible.

Lightning is frequent in the ponderosa
pine region, and the Indians set many
fires there. Tree rings show that the forests used to burn regularly at intervals
of three to 10 years. The mosaic pattern
of the forest has developed under the
influence of recurrent light fires. Each
even-aged group springs up in an opening left by the death of a predecessor.
(After remaining intact for 300 years or
more, groups break up quite suddenly—
often in less than 20 years.) The first
fire that passes through consumes the
dead trees, and leaves a good seedbed
of ash and mineral soil, into which seed
drifts from surrounding trees. Young
ponderosa seedlings cannot withstand
even a light surface fire, but in the newly seeded opening they are protected by

**PRIMEVAL DOUGLAS FIR FORESTS** of western U. S. have
origin in fires of previous centuries. Young Douglas firs, which
are intolerant of shade, cannot grow beneath mature Douglas fir
forest (*a*), yield to cedars and hemlocks, which make up the climax

**REPLACEMENT OF DOUGLAS FIRS** by hardwoods is in part
attributable to exclusion of fire. Cedar and hemlock saplings (*a*),
unlike young Douglas firs, grow well in shade of mature Douglas
fir forest, take over as older firs die (*b*). As cedar and hemlock

the lack of dry pine needles to fuel such fires. Consequently the young stand escapes burning for the first few years. Eventually the saplings drop enough needles to support a light surface fire, which kills many smaller saplings but leaves most of the larger ones alive. The roots of the survivors quickly appropriate the soil made vacant, and their growth is stimulated.

The degree of thinning accomplished by a fire depends upon the quantity of fuel on the ground. The denser the sapling stand, the more needles it drops and the hotter the fire it will support. The process is thus a sort of self-regulating feedback mechanism governed by the density of the stand. Thinning by fire is less efficient than the forester might wish, but it does help to prevent the stagnation resulting from extreme overcrowding.

As a group of trees grows toward maturity, new seedlings germinate beneath

vegetation of the region. Succession was interrupted by frequent small fires that burned out cedar and hemlock trees (*b*). Douglas fir seeds from adjacent stands blew into new openings (*c*), grew well in seedbed of ashes and became pure stands of Douglas fir (*d*).

trees grow (*c*), they diminish remaining opportunities for Douglas fir seedlings to survive. Climax vegetation that results is composed of cedar and hemlock (*d*). These illustrations, like those on preceding and following pages, are drawn from same point of view.

it. The volume of dry fuel dropped by the older trees, however, supports fires hot enough to eradicate the seedlings entirely. Fire and shade together prevent younger trees from developing; the even-aged character of the group is maintained throughout its life.

Wild-land managers have historically, and properly, concentrated on suppressing accidental fires in forests and grasslands and on discouraging deliberate overburning by man. While fire may favor the establishment of jack pine forests, the annual burning long practiced in the South will prevent the growth of any forest at all. By the same token, occasional fires may be needed to maintain African grasslands, but deliberately setting fire to the country every few months has unquestionably damaged them seriously. It is time to relax many of the ingrained prejudices against fire and to utilize it, judiciously, as a tool in the management of both forests and grasslands.

PARKLIKE PONDEROSA PINE FORESTS of Southwest were typically a mosaic of even-aged groups (*mature stand in middle distance of "a"; young stand in background*). Frequent fires kept forest debris from accumulating (*b*); thus the fires were mild and created openings for seedlings (*c*), which cannot grow in shade. As new trees matured, they dropped more needles, providing more fuel for hotter fires, which killed new seedlings (*d*). Mosaic and parklike character of the forest was thereby maintained.

CLUTTERED PONDEROSA PINE FORESTS (*a*), in contrast to those illustrated on page 254, result from the elimination of the periodic fires that occurred naturally. Saplings that would have been thinned out by fire now vie for space in the formerly open avenues between trees, the grass cover is reduced and forest debris and undergrowth have accumulated to the point (*b*) that fires that formerly would have been mild and easily controlled often explode into holocausts (*c*) that destroy the entire stand of trees (*d*).

# 31 The Black Death

WILLIAM L. LANGER · February 1964

In the three years from 1348 through 1350 the pandemic of plague known as the Black Death, or, as the Germans called it, the Great Dying, killed at least a fourth of the population of Europe. It was undoubtedly the worst disaster that has ever befallen mankind. Today we can have no real conception of the terror under which people lived in the shadow of the plague. For more than two centuries plague has not been a serious threat to mankind in the large, although it is still a grisly presence in parts of the Far East and Africa. Scholars continue to study the Great Dying, however, as a historic example of human behavior under the stress of universal catastrophe. In these days when the threat of plague has been replaced by the threat of mass human extermination by even more rapid means, there has been a sharp renewal of interest in the history of the 14th-century calamity. With new perspective, students are investigating its manifold effects: demographic, economic, psychological, moral and religious.

Plague is now recognized as a well-marked disease caused by a specific organism (*Bacillus pestis*). It is known in three forms, all highly fatal: pneumonic (attacking primarily the lungs), bubonic (producing buboes, or swellings, of the lymph glands) and septicemic (killing the victim rapidly by poisoning of the blood). The disease is transmitted to man by fleas, mainly from black rats and certain other rodents, including ground squirrels. It produces high fever, agonizing pain and prostration, and it is usually fatal within five or six days. The Black Death got its name from dark blotches produced by hemorrhages in the skin.

There had been outbreaks of plague in the Roman Empire in the sixth century and in North Africa earlier, but for some reason epidemics of the disease in Europe were comparatively rare after that until the 14th century. Some historians have suggested that the black rat was first brought to western Europe during the Crusades by expeditions returning from the Middle East. This seems unlikely: remains of the rat have been found in prehistoric sites in Switzerland, and in all probability the houses of Europe were infested with rats throughout the Middle Ages.

In any event, the 14th-century pandemic clearly began in 1348 in the ports of Italy, apparently brought in by merchant ships from Black Sea ports. It gradually spread through Italy and in the next two years swept across Spain, France, England, central Europe and Scandinavia. It advanced slowly but pitilessly, striking with deadliest effect in the crowded, unsanitary towns. Each year the epidemic rose to a peak in the late summer, when the fleas were most abundant, and subsided during the winter, only to break out anew in the spring.

The pandemic of 1348–1350 was followed by a long series of recurrent outbreaks all over Europe, coming at intervals of 10 years or less. In London there were at least 20 attacks of plague in the 15th century, and in Venice the Black Death struck 23 times between 1348 and 1576. The plague epidemics were frequently accompanied by severe outbreaks of typhus, syphilis and "English sweat"—apparently a deadly form of influenza that repeatedly afflicted not only England but also continental Europe in the first half of the 16th century.

From the 13th to the late 17th century Europe was disease-ridden as never before or since. In England the long affliction came to a climax with an epidemic of bubonic plague in 1665 that killed nearly a tenth of London's estimated population of 460,000, two-thirds of whom fled the city during the outbreak. Thereafter in western and central Europe the plague rapidly died away as mysteriously as it had come. The theories advanced to explain its subsidence are as unconvincing as those given for its rise. It was long supposed, for instance, that an invasion of Europe early in the 18th century by brown rats, which killed off the smaller black rats, was responsible for the decline of the disease. This can hardly be the reason; the plague had begun to subside decades before, and the brown rat did not by any means exterminate the black rat. More probably the answer must be sought in something that happened to the flea, the bacillus or the living conditions of the human host.

This article, however, is concerned not with the medical but with the social aspects of the Black Death. Let us begin by examining the dimensions of the catastrophe in terms of the death toll.

As reported by chroniclers of the time, the mortality figures were so incredibly high that modern scholars long regarded them with skepticism. Recent detailed and rigorously conducted analyses indicate, however, that many of the reports were substantially correct. It is now generally accepted that at least a quarter of the European population was wiped out in the first epidemic of 1348 through 1350, and that in the next 50 years the total mortality rose to more than a third of the population. The incidence of the disease and the mortality rate varied, of course, from place to place. Florence was reduced in population from 90,000 to 45,000, Siena from 42,000 to 15,000; Hamburg apparently lost almost two-thirds of its inhabitants. These estimates are borne out by accurate records that were kept in later epidemics. In Venice, for example, the Magistrato della Sanità (board of health) kept a meticulous count of the victims of a severe plague attack in 1576 and 1577; the deaths totaled 46,721 in a total estimated population of about 160,000. In 1720 Marseilles lost 40,000 of a population of 90,000, and in Messina about half of the inhabitants died in 1743.

It is now estimated that the total population of England fell from about 3.8 million to 2.1 million in the period from 1348 to 1374. In France, where the loss of life was increased by the Hundred Years' War, the fall in population was even more precipitate. In western and central Europe as a whole the mortality was so great that it took nearly two centuries for the population level of 1348 to be regained.

The Black Death was a scourge such as man had never known. Eighty per cent or more of those who came down with the plague died within two or three days, usually in agonizing pain. No one knew the cause of or any preventive or cure for the disease. The medical profession was all but helpless, and the desperate measures taken by town authorities proved largely futile. It is difficult to imagine the growing terror with which the people must have watched the inexorable advance of the disease on their community.

They responded in various ways. Almost everyone, in that medieval time, interpreted the plague as a punishment by God for human sins, but there were arguments whether the Deity was sending retribution through the poisoned arrows of evil angels, "venomous moleculae" or earthquake-induced or comet-borne miasmas. Many blamed the Jews,

accusing them of poisoning the wells or otherwise acting as agents of Satan. People crowded into the churches, appealing for protection to the Virgin, to St. Sebastian, to St. Roch or to any of 60 other saints believed to have special influence against the disease. In the streets half-naked flagellants, members of the century-old cult of flagellantism, marched in processions whipping each other and warning the people to purge themselves of their sins before the coming day of atonement.

Flight in the face of approaching danger has always been a fundamental human reaction, in modern as well as ancient times. As recently as 1830, 60,-000 people fled from Moscow during an epidemic of cholera, and two years later, when the first cases of this disease turned up in New York City, fully a fourth of the population of 220,000 took flight in

RAPHAEL'S "LA PÈSTE" ("The Plague") reflects the preoccupation of European art with plague and its consequences during the plague-ridden three centuries following the Black Death. This picture, now worn with time, is divided into two parts: night at right and day at left. Among other plague themes of artists were the dance of death and the terrors of the Last Judgment.

steamboats, stagecoaches, carts and even wheelbarrows. The plague epidemics of the 14th to 16th century of course produced even more frightened mass migrations from the towns. Emperors, kings, princes, the clergy, merchants, lawyers, professors, students, judges and even physicians rushed away, leaving the common people to shift for themselves. All who could get away shut themselves up in houses in the country.

At the same time drastic efforts were made to segregate those who were forced to remain in the towns. In an epidemic in 1563 Queen Elizabeth took refuge in Windsor Castle and had a gallows erected on which to hang anyone who had the temerity to come out to Windsor from plague-ridden London. Often when a town was hit by the plague a cordon of troops would be thrown around the town to isolate it, allowing no one to leave or enter. In the afflicted cities entire streets were closed off by chains, the sick were quarantined in their houses and gallows were installed in the public squares as a warning against the violation of regulations. The French surgeon Ambroise Paré, writing of a plague epidemic in 1568,

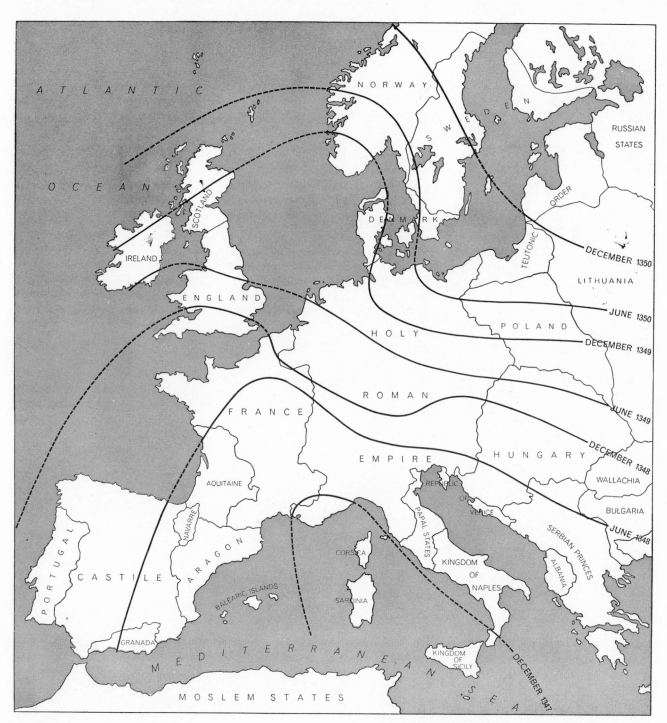

**APPROXIMATE CHRONOLOGY** of the Black Death's rapid sweep through Europe in the middle of the 14th century is indicated on this map, which shows the political divisions as they existed at the time. The plague, which was apparently brought from Asia by ships, obtained a European foothold in the Mediterranean in 1347; during the succeeding three years only a few small areas escaped.

reported that husbands and wives deserted each other, that parents sometimes even abandoned their children and that people went mad with terror and committed suicide.

Victims of the disease often died in the streets, as is shown in Raphael's "La Pèste," now in the Uffizi Gallery in Florence. Gravediggers were understandably scarce. For the most part those hired for the job, at fantastic wages, were criminals and tramps—men who could not be expected to draw fine distinctions between the dying and the dead. The corpses and the near corpses were thrown into carts and dumped indiscriminately into huge pits outside the town walls.

The sufferings and reactions of humanity when the plague came have been depicted vividly by writers such as Boccaccio, Daniel Defoe, Alessandro Manzoni and the late Albert Camus (in his novel *The Plague*) and by artists from Raphael and Holbein to Delacroix. Boccaccio's *Decameron*, an account of a group of well-to-do cavaliers and maidens who shut themselves up in a country house during the Black Death in Florence and sought to distract themselves with revelry and spicy stories, illustrates one of the characteristic responses of mankind to fear and impending disaster. It was most simply described by Thucydides in his report of the "Plague of Athens" in 430 B.C.:

"Men resolved to get out of life the pleasures which could be had speedily and would satisfy their lusts, regarding their bodies and their wealth alike as transitory.... No fear of gods or law of men restrained them; for, on the one hand, seeing that all men were perishing alike, they judged that piety or impiety came to the same thing, and, on the other hand, no one expected that he would live to be called to account and pay the penalty for his misdeeds. On the contrary, they believed that the penalty already decreed against them and now hanging over their heads was a far heavier one, and that before it fell it was only reasonable to get some enjoyment out of life."

From this philosophy one might also develop the rationalization that hilarity and the liberal use of liquor could ward off the plague. In any event, many people of all classes gave themselves up to carousing and ribaldry. The Reformation theologian John Wycliffe, who survived the Black Death of the 14th century, wrote with dismay of the lawlessness and depravity of the time. Everywhere, wrote chroniclers of the

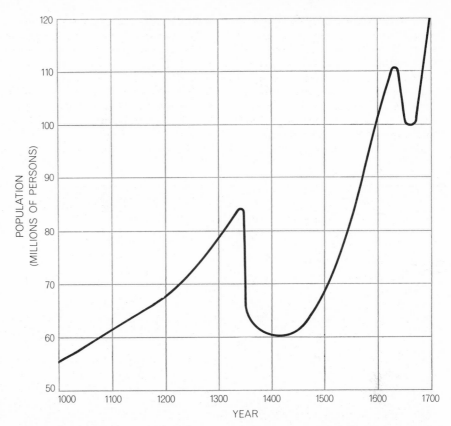

IMPACT ON POPULATION from recurrent plagues in Europe is indicated. For more than 300 years after 1347 the plagues checked the normal rise in population; sometimes, as in the 14th and 17th centuries, they resulted in sharp reductions. The figures shown on this chart derive from estimates by students of population; actual data for the period are scarce.

epidemics in London then and later, there was "drinking, roaring and surfeiting.... In one house you might hear them roaring under the pangs of death, in the next tippling, whoring and belching out blasphemies against God." Even the sober Samuel Pepys admitted to his diary that he had made merry in the shadow of death, indulging himself and his wife in a "great store of dancings." The university town of Oxford, like London, also was the scene of much "lewd and dissolute behavior."

The outbreak of an epidemic of plague was almost invariably the signal for a wave of crime and violence. As Boccaccio wrote, "the reverend authority of the laws, both human and divine, was all in a manner dissolved and fallen into decay, for lack of the ministers and executors thereof." In the midst of death, looting and robbery flourished. Burial gangs looted the houses of the dead and stripped the corpses of anything of value before throwing them into the pits. On occasion they even murdered the sick.

Just as desperation drove some to a complete abandonment of morality, it drove others, perhaps the majority, to

pathetic extravagances of religiosity or superstition. The poet George Wither noted this contrast in the London epidemic of 1625:

*Some streets had Churches full*
*  of people, weeping;*
*Some others, Tavernes had, rude-revell*
*  keeping;*
*Within some houses Psalmes*
*  and Hymnes were sung;*
*With raylings and loud scouldings*
*  others rung.*

Many people threw themselves on God's mercy, showered the church with gifts and made extravagant vows for the future. Others hunted down Jews and witches as the originators of the plague. The Black Death generated a startling spread of belief in witchcraft. Even as learned a scholar and theologian as John Calvin was convinced that a group of male and female witches, acting as agents of Satan, had brought the plague to Geneva. In the cult of Satanism, as in that of flagellantism, there was a strong strain of sexuality. It was believed that the women accused of being witches had intercourse with the

Devil and could strike men with sexual impotence. From the psychoanalytic point of view this belief may have stemmed from an unconscious reaction to the tremendous shrinkage of the population.

Jews and witches were not the only victims of the general panic. The wrath of the people also fell on physicians. They were accused of encouraging or helping the spread of the plague instead of checking it. Paré tells us that some of them were stoned in the streets in France. (In the 19th century physicians were similarly made scapegoats during epidemics of cholera. Some people accused them of poisoning public water supplies, at the behest of the rich, in order to kill off the excessive numbers of the poor.)

Although we have fairly accurate knowledge of the immediate effects of the great plagues in Europe—they were fully and circumstantially chronicled by many contemporary writers—it is not so

easy to specify the long-term effects of the plagues. Many other factors entered into the shaping of Europe's history during and after the period of the plague epidemics. Nevertheless, there can be no doubt that the Great Dying had a profound and lasting influence on that history.

In its economic life Europe suffered a sudden and drastic change. Before the Black Death of 1348–1350 the Continent had enjoyed a period of rather rapid population growth, territorial expansion and general prosperity. After the pandemic Europe sank into a long depression: a century or more of economic stagnation and decline. The most serious disruption took place in agriculture.

For a short time the towns and cities experienced a flush of apparent prosperity. Many survivors of the epidemic had suddenly inherited substantial amounts of property and money from

the wholesale departure of their relatives. They built elegant houses and went on a buying spree that made work (and high prices) for the manufacturing artisans. The churches and other public institutions, sharing in the wealth of the new rich, also built imposing and expensive structures.

The rural areas, on the other hand, virtually collapsed. With fewer people to feed in the towns and cities, the farmers lost a large part of the market for their crops. Grain prices fell precipitately. So did the farm population. Already sadly depleted by the ravages of the plague, it was now further reduced by a movement to the towns, which offered the impoverished farmers work as artisans. In spite of strenuous efforts by landlords and lords of the manor to keep the peasants on the land by law and sometimes by force, the rural population fled to the cities en masse. Thousands of farms and villages were deserted. In central Germany some 70

**DESERTED ENGLISH VILLAGE,** typical of many medieval communities made ghost towns by the Black Death and succeeding plagues, occupied the site shown in this aerial photograph. This site is Tusmore in Oxfordshire; most of the lines are earthworks that bounded farm enclosures behind cottages. Aerial photography has been used to locate many abandoned medieval villages.

per cent of all the farm settlements were abandoned in the period following the Black Death. (Many of these "lost" farms and villages, long overgrown, have recently been located by aerial photography.)

Farms became wilderness or pasture. Rents and land values disappeared. The minor land-owning gentry sank into poverty. In the words of the 14th-century poet Petrarch, "a vast and dreadful solitude" settled over the land. And of course in the long run the depression of agriculture engulfed the cities in depression as well.

Some authorities believe that Europe had begun to fall into a period of economic decay before the Black Death and that the epidemics only accentuated this trend. The question is certainly a complicated one. Wars and other economic forces no doubt played their part in Europe's long recession. It seems probable, however, that the decisive factor was the repeated onslaught of epidemics that depleted and weakened the population. The present consensus on the subject is that population change is a main cause of economic change rather than vice versa. Surely it must be considered significant that Europe's economic revival in the 17th and 18th centuries coincided with the disappearance of the plague and a burst of rapid population growth [see "Population," by Kingsley Davis; SCIENTIFIC AMERICAN, September, 1963].

The psychological effects of the ordeal of the plague are at least as impressive as the economic ones. For a long time it held all of Europe in an apocalyptic mood, which the Dutch historian Johan Huizinga analyzed brilliantly a generation ago in his study The Waning of the Middle Ages. As Arturo Castiglioni, the eminent Yale University historian of medicine, has written: "Fear was the sovereign ruler of this epoch." Men lived and worked in constant dread of disease and imminent death. "No thought is born in me that has not 'Death' engraved upon it," wrote Michelangelo.

Much of the art of the time reflected a macabre interest in graves and an almost pathological predilection for the manifestations of disease and putrefaction. Countless painters treated with almost loving detail the sufferings of Christ, the terrors of the Last Judgment and the tortures of Hell. Woodcuts and paintings depicting the dance of death, inspired directly by the Black Death, enjoyed a morbid popularity. With pitiless realism these paintings portrayed Death as a horridly grinning skeleton that seized, without warning, the prince and the peasant, the young and the old, the lovely maiden and the hardened villain, the innocent babe and the decrepit dotard.

Along with the mood of despair there was a marked tendency toward wild defiance—loose living and immoralities that were no doubt a desperate kind of reassertion of life in the presence of death. Yet the dominant feature of the time was not its licentiousness but its overpowering feelings of guilt, which arose from the conviction that God had visited the plague on man as retribution for his sins. Boccaccio, a few years after writing his Decameron, was overcome by repentance and a sense of guilt verging on panic. Martin Luther suffered acutely from guilt and fear of death, and Calvin, terror-stricken by the plague, fled from each epidemic. Indeed, entire communities were afflicted with what Freud called the primordial sense of guilt, and they engaged in penitential processions, pilgrimages and passionate mass preaching.

Some 70 years ago the English Catholic prelate and historian (later cardinal) Francis Gasquet, in a study entitled The Great Pestilence, tried to demonstrate that the Black Death set the stage for the Protestant Reformation by killing off the clergy and upsetting the entire religious life of Europe. This no doubt is too simple a theory. On the other hand, it is hard to deny that the catastrophic epidemics at the close of the Middle Ages must have been a powerful force for religious revolution. The failure of the Church and of prayer to ward off the pandemic, the flight of priests who deserted their parishes in the face of danger and the shortage of religious leaders after the Great Dying left the people eager for new kinds of leadership. And it is worth noting that most if not all of the Reformation leaders—Wycliffe, Zwingli, Luther, Calvin and others—were men who sought a more intimate relation of man to God because they were deeply affected by mankind's unprecedented ordeal by disease.

This is not to say that the epidemics of the late Middle Ages suffice to explain the Reformation but simply that the profound disturbance of men's minds by the universal, chronic grief and by the immediacy of death brought fundamental and long-lasting changes in religious outlook. In the moral and religious life of Europe, as well as in the economic sphere, the forces that make for change were undoubtedly strengthened and given added impetus by the Black Death.

# 32 Population Control in Animals

V. C. WYNNE-EDWARDS · August 1964

In population growth the human species is conspicuously out of line with the rest of the animal kingdom. Man is almost alone in showing a long-term upward trend in numbers; most other animals maintain their population size at a fairly constant level. To be sure, many of them fluctuate in number from season to season, from year to year or from decade to decade; notable examples are arctic lemmings, migratory locusts living in the subtropical dry belt, many northern game birds and certain fur-bearing animals. Such fluctuations, however, tend to swing erratically around a constant average value. More commonly animal populations maintain a steady state year after year and even century after century. If and when the population does rise or fall permanently, because of some change in the environment, it generally stabilizes again at a new level.

This well-established fact of population dynamics deserves to be studied with close attention, because the growth of human populations has become in recent years a matter of increasing concern. What sort of mechanism is responsible for such strict control of the size of populations? Each animal population, apart from man's, seems to be regulated in a homeostatic manner by some system that tends to keep it within not too wide limits of a set average density. Ecologists have been seeking to discover the nature of this system for many years. I shall outline here a new hypothesis that I set forth in full detail in a recently published book, *Animal Dispersion in Relation to Social Behaviour*.

The prevailing hypothesis has been that population is regulated by a set of negative natural controls. It is assumed that animals will produce young as fast as they efficiently can, and that the main factors that keep population density within fixed limits are predators, starvation, accidents and parasites causing disease. On the face of it this assumption seems entirely reasonable; overcrowding should increase the death toll from most of these factors and thus act to cut back the population when it rises to a high density. On close examination, however, these ideas do not stand up.

The notions that predators or disease are essential controllers of population density can be dismissed at once. There are animals that effectively have no predators and are not readily subject to disease and yet are limited to a stable level of population; among notable examples are the lion, the eagle and the skua [see "The Antarctic Skua," by Carl R. Eklund; SCIENTIFIC AMERICAN, February]. Disease per se does not act on a large scale to control population growth in the animal world. This leaves starvation as the possible control. The question of whether starvation itself acts directly to remove a population surplus calls for careful analysis.

Even a casual examination makes it clear that in most animal communities starvation is rare. Normally all the individuals in the habitat get enough food to survive. Occasionally a period of drought or severe cold may starve out a population, but that is an accident of weather—a disaster that does not arise from the density of population. We must therefore conclude that death from hunger is not an important density-dependent factor in controlling population size except in certain unusual cases.

Yet the density of population in the majority of habitats does depend directly on the size of the food supply; the close relation of one to the other is clear in representative situations where both variables have been measured [see *illustration on page 265*]. We have, then, the situation that no individual starves but the population does not outgrow the food supply available in its habitat under normal conditions.

For many of the higher animals one can see therefore that neither predators, disease nor starvation can account for the regulation of numbers. There is of course accidental mortality, but it strikes in unpredictable and haphazard ways, independently of population density, and so must be ruled out as a stabilizer of population. All these considerations point to the possibility that the animals themselves must exercise the necessary restraint!

Man's own history provides some vivid examples of what is entailed here. By overgrazing he has converted once rich pastures into deserts; by overhunting he has exterminated the passenger pigeon and all but eliminated animals such as the right whale, the southern fur seal and, in many of their former breeding places, sea turtles; he is now threatening to exterminate all five species of rhinoceros inhabiting tropical Africa and Asia because the horns of those animals are valued for their alleged aphrodisiac powers. Exploiting the riches of today can exhaust and destroy the resources of tomorrow. The point is that animals face precisely this danger with respect to their food supply, and they generally handle it more prudently than man does.

Birds feeding on seeds and berries in the fall or chickadees living on hibernating insects in winter are in such a situation. The stock of food to begin with is so abundant that it could feed an enormous population. Then, however, it would be gone in hours or days, and the birds must depend on this food supply for weeks or months. To make it

**UNEMPLOYED BIRDS** are visible at a gannetry on Cape St. Mary in Newfoundland. They are the ones on the slope at left; the main colony is on the large adjacent slope. The unemployed gannets are excluded from breeding, apparently as part of the colony's automatic mechanisms for controlling the population level. These birds do, however, constitute a reserve for raising the population level.

MASSED MANEUVERS by starling flocks occur frequently on fine evenings, particularly in the fall. The maneuvers are an example of communal activity that appears to have the purpose of provid- ing the flock with an indication of population density. If the density is too high or too low in relation to the food supply, the flock automatically increases the activities that will improve the balance.

last through the season the birds must restrict the size of their population in advance. The same necessity holds in situations where unlimited feeding would wipe out the sources that replenish the food supply. Thus the threat of starvation tomorrow, not hunger itself today, seems to be the factor that decides what the density of a population ought to be. Long before starvation would otherwise occur, the population must limit its growth in order to avoid disastrous overexploitation of its food resources.

All this implies that animals restrict their population density by some artificial device that is closely correlated with the food supply. What is required is some sort of automatic restrictive mechanism analogous to the deliberate conventions or agreements by which nations limit the exploitation of fishing grounds.

One does not need to look far to realize that animals do indeed possess conventions of this kind. The best-known is the territorial system of birds. The practice of staking out a territory for nesting and rearing a family is common among many species of birds. In the breeding season each male lays claim to an area of not less than a certain minimum size and keeps out all other males of the species; in this way a group of males will parcel out the available ground as individual territories and put a limit on crowding. It is a perfect example of an artificial mechanism geared to adjusting the density of population to the food resources. Instead of competing directly for the food itself the members compete furiously for pieces of ground, each of which then becomes the exclusive food preserve of its owner. If the standard territory is large enough to feed a family, the entire group is safe from the danger of overtaxing the food supply.

The territorial convention is just one example of a convention that takes many other forms, some of them much more sophisticated or abstract. Seabirds, for instance, being unable to stake out a territory or nest on the sea itself,

PLACE IN HIERARCHY is at stake in this contest between male black bucks in India. Many mammal and bird groups have a hierarchical system or a system of defended territories. Successful individuals acquire food and breeding rights; the others leave, or perhaps stay as a reserve available for breeding if needed. By such means the group correlates its population with food resources.

adopt instead a token nesting place on the shore that represents their fishing rights. Each nesting site occupies only a few square feet, but the birds' behavior also limits the overall size of their colony, thereby restricting the number that will fish in the vicinity. Any adults that have not succeeded in winning a site within the perimeter of the colony are usually inhibited from nesting or starting another colony nearby.

Other restrictive conventions practiced by animals are still more abstract. Often the animals compete not for actual property, such as a nesting site, but merely for membership in the group, and only a certain number are accepted. In all cases the effect is to limit the density of the group living in the given habitat and unload any surplus population to a safe distance.

Not the least interesting fact is that the competition itself tends to take an abstract or conventional form. In their contest for a territory birds seldom actually draw blood or kill each other. Instead they merely threaten with aggressive postures, vigorous singing or displays of plumage. The forms of intimidation of rivals by birds range all the way from the naked display of weapons to the triumph of splendor revealed in the peacock's train.

This hypothesis about the mechanism of population control in animals leads to a generalization of broader scope, namely that this was the origin or root of all social behavior in animals, including man. Surprisingly there has been no generally acceptable theory of how the first social organizations arose. One can now argue logically, however, that the kind of competition under conventional rules that is typified by the territorial system of birds was the earliest form of social organization. Indeed, a society can be defined as a group of individuals competing for conventional prizes by conventional methods. To put it another way, it is a brotherhood tempered by rivalry. One does not need to ponder very deeply to see how closely this cap fits even human societies.

A group of birds occupying an area divided into individual territories is plainly a social organization, and it exhibits a considerable range of characteristically social behavior. This is well illustrated by the red grouse of Scotland—a bird that is being studied intensively in a long-term research project near Aberdeen.

The grouse population on a heather moor consists of individuals known to one another and differing among them-

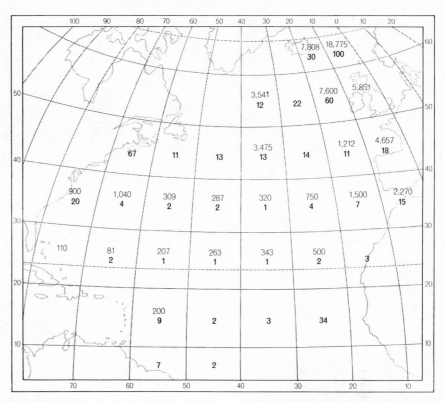

POPULATION AND FOOD SUPPLY show a correlation in the North Atlantic Ocean. The figures in light type give the average volume of plankton found per cubic centimeter of water; the darker figures show the average daily count of ocean birds that feed on plankton.

selves in social standing. The dominant males hold territories almost all year round, the most aggressive claiming on the average the largest territories. Their individual domains cover the moor like a mosaic [see top illustration on page 267]. The community admits as members some socially subordinate males and unmated hens that have no territories of their own, but with the onset of winter, or with a decline in the food supply for some other reason, these supernumeraries at the bottom of the social ladder get squeezed out. Only as many as can be supported by the lowered food level are allowed to stay. Thus the social hierarchy of the red grouse works as a safety valve or overflow mechanism, getting rid of any excess that would overtax the food resources. The existence of the peck-order system among birds has been known for some time, but its functional reason for being has been unclear; it now appears that the lowest members of the order serve as a dispensable reserve that can fill in as replacements for casualties among the established members or be dropped as circumstances require.

Certain definite rules mark the competition of the red grouse males for territory and status. One is that, at least in the fall, they crow and threaten only on fine mornings between first light

and two or three hours later. So aggressive is this struggle that the stress forces some of the losers to make a break away from the moor; on unfamiliar ground and without their usual food they soon weaken and are killed by predators or disease. Once the early-morning contest is over, however, those birds that remain in the habitat flock together amicably and feed side by side for the rest of the day.

The convention of competing at dawn or at dusk and leaving the rest of the day free for feeding and other peaceable activities is exceedingly common among animals of various kinds. The changes of light at dawn and dusk are, of course, the most conspicuous recurrent events of the day, and this no doubt explains why they serve so often as a signal for joint or communal activities. There are many familiar manifestations of this timing: the dawn chorus of songbirds and crowing cocks, the flight of ducks at dusk, the massed maneuvers of starlings and blackbirds at their roosts as darkness falls; the evening choruses of almost innumerable other birds, various tropical bats, frogs, cicadas and fishes such as the croaker, and the morning concerts of howler monkeys.

All these synchronized outbursts give an indication of the numbers present in the respective populations. They provide an index of the population density in the habitat from day to day, and so feed to the group information that causes it, not deliberately but automatically, to step up those activities that may be necessary to restore the balance between the density and the food supply.

The daily community display puts a changing pressure on the members taking part. If the stress is great enough, a reduction in the population can be triggered off; if it is felt lightly or not at all, there is room for new recruits. Overcrowding will lead to expulsion of the population surplus, as in the case of the red grouse. In the breeding season the density index, in the form of the daily display, can influence the proportion of adults that mate and breed; likewise the number of young can be restricted in a variety of other ways to the quota that the habitat will allow.

In the light of this hypothesis one would expect these "epideictic" displays (that is, population-pressure demonstrations) to be particularly prominent at the outset of the breeding season. That is actually the case. In birds the demonstrators are usually the males; they can be called the epideictic sex. They may swarm and dance in the air (as many flying insects do) or engage in ritual tournaments, gymnastics or parades (characteristic of sage grouse, prairie chickens, tropical hummingbirds, manakins and birds-of-paradise). The intensity of these activities depends on the density of the population: the more males there are, the keener the competition. The new hypothesis suggests that this will result in greater stress among the males and sharper restriction of the size of the population.

In many animals the males have vocal abilities the females lack; this is true of songbirds, cicadas, most crickets and katydids, frogs, drumfishes, howler monkeys and others. Contrary to what was once thought, these males use their voices primarily not to woo females but in the contest with their fellow males for real estate and status. The same applies to many of the males' adornments and scent glands, as well as to their weapons. This newly recognized fact calls for some rethinking of the whole vexed subject of sexual selection.

Epideictic displays rise to a height not only as a prelude to the breeding season but also at the time of animal migrations. They show the scale of the impending change in the population density of the habitat and, during the migration, give an indication of the size of the flocks that have gathered at the stopping places, thereby enabling the migrants to avoid dangerous congestion at any one place. Locusts build up for a great flight with spectacular massed maneuvers, and comparable excitement marks the nightly roosting of migratory chimney swifts and other big gatherings of birds, fruit bats and insects.

Altogether the hypothesis that animal populations regulate themselves through the agency of social conventions of this kind seems to answer satisfactorily several of the major questions that have concerned ecologists. Basically the average population level is set by the long-term food resources of the habitat. A system of behavioral conventions acts as homeostatic machinery that prevents the growth of the population from departing too far from the optimal density. Fluctuations from this average can be explained as being due partly to temporary accidents (such as climatic extremes) and partly to the working of the homeostatic machinery itself, which allows the population density to build up when the food yields are good and thins it down when the yields fall below average. At any particular time the availability of food in relation to the number of mouths to be fed—in other words, the standard of living at the moment—determines the response of the regulating mechanism. The mechanism acts by controlling the rate of recruitment, by creating a pressure to emigrate or sometimes by producing stresses that result in large-scale mortality.

It has been particularly gratifying to find that the hypothesis offers explanations of several social enigmas on which there has been no good theory, such as the biological origin of social behavior; the function of the social hierarchy, or peck-order system, among birds; the chorus of birds and similar social events synchronized at dawn and dusk.

The theory has wide ramifications, which I have discussed at length in my book. The one that interests us most,

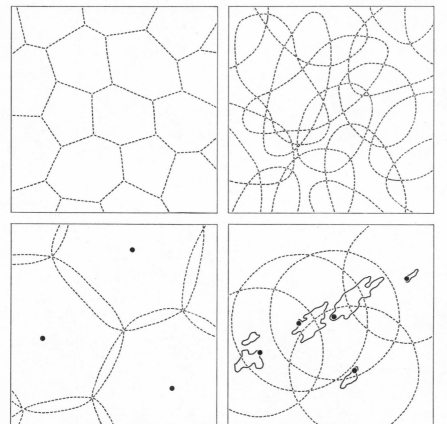

POPULATION-CONTROL DEVICES include the territory, of which the four basic types are depicted. Birds or mammals with territories have an established right to the available food; they also are the ones that breed. The others are in effect squeezed out. At top are two types of territory occupied by single males and their mates. At bottom are the types occupied by animals that live in colonies. One is virtually exclusive. The other is overlapping; shown here are islands from which five seabird colonies fan out within a maximum radius.

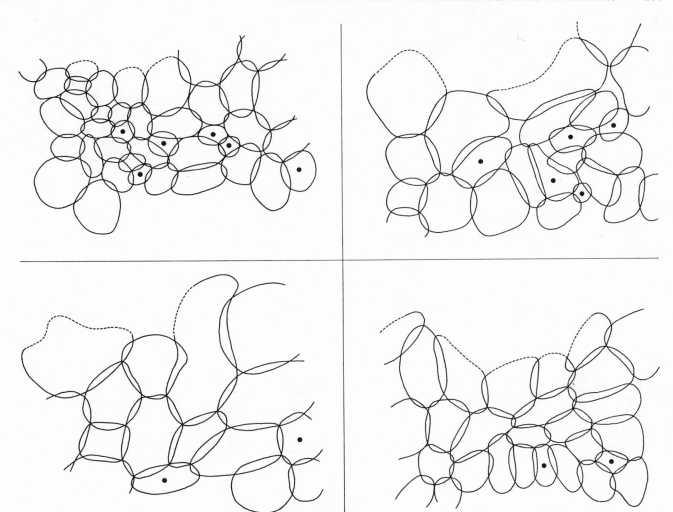

**TERRITORIAL VARIATIONS** of Scottish red grouse males reflect a form of population control. The drawings show the territorial holdings of individual cocks in four successive springs (1958–1961) on the same 140 acres of moorland. Some of the smaller territories, marked by dots, were held by males who remained unmated. Av-

erage territory size varies from year to year, thus affecting the density of breeding; in these four years the number of territories ranged between 40 in 1958 (*top left*) and 16 in 1960 (*bottom left*). The density of breeding is correlated with the food supply, which is to say with the quantity and quality of the heather.

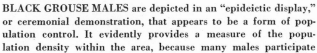

**BLACK GROUSE MALES** are depicted in an "epideictic display," or ceremonial demonstration, that appears to be a form of population control. It evidently provides a measure of the population density within the area, because many males participate

simultaneously on a communal strutting ground. It also serves as a means of excluding some less prominent males, who seldom display and often are chased away by the dominant birds. Epideictic displays also occur among many other bird and mammal species.

of course, is its bearing on the problem of the unchecked growth of the human population. The hypothesis opens up to clearer view the differences between man's demographic history and that of other animals.

There are two outstanding differences. In the first place, the homeostatic control of animal populations is strictly automatic: even the social conventions of behavior are innate rather than deliberately arrived at. In part the density-dependent control in many animals, including some of the mammals, is exercised by means of a biological reaction—either reduction of the rate of ovulation through a change in the output of hormones, or resorption of the embryos in the uterus as a result of stress (as occurs in rabbits, foxes and deer). Man's fertility and population growth, on the other hand, are subject only to his conscious and deliberate behavior. The second important difference is that modern man has progressively and enormously increased the food productivity of his habitat.

Primitive man, limited to the food he could get by hunting, had evolved a system for restricting his numbers by tribal traditions and taboos, such as prohibiting sexual intercourse for mothers while they were still nursing a baby, practicing compulsory abortion and infanticide, offering human sacrifices, conducting headhunting expeditions against rival tribes and so forth. These customs, consciously or not, kept the population density nicely balanced against the feeding capacity of the hunting range. Then, some 8,000 to 10,000 years ago, the agricultural revolution removed that limitation. There was no longer any reason to hold down the size of the tribe; on the contrary, power and wealth accrued to those tribes that allowed their populations to multiply, to develop farms, villages and even towns. The old checks on population growth were gradually discarded and forgotten. The rate of reproduction became a matter of individual choice rather than of tribal or community control. It has remained so ever since.

Given opportunity for procreation and a low death rate, the human population, whether well fed or hungry, now shows a tendency to expand without limit. Lacking the built-in homeostatic system that regulates the density of animal populations, man cannot look to any natural process to restrain his rapid growth. If the growth is to be slowed down, it must be by his own deliberate and socially applied efforts.

# 33 Population Density and Social Pathology

JOHN B. CALHOUN · February 1962

In the celebrated thesis of Thomas Malthus, vice and misery impose the ultimate natural limit on the growth of populations. Students of the subject have given most of their attention to misery, that is, to predation, disease and food supply as forces that operate to adjust the size of a population to its environment. But what of vice? Setting aside the moral burden of this word, what are the effects of the social behavior of a species on population growth—and of population density on social behavior?

Some years ago I attempted to submit this question to experimental inquiry. I confined a population of wild Norway rats in a quarter-acre enclosure. With an abundance of food and places to live and with predation and disease eliminated or minimized, only the animals' behavior with respect to one another remained as a factor that might affect the increase in their number. There could be no escape from the behavioral consequences of rising population density. By the end of 27 months the population had become stabilized at 150 adults. Yet adult mortality was so low that 5,000 adults might have been expected from the observed reproductive rate. The reason this larger population did not materialize was that infant mortality was extremely high. Even with only 150 adults in the enclosure, stress from social interaction led to such disruption of maternal behavior that few young survived.

With this background in mind I turned to observation of a domesticated albino strain of the Norway rat under more controlled circumstances indoors. The data for the present discussion come from the histories of six different populations. Each was permitted to increase to approximately twice the number that my experience had indicated could occupy the available space with only moderate stress from social interaction. In each case my associates and I maintained close surveillance of the colonies for 16 months in order to obtain detailed records of the modifications of behavior induced by population density.

The consequences of the behavioral pathology we observed were most apparent among the females. Many were unable to carry pregnancy to full term or to survive delivery of their litters if they did. An even greater number, after successfully giving birth, fell short in their maternal functions. Among the males the behavior disturbances ranged from sexual deviation to cannibalism and from frenetic overactivity to a pathological withdrawal from which individuals would emerge to eat, drink and move about only when other members of the community were asleep. The social organization of the animals showed equal disruption. Each of the experimental populations divided itself into several groups, in each of which the sex ratios were drastically modified. One group might consist of six or seven females and one male, whereas another would have 20 males and only 10 females.

The common source of these disturbances became most dramatically apparent in the populations of our first series of three experiments, in which we observed the development of what we called a behavioral sink. The animals would crowd together in greatest number in one of the four interconnecting pens in which the colony was maintained. As many as 60 of the 80 rats in each experimental population would assemble in one pen during periods of feeding. Individual rats would rarely eat except in the company of other rats. As a result extreme population densities developed in the pen adopted for eating, leaving the others with sparse populations.

Eating and other biological activities were thereby transformed into social activities in which the principal satisfaction was interaction with other rats. In the case of eating, this transformation of behavior did not keep the animals from securing adequate nutrition. But the same pathological "togetherness" tended to disrupt the ordered sequences of activity involved in other vital modes of behavior such as the courting of sex partners, the building of nests and the nursing and care of the young. In the experiments in which the behavioral sink developed, infant mortality ran as high as 96 per cent among the most disoriented groups in the population. Even in the absence of the behavioral sink, in the second series of three experiments, infant mortality reached 80 per cent among the corresponding members of the experimental populations.

The design of the experiments was relatively simple. The three populations of the first series each began with 32 rats; each population of the second series began with 56 rats. In all cases the animals were just past weaning and were evenly divided between males and females. By the 12th month all the populations had multiplied and each comprised 80 adults. Thereafter removal of the infants that survived birth and weaning held the populations steady. Although the destructive effects of population density increased during the course of the experiments, and the mortality rate among the females and among the young was much higher in the 16th month than it was earlier, the number of young that survived to weaning was always large enough to offset the effects of adult mortality and actually to increase the population. The evidence indicates, however, that in time failures of reproductive function would have caused the colonies to die out. At the end of the first series of experiments eight rats—the four healthi-

**EFFECT OF POPULATION DENSITY** on the behavior and social organization of rats was studied by confining groups of 80 animals in a 10-by-14-foot room divided into four pens by an electrified fence. All pens (numbered 1, 2, 3 and 4 clockwise from door) were complete dwelling units. Conical objects are food hoppers; trays with three bottles are drinking troughs. Elevated burrows, reached by winding staircases, each had five nest boxes, seen in pen 1, where top of burrow has been removed. Ramps connected all pens but 1 and 4. Rats therefore tended to concentrate in pens 2 and 3. Development of a "behavioral sink," which further increased population in one pen, is reflected in pen 2, where three rats are eating simultaneously. Rat approaching ramp in pen 3 is an estrous female

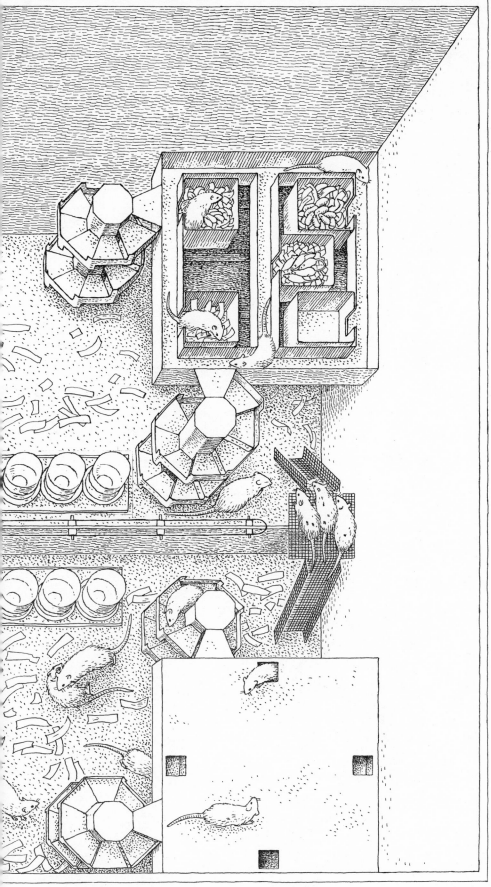

est males and the four healthiest females in each of two populations—were permitted to survive. These animals were six months old at the time, in the prime of life. Yet in spite of the fact that they no longer lived in overpopulated environments, they produced fewer litters in the next six months than would normally have been expected. Nor did any of the offspring that were born survive to maturity.

The males and females that initiated each experiment were placed, in groups of the same size and sex composition, in each of the four pens that partitioned a 10-by-14-foot observation room. The pens were complete dwelling units; each contained a drinking fountain, a food hopper and an elevated artificial burrow, reached by a winding staircase and holding five nest boxes. A window in the ceiling of the room permitted observation, and there was a door in one wall. With space for a colony of 12 adults in each pen—the size of the groups in which rats are normally found—this setup should have been able to support 48 rats comfortably. At the stabilized number of 80, an equal distribution of the animals would have found 20 adult rats in each pen. But the animals did not dispose themselves in this way.

Biasing factors were introduced in the physical design of the environment to encourage differential use of the four pens. The partitions separating the pens were electrified so that the rats could not climb them. Ramps across three of the partitions enabled the animals to get from one pen to another and so traverse the entire room. With no ramps to permit crossing of the fourth partition, however, the pens on each side of it became the end pens of what was topologically a row of four. The rats had to make a complete circuit of the room to go from the pen we designated 1 to the pen designated 4 on the other side of the partition separating the two. This arrangement of ramps immediately skewed the mathematical probabilities in favor of a higher population density in pens 2 and 3 than in pens 1 and 4. Pens 2 and 3 could be reached by two ramps, whereas pens 1 and 4 had only one each.

The use of pen 4 was further discouraged by the elevation of its burrow to a height greater than that of the burrow in the other end pen. The two middle pens were similarly distinguished from each other, the burrow in pen 3 being higher than that in pen 2. But here the differential appears to have played a smaller role, although pen 2 was used somewhat more often than pen 3.

With the distribution of the rats

pursued by a pack of males. In pens 2 and 3, where population density was highest, males outnumbered females. In pens 1 and 4, a dominant male was usually able to expel all other males and possess a harem of females. Dominant males are sleeping at the base of the ramps in pens 1 and 4. They wake when other males approach, preventing incursions into their territories. The three rats peering down from a ramp are probers, one of the deviant behavioral types produced by the pressures of a high population density.

biased by these physical arrangements, the sizes of the groups in each pen could have been expected to range from as few as 13 to as many as 27. With the passage of time, however, changes in behavior tended to skew the distribution of the rats among the pens even more. Of the 100 distinct sleeping groups counted in the 10th to 12th month of each experiment, only 37 fell within the expected size range. In 33 groups there were fewer than 13 rats, and in 30 groups the count exceeded 27. The sex ratio approximated equality only in those groups that fell within the expected size range. In the smaller groups, generally composed of eight adults, there were seldom more

than two males. In the larger groups, on the other hand, there were many more males than females. As might be expected, the smaller groups established themselves in the end pens, whereas the larger groups were usually observed to form in the middle pens. The female members of the population distributed themselves about equally in the four pens, but the male population was concentrated almost overwhelmingly in the middle pens.

One major factor in the creation of this state of affairs was the struggle for status that took place among the males. Shortly after male rats reach maturity, at about six months of age, they enter into

a round robin of fights that eventually fixes their position in the social hierarchy. In our experiments such fights took place among the males in all the pens, both middle and end. In the end pens, however, it became possible for a single dominant male to take over the area as his territory. During the period when the social hierarchy was being established, the subordinate males in all pens adopted the habit of arising early. This enabled them to eat and drink in peace. Since rats generally eat in the course of their normal wanderings, the subordinate residents of the end pens were likely to feed in one of the middle pens. When, after feeding, they wanted to

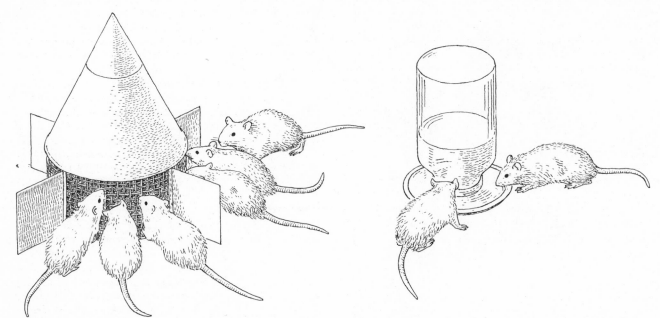

FOOD HOPPER used in first series of experiments is seen at the left in this drawing. Water tray is at the right. The hopper, covered with wire grating and holding hard pellets of food, made eating a lengthy activity during which one rat was likely to meet another.

Thus it fostered the development of a behavioral sink: the animals would eat only in the presence of others, and they preferred one of the four hoppers in the room to all the others. In time 75 per cent of the animals crowded into the pen containing this hopper to eat.

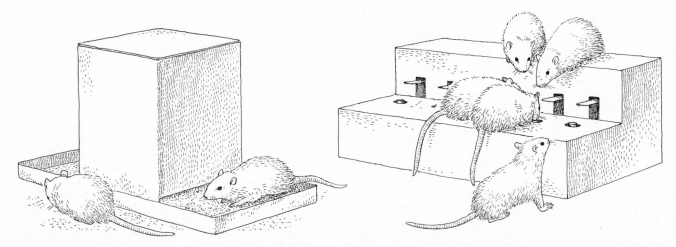

WATER FOUNTAIN used in second series of experiments is seen at the right in this drawing. Food hopper is at the left. The fountain was operated by pressing a lever. Thus it made drinking a lengthy activity, associated with the presence of others. But it

did not create a behavioral sink. Although the rats would drink only if other animals were present, they engaged in this activity in their home pens, immediately after awakening. The fountain therefore acted to produce an even distribution of the population.

return to their original quarters, they would find it very difficult. By this time the most dominant male in the pen would probably have awakened, and he would engage the subordinates in fights as they tried to come down the one ramp to the pen. For a while the subordinate would continue its efforts to return to what had been its home pen, but after a succession of defeats it would become so conditioned that it would not even make the attempt. In essence the dominant male established his territorial dominion and his control over a harem of females not by driving the other males out but by preventing their return.

Once a male had established his dominion over an end pen and the harem it contained, he was usually able to maintain it. Although he slept a good deal of the time, he made his sleeping quarters at the base of the ramp. He was, therefore, on perpetual guard. Awakening as soon as another male appeared at the head of the ramp, he had only to open his eyes for the invader to wheel around and return to the adjoining pen. On the other hand, he would sleep calmly through all the comings and goings of his harem; seemingly he did not even hear their clatterings up and down the wire ramp. His conduct during his waking hours reflected his dominant status. He would move about in a casual and deliberate fashion, occasionally inspecting the burrow and nests of his harem. But he would rarely enter a burrow, as some other males did, merely to ferret out the females.

A territorial male might tolerate other males in his domain provided they respected his status. Such subordinate males inhabited the end pens in several of the experiments. Phlegmatic animals, they spent most of their time hidden in the burrow with the adult females, and their excursions to the floor lasted only as long as it took them to obtain food and water. Although they never attempted to engage in sexual activity with any of the females, they were likely, on those rare occasions when they encountered the dominant male, to make repeated attempts to mount him. Generally the dominant male tolerated these advances.

In these end pens, where population density was lowest, the mortality rate among infants and females was also low. Of the various social environments that developed during the course of the experiments, the brood pens, as we called them, appeared to be the only healthy ones, at least in terms of the survival of the group. The harem females generally made good mothers. They nursed their young, built nests for them and protected them from harm. If any situation arose that a mother considered a danger to her pups, she would pick the infants up one at a time and carry them in her mouth to a safer place. Nothing would distract her from this task until the entire litter had been moved. Half the infants born in the brood pens survived.

The pregnancy rates recorded among the females in the middle pens were no lower than those recorded in the end pens. But a smaller percentage of these pregnancies terminated in live births. In the second series of experiments 80 per cent of the infants born in the middle pens died before weaning. In the first series 96 per cent perished before this time. The males in the middle pens were no less affected than the females by the pressures of population density. In both series of experiments the social pathology among the males was high. In the first series, however, it was more aggravated than it was in the second.

This increase in disturbance among the middle-pen occupants of the first series of experiments was directly related to the development of the phenomenon of the behavioral sink—the outcome of any behavioral process that collects animals together in unusually great numbers. The unhealthy connotations of the term are not accidental: a behavioral sink does act to aggravate all forms of pathology that can be found within a group.

The emergence of a behavioral sink was fostered by the arrangements that were made for feeding the animals. In these experiments the food consisted of small, hard pellets that were kept in a circular hopper formed by wire mesh. In consequence satisfaction of hunger required a continuous effort lasting several minutes. The chances therefore were good that while one rat was eating another would join it at the hopper. As was mentioned earlier, rats usually eat intermittently throughout their waking hours, whenever they are hungry and food is available. Since the arrangement of the ramps drew more rats into the middle pens than into the end ones, it was in these pens that individuals were most likely to find other individuals eating. As the population increased, the association of eating with the presence of other animals was further reinforced. Gradually the social aspect of the activity became determinant: the rats would rarely eat except at hoppers already in use by other animals.

At this point the process became a vicious circle. As more and more of the rats tended to collect at the hopper in one of the middle pens, the other hoppers became less desirable as eating places. The rats that were eating at these undesirable locations, finding themselves deserted by their groupmates, would transfer their feeding to the more crowded pen. By the time the three experiments in the first series drew to a close half or more of the populations were sleeping as well as eating in that pen. As a result there was a decided increase in the number of social adjustments each rat had to make every day. Regardless of which pen a rat slept in, it would go to one particular middle pen several times a day to eat. Therefore it was compelled daily to make some sort of adjustment to virtually every other rat in the experimental population.

No behavioral sinks developed in the second series of experiments, because we offered the rats their diet in a different way. A powdered food was set out in an open hopper. Since it took the animals only a little while to eat, the probability that two animals would be eating simultaneously was considerably reduced. In order to foster the emergence of a behavioral sink I supplied the pens with drinking fountains designed to prolong the drinking activity. The effect of this arrangement was unquestionably to make the animals social drinkers; they used the fountain mainly when other animals lined up at it. But the effect was also to discourage them from wandering and to prevent the development of a behavioral sink. Since rats generally drink immediately on arising, drinking and the social interaction it occasioned tended to keep them in the pens in which they slept. For this reason all social pathology in the second series of experiments, although severe, was less extreme than it was in the first series.

Females that lived in the densely populated middle pens became progressively less adept at building adequate nests and eventually stopped building nests at all. Normally rats of both sexes build nests, but females do so most vigorously around the time of parturition. It is an undertaking that involves repeated periods of sustained activity, searching out appropriate materials (in our experiments strips of paper supplied an abundance), transporting them bit by bit to the nest and there arranging them to form a cuplike depression, frequently sheltered by a hood. In a crowded middle pen, however, the ability of females to persist in this biologically essential activity became markedly impaired. The first sign of disruption was a failure to build the nest to normal specifications.

These females simply piled the strips of paper in a heap, sometimes trampling them into a pad that showed little sign of cup formation. Later in the experiment they would bring fewer and fewer strips to the nesting site. In the midst of transporting a bit of material they would drop it to engage in some other activity occasioned by contact and interaction with other individuals met on the way. In the extreme disruption of their behavior during the later months of the population's history they would build no nests at all but would bear their litters on the sawdust in the burrow box.

The middle-pen females similarly lost the ability to transport their litters from one place to another. They would move only part of their litters and would scatter them by depositing the infants in different places or simply dropping them on the floor of the pen. The infants thus abandoned throughout the pen were seldom nursed. They would die where they were dropped and were thereupon generally eaten by the adults.

The social stresses that brought about this disorganization in the behavior of the middle-pen females were imposed with special weight on them when they came into heat. An estrous female would be pursued relentlessly by a pack of males, unable to escape from their soon

unwanted attentions. Even when she retired to a burrow, some males would follow her. Among these females there was a correspondingly high rate of mortality from disorders in pregnancy and parturition. Nearly half of the first- and second-generation females that lived in the behavioral-sink situation had died of these causes by the end of the 16th month. Even in the absence of the extreme stresses of the behavioral sink, 25 per cent of the females died. In contrast, only 15 per cent of the adult males in both series of experiments died.

A female that lived in a brood pen was sheltered from these stresses even though during her periods of estrus she would leave her pen to mate with males

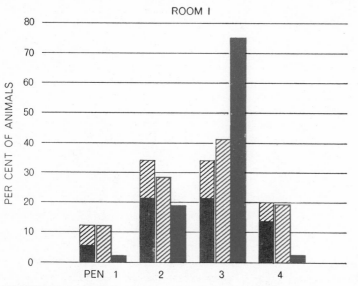

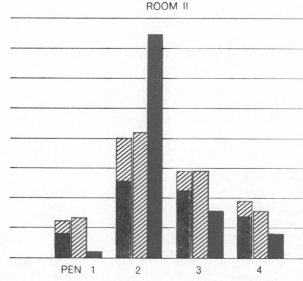

**BEHAVIORAL SINK** developed in the first series of three experiments, drawing half the rats either into pen 2 or pen 3 of each room to drink and sleep, and even more into that pen to eat. Chart describes the situation in the 13th month of the experiment. By then the population distributions were fairly stable and many females in the densely populated pens had died. One male in room

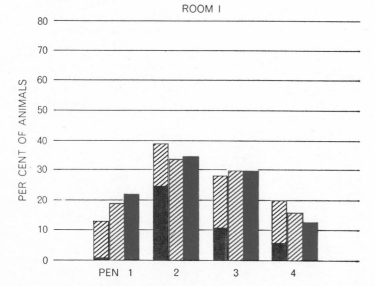

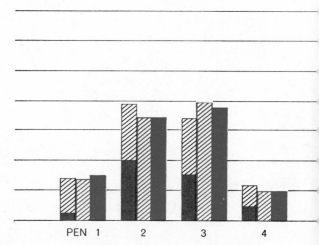

**POPULATION DISTRIBUTIONS** in the second series of three experiments, in which no behavioral sink developed, were more even than they were in the first series, and the death rate among females and infants was lower. Chart shows the situation in the 13th month, when one male had established pens 3 and 4 of room III as his territory, and another was taking over pen 2, thus

in the other pens of the room. Once she was satiated, however, she could return to the brood pen. There she was protected from the excessive attention of other males by the territorial male.

For the effect of population density on the males there is no index as explicit and objective as the infant and maternal mortality rates. We have attempted a first approximation of such an index, however, by scoring the behavior of the males on two scales: that of dominance and that of physical activity. The first index proved particularly effective in the early period of the experiments, when the males were approaching adulthood and beginning the fights that eventually fixed their status in the social hierarchy.

ROOM III

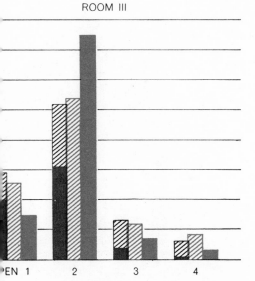

PEN   1        2        3        4

III had established pens 3 and 4 as his territory. Subsequently a male in room I took over pen 1, expelling all the other males.

ROOM III

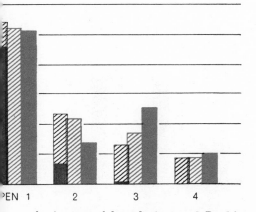

PEN   1        2        3        4

forcing most of the males into pen 1. Pen 1 in rooms I and II had also become territories; later pen 4 in room II became a territory.

The more fights a male initiated and the more fights he won, the more likely he was to establish a position of dominance. More than half the animals in each experiment gave up the struggle for status after a while, but among those that persisted a clear-cut hierarchy developed.

In the crowded middle pens no one individual occupied the top position in this hierarchy permanently. In every group of 12 or more males one was the most aggressive and most often the victor in fights. Nevertheless, this rat was periodically ousted from his position. At regular intervals during the course of their waking hours the top-ranking males engaged in free-for-alls that culminated in the transfer of dominance from one male to another. In between these tumultuous changings of the guard relative calm prevailed.

The aggressive, dominant animals were the most normal males in our populations. They seldom bothered either the females or the juveniles. Yet even they exhibited occasional signs of pathology, going berserk, attacking females, juveniles and the less active males, and showing a particular predilection —which rats do not normally display— for biting other animals on the tail.

Below the dominant males both on the status scale and in their level of activity were the homosexuals—a group perhaps better described as pansexual. These animals apparently could not discriminate between appropriate and inappropriate sex partners. They made sexual advances to males, juveniles and females that were not in estrus. The males, including the dominants as well as the others of the pansexuals' own group, usually accepted their attentions. The general level of activity of these animals was only moderate. They were frequently attacked by their dominant associates, but they very rarely contended for status.

Two other types of male emerged, both of which had resigned entirely from the struggle for dominance. They were, however, at exactly opposite poles as far as their levels of activity were concerned. The first were completely passive and moved through the community like somnambulists. They ignored all the other rats of both sexes, and all the other rats ignored them. Even when the females were in estrus, these passive animals made no advances to them. And only very rarely did other males attack them or approach them for any kind of play. To the casual observer the passive animals would have appeared to be the healthiest and most attractive

members of the community. They were fat and sleek, and their fur showed none of the breaks and bare spots left by the fighting in which males usually engage. But their social disorientation was nearly complete.

Perhaps the strangest of all the types that emerged among the males was the group I have called the probers. These animals, which always lived in the middle pens, took no part at all in the status struggle. Nevertheless, they were the most active of all the males in the experimental populations, and they persisted in their activity in spite of attacks by the dominant animals. In addition to being hyperactive, the probers were both hypersexual and homosexual, and in time many of them became cannibalistic. They were always on the alert for estrous females. If there were none in their own pens, they would lie in wait for long periods at the tops of the ramps that gave on the brood pens and peer down into them. They always turned and fled as soon as the territorial rat caught sight of them. Even if they did not manage to escape unhurt, they would soon return to their vantage point.

The probers conducted their pursuit of estrous females in an abnormal manner. Mating among rats usually involves a distinct courtship ritual. In the first phase of this ritual the male pursues the female. She thereupon retires for a while into the burrow, and the male lies quietly in wait outside, occasionally poking his head into the burrow for a moment but never entering it. (In the wild forms of the Norway rat this phase usually involves a courtship dance on the mound at the mouth of the burrow.) The female at last emerges from the burrow and accepts the male's advances. Even in the disordered community of the middle pens this pattern was observed by all the males who engaged in normal heterosexual behavior. But the probers would not tolerate even a short period of waiting at the burrows in the pens where accessible females lived. As soon as a female retired to a burrow, a prober would follow her inside. On these expeditions the probers often found dead young lying in the nests; as a result they tended to become cannibalistic in the later months of a population's history.

Although the behavioral sink did not develop in the second series of experiments, the pathology exhibited by the populations in both sets of experiments, and in all pens, was severe. Even

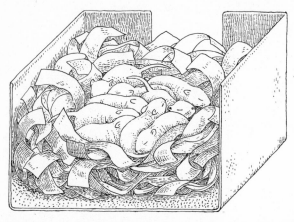

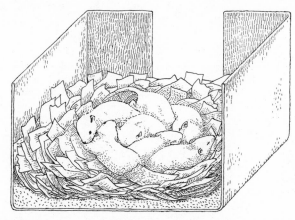

**NORMAL MATERNAL BEHAVIOR** among rats includes building a fluffy, well-shaped nest for the young. The drawing at the left shows such a nest, holding a recently born litter. The drawing at the right shows this same nest about two weeks later. It has been flattened by the weight of the animals' bodies but it still offers ample protection and warmth, and the remaining pups can still rest comfortably. In these experiments half the offspring of normal mothers survived infancy and were successfully weaned.

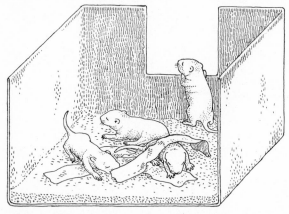

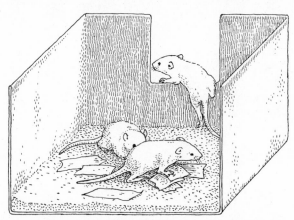

**ABNORMAL MATERNAL BEHAVIOR,** shown by females exposed to the pressures of population density, includes failure to build adequate nests. The drawing at the left shows the recently born young of a disturbed female. She started to make a nest but never finished it. The drawing at the right shows her young about two weeks later. One pup has already left and another is leaving. Neither can survive alone. In these experiments the mortality rate among infants of disturbed mothers was as high as 96 per cent.

in the brood pens females could raise only half their young to weaning. Nor does the difference in infant mortality between the middle pens of the first and second series—96 per cent in the first as opposed to 80 per cent in the second— represent a biologically significant improvement. It is obvious that the behavioral repertory with which the Norway rat has emerged from the trials of evolution and domestication must break down under the social pressures generated by population density. In time, refinement of experimental procedures and of the interpretation of these studies may advance our understanding to the point where they may contribute to the making of value judgments about analogous problems confronting the human species.

*Man-Created Problems*

# Man-Created Problems

## INTRODUCTION

Having overcome almost all his other enemies (microbes have not quite surrendered yet), man now faces the most intractable enemy of all: himself. Part of the trouble stems from the way in which we use language to describe our trouble: we speak of "man" when we mean an unidentified fraction of some three billion people; we complain of what "they" are doing to "our" world. The referents of these terms are pretty fuzzy.

I should always assume that "they" refers to *me. I* pollute the waters and the air—I and many others no better and no worse (and equally unthinking). The harm that is done is a function of numbers. It was all right for a frontiersman to defecate almost anyplace; natural processes of microbial digestion soon reestablished pristine purity. But when the frontier was replaced by a city, explicit technological arrangements had to be made to dispose of the products of the animal functions. Individual freedom necessarily had to be curtailed for the well-being of all: this is the price of population.

In recent decades we have come to realize that we must do something about the wastes we have hitherto thrown unthinkingly into the air. This is not wholly a new problem, having been recognized earlier in the dirty clouds of smoke emitted by large industrial works. Some, though not enough, progress had been made in controlling this kind of aerial garbage when the problem of control was exacerbated by the multiplication of automobiles. With almost 100 million internal combustion vehicles registered in the United States, Everyman becomes the culprit—of whom every man complains. The results are described by A. J. Haagen-Smit in "The Control of Air Pollution." We clearly must give up some of our previous freedoms—but which ones? We can foresee political troubles lasting many years.

E. Cuyler Hammond discusses a different sort of man-created problem in "The Effects of Smoking." The truth about tobacco has been hard to accept because it is based on statistical evidence, which is subtle. Acknowledgment of the truth implies a change in a socially supported habit—and that is hard to accept. Seeking to deny unpleasant truths, many well-meaning critics (some of them scientists) have thrown up a great barrage of statistical flimflam to impugn the assertion that smoking is unhealthy. (Most notable was the late R. A. Fisher, a heavy smoker and a superb statistician.) Of course the evidence for any positive scientific statement is only probabilistic. We can deny it if we wish, but we should try to recognize the role of irrational desires in our denials. It is not *absolutely* certain that smoking is unhealthy—but as one commentator remarked, "If tobacco were spinach it would have been outlawed years ago."

Even positive attempts to improve our well-being may produce new troubles. A basic working hypothesis of ecologists is, "We can never do merely one thing," and this applies also to therapeutics. We must assume that every new medicine will produce some unwanted "side effects"; the question is, what, and how serious, are they? A particularly harrowing experience is discussed by Helen B. Taussig in "The Thalidomide Syndrome." The drug thalidomide was adequately tested on experimental animals before human use, but the particular danger of it was not revealed. (Scientists have since succeeded in demonstrating the teratogenic effects of thalidomide on non-human animals, but only after human beings had served as the first guinea pigs. The belated animal demonstration was of little help.) The thalidomide danger is now part of history. But how shall we anticipate similar unknown dangers in the future? Interesting ethical questions are raised by this experience.

The most acute man-created problem of all, of course, is the danger that the human race will be extinguished by *Homo sapiens* (in which case, retrospectively, the specific name will seem ironic). No other animal has ever faced such a threat. Irenäus Eibl-Eibesfeldt discusses "The Fighting Behavior of Animals" and shows how their instincts ensure that violence will not be escalated to the point at which it endangers the existence of the species. The evolution of the necessary instinctive reactions must have been brought about by natural selection operating at the level of the individual. (Most modern biologists find it difficult to accept any other explanation.) But the reader may well wonder if a strict Darwinian explanation is sufficient to account for the phenomena described by Eibl-Eibesfeldt.

Turning our attention to man, we have a careful scientific discussion of "National Security and the Nuclear-Test Ban" by Jerome B. Wiesner and Herbert F. York. These men, who have operated at the highest levels of government-scientific councils, give the logical reasons why it seems highly probable that defense will always be inferior to offense—at the technical level. If we are to survive we must find a solution that transcends technology (as we now understand it). A quasi-solution is described by Arthur I. Waskow in "The Shelter-Centered Society."

These are inevitably times when we recall the lines of A. E. Housman:

> And how am I to face the odds
> Of man's bedevilment and God's?
> I, a stranger and afraid
> In a world I never made.

Recalling these, we may momentarily think of giving up. But if we identify with humanity we must accept the responsibility for having made this world, sorry though it may be, and suspect—hope—that the ingenuity that created the problems is still available and equal to the solution of them.

# 34 The Control of Air Pollution

A. J. HAAGEN-SMIT · January 1964

The past decade has seen a change in the public's attitude toward air pollution. Formerly the tendency was to deplore smog but to regard it as one of the inescapable adjuncts of urban life. Now there is a growing realization that smog, beyond being a vexatious nuisance, may indeed present hazards to health, and that in any case the pollution of the air will inevitably grow worse unless something is done about it. As a result many communities have created agencies to deal with air pollution and have, with varying degrees of effectiveness, backed the agencies with laws.

Going considerably beyond these efforts is the program in Los Angeles, a city rather widely regarded as the smog capital of the U.S. There the authorities have adopted the attitude that it is not enough to know smog exists; they have undertaken extensive studies to ascertain its components and to understand something of the complex processes by which it is created. Moreover, with help from the state they have taken pioneering steps toward curbing the emissions of the automobile, which is both a major cause of air pollution and a far more difficult source to control than such stationary installations as petroleum refineries

LOS ANGELES SMOG, shown in photograph on opposite page, casts thick pall over city. Persistence and severity of smogs led the city to undertake pioneering and extensive programs to curb air pollution.

and electric power plants. As a result of California's activities a device to control the emissions from the crankcases of automobiles is now standard equipment on all new cars in the U.S. The state is also working toward a program that will result in a measure of control over emissions from the automobile exhaust.

Complaints about polluted air go far back in time. As long ago as 1661 the English diarist John Evelyn declared in a tract entitled *Fumifugium, or the inconvenience of the Aer and Smoak of London* that the city "resembles the face Rather of Mount Aetna, the Court of Vulcan, Stromboli, or the Suburbs of Hell than an Assembly of Rational Creatures and the Imperial seat of our Incomparable Monarch." Air pollution has drawn similar complaints in many cities over the centuries.

For a long time, however, these complaints were like voices in the wilderness. Among the few exceptions in the U.S. were St. Louis and Pittsburgh, where the residents decided at last that they had inhaled enough soot and chemicals and took steps several years ago to reduce air pollution, primarily by regulating the use of coal. These, however, were isolated cases that did not deeply penetrate the consciousness of people in other parts of the country.

It was probably the recurrence of crises over smog in Los Angeles that awakened more of the nation to the possibility that the same thing could happen elsewhere and to the realization that air,

like water, should be considered a precious resource that cannot be used indiscriminately as a dump for waste materials. By the time residents of Washington, D.C., complained of eye irritation and neighboring tobacco growers suffered extensive crop damage, it was clear that Los Angeles smog was not just a subject for jokes but a serious problem requiring diligent efforts at control. As a result the pace of antipollution activity has quickened at all levels of government. In addition to the community efforts already mentioned, a national air-sampling network now exists to assemble data on the extent of air pollution, and extensive studies of the effects of smog on health and the economy are under way.

Still, these efforts seem modest when viewed against the size of the problem. Surgeon General Luther L. Terry spoke at the second National Conference on Air Pollution late in 1962 of "how far we have to go." He said: "Approximately 90 per cent of the urban population live in localities with air-pollution problems—a total of about 6,000 communities. But only half of this population is served by local control programs with full-time staffs. There are now about 100 such programs, serving 342 local political jurisdictions. The median annual expenditure is about 10 cents per capita, an amount clearly inadequate to do the job that is necessary."

Enough has been done, however, to demonstrate that a concerted attack on the smog problem can produce a clearing of the air. Los Angeles, which Terry has called "the area in the United States that's devoting more money and more effort toward combating the problem than any other city," provides an example of the possibilities, the difficulties and the potential of such an attack.

Los Angeles certainly qualifies as a community where air pollution has created an annoying and at times dangerous situation. Two-thirds of the year

smog is evident through eye irritation, peculiar bleachlike odors and a decrease in visibility that coincides with the appearance of a brownish haze. According to the California Department of Public Health, 80 per cent of the population in Los Angeles County is affected to some extent.

The city's decision to attack the smog problem dates from a report made in 1947 by Raymond R. Tucker, who as an investigator of air-pollution problems played a major role in the St. Louis smog

battle and is now the mayor of that city. His report on Los Angeles enumerated the sources of pollution attributable to industry and to individuals through the use of automobiles and the burning of trash. The report recommended immediate control of known sources of pollution and a research program to determine if there were any other things in the air that should be controlled.

Largely on the basis of the Tucker report, *The Los Angeles Times* started with the aid of civic groups a campaign to inform and arouse the public about smog. As a result the state legislature in 1948 passed a law permitting the formation of air-pollution control districts empowered to formulate rules for curbing smog and endowed with the necessary police power for enforcement of the rules. Los Angeles County created such a district the same year.

The district began by limiting the dust and fumes emitted by steel factories, refineries and hundreds of smaller industries. It terminated the use of a million home incinerators and forbade the widespread practice of burning in public dumps. These moves reduced dustfall, which in some areas had been as much as 100 tons per square mile per month, by two-thirds, bringing it back to about the level that existed in 1940 before smog became a serious problem in the community. That achievement should be measured against the fact that since 1940 the population of Los Angeles and the number of industries in the city have doubled.

Although the attack on dustfall produced a considerable improvement in visibility, the typical smog symptoms of eye irritation and plant damage remained. The district therefore undertook a research program to ascertain the origin and nature of the substances that caused the symptoms. One significant finding was that the Los Angeles atmosphere differs radically from that of most other heavily polluted communities. Ordinarily polluted air is made strongly reducing by sulfur dioxide, a product of the combustion of coal and heavy oil. Los Angeles air, on the other hand, is often strongly oxidizing. The oxidant is mostly ozone, with smaller contributions from oxides of nitrogen and organic peroxides.

During smog attacks the ozone content of the Los Angeles air reaches a level 10 to 20 times higher than that elsewhere. Concentrations of half a part of ozone per million of air have repeatedly been measured during heavy smogs. To establish such a concentration directly would require the dispersal of about

SMOG CURTAIN falls over the view from the campus of the California Institute of Technology. At top is the scene on a weekday morning; at bottom, the same scene that afternoon.

1,000 tons of ozone in the Los Angeles basin. No industry releases significant amounts of ozone; discharges from electric power lines are also negligible, amounting to less than a ton a day. A considerable amount of ozone is formed in the upper atmosphere by the action of short ultraviolet rays, but that ozone does not descend to earth during smog conditions because of the very temperature inversion that intensifies smog. In such an inversion warm air lies atop the cold air near the ground; this stable system forms a barrier not only to the rise of pollutants but also to the descent of ozone.

Exclusion of these possibilities leaves sunlight as the only suspect in the creation of the Los Angeles ozone. The cause cannot be direct formation of ozone by sunlight at the earth's surface because that requires radiation of wavelengths shorter than 2,000 angstrom units, which does not penetrate the atmosphere to ground level. There was a compelling reason, however, to look for an indirect connection between smog and the action of sunlight: high oxidant or ozone values are found only during daylight hours. Apparently a photochemical reaction was taking place when one or more ingredients of smog were exposed to sunlight—which is of course abundant in the Los Angeles area.

In order for a substance to be affected by light it has to absorb the light, and the energy of the light quanta has to be sufficiently high to rupture the chemical bonds of the substance. A likely candidate for such a photochemical reaction in smog is nitrogen dioxide. This dioxide is formed from nitrogen oxide, which originates in all high-temperature combustion through a combining of the nitrogen and oxygen of the air. Nitrogen dioxide has a brownish color and absorbs light in the region of the spectrum from the blue to the near ultraviolet. Radiation from the sun can readily dissociate nitrogen dioxide into nitric oxide and atomic oxygen. This reactive oxygen attacks organic material, of which there is much in the unburned hydrocarbons remaining in automobile exhaust. The result is the formation of ozone and various other oxidation products. Some of these products, notably peracylnitrates and formaldehyde, are eye irritants. Peracylnitrates and ozone also cause plant damage. Moreover, the oxidation reactions are usually accompanied by the formation of aerosols, or hazes, and this combination aggravates the effects of the individual components in the smog complex.

The answer to the puzzle of the oxi-

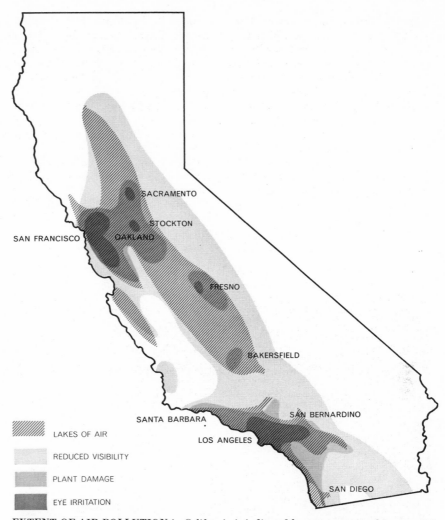

LAKES OF AIR

REDUCED VISIBILITY

PLANT DAMAGE

EYE IRRITATION

**EXTENT OF AIR POLLUTION** in California is indicated by gray areas on this map. Colored areas show the main natural airsheds, or lakes of air, into which pollutants flow. Sunlight acting on pollutants produces substances that irritate eyes and damage plants.

dizing smog of the Los Angeles area thus lay in the combination of heavy automobile traffic and copious sunlight. Similar photochemical reactions can of course occur in other cities, and the large-scale phenomenon appears to be spreading.

The more or less temporary effects of smog alone would make a good case for air-pollution control; there is in addition the strong likelihood that smog has adverse long-range effects on human health [see "Air Pollution and Public Health," by Walsh McDermott; SCIENTIFIC AMERICAN offprint 612]. Workers of the U.S. Public Health Service and Vanderbilt University reported to the American Public Health Association in November that a study they have been conducting in Nashville, Tenn., has established clear evidence that deaths from respiratory diseases rise in proportion to the degree of air pollution.

For the control of air pollution it is of central importance to know that

organic substances—olefins, unsaturated hydrocarbons, aromatic hydrocarbons and the derivatives of these various kinds of molecules—can give rise to ozone and one or more of the other typical manifestations of smog. Control measures must be directed against the release of these volatile substances and of the other component of the smog reaction: the oxides of nitrogen. The organic substances originate with the evaporation or incomplete combustion of gasoline in motor vehicles, with the evaporative losses of the petroleum industry and with the use of solvents. A survey by the Los Angeles Air Pollution Control District in 1951 showed that losses at the refineries were more than 400 tons a day; these have since been reduced to an estimated 85 tons.

This reduction of one source was offset, however, by an increase in the emissions from motor vehicles. In 1940 there were about 1.2 million vehicles in the Los Angeles area; in 1950 there were

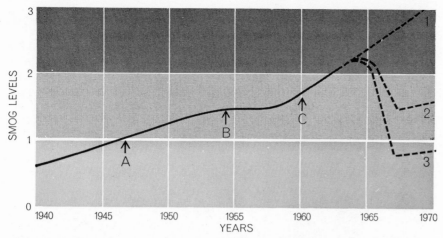

POLLUTION LEVELS in Los Angeles are plotted on scale (*left*) where *1* is 1947 level, *2* double and *3* triple that. *A* represents state pollution control law; *B*, control over refineries; *C*, motor vehicle controls. Broken lines indicate smog potential without new controls (*1*), with hydrocarbon controls (*2*) and with both hydrocarbon and nitrogen oxide controls (*3*).

two million; today there are 3.5 million. These vehicles burn about seven million gallons, or 21,500 tons, of gasoline a day. They emit 1,800 tons of unburned hydrocarbons, 500 tons of oxides of nitrogen and 9,000 tons of carbon monoxide daily. These emissions outweigh those from all other sources.

When motor vehicles emerged as a major source of air pollution, it was evident that state rather than local government could best cope with these moving sources. As a first step, and a pioneering one for the U.S., the California Department of Public Health adopted community standards for the quality of the air [*see top illustration on page 287*].

The adoption of these standards provided a sound basis for a program of controlling automobile emissions. Of special importance for that program was the establishment of the figure of .15 part per million by volume as the harmful level of oxidant. Years of observation have demonstrated that when the oxidant goes above .15 part per million, a significant segment of the population complains of eye irritation, and plant damage is readily noticeable. The standards also set the harmful level for carbon monoxide at 30 parts per million by volume for eight hours, on the basis of observations that under those conditions 5 per cent of the human body's hemoglobin is inactivated. A further stipulation of the standards was that these oxidant and carbon monoxide levels should not be reached on more than

four days a year. To attain such a goal in Los Angeles by 1970 would require the reduction of hydrocarbons and carbon monoxide by 80 and 60 per cent.

On the basis of these standards the California legislature in 1960 adopted the nation's first law designed to require control devices on motor vehicles. The law created a Motor Vehicle Pollution Control Board to set specifications and test the resulting devices. In its work the board has been concerned with two kinds of vehicular emission: that from the engine and that from the exhaust.

About 30 per cent of the total emission of the car, or 2 per cent of the supplied fuel, escapes from the engine. This "blowby" loss results from seepage of gasoline past piston rings into the crankcase; it occurs even in new cars. Evaporation from the carburetor and even from the fuel tank is substantial, particularly on hot days. Until recently crankcase emissions were vented to the outside through a tube. California's Motor Vehicle Polution Control Board began in 1960 a process leading to a requirement that all new cars sold in the state have by 1963 a device that carries the emissions back into the engine for recombustion. The automobile industry thereupon installed the blowby devices in all 1963 models, so that gradually crankcase emissions will come under control throughout the U.S. California is going a step further: blowby devices will have to be installed soon on certain used cars and commercial vehicles.

Two-thirds of the total automobile emission, or 5.4 per cent of the supplied fuel, leaves through the tail pipe as a result of incomplete combustion. For complete combustion, which would produce harmless gases, the air-fuel ratio should be about 15 to 1. Most cars are built to operate on a richer mixture, containing more gasoline, for smoother operation and maximum power; consequently not all the gasoline can be burned in the various driving cycles.

The exhaust gases consist mainly of nitrogen, oxygen, carbon dioxide and water vapor. In addition there are lesser quantities of carbon monoxide, partially oxidized hydrocarbons and their oxidation products, and oxides of nitrogen and sulfur. Most proposals for control of these gases rely on the addition of an afterburner to the muffler. Two approaches appear most promising. The direct-flame approach uses a spark plug or pilot light to ignite the unburned gases. The catalytic type passes them through a catalyst bed that burns them at lower temperatures than are possible

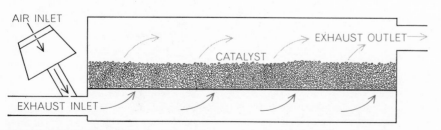

SECOND TYPE of afterburner involves leading exhaust gases through a catalyst bed; they can then be burned at lower temperatures than are possible in a direct-flame afterburner.

with direct-flame burners [*see bottom illustrations on opposite page*].

Building a successful afterburner presents several problems. The high temperatures require more costly materials, thereby increasing initial and replacement costs. Complications in operation arise from the burning of a mixture of gases and air of highly variable concentration. During deceleration the mixture may be so rich that without a bypass ceramics and catalysts will melt. In other cycles of operation there may not be enough fuel to keep the flame going. Moreover, the California law on exhaust-control devices stipulates that they must not be a fire hazard, make excessive noise or adversely affect the operation of the engine by back pressure.

Nine makes of afterburner—six catalytic and three direct-flame—are now under test by the California Motor Vehicle Pollution Control Board. Much testing and modification will be necessary before they are ready for the rough treatment to which they will be subjected when they are attached to all cars. Even after they have been installed a rigorous inspection program will be necessary to make certain that they are properly maintained and periodically replaced.

A preferable method of controlling hydrocarbon emissions from automobile tail pipes would be better combustion in the engine. Automobile engineers have indicated that engines of greater combustion efficiency will appear in the next few years. How efficient these engines will be remains to be seen; so does the effect of the prospective changes on emissions of oxides of nitrogen.

From all the emissions of an automobile the total loss in fuel energy is about 15 per cent; in the U.S. that represents a loss of about $3 billion annually. It is remarkable that the automobile industry, which has a reputation for efficiency, allows such fuel waste. Perhaps pressure for greater efficiency and for control of air pollution will eventually produce a relatively smogless car.

In any case it appears that the proposed 80 per cent control over motor vehicle emissions is a long way off. An alternative is to accept temporary controls at lower levels of effectiveness. It is possible to reduce unburned hydrocarbons and carbon monoxide by modification of the carburetor in order to limit the flow of fuel during deceleration, and by changing the timing of the ignition spark. Proper maintenance can reduce emissions by 25 to 50 per cent, depending on the condition of the car.

Accepting more practical but less ef-ficient means of curbing vehicular emissions requires making up the deficiency in the smog control program some other way. This can be done by control of the other smog ingredient: oxides of nitrogen. At one time it was thought that control of these oxides would be very difficult, and that was why the California law concentrated on curbing emissions of hydrocarbons. It has now been shown, however, that control of oxides of nitrogen, from stationary sources as well as from motor vehicles, is feasible. Oil-burning electric power plants have reduced their contribution by about 50 per cent through the use of a special two-phase combustion system. Research on automobiles has shown that a substantial reduction of oxides of nitrogen is feasible with a relatively simple method of recirculating some of the exhaust gases through the engine.

To arrive at an acceptable quality of air through the limitation of hydrocar-

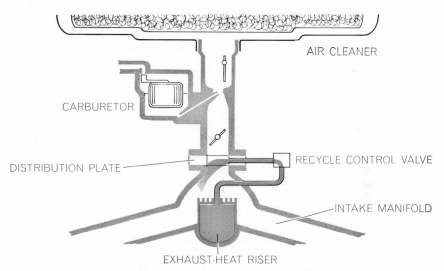

**OXIDES OF NITROGEN** emitted by automobiles may be curbed by this system, which takes exhaust gases before they leave the engine and recycles them through the combustion process.

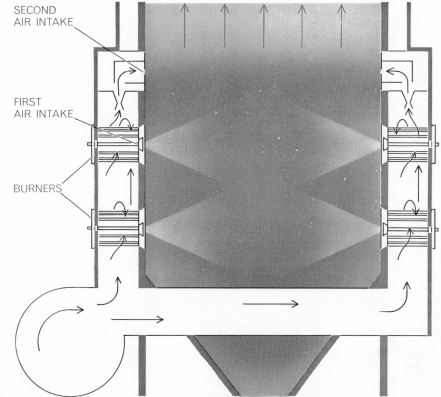

**INDUSTRIAL FURNACES** have curbed emissions of oxides of nitrogen by two-phase combustion. It lowers temperatures by introducing air at two stages of the burning process.

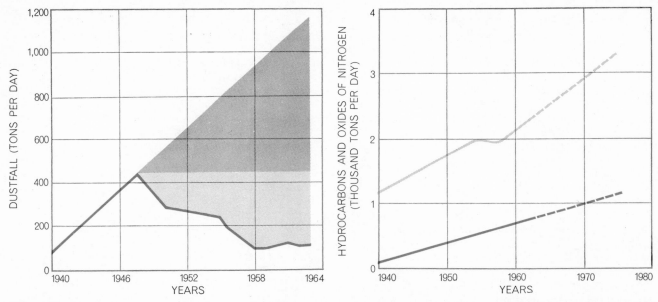

MAJOR POLLUTANTS in Los Angeles County are charted. Dustfall (*left*) has been visibly reduced (*light color*) by control measures; potential without controls is indicated by darker color. At right, light line shows actual and potential levels of hydrocarbons; dark line similarly represents oxides of nitrogen. Rises in spite of controls reflect growth of population and number of vehicles.

bons alone would require a reduction in the hydrocarbons of about 80 per cent, which could be achieved only with rigorous and efficient controls. The plateau of clean air can also be reached, however, by dealing with both hydrocarbons and oxides of nitrogen. The advantage of such an approach is that each one of the reductions would have to be less complete. An over-all reduction of the two major smog components by half would achieve the desired air quality [*see bottom illustration on opposite page*].

This combined approach offers the only practically feasible way to return to a reasonably smog-free atmosphere in Los Angeles as well as in other metropolitan areas plagued by photochemical smog. The California Department of Public Health is now considering the ex-

pansion of the smog control program to include curbs on emission of oxides of nitrogen. For such a program to succeed, however, there would have to be regular inspection of motor vehicles, control of carburetor and fuel tank losses, stringent additional controls over industry and the co-operation of citizens. Moreover, these efforts must be organized in such a way that they take into account the area's rapid population growth, which will mean proportionate rises in motor vehicle and industrial emissions.

Beyond the efforts to control industries and vehicles lie some other possibilities, all of which would have the broad objective of reducing the amount of gasoline burned in the area. They include electric propulsion, economy cars, increased use of public transportation

and improvement of traffic flow. A strong argument for resorting to some of or all these possibilities can be found in an examination of the carbon monoxide readings at a monitoring station in downtown Los Angeles. The readings show clear peaks resulting from commuter traffic. The carbon monoxide increase during a rush period is about 200 tons, representing the emission of about 100,000 cars. That figure agrees well with vehicular counts made during the hours of heavy commuting.

Greater use of public transportation would produce a considerable reduction of peak pollution levels. So would improved traffic flow, both on the main commuter arteries and on the roads that connect with them. Reduction of the frequent idling, acceleration and deceleration characteristic of stop-and-go driving

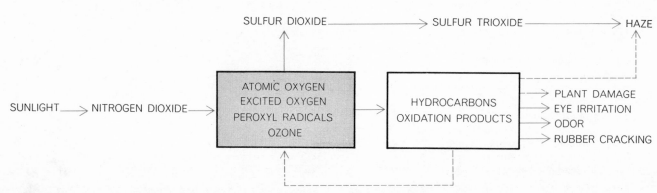

PHOTOCHEMICAL REACTION playing a major role in smog formation begins with sunlight acting on nitrogen dioxide, a product of combustion, to yield oxidants (*gray box*). They attack hydrocarbons, which come mainly from automobile exhausts, to produce irritating materials. Oxidants also attack sulfur dioxide, a product of coal and oil burning. Broken lines indicate interactions.

—the very cycles that produce the most hydrocarbons and oxides of nitrogen—could curb vehicular emissions by 50 per cent or more over a given distance. Detroit has a system of computing the optimum speed on certain freeways according to the density and flow of traffic; the speed is then indicated on large lighted signs. The result is a smoother flow. More techniques of this kind, more imaginative thinking about transportation in general, are necessary for a successful attack on smog.

There can be no doubt that the smogs of Los Angeles represent an extreme manifestation of a problem that is growing in every heavily populated area. Similarly, the control steps taken by Los Angeles will have to be duplicated to some degree in other cities. In those cities, as in Los Angeles, there will be difficulties. One is the cost of air-pollution control for communities that already find their budgets stretched; the Detroit City Council annually votes down an ordinance to ban the burning of leaves because it believes the city cannot afford the estimated cost of $500,-000 for carting the leaves off to dumps. Industry also may balk at smog controls out of concern for maintaining a competitive position. There is a related problem of co-ordination: industries are reluctant to install devices for curbing smoke while the city burns trash in open dumps.

Another problem involves mobilizing the public behind air-pollution control programs. Even though smog looks unpleasant, is occasionally offensive to the smell and irritating to the eye, and sometimes precipitates a public health disaster (as in Donora, Pa., in 1948 and in London in 1952), it nonetheless tends to be regarded as a fact of urban life and something that communities can live with if they must. Moreover, so many political jurisdictions must be involved in an effective attack on air pollution that any one community attempting a clean-up may find its efforts vitiated by another community's smog.

Nevertheless, a growing segment of the public is alert to the dangers of air pollution and determined to do something about it. If anything effective is to be done, however, it will require intelligent planning, aggressive public-education programs and resoluteness on the part of public officials. Then leadership by government and civic groups at all levels, united behind well-designed plans, could generate progress toward the goal of cleaner air.

| POLLUTANT | PARTS PER MILLION FOR ONE HOUR | | |
|---|---|---|---|
| | "ADVERSE" LEVEL | "SERIOUS" LEVEL | "EMERGENCY" LEVEL |
| CARBON MONOXIDE | | 120 | 240 |
| ETHYLENE | .5 | | |
| HYDROGEN SULFIDE | .1 | 5 | |
| SULFUR DIOXIDE | 1 | 5 | 10 |
| HYDROCARBONS | | | |
| NITROGEN DIOXIDE | | | |
| OXIDANT | .15 ON "OXIDANT INDEX" | NOT ESTABLISHED | NOT ESTABLISHED |
| OZONE | | | |
| AEROSOLS | | | |

**AIR-QUALITY STANDARDS** adopted by California set three levels of pollution: "adverse," at which sensory irritation and damage to vegetation occur; "serious," where there is danger of altered bodily function or chronic disease; "emergency," where acute sickness or death may occur in groups of sensitive persons. Blanks mean "not applicable." Pollutants listed in colored type are involved in or are the products of photochemical reaction. These standards, the first adopted by any state, provided a basis for pollution control measures.

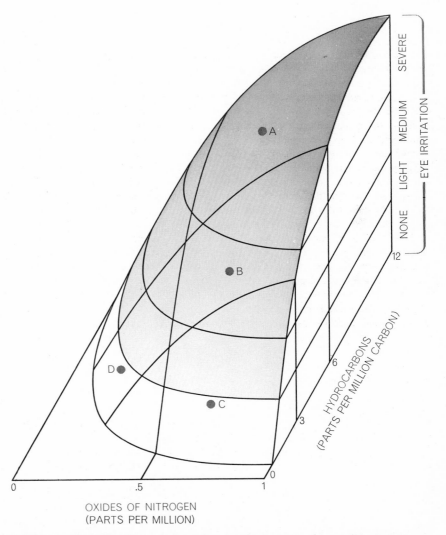

**CONTROL POTENTIALS** are depicted. Los Angeles is at *A* in degree of eye irritation on a day of heavy smog. Controls reducing hydrocarbons by 50 per cent would bring city down the slope to *B*, still not in clear zone shown in white. Hydrocarbon controls to *C* are impractical; control of both hydrocarbons and oxides of nitrogen would attain clear zone at *D*.

# $\mathbb{35}$ The Effects of Smoking

E. CUYLER HAMMOND · July 1962

In 1560 Jean Nicot, the French ambassador to Portugal, wrote that an American Indian herb he had acquired had marvelous curative powers. For a time his view was widely accepted, and in his honor the herb was given the generic name *Nicotiana*. The species *Nicotiana rustica,* first introduced into Europe for smoking in pipes, was harsh and rather disagreeable. Later it was supplanted by *Nicotiana tabacum,* which produces a pleasanter smoke. *N. rustica* is still grown in the U.S.S.R. and other parts of Asia, but *N. tabacum* is now the chief source of smoking tobacco and is the only species cultivated in the U.S.

Skepticism about the medical value of tobacco developed near the end of the 16th century; not long thereafter smoking was condemned as a pernicious habit responsible for all manner of ills. This did not prevent smoking from becoming an almost universal habit among men in Europe and the American colonies. Actually there was no scientific evidence for any harmful effects of tobacco until the middle of the 19th century.

It appears that M. Bouisson, an obscure French physician, deserves credit for the first well-documented clinical study of the matter. In 1859, reporting on patients in the hospital at Montpellier, he observed that of 68 patients with cancer of the buccal cavity (45 of the lip, 11 of the mouth, seven of the tongue and five of the tonsil) 66 smoked pipes, one chewed tobacco and one apparently used tobacco in some form. He noted

that cancer of the lower lip ordinarily developed at the point where the pipe was held in the mouth. He further noted that lip cancer occurred more frequently among individuals who smoked short-stemmed pipes (then called "mouth burners") than among those who smoked long-stemmed clay pipes or pipes with stems made of a substance that does not conduct heat. He suggested that the cancer resulted from irritation of the tissue by tobacco products and heat.

Bouisson's observations were confirmed repeatedly over the next half-century, but since mouth cancer did not loom as a major medical problem the effect on smoking habits was insignificant. Another statistically unimportant problem early recognized as being associated with smoking was Buerger's disease, a rare affliction of the peripheral arteries. It was found to occur exclusively among smokers and to subside when the patient stopped smoking. In 1936, however, two New Orleans surgeons, Alton Ochsner and Michael E. De Bakey, observed that nearly all their lung cancer patients were cigarette smokers. Noting that lung cancer seemed to be on the increase and that it was paralleled by a general rise in cigarette smoking, they suggested a causal connection between the two phenomena. In 1938 Raymond Pearl, the noted Johns Hopkins University medical statistician, reported that smokers had a far shorter life expectancy than those who did not

use tobacco. The effect was so great as to indicate that smoking must be associated with diseases other than cancer. The first experimental evidence for an association between tobacco and cancer came in 1939, when A. H. Roffo of Argentina reported that he had produced cancer by painting tarlike tobacco extracts on the backs of rabbits. After World War II there was renewed interest in the subject of smoking and health, due partly to trends in tobacco consumption and partly to trends in death rates.

Before 1914 tobacco had been consumed mainly in pipes, cigars, chewing tobacco and snuff [see illustration on page 291[. Cigarettes began to be popular during World War I. In the period from the early 1920's to 1960 the consumption of manufactured cigarettes in the U.S. rose from about 750 per adult per year to 3,900 per adult per year. During the same period the consumption of tobacco in all other forms declined by about 70 per cent. The net result was that consumption of all tobacco products rose about 30 per cent.

The changes in smoking habits are more significant than the over-all rise in tobacco consumption. Smoke from cigars and pipes is heavy and as a rule slightly alkaline. Few people can inhale it without coughing or becoming dizzy or nauseated. Cigarette smoke, on the other hand, is relatively light, nearly neutral and can be inhaled readily. Most habit-

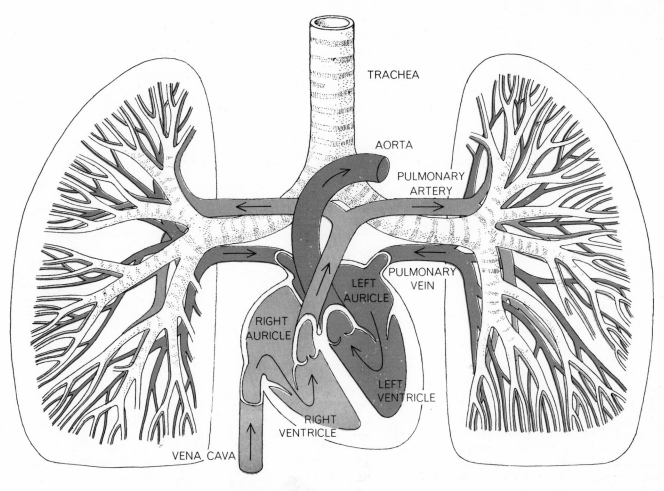

**HEART AND LUNGS** are both affected by inhaled tobacco smoke, which travels down the trachea, through the bronchial tubes to the alveoli. "Tars" deposit on the epithelium and lead to clogging of alveoli. These and the capillaries are often ruptured by coughing. The heart must then pump blood through a smaller number of capillaries, against increased pressure, on a reduced oxygen supply.

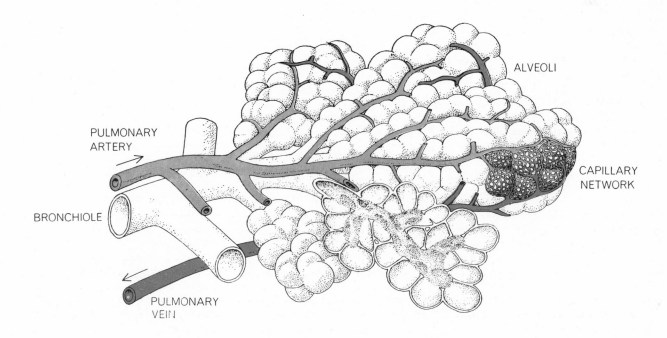

**ALVEOLI** of the lungs are air sacs formed by terminal expansion of the bronchioles. Oxygen is supplied to the blood through the capillaries embedded in the alveolar walls. Destruction of this tissue thus reduces the rate at which the lungs can take up oxygen.

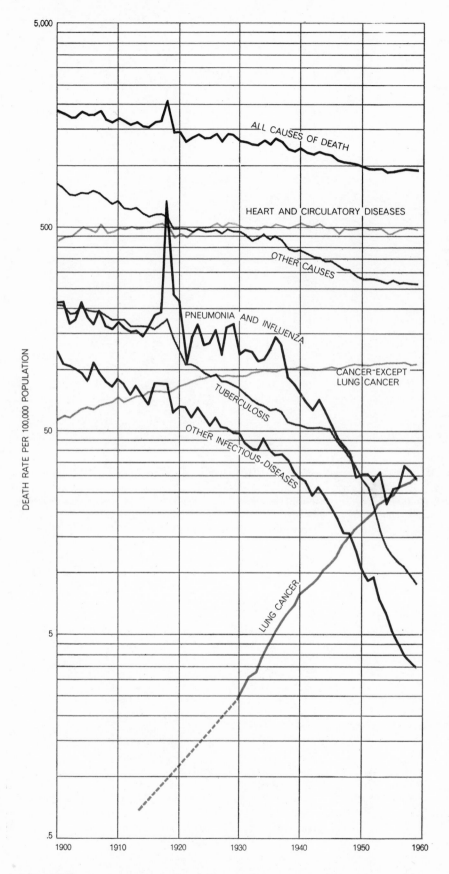

DEATH RATE PER 100,000 POPULATION

ALL CAUSES OF DEATH

HEART AND CIRCULATORY DISEASES

OTHER CAUSES

PNEUMONIA AND INFLUENZA

CANCER-EXCEPT LUNG CANCER

TUBERCULOSIS

OTHER INFECTIOUS DISEASES

LUNG CANCER

**RISE IN LUNG CANCER DEATHS** runs counter to the 60-year downtrend in total death rates among U.S. men. In 1959 lung cancer accounted for 29,335 deaths. Colon and rectal cancers, next in order of frequency, caused 19,129 male deaths. The nearly steady death rate for heart and circulatory diseases conceals a significant rise in coronary artery disease, which is offset by a long-term decline in other forms of heart disease. Curves are age-adjusted so that death rates are not spuriously shifted by changing age composition of the population.

ual cigarette smokers inhale to some degree, and heavy cigarette smokers tend to inhale deeply. In a recent study conducted by the American Cancer Society detailed information has been obtained on the smoking habits of 43,068 men and women. Only 7 per cent of the cigarette smokers among the men said that they did not inhale, whereas noninhalation was reported by 53 per cent of the pipe smokers and 71 per cent of the cigar smokers. Deep inhalation was reported by 24 per cent of the cigarette smokers compared with only 3 per cent of the pipe smokers and 1.5 per cent of the cigar smokers. Women who smoke inhale to a lesser degree than men smokers do. Furthermore, women over the age of 40 smoke far fewer cigarettes than men of the same age do, and few women over 55 smoke as much as a pack a day. Among current cigarette smokers now over 50, the majority of the men started the habit before they were 20, whereas the majority of the women did not begin until they were over 35.

During the past half-century total death rates—including death rates from almost all infectious diseases and some noninfectious ones—have declined rapidly. Lung cancer is a striking exception. Deaths from lung cancer in the U.S. have climbed from 4,000 in 1935 to 11,000 in 1945 and to 36,000 in 1960. The toll in 1960 was approximately equal to the number of deaths caused by traffic accidents. In 1960, 86 per cent of those who died from lung cancer were men. Between 1935 and 1960 the age-standardized death rate from lung cancer among U.S. men (the death rate adjusted for age differences in the composition of the population) increased 600 per cent; among women it increased 125 per cent. And for the past several years lung cancer has been the principal form of fatal cancer among men.

Painstaking studies have clearly demonstrated that the increase in lung cancer is real and not attributable merely to improvement in diagnosis. Lung cancer (that is, bronchogenic carcinoma) arises in the epithelium, or lining, of the bronchial tubes. The increase seems to be confined to two closely related forms of the disease: epidermoid carcinoma and undifferentiated carcinoma. There seems to be little, if any, increase in another form of the disease: adenocarcinoma. (In adenocarcinoma the diseased cells assume an arrangement resembling that of the cells in a gland.)

Lung cancer accounted for about 2 per cent of all U.S. deaths in 1960, and for about 6 per cent of deaths among men in their late 50's and 60's. The leading cause of death in the U.S. is coronary artery disease of the heart, which accounted in 1960 for nearly 29 per cent of all deaths, and for about 35 per cent of deaths among men still in their 40's and 50's. As in the case of lung cancer, coronary artery disease is less common among women, accounting for only about 16 per cent of the deaths occurring between the ages of 40 and 59.

In the late 1940's, when a number of investigators became concerned with lung cancer, cigarette smoking was only one of several factors suggested as possible causes for the increase in the disease. It was already well known that lung cancer could result from prolonged and heavy occupational exposure to certain industrial dusts and vapors. These include chromates, nickel carbonyl and dusts containing radioactive particles. Moreover, they result in epidermoid or undifferentiated carcinoma of the bronchial tubes and not in the less common adenocarcinoma.

This led to the hypothesis that the increase in lung cancer was due to increased exposure of the human population to air contamination of some sort. The factor involved had to be widespread and not confined to any particular occupational group. (In all countries with adequate mortality statistics lung cancer was found to have increased.) Three factors that met the requirements were: fumes from the combustion of solid and liquid fuels, dust from asphalt roads and the tires of motor vehicles, and cigarette smoking. The first two have not been ruled out as possibly contributing somewhat to the occurrence of lung cancer. It is the third that concerns us here.

As a first step a number of studies were made comparing the smoking habits of lung cancer patients with the smoking habits of individuals free of the disease. The results confirmed the 1936 observation of Ochsner and De Bakey. In every such study a far larger percentage of cigarette smokers was found in the lung cancer group than in the control group. Indeed, virtually all patients with epidermoid or undifferentiated carcinoma of the bronchial tubes admitted to smoking. There appeared to be less association, if there was any at all, between smoking habits and adenocarcinoma of the lung.

Cancer was not the only disease studied in relation to smoking habits. Knowing the acute effects of nicotine on the circulatory system, many physicians believed that smoking might be bad for patients with heart disease. In fact, a

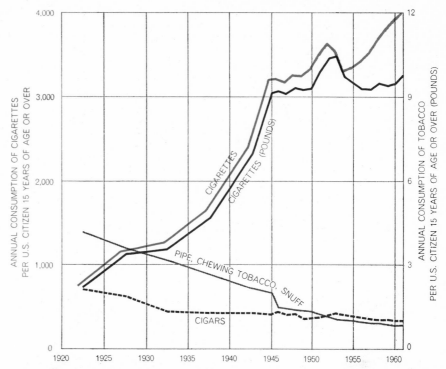

CHANGES IN TOBACCO USE produced a fivefold rise in cigarette consumption between the early 1920's and 1961, and a drop of nearly 70 per cent in consumption of all other tobacco products. Cigarettes are plotted both in units (*color*) and in pounds of unstemmed-tobacco equivalent. Other tobacco products are shown only in pounds. Filter cigarettes, which use less tobacco than nonfilter types, have been growing in popularity since 1954.

study made at the Mayo Clinic in 1940 by John P. English, Fredrick A. Willius and Joseph Berkson had indicated a considerable degree of association between smoking habits and coronary artery disease. Furthermore, many doctors were under the impression that smoking had a bad effect on patients with gastric and duodenal ulcers.

A number of investigators, myself among them, were uncertain as to the validity of these "clinical impressions" and "retrospective studies." A useful way to minimize bias and other difficulties in looking for an association between a disease and its possible causes is to employ the "prospective," or "follow up," method of investigation. The method consists of questioning a large number of presumably healthy individuals, keeping in touch with them for a number of years and finally ascertaining whether or not deaths in later years are associated with habits reported by the subjects before they became ill.

Two such prospective studies were undertaken in the fall of 1951, one in Britain by W. Richard Doll and A. Bradford Hill and the other in the U.S. by Daniel Horn and me. Under the auspices of the British Medical Research Council, Doll and Hill initiated their investigation by mailing questionnaires on smoking habits to all British physicians. They ob-

tained information on all deaths among British physicians by checking death certificates. Their study is still in progress. Several years later similar investigations were undertaken by Harold F. Dorn, who studied U.S. veterans holding life insurance; by E. W. R. Best, G. H. Josie and C. B. Walker, who are studying Canadian veterans and pensioners; and by John Edward Dunn, Jr., George Linden and Lester Breslow, who are studying men employed in certain occupations in California. In 1959 I started a new and more extensive prospective study in which smoking is included as only one of many factors under investigation.

The findings in all these investigations are remarkably similar; indeed, they are as close as could possibly be expected considering that the subjects were drawn from different populations and were of different ages. In the interest of brevity, therefore, I shall present data only from two studies with which I am personally concerned. The first of these was carried out as follows:

After designing and pretesting a questionnaire in the fall of 1951, we trained more than 22,000 American Cancer Society volunteers as researchers for the study. Between January 1 and May 31 of 1952 they enrolled subjects in 394 counties in nine states. The subjects, all men between the ages of 50 and 69, answered a simple confidential questionnaire on their smoking habits, both past and present. A total of 187,783 men were enrolled, filled out usable questionnaires and were successfully kept track of for the next 44 months. Death certificates were obtained for all who died, and additional medical information was gathered for those who were reported to have died of cancer. All together 11,870

deaths were reported, of which 2,249 were attributed to cancer.

The most important finding was that the total death rate (from all causes of death combined) is far higher among men with a history of regular cigarette smoking than among men who never smoked, but only slightly higher among pipe and cigar smokers than among men who never smoked. This is illustrated in the first of the series of charts on pages

294, 295, and 296. The death rates have been adjusted for age, and for ease of comparison the death rate of men who never smoked has been set at one.

Men who had smoked cigarettes regularly and exclusively were classified according to their cigarette consumption at the time they were enrolled in the study. It was found that death rates rose progressively with increasing number of cigarettes smoked per day, as shown in the second chart in the series. The death rate of those who smoked two or more packs of cigarettes a day was approximately two and a quarter times higher than the death rate of men who never smoked.

Being a heavy cigarette smoker myself at the time, I was curious to know the death rate of ex-cigarette smokers. This is shown in the third chart in the series. The death rate of men who had given up cigarette smoking a year or more prior to enrollment was considerably lower than that of men who were still smoking cigarettes when they were enrolled in the study.

Next we analyzed the data in relation to cause of death as reported on death certificates. Such information is subject to error, but on checking medical records we found that the diagnosis of cancer had been confirmed by microscopic examination of tissue in 79 per cent of the deaths ascribed to this disease. Even in some of these cases, however, the site of origin of the cancer was unknown or open to question. This is because cancer, unless successfully treated at an early stage, spreads through the body and its source is often difficult to determine. There is another difficulty that has to do with other causes of death. People in the older age groups not infrequently suffer from two or more diseases, one or another of which could be fatal. Since death can result from the combined effects of these diseases, it is difficult, and perhaps illogical, to ascribe death to one alone. These difficulties should be kept in mind in evaluating the following findings.

During the course of the study 7,316 deaths occurred among subjects with a history of regular cigarette smoking (some of whom smoked pipes and/or cigars as well as cigarettes). We divided these deaths according to primary cause as reported on death certificates. This is shown in the table on the opposite page under the heading "Observed deaths." Only 4,651 of these cigarette smokers would have died during the course of the study if their death rates had exactly matched those of men of the same age who had never smoked. This is shown in

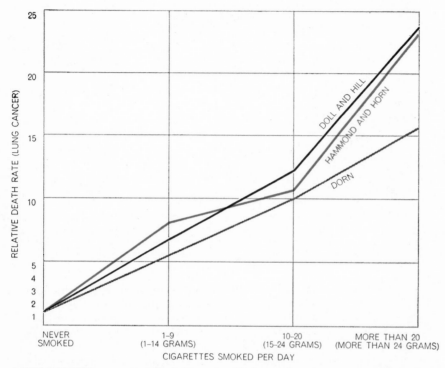

LUNG CANCER as a cause of death increases with the number of cigarettes (or gram equivalent) consumed per day, according to three major studies cited in the text. "Relative death rate" is the death rate among smokers divided by the death rate found among nonsmokers.

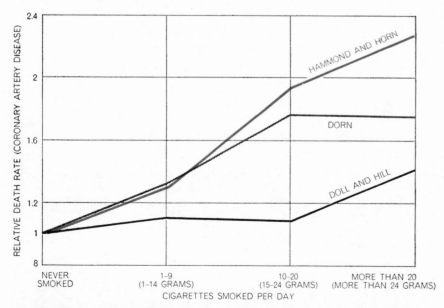

CORONARY ARTERY DISEASE as a cause of death also increases with the cigarettes smoked per day. The relative death rates are lower than for lung cancer because coronary artery disease is the leading cause of death among nonsmokers as well as among smokers.

the table under the heading "Expected deaths." The difference of 2,665 deaths (7,316 minus 4,651) can be considered the "Excess deaths" associated with a history of regular cigarette smoking. Of these excess deaths 52.1 per cent were attributed to coronary artery disease of the heart, 13.5 per cent to lung cancer and the remainder to other diseases. From this it is apparent that as a cause of death coronary artery disease is by far the most important disease associated with cigarette smoking.

From the standpoint of attempting to determine causal relations, it is best to study the figures in the table under the heading "Relative death rate." This is the observed number of deaths divided by the expected number of deaths, which in essence is the death rate of cigarette smokers divided by the death rate of subjects who never smoked.

Since coronary artery disease is the leading cause of death among men in the U.S. today, it is not surprising that we found it to be the leading cause of death among nonsmokers as well as among cigarette smokers. But the rate was 70 per cent higher among cigarette smokers. As shown in the fourth chart in the series on the next three pages, the death rate attributed to coronary artery disease increased progressively with the amount of cigarette smoking. We also found that ex-cigarette smokers had a lower death rate from this disease than did men who were still smoking cigarettes at the start of the study.

Lung cancer is an extremely rare cause of death among nonsmokers, except for those who have had prolonged and heavy occupational exposure to certain dusts and fumes. Taking death-certificate diagnosis at face value, the lung cancer death rate was more than 10 times higher among cigarette smokers than among nonsmokers. On obtaining medical records we found that, of 448 deaths attributed to this cause, the diagnosis of bronchogenic carcinoma was established by microscopic examination in addition to other evidence in 327 cases, of which 32 were adenocarcinoma. The fifth chart in the series shows age-standardized death rates by amount of cigarette smoking based on the 295 deaths from well-verified cases of bronchogenic carcinoma other than adenocarcinoma. The rate was very low for men who had never smoked, it increased with the amount of cigarette smoking, and it was very high for men who smoked two or more packs of cigarettes a day. When standardized both for age and for the amount of smoking, the rate for ex-cigarette smokers who had given up the

habit for a year or more was considerably lower than the rate for men who were smoking cigarettes regularly at the start of the study. The lung cancer death rate of cigar and pipe smokers was very low compared with that of cigarette smokers, although higher than the rate for nonsmokers.

All together 127 deaths were attributed to cancer of other tissues (mouth, tongue, lip, larynx, pharynx and esophagus) that are directly exposed to tobacco smoke and material condensed from tobacco smoke. In 114 of these cases the diagnosis was confirmed by microscopic examination. Of these 114 men, 110 were smokers and only four had never smoked. The figures suggest that pipe and cigar smoking may be more important than cigarette smoking in relation to cancer of one or more sites included in this group, but the number of cases was not sufficient for a reliable evaluation of this point. Nevertheless, these cancers were the only causes of death for which the death rate of pipe and cigar smokers was found to be far higher than the death rate of nonsmokers.

Other reported causes of death showing a fairly high degree of association with cigarette smoking were gastric and duodenal ulcers, certain diseases of the arteries, pulmonary diseases (including pneumonia and influenza), cancer of the bladder and cirrhosis of the liver. Many other diseases appeared to be somewhat associated with cigarette smoking.

In 1959 I started a new study considerably larger than the first one. By securing the services of some 68,000 volunteer workers of the American Cancer Society in 1,121 counties in 25 states, we enrolled as subjects 1,079,000 men and women over the age of 30. Each of them filled out a lengthy confidential questionnaire including questions on family history, diseases and physical complaints, diet, smoking and other habits, residence history, occupational exposures and many other factors not included in previous studies. We plan to follow these subjects for six years. So far follow-up information is available only for the first 10½ months of observation.

The early findings on smoking are in close agreement with findings in all previous studies. In this study smokers were asked the degree to which they inhaled the smoke. It was found that, in relation to total death rates, the degree of inhalation is as important, and perhaps more important, than the amount of smoking [see illustration on page 297].

The new study has also revealed a high degree of association between cigarette smoking and a number of physical complaints, most particularly coughing, shortness of breath, loss of appetite and loss of weight [see illustration on page 298]. These complaints were related to the degree of inhalation as well as to the amount of smoking. They were reported less frequently by cigar and pipe smokers (most of whom do not inhale) than by cigarette smokers (most of whom

| CAUSE OF DEATH | OBSERVED DEATHS | EXPECTED DEATHS | EXCESS DEATHS | PERCENTAGE OF EXCESS | RELATIVE DEATH RATE |
|---|---|---|---|---|---|
| TOTAL DEATHS (ALL CAUSES) | 7,316 | 4,651 | 2,665 | 100.0 | 1.57 |
| CORONARY ARTERY DISEASE | 3,361 | 1,973 | 1,388 | 52.1 | 1.70 |
| OTHER HEART DISEASES | 503 | 425 | 78 | 2.9 | 1.18 |
| CEREBRAL VASCULAR LESIONS | 556 | 428 | 128 | 4.8 | 1.30 |
| ANEURYSM AND BUERGER'S DISEASE | 86 | 29 | 57 | 2.1 | 2.97 |
| OTHER CIRCULATORY DISEASES | 87 | 68 | 19 | 0.7 | 1.28 |
| LUNG CANCER | 397 | 37 | 360 | 13.5 | 10.73 |
| CANCER OF THE BUCCAL CAVITY, LARYNX OR ESOPHAGUS | 91 | 18 | 73 | 2.7 | 5.06 |
| CANCER OF THE BLADDER | 70 | 35 | 35 | 1.3 | 2.00 |
| OTHER CANCERS | 902 | 651 | 251 | 9.4 | 1.39 |
| GASTRIC AND DUODENAL ULCER | 100 | 25 | 75 | 2.8 | 4.00 |
| CIRRHOSIS OF THE LIVER | 83 | 43 | 40 | 1.5 | 1.93 |
| PULMONARY DISEASE (EXCEPT CANCER) | 231 | 81 | 150 | 5.6 | 2.85 |
| ALL OTHER DISEASES | 486 | 453 | 33 | 1.2 | 1.07 |
| ACCIDENT, VIOLENCE, SUICIDE | 363 | 385 | −22 | −0.8 | 0.94 |

DEATHS AMONG REGULAR CIGARETTE SMOKERS, labeled "Observed deaths," are compared with the number of deaths "expected" if the death rates for each age group among smokers had been the same as those found among nonsmokers. The table summarizes the results of the study conducted by the author and Daniel Horn. The column "Excess deaths" can be considered as the excess number of deaths associated with cigarette smoking. "Relative death rate" is the observed number of deaths divided by the expected number.

inhale either moderately or deeply).

Two prospective studies of smoking in relation to the occurrence of coronary artery disease have been carried out in Framingham, Mass., and Albany, N.Y. The combined findings from these were published on April 19, 1962 in *The New England Journal of Medicine* by Joseph T. Doyle, Thomas R. Dawber, William B. Kannel, A. Sandra Heslin and Harold A. Kahn. On enrollment in these studies each subject was given a medical examination. No symptoms of coronary artery disease were initially found in 4,120 men. These men were re-examined from time to time for a number of years. Symptoms of coronary artery disease (as well as death from this disease) were found far more frequently among those who smoked cigarettes regularly than among those who did not smoke. The total death rate was more than twice as high among men who smoked more than 20 cigarettes a day as among men who had never smoked. Ex-smokers and cigar and pipe smokers had morbidity and mortality records similar to the records of those who had never smoked. Thus the findings in this study based on medical examination of subjects were in close agreement with findings in the other U.S. studies.

Although all the studies have shown essentially the same results, there are some interesting differences between the results in Britain and the U.S. Lung cancer death rates are about twice as high in Britain as they are in the U.S.; chronic bronchitis is reported to be a common cause of death by British physicians but is seldom mentioned as a cause of death in the U.S.; death rates from coronary artery disease (as reported on death certificates) are far lower in Britain than they are in the U.S. No one really knows the reasons for these differences. Speculations on the subject may be briefly summarized as follows.

Climate, the method of heating houses, exposure to air pollutants and occupational exposure to dusts and fumes have all been suggested as possible reasons why both lung cancer and chronic bronchitis appear to occur more frequently in Britain than in this country. Differences in smoking habits have also been suggested as a possible factor. Doll and Hill have studied the length of discarded cigarette butts in England and Wales, and Ernest L. Wynder of the Sloan-Kettering Institute for Cancer Research and I have made similar studies on this side of the Atlantic. The average length of the butts was found to be 18.7 millimeters in England and Wales (where cigarettes are quite expensive), compared with 27.9 mm. in Canada and 30.9 mm. in the U.S. Therefore British smokers consume more of each cigarette and so receive a higher amount of nicotine and tobacco tar than Canadian and U.S. smokers do.

Diet has been suggested as a possible reason why death rates from coronary artery disease appear to be higher in the U.S. than they are in Britain. This apparent difference may be at least partly due to difference in diagnosis of the cause of death. Death can result from the combined effects of heart disease and lung ailments, particularly in older people. In the case of heart failure in a person suffering from a lung disease it is sometimes difficult to decide which to record as the principal cause of death. Thus the apparent high death rate reported as due to chronic bronchitis in Britain may be related to the comparatively low death rate reported as due to coronary artery disease in that country. Be that as it may, the Doll and Hill study showed less of a relation between smoking and coronary artery disease than did our U.S. study [*see lower illustration on page 292*]. On the other hand, Doll and Hill found a very high relation between smoking and death from chronic bronchitis.

In recent years considerable attention has been given to the chemical composition of tobacco smoke. A great many compounds have been identified, most of which are present in very small amounts. Some are distilled out of the tobacco and others are products of combustion. Included are numerous poisons (such as nicotine), various agents that are highly irritating to mammalian tissues, several carcinogenic (cancer-

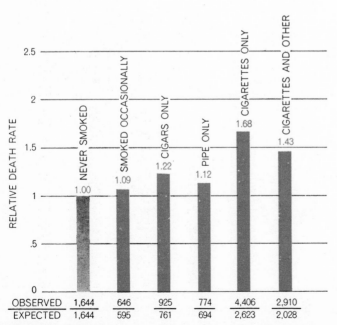

**DEATH RATE FROM ALL CAUSES** in Hammond and Horn study was far higher among cigarette smokers than among men who never smoked, but only slightly higher among pipe and cigar smokers.

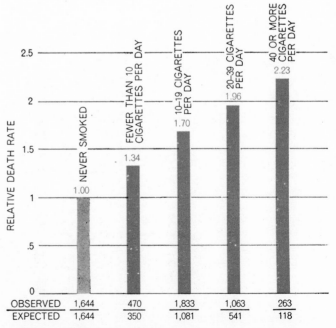

**DAILY CIGARETTE CONSUMPTION** showed a direct correlation with relative death rate from all causes. The study followed 187,783 men between the ages of 50 and 69 for 44 months.

producing) compounds and some co-carcinogenic compounds (materials that increase the potency of carcinogens). Most of this material is suspended in small particles, which together with carbon monoxide, air and other gases constitute tobacco smoke.

Ernest Wynder and his various collaborators have shown that tobacco-smoke condensate, or "tar," produces cancer in mice and rabbits if applied repeatedly to the skin over a long period of time. A number of investigators have confirmed these findings. The cancers so produced in rodents are of a type known as epidermoid carcinoma. (A synonym is squamous cell carcinoma, because the cells tend to be flattened, or squamous.) Different strains of animals vary in susceptibility, some being highly susceptible and others highly resistant.

Many investigators who have tried to produce lung cancer in rodents by exposing them to tobacco smoke have not succeeded in doing so. This may be because of two serious difficulties. Whereas a human smoker takes in smoke through his mouth, mice and other small rodents breathe through their noses, and in rodents this organ has developed into a remarkably efficient filter for preventing particulate matter from being drawn into the lung. Moreover, mice are sensitive to the acute toxic effects of tobacco smoke.

Several years ago I exposed mice to cigarette smoke under such conditions that they were forced to breathe smoke of approximately the same concentration as that of smoke taken in by human cigarette smokers. Unfortunately many of my animals went into convulsions and died within a few minutes. The remaining animals lived only a short time. By reducing the concentration of smoke the animals can be kept alive, but under such conditions it is doubtful whether or not their lungs are any more heavily exposed to the particulate matter of cigarette smoke than are the lungs of a nonsmoker sitting in a small room with several heavy smokers.

Nevertheless, by subjecting mice to tolerable concentrations of tobacco smoke Cecilie and Rudolph Leuchtenberger and Paul F. Doolon of the Children's Cancer Research Foundation in Boston have succeeded in producing various changes in the lining of the bronchial tubes of mice. These changes are similar to changes found in the bronchial tubes of human cigarette smokers. So far no cancers have been produced in mice thereby. This is consistent with the finding that lung cancer rarely occurs in human beings who are only slightly exposed to tobacco smoke.

During smoking the tissues first exposed to tobacco smoke are the lips, the tongue and the mucous membrane of the mouth. Some of the components of tobacco smoke (including known carcinogens) fluoresce under ultraviolet light. Robert C. Mellors of the Cornell University Medical College has shown that this material penetrates the cells of the lining of the mouth. The type of cancer that arises in this tissue is epidermoid carcinoma—the same type of cancer that is produced when tobacco tar is applied to the skin of experimental animals. Furthermore, the amount of tar required to produce epidermoid carcinoma of the skin in mice is roughly comparable to the exposure of a heavy smoker who develops epidermoid carcinoma of the lip or mouth.

In study after study a high degree of association has been found between smoking of all types (as well as the chewing of tobacco) and the occurrence of cancer of these tissues. It is hard to escape the conclusion that this association reflects a direct causal relation. This does not preclude the possibility that other factors (such as host susceptibility or exposure to other carcinogenic materials) are involved in at least some cases.

What has just been said of smoking in relation to cancer of the lips, mouth and tongue also applies to cancer of the pharynx and cancer of the larynx. The situation is slightly different in cancer of the esophagus; this passageway is exposed to ingested tobacco-smoke condensate but not directly to the smoke. The strong association between smoking and epidermoid carcinoma of the esophagus, however, would seem to point to the same conclusion.

When inhaled, tobacco smoke travels

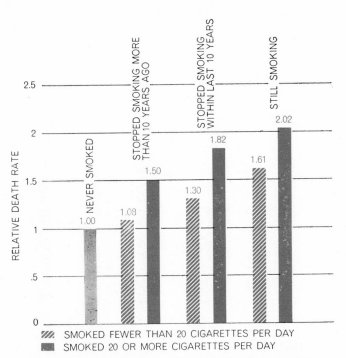

FORMER SMOKERS had a lower relative death rate than those still smoking, particularly if they had smoked fewer than 20 cigarettes a day and had stopped smoking for at least 10 years.

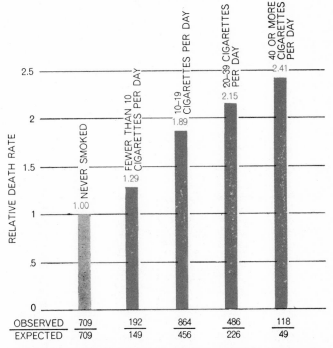

CORONARY ARTERY DISEASE, which accounted for 52.1 per cent of excess deaths among regular smokers of cigarettes, was also correlated very closely with the smoker's daily cigarette consumption.

down the trachea to the bronchial tubes of the lungs. All but a few cases of lung cancer originate in the lining, or epithelium, of these tubes. This is remarkable tissue, well worth describing here. Normally it consists of just two layers of cells that rest on a thin mat of tiny fibers called the basement membrane. This membrane separates the epithelium from the underlying tissue. Directly on top of the basement membrane is a layer of small, round cells with relatively small nuclei. They are called basal cells. On top of the basal cells is a single layer of cells known as columnar cells (because from the side they look like columns) interspersed with a few goblet cells (which look like little wine goblets). The goblet cells secrete a sticky fluid onto the surface. This is augmented by fluid secreted by glands located below the basement membrane. Protruding from the top of the columnar cells are short, hairlike cilia, which constantly move in a whiplike manner. This causes fluid on the epithelium to move up through the bronchial tubes and the trachea into the mouth, where it is either swallowed or expectorated.

The cilia and the fluid perform an extremely important function in cleansing the lungs. Small particles of dust or smoke that settle on the surface of the bronchial tubes are trapped in the fluid and, together with the fluid, are moved up and out of the lungs.

It has been shown by Anderson C. Hilding of St. Luke's Hospital in Duluth, Minn., by Paul Kotin of the University of Southern California School of Medicine and by others that tobacco smoke inhibits the movement of the cilia to such a degree that the flow of fluid is slowed down, if not stopped altogether. This allows an accumulation of tobacco-smoke products and whatever other material happens to fall on the lining of the bronchial tubes. Smokers and nonsmokers alike—particularly those living in cities with polluted air and those engaged in certain occupations—inhale dust of various types, and some of the dusts contain carcinogenic substances.

For a number of years I have been cooperating in an extensive study of human lung tissue with Oscar Auerbach, a pathologist at the Veterans Administration Hospital in East Orange, N.J., and with Arthur Purdy Stout of the Columbia University College of Physicians and Surgeons. Some of our findings can be summarized as follows.

At the East Orange Veterans Hospital and at a number of hospitals in upstate New York the lungs are routinely removed at autopsy. The trachea and bronchial tubes are dissected out of the lungs and systematically divided into 208 portions, each of which is embedded in paraffin. A thin section of tissue is cut from each of these portions, mounted on a glass slide and stained with a suitable dye for microscopic examination. Independently, under the supervision of Lawrence Garfinkel of my staff, an interviewer is sent to the home of each patient to obtain information on his or her occupational history, residence history and smoking habits. We do not include a case unless this information can be obtained. All told we have studied tissue from the bronchial tubes of more than 1,000 individuals.

In each of our studies microscope slides from a number of different patients have been put in completely random order by the use of a table of random numbers. They are then labeled with a serial number that gives no clue to their identity. All the slides are studied microscopically by Auerbach and samples of them are checked by Stout. After the slides are examined, the serial numbers are decoded so that the microscopic findings can be analyzed in relation to other information about the subjects.

Three major types of change occur in bronchial epithelium: hyperplasia (an increase in the number of layers of cells), loss of ciliated columnar cells and changes in the nuclei of cells [see illustration on page 299]. Hyperplasia is the usual reaction of surface tissues to almost any type of irritation, either chemical or mechanical. A familiar example is the formation of calluses on the hands. We found some degree of hyperplasia in 10 to 18 per cent of slides from nonsmokers, in more than 80 per cent of slides from light cigarette smokers and in more than 95 per cent of slides from heavy cigarette smokers. Extensive hyperplasia (defined as five or more layers of cells between the basement mem-

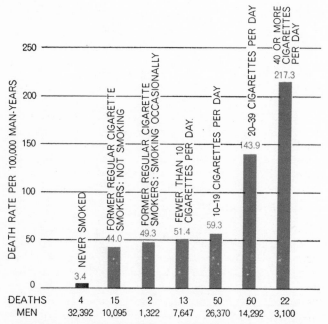

LUNG CANCER DEATH RATES, age-standardized and based on well-established cases exclusive of adenocarcinoma, rose sharply for men smoking more than a pack a day in the Hammond and Horn study. But the death rate among former smokers was much lower.

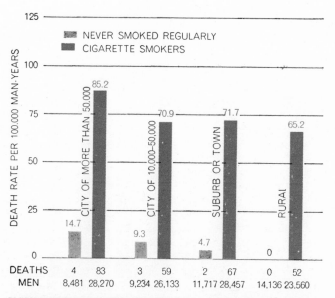

NONSMOKERS IN THE CITY sometimes die of lung cancer, but the death rate was only a fraction of that found among cigarette smokers who lived in the country. The death rates are based on well-established cases of lung cancer, exclusive of adenocarcinoma.

brane and the columnar cells) was frequently found in heavy cigarette smokers but rarely in other subjects.

Loss of ciliated columnar cells was observed in nonsmokers but far more frequently in cigarette smokers, and the frequency of this observation increased with the amount of cigarette smoking. The implication is that foreign material tends not to be removed, and thus can accumulate where the cilia have been destroyed.

An important finding was the occurrence of cells with atypical nuclei. The nuclei of cancer cells are usually large, irregular in shape and characteristically have an abnormal number of chromosomes. A few cells with nuclei that have such an appearance are occasionally found in the bronchial epithelium of men and women who have never smoked. Presumably they result from somatic mutation or some similar process. In nonsmokers the frequency of such cells does not increase with age.

Large numbers of cells with atypical nuclei of this kind were found in slides from cigarette smokers, and the number increased greatly with the amount of smoking. In heavy cigarette smokers we found many lesions composed entirely of cells with atypical nuclei and lacking cilia. Fewer such lesions were found in light cigarette smokers and none were found in nonsmokers. Among heavy cigarette smokers the number of cells with atypical nuclei increased markedly with advancing age.

In our latest study of bronchial epithelium we matched 72 ex-cigarette smokers, 72 men who had smoked cigarettes regularly up to the time of their terminal illness and 72 men who had never smoked. None of the men had died of lung cancer. Within each of the 72 triads, the three men were the same age, had similar employment histories and similar residence histories. Somewhat more changes were found in slides from ex-cigarette smokers than in slides from men who had never smoked. The important finding, however, was that the cellular changes, particularly the occurrence of cells with atypical nuclei, were fairly rare in ex-cigarette smokers compared with men who had smoked up to the time of their terminal illness. The study indicated that the number of cells with atypical nuclei declines when a cigarette smoker gives up the habit. This probably occurs slowly over a period of years.

The location of lesions is also significant and correlates with an observation one can make by passing cigarette smoke through glass tubing. Some years ago I found that when smoke was passed through a tube with a Y-shaped bifurcation, more tar precipitated where the tube branched than elsewhere. Acting on this lead, we have studied changes in bronchial epithelium in relation to bifurcations. There are numerous such points in the bronchial tree, because the tubes divide and redivide into smaller and smaller tubes. We found that lesions composed entirely of cells with atypical nuclei occur far more frequently at bifurcations than elsewhere.

In order to determine the significance of these changes we studied the bronchial epithelium of men who had died of bronchogenic carcinoma. Carcinoma is defined as a tumor, composed of cells with atypical nuclei, that originated in the epithelium and has penetrated the basement membrane and "invaded" the underlying tissue. Once such an invasion has occurred, the tumor grows—often to considerable size—and spreads to many parts of the body. In men who had died of lung cancer we found large numbers of cells with atypical nuclei, as well as many lesions composed entirely of such cells, scattered throughout the epithelium of the bronchial tubes of both lungs. In a few instances we found tiny independent carcinomas in which the tumor cells had broken through the basement membrane at just one small spot. These carcinomas looked exactly like many of the other lesions composed entirely of cells with atypical nuclei, except that in the other lesions we did not find any cells that had broken through the basement membrane. We are of the opinion that many, if not all, of the lesions composed entirely of atypical cells represent an early, preinvasive stage of carcinoma. This is a well-known occurrence in the cervix of the uteri of women and is called carcinoma *in situ*.

Judging from experimental evidence as well as from our findings in human beings, we are of the opinion that carcinoma of bronchial epithelium originates with a change in the nuclei of a few cells; that by cell division the number of such cells gradually increases; that finally lesions composed entirely of atypical cells are formed; and that occasionally cells in such a lesion penetrate the basement membrane, producing the disease known as carcinoma. Apparently the process is reversible up to the time the cells with atypical nuclei break through the basement membrane.

Where does the inhalation of tobacco smoke fit into this picture? There appear to be three possibilities:

1. It may be that exposure to tobacco smoke induces changes in the nuclei of

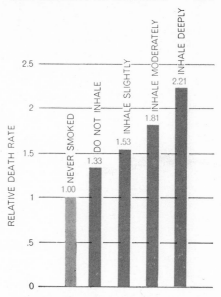

DEGREE OF INHALATION among cigarette smokers is charted against relative death rates from all causes. Rates are based on the author's new study of 1,079,000 men and women, which was begun in 1959.

cells. This would account for the increase of such cells both with the amount of smoking and with the number of years of smoking. It would not, however, in itself account for the finding of a decrease in the number of such cells when a cigarette smoker gives up the habit.

2. It may be that exposure to tobacco smoke simply increases the probability of changes taking place in the nuclei of cells as a result of exposure to inhaled carcinogenic agents other than those in tobacco smoke. The inhibition of ciliary movement by tobacco smoke may be the major factor involved in such a relation. Again this would not in itself account for the decrease in cells with atypical nuclei following cessation of cigarette smoking.

3. It may be that exposure to tobacco smoke produces a change in the local environment of bronchial epithelium so as to favor the survival and reproduction of certain mutant cells that have atypical nuclei of the type observed, as opposed to the survival and reproduction of normal cells. On this hypothesis the development of cancer results from natural selection under conditions of greatly altered environment. It is unnecessary to assume that tobacco smoke causes mutations, since a few cells with atypical nuclei are sometimes found in the bronchial epithelium of nonsmokers. This hypothesis suggests that normal cells are best adapted to an environment free of tobacco smoke, whereas cells with atypical nuclei are best adapted to an environment that includes smoke. The hypothesis thus accounts for the decline in the number of cells with atypical nu-

clei on the cessation of cigarette smoking.

I favor the last of these three hypotheses. It appears to account for all the findings, whereas the other two hypotheses account for only some of them. The three hypotheses are not, however, mutually exclusive.

To account for the association between cigarette smoking and certain other diseases, such as lung infections and coronary artery disease, other plausible mechanisms exist. On inhalation, air and any smoke it may contain passes through bronchial tubes of decreasing diameter, which finally deliver it to the tiny sacs called alveoli. The alveoli have thin walls supported by fibers of connective tissue. These walls contain capillary tubes through which blood flows from the pulmonary arteries to the pulmonary veins. During its passage through these capillaries the blood releases carbon dioxide and absorbs oxygen. At the same time carbon monoxide, nicotine and other impurities that may be present in the air or smoke are absorbed into the blood.

The small bronchial tubes are subject to being plugged with mucus. This frequently occurs in infectious diseases of the lung, with the result that secretions and bacteria are trapped in the alveolar spaces, thereby producing pneumonia. In cigarette smokers the interior diameter of the small bronchial tubes is considerably reduced by hyperplasia, so that the opening is very small indeed. In addition we find that smoking results in increased activity of the glands that secrete mucus into the bronchial tubes. This combination almost certainly increases the likelihood of the tubes being plugged by mucus. In my opinion this is enough to explain the finding that death rates from infectious diseases of the lung are considerably higher among cigarette smokers than among nonsmokers.

The occlusion of a bronchial tube by mucus (or by a spasm) often traps air in the alveoli to which that tube leads. If the person then happens to cough, the pressure of the trapped air can be increased to such a degree that the thin walls of the alveoli rupture. Coughing, excess mucus and reduction in the diameter of the small bronchial tubes increase the likelihood of such rupture.

Recently we have studied the alveoli in relation to cigarette smoking. We found extensive rupturing of the walls of a great many alveoli in the lungs of heavy cigarette smokers, a considerable amount in lighter cigarette smokers and very little in nonsmokers. The rupturing of the walls is usually accompanied by

a fibrous thickening of the remaining alveolar walls, together with a fibrous thickening of the walls of the small blood vessels in the vicinity. This probably results from the mechanism outlined above, since cigarette smoking produces coughing as well as hyperplasia of the bronchial tubes and increased secretion of mucus.

Ruptures in the walls of the alveoli destroy the capillary tubes located in the walls. If many are destroyed, far greater pressure is required to force the same quantity of blood through the remaining capillaries. All the blood must pass through them each time it circulates through the body, and the right ventricle of the heart has to supply the pressure. As a result the work load of the heart is increased in proportion to the degree of destruction of the alveoli.

Since oxygen is supplied to the blood through the capillaries in the alveoli, destruction of this tissue reduces the oxygen supply on which all the tissues of the body depend. In smokers this is compounded by the inhalation of carbon monoxide, which combines with hemoglobin more readily than oxygen does. This combination is enough to account for the shortness of breath often reported by cigarette smokers.

Because of its great activity heart muscle requires an abundant supply of oxygen. The inhalation of tobacco smoke increases the work load of this muscle and at the same time reduces the quantity of oxygen available to the muscle. In addition the action of nicotine on the

**BRONCHIAL EPITHELIUM is the original site of almost all lung cancer, which often develops as shown on the opposite page. The photomicrographs (1 through 5), made by Oscar Auerbach of the East Orange, N.J., Veterans Administration Hospital, magnify human epithelial tissue 325, 250, 250, 75 and 110 diameters respectively. One of the first effects of smoking on normal epithelium (1) is hyperplasia (2), an increase in the number of basal cells. The cila disappear and the cells become squamous, or flattened (3). When the cells develop atypical nuclei and become disordered (4), the result is called carcinoma in situ. When these cells break through the basement membrane (5), the cancer may spread through lungs and to the rest of the body.**

nervous system produces a temporary increase in the heart rate and a constriction of the peripheral blood vessels, which in turn produces a temporary increase in blood pressure. This also puts an added strain on the heart. Since a normal heart has extraordinary reserve powers, it can probably withstand these effects of smoking. A diseased heart may not be able to do so.

Autopsy studies (including a study of young men killed in the Korean war) have shown that the great majority of American men have at least some degree of atherosclerosis of the coronary arteries that supply blood to the muscle of the heart. Atherosclerosis consists of the progressive development of plaques (composed largely of cholesterol) with-

| COMPLAINT | CIGARETTE SMOKERS (PER CENT) | NONSMOKERS (PER CENT) | RATIO (SMOKERS TO NONSMOKERS) |
|---|---|---|---|
| COUGH | 33.2 | 5.6 | 5.9 |
| LOSS OF APPETITE | 3.3 | 0.9 | 3.7 |
| SHORTNESS OF BREATH | 16.3 | 4.7 | 3.5 |
| CHEST PAINS | 7.0 | 3.7 | 1.9 |
| DIARRHEA | 3.3 | 1.7 | 1.9 |
| EASILY FATIGUED | 26.1 | 14.9 | 1.8 |
| ABDOMINAL PAINS | 6.7 | 3.8 | 1.8 |
| HOARSENESS | 4.8 | 2.6 | 1.8 |
| LOSS OF WEIGHT | 7.3 | 4.5 | 1.6 |
| STOMACH PAINS | 6.0 | 3.8 | 1.6 |
| INSOMNIA | 10.2 | 6.8 | 1.5 |
| DIFFICULTY IN SWALLOWING | 1.4 | 1.0 | 1.4 |

**PHYSICAL COMPLAINTS are more frequent among people who smoke a pack of cigarettes or more a day than among nonsmokers. The figures are from the author's large new study.**

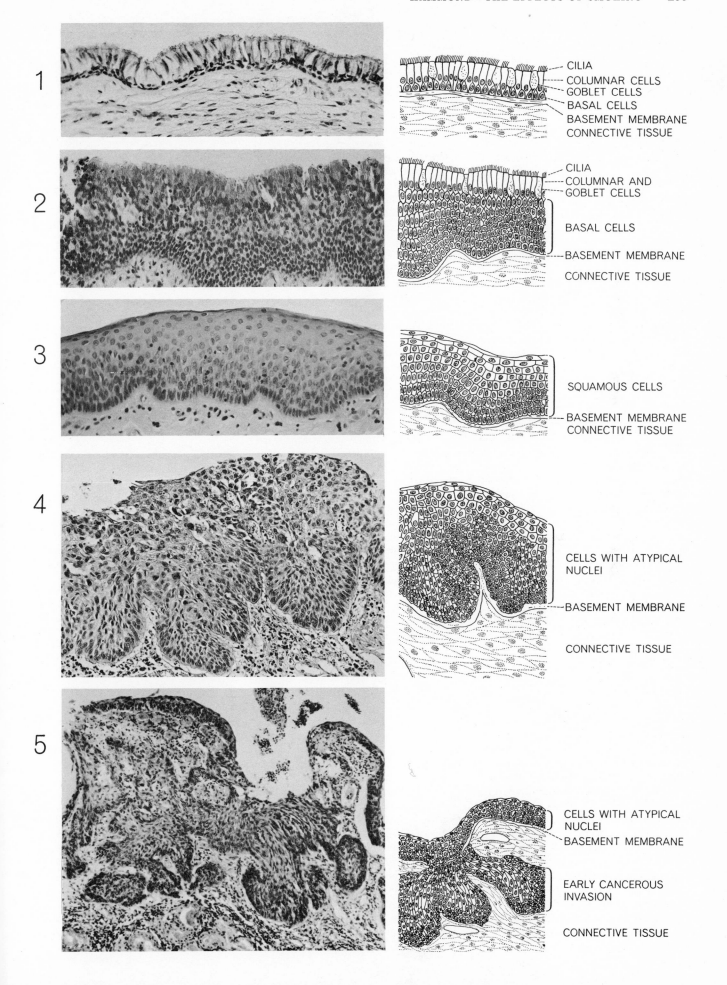

1

CILIA
COLUMNAR CELLS
GOBLET CELLS
BASAL CELLS
BASEMENT MEMBRANE
CONNECTIVE TISSUE

2

CILIA
COLUMNAR AND
GOBLET CELLS

BASAL CELLS

BASEMENT MEMBRANE

CONNECTIVE TISSUE

3

SQUAMOUS CELLS

BASEMENT MEMBRANE
CONNECTIVE TISSUE

4

CELLS WITH ATYPICAL
NUCLEI

BASEMENT MEMBRANE

CONNECTIVE TISSUE

5

CELLS WITH ATYPICAL
NUCLEI
BASEMENT MEMBRANE

EARLY CANCEROUS
INVASION

CONNECTIVE TISSUE

in the walls of these relatively small blood vessels, which thereby reduces their interior diameter. This in turn reduces the supply of blood to the heart muscle. Eventually it may completely cut off the supply of blood to a portion of the heart muscle, and this portion dies. Moreover, blood clots often form in diseased coronary arteries. This can also shut off the blood and cause the death of heart tissues. The common symptom of a stoppage in coronary blood flow is a heart attack.

As described above, cigarette smoking decreases the quantity of oxygen per unit volume of blood. Atherosclerosis of the coronary arteries tends to reduce the volume of blood delivered to the heart muscle per minute. Therefore if a person with atherosclerosis of the coronary arteries is also a cigarette smoker, his heart muscle receives far less than the normal supply of oxygen per minute. At the same time, because of the effects of smoking, a heavy work load is placed on his heart muscle. In my opinion this combination of conditions is sufficient to account for the finding that the death rate from coronary artery disease is higher in cigarette smokers than it is in men who never smoked, that the rate increases with the amount of cigarette smoking, and that it is lower in ex-cigarette smokers than it is in men who continue to smoke cigarettes.

Not only the heart but also all other organs of the body require oxygen obtained through the alveoli of the lungs and distributed by the blood. Thus a reduction in oxygen supply resulting from smoking may have a serious effect on any diseased organ, and in some instances it can make the difference between life and death. Perhaps this accounts for the finding that death rates from a multiplicity of chronic diseases are slightly higher among cigarette smokers than among nonsmokers.

I shall touch only briefly on two other diseases that appear to be significantly associated with cigarette smoking: gastric and duodenal ulcers and cancer of the bladder. In our first study cigarette smokers, compared with nonsmokers, had four times the relative death rate from the two kinds of ulcer and twice the death rate from cancer of the bladder. Doll and his associates in England recently performed a controlled clinical experiment demonstrating that smoking is indeed harmful to patients with gastric ulcer. Eighty patients who were regular smokers were divided at random into two groups, one allowed to continue smoking, the other advised to stop. Among the 40 patients who con-

tinued to smoke, the ulcers healed at a significantly slower rate than they did among the 40 patients who cut down on their smoking or stopped altogether. The mechanism by which smoking evidently retards recovery is unknown. It may be due to indirect effects, such as the effect of nicotine in the bloodstream, or to direct action of ingested tobacco smoke on the lining of the stomach.

As for cancer of the bladder, it is well known that exposure to carcinogenic agents can produce cancer in parts of the body remote from the tissue to which the agent is applied. For example, prolonged exposure to beta-naphthylamine often produced cancer of the bladder in workers in aniline dye plants. Conceivably some agent in tobacco smoke works in the same way, but until the problem is thoroughly investigated judgment should be deferred.

After reviewing the evidence, the mildest statement I can make is that, in my opinion, the inhalation of tobacco smoke produces a number of very harmful effects and shortens the life span of human beings. The simplest way to avoid these possible consequences is not to smoke at all. But one can avoid the most serious of them by smoking cigars or a pipe instead of cigarettes, provided that one does not inhale the smoke. An individual who chooses to smoke cigarettes can minimize the risks by restricting his consumption and by not inhaling.

The individual solution to the problem apparently requires more will power than many cigarette smokers have or are inclined to exert. I am confident, however, that more generally acceptable solutions can be found. There is good reason to suppose that the composition of tobacco smoke, both qualitative and quantitative, is a matter of considerable importance. Until several years ago the mainstream smoke of most U.S. cigarettes contained about 35 milligrams of "tar" per cigarette, of which about 2.5 milligrams was nicotine. The smoke from filter-tip cigarettes now on the market ranges in tar content from as low as 5.7 milligrams per cigarette to nearly 30 milligrams and the nicotine content from .4 to 2.5 milligrams. It is apparent that by selection of tobacco and by means of an effective filter, the nicotine and tar content of cigarette smoke can be markedly reduced. Some filters are selective in their action. For example, Wynder and Dietrich Hoffmann have recently found that a certain type of filter, which passes a reasonable amount of smoke, removes almost all the phenols. This may be important, since the same in-

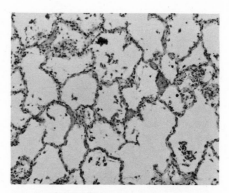

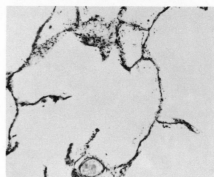

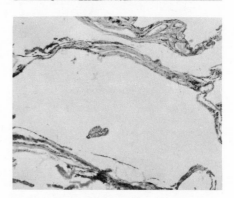

RUPTURE OF ALVEOLAR WALLS is a progressive process, from the normal state (*top*) to the rupture of some walls (*middle*) to the disappearance in certain areas of all the alveolar tissue (*bottom*). These photomicrographs, made by Auerbach, magnify the tissue approximately 120 diameters.

vestigators have reported that the phenols in cigarette smoke strongly inhibit the action of cilia in the bronchial tubes, and that some phenols increase the action of known carcinogenic agents. Furthermore, by various processes it is possible to alter the chemical composition of the smoke before it reaches the filter.

Considering this, I believe that extensive research should be undertaken to determine the effects of various constituents of cigarette smoke and to find means of removing those that are most harmful. Until this has been accomplished it seems advisable to reduce the total tar and nicotine content of cigarette smoke by the means now available.

# 36 The Thalidomide Syndrome

HELEN B. TAUSSIG · August 1962

Two grossly deformed infants were the subject of an exhibit at the annual meeting of the pediatricians of the Federal Republic of Germany held in October, 1960, in the city of Kassel. Photographs and X-ray pictures showed that the long bones of the infants' arms had almost completely failed to grow; their arms were so short that their hands extended almost directly from their shoulders. Their legs were less affected but showed signs of a similar distortion of growth. Both infants were also marked by a large hemangioma (strawberry mark) extending from the forehead down the nose and across the upper lip; one of them was also found to have a duodenal stenosis, that is, a constriction of the beginning of the small intestine. The physicians who presented these cases, W. Kosenow and R. A. Pfeiffer, members of the staff of the Institute of Human Genetics in Münster, had never seen quite this combination of anomalies in a single infant. They regarded it as a new clinical entity.

The deformity of the limbs was characteristic of a malformation known as phocomelia, from the Greek words *phoke,* meaning seal, and *melos,* meaning limb. Phocomelia is so rare that most physicians never see it in a lifetime; moreover, it usually affects only one limb. Kosenow and Pfeiffer reported that they could find no hereditary indication for the condition in the history of either family, no incompatibility in the blood types of the parents and no

abnormality in the chromosomes of the tissue cells of either child. Guido Fanconi, a Swiss pediatrician who has long been interested in congenital deformities, declared that he too had never seen infants afflicted this way. Otherwise little note was taken of the exhibit. I missed it myself, although I was at the meeting.

In retrospect it is surprising that the exhibit did not attract a great deal of attention. During 1960 almost every pediatric clinic in West Germany had seen infants suffering such defects. In Münster there had been 27, in Hamburg 30 and in Bonn 19. There had been perhaps a dozen cases of phocomelia in 1959, whereas in the preceding decade there had been perhaps 15 in all of West Germany. During 1961 the incidence of phocomelia increased rapidly; hundreds of afflicted infants were born.

When the West German pediatricians gathered for their 1961 meeting in November at Düsseldorf, almost all of them were aware of the mysterious outbreak of phocomelia. At the meeting Widukind Lenz of Hamburg made the disclosure that he had tentatively traced the disease to a new drug that had come into wide use in sedatives and sleeping tablets. The generic name of the drug was thalidomide. Under the trade name Contergan, it had been marketed as freely as aspirin in West Germany from 1959 into the spring of 1961. Lenz had found that many mothers of "seal limb" infants admitted to the Hamburg clinic had taken this drug early in pregnancy. Contergan

and other preparations containing thalidomide have now been withdrawn from sale. But infants injured by the drug are still in gestation. When the last of them has been born by the end of this summer or early in the autumn, thalidomide will have produced deformities in 4,000 or even as many as 6,000 infants in West Germany alone, and probably more than 1,000 in other countries where it has been marketed. The one-third who are so deformed that they die may be the luckier ones.

It happens that thalidomide-containing drugs did not reach the market in the U.S. This was because of a lucky combination of circumstances and the alertness of a staff physician at the Food and Drug Administration—not because of the existence of any legal requirement that the drug might have failed to meet. If thalidomide had been developed in this country, I am convinced that it would easily have found wide distribution before its terrible power to cause deformity had become apparent. The marketing techniques of the pharmaceutical industry, which can saturate the country with a new drug almost as soon as it leaves the laboratory, would have enabled thalidomide to produce thousands of deformed infants in the U.S. I believe that it is essential to improve both the techniques for testing and the legal controls over the release of new drugs.

The news that a large number of malformed infants had been born in West

Germany and that a sleeping tablet was suspected as the cause first came to me in late January of this year. I was particularly concerned because of my lifelong interest in malformations. That a drug was implicated was of especial interest, because little is known about the cause of the various congenital anomalies that arise in the course of gestation. I immediately went to West Germany to investigate the situation, and I have also conferred and corresponded with physicians in other countries where thalidomide, under various names, has been sold.

In West Germany I was told that a Swiss pharmaceutical house, interested in producing a new sedative, had first synthesized thalidomide in 1954. Because it showed no effects on laboratory animals the company discarded it. Then the West German firm Chemie Grünenthal undertook the development of the compound. Once again thalidomide showed no effect on laboratory animals. Since the structure of the molecule suggested that it should work as a sedative, Grünenthal tried it as an anticonvulsant for epileptics. It did not prevent convulsions, but it worked as a hypnotic, acting promptly to give a deep, "natural" all-night sleep without a hangover. Given the trade name Contergan, it became during 1960 the favorite sleeping tablet of West Germany, inexpensively available without a prescription and widely used in homes, hospitals and mental institutions. It turned out to be as safe for humans as for animals. Would-be suicides who tried it after it came on the market survived large doses of it without harm.

Grünenthal combined thalidomide with aspirin and other medicines. Germans consumed these compounds—Algosediv, Peracon Expectorans, Grippex and Polygrippan—for such conditions

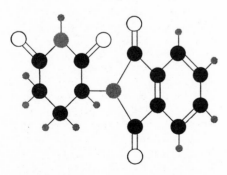

**THALIDOMIDE is a synthetic drug. In this diagram of its molecule, carbon atoms are represented by black balls, hydrogen by small gray balls, oxygen by white balls and the two nitrogen atoms by large gray balls.**

as colds, coughs, grippe, nervousness, neuralgia, migraine and other headaches and asthma. A liquid form made especially for children became West Germany's baby sitter. Hospitals employed it to quiet children for electroencephalographic studies. As an antiemetic, it helped to combat the nausea of pregnancy, and of course Contergan gave many a pregnant woman a good night's sleep. Grünenthal was manufacturing it almost by the ton.

Soon pharmaceutical companies in other countries began to make or market thalidomide under license from Grünenthal. Distillers (Biochemicals) Ltd. sold it as Distaval in the British Isles, Australia and New Zealand. Combinations received the trade names of Valgis, Tensival (a tranquilizer), Valgraine and Asmaval. An advertisement in Great Britain emphasized the safety of the drug with a picture of a small child taking a bottle from a medicine shelf. From Portugal it went into local and international channels of distribution as Softenon. In Canada Frank W. Horner Ltd. of Montreal marketed it as Talimol and the Canadian branch of the Wm. S. Merrell Company of Cincinnati as Kevadon. In September, 1960, the Merrell Company applied to the Food and Drug Administration for clearance to sell Kevadon in the U.S.

At that time no one had reported any untoward side effects from thalidomide. During the next few months, however, German medical journals carried reports of a new polyneuritis associated with long-term use of the drug. Patients complained of tingling hands, sensory disturbances and, later, motor disturbances and atrophy of the thumb. By April, 1961, there was a sufficient number of ill effects reported in West Germany following the use of the drug to place the thalidomide compounds on the list of drugs for which prescriptions were required. (It was under prescription from the beginning in most other countries.) Nevertheless, thalidomide remained popular and continued in widespread use in the home and in hospitals.

By the summer of 1961 physicians all over West Germany were realizing with alarm that an increasing number of babies were being born with disastrous deformities of their arms and legs. In Kiel, Münster, Bonn and Hamburg four different investigations were under way. From a study of 32 cases in Kiel and its environs H. R. Wiedemann found that the malformations followed a specific pattern, although they varied in severity.

Abnormality of the long bones of the arms characterizes the great majority of the cases, with the legs involved in half of these. The radius or ulna (the forearm bones) or both may be absent or defective. In extreme cases the humerus (upper-arm bone) also fails to appear. Typically both arms are affected, although not necessarily equally. When the legs are involved, the hip girdle is not fully developed. Dislocation of the hip and outward rotation of the stub of the femur turns the deformed feet outward. The worst cases have neither arms nor legs; since they cannot turn over in the crib or exercise they usually succumb to pneumonia.

The hemangioma of the face, as Pfeiffer and Kosenow pointed out, is possibly the most characteristic feature of the syndrome. It is, however, neither harmful nor permanent. A saddle-shaped or flattened nose is common. In some cases the external ear is missing and the internal auditory canal is situated abnormally low in the head. In spite of this deformity hearing tends to be fairly good if not normal. Many of the children display paralysis of one side of the face. Many suffered from a variety of malformations of their internal organs, involving the alimentary tract and also the heart and circulatory system. Most of the children seem to be normally intelligent.

Pfeiffer and Kosenow in Münster had found no evidence that the phocomelia in their first two cases was hereditary. Eventually they completed detailed studies of 34 cases, with the same result. This was surprising because many of the previous cases of phocomelia could be traced back in the family. These two investigators concluded that an unknown agent from the environment, affecting the embryo at some time between the third and sixth week of pregnancy, had caused the damage. During this period, when most women do not yet know they are pregnant, the embryo goes through the principal stages of development.

Was the unknown agent a virus? An infection by rubella, or German measles, during this critical period of gestation results in severe malformations but not in phocomelia. That it might be some other virus seemed to be ruled out by the fact that the increase in the incidence of phocomelia had been steady, not abrupt, and by the fact that the cases were confined within the boundaries of West Germany. By the time of last year's pediatric meeting at Düsseldorf in late

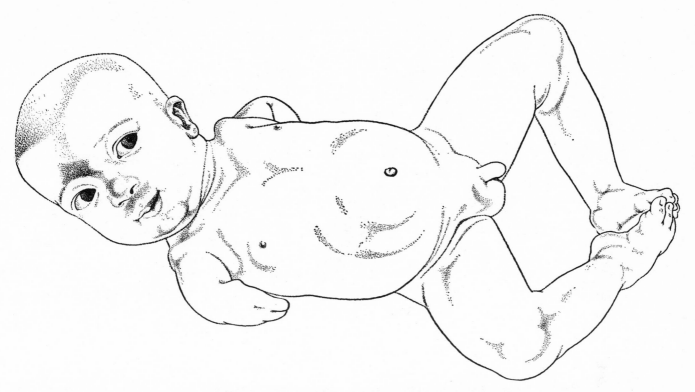

**VICTIM OF THALIDOMIDE SYNDROME** typically has short, deformed and useless arms and hands. The actual case shown in this drawing displays the hemangioma, or strawberry mark, on the forehead, nose and upper lip, which is the most characteristic (although harmless) feature of syndrome. Other abnormalities that may occur include deformed legs and feet and a wide variety of deformations of the ears, digestive tract, heart and large blood vessels. Most of the afflicted children have normal intelligence.

November the range of speculation included radioactive fallout.

Lenz meanwhile had formed a new suspicion. Like the other investigators, he had been sending out lengthy questionnaires to the parents of deformed infants and to the physicians who attended them, asking about X-ray exposure, drugs, hormones, detergents, foods and food preservatives, contraceptive measures and tests for pregnancy. In his initial returns he noted that approximately 20 per cent of the mothers reported taking Contergan during pregnancy. On November 8, he recalls, it occurred to him that Contergan might be the cause. He now asked all the parents specifically about Contergan, and 50 per cent reported use of the drug. Many of the mothers said that they had considered the drug too innocuous to mention on the questionnaire.

On November 15 Lenz warned Grünenthal that he suspected Contergan of causing the catastrophic outbreak of phocomelia and he urged the firm to withdraw it from sale. On November 20, at the pediatric meeting, he announced that he suspected a specific but unnamed drug as the cause of the "Wiedemann syndrome" and said that he had warned the manufacturer. That night a physician came up to Lenz and said: "Will you tell me confidentially, is the drug Contergan? I ask because we have such a child and my wife took Contergan." Before the meeting was over the doctors generally knew that Lenz suspected Contergan.

On November 26 Grünenthal withdrew the drug and all compounds containing it from the market. Two days later the West German Ministry of Health issued a firm but cautious statement that Contergan was suspected as the major factor in causing phocomelia. Radio and television stations and the front pages of newspapers promptly carried announcements warning women not to take the drug.

On the other side of the world W. G. McBride, a physician in New South Wales, Australia, saw three newborn babies with severe phocomelia during April, 1961. In October and November he saw three more. From the histories of the mothers he found that all six had taken Distaval in early pregnancy. McBride notified the Australian branch of Distillers Ltd. and it cabled his findings to the London headquarters on November 27. This and the news from Germany caused the firm to withdraw the drug on December 3. Because of the demand by physicians it has been returned to limited sale in England, but in Germany it is now illegal to possess thalidomide.

The news of the Australian experience prompted A. L. Speirs, a physician of Stirlingshire, Scotland, to review 10 cases of phocomelia that he had seen in his practice during the preceding months. By checking prescription records and medicine cabinets in the victims' homes, he obtained positive proof that eight of the mothers had taken Distaval in early pregnancy.

Thus in the last weeks of 1961 circumstantial evidence accumulating in various parts of the world indicated that thalidomide played an important role in the causation of phocomelia. Physicians now began asking women who were still pregnant about their experience with the drug. One obstetrician in Germany asked 65 pregnant women if they had taken Contergan in early pregnancy. Only one said that she had. The physician declared that if she had an abnormal baby, he would believe Lenz. She did!

Among 350 pregnant women in Lübeck, W. von Massenbach found that 13 had taken Contergan, six during the second half of pregnancy and seven in the first four and a half months. Of the seven, two had babies with phocomelia, one had a baby with a closed anus and four had normal infants. By March, 1961, clinical records in Düsseldorf showed that 300 women who had not taken Contergan had given birth to healthy infants, whereas half of those who reported taking Contergan bore deformed infants. At Hamburg, meanwhile, Lenz had set out to investigate the exact connection between phocomelia and the drug and to fix reliably the date or dates of exposure to the drug in each case. He considered the use of Contergan to be proved only by a photostatic copy of a prescription or by a hospital record. This was difficult because the drug had been sold without prescription before April, 1961, and because nurses in German hospitals dispense sleeping tablets as freely as nurses in the U.S. give laxatives. In one case, Lenz told me, the attending physician swore that the mother had not received Contergan, although her baby had been born with phocomelia. The physician insisted that he had prescribed a different sedative. At the pharmacy Lenz found the prescription marked by the druggist: "Drug not in stock. Contergan given instead."

By the middle of March of this year Lenz had assembled histories on 50 cases in which he had established documentary evidence for use of the drug and had determined the date of the last menstrual period before pregnancy. He had proof in each case of the date or dates on which Contergan had been taken. All but five of the women had taken the drug between the 30th and 50th day after the last menstrual period and the five had taken it between the 50th and 60th day. In the 21 instances in which Lenz managed to ascertain the date of conception, the mother had taken Contergan between the 28th and 42nd day after conception. Thus the exact time when thalidomide can damage the embryo varies somewhat, but the period in which the embryo is especially vulnerable to the drug appears to be relatively brief.

In the human embryo the first signs of future limbs can be discerned with a microscope when the embryo is only 10 days old. By 42 days the tiny limbs are visible to the naked eye, although the embryo is only a little more than an inch long. The fact that the arm buds develop slightly earlier than those of the legs may be of significance in accounting for the greater frequency of arm damage. As the malformations indicate, the drug arrests and deranges those processes of development that are in progress when the embryo is exposed to it. Just how thalidomide interferes with growth remains to be determined. Some German doctors still doubt that Contergan is the sole

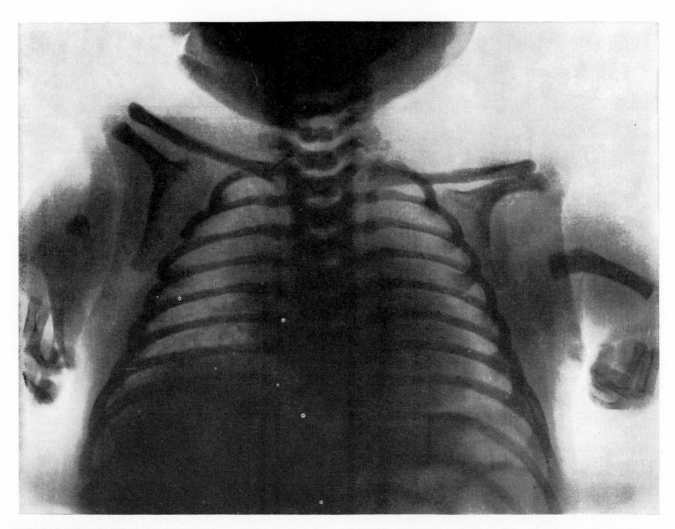

TYPICAL PHOCOMELIA, or "seal limb," is readily apparent in this X ray of chest, shoulders and arms of West German infant. In "classic" phocomelia usually only one arm was affected. Phocomelia caused by thalidomide almost always deforms both arms.

cause of the phocomelia syndrome, and a number of English physicians hold that some other substance or factor also causes phocomelia because they cannot get a history of Distaval or compounds containing it in every case. Furthermore, there is apparently no relation between the amount of the drug ingested and the severity of the malformation. A single dose of 100 milligrams appears to be enough to cause severe phocomelia, yet in other instances the same doses may produce only a mild abnormality. This must be due to a lack of susceptibility or to the fact that the drug was not taken in the sensitive period.

A drug with a molecular structure similar to that of thalidomide is Doriden, also used as a sedative. Although in a few cases of phocomelia the mother says she took Doriden, not Contergan, Doriden has been widely used in Switzerland since 1955, and phocomelia did not appear there until 1961. Almost all the few Swiss cases have been traced to Contergan from Germany.

Little is known about the metabolism of thalidomide, how the body excretes it or how long the deformity-producing factor persists in the body. About all that is certain is that it is insoluble in water and in fat. Obviously the usual laboratory animals metabolize it differently from human beings; it does not induce sleep in the animals. Investigators at the Grünenthal laboratories have tried unsuccessfully to produce phocomelia in rats, mice and rabbits. They have shown that the drug passes through the placenta of rabbits, but the offspring were normal in these experiments. G. F. Somers of the Distillers Ltd. laboratories has fed massive doses to pregnant rabbits. The rabbits did not sleep; they did, however, produce offspring with abnormalities remarkably similar to those in human infants. Since thalidomide makes a horse sleep, it may be that the horse will react in other ways as man does. Experiments with monkeys and apes will also be of interest. When the proper experimental animal is found, thalidomide does offer the possibility of studying the origin of malformations.

It is not yet possible to determine the exact number of infants born with phocomelia in West Germany, but the outbreak was devastating. The records of the Institute of Human Genetics in Münster show three cases of bilateral phocomelia in 1959, 26 cases in 1960 and 96 in 1961. Up to this spring 13 pairs of twins afflicted with phocomelia had been

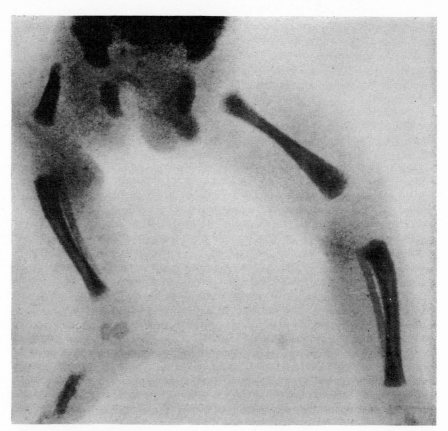

**DEFORMITY OF LEG,** here a very short femur, or thighbone (*left*), characterizes quite a few cases of the thalidomide syndrome. The bones of the hip girdle are also abnormal.

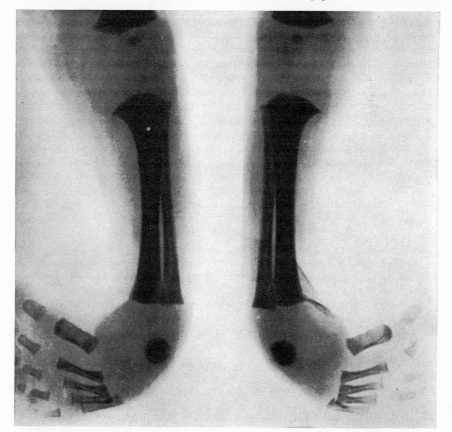

**FEET ROTATE OUTWARD** in this case. Even though badly deformed, this child may be able to learn to walk. Widukind Lenz, Hamburg pediatrician, supplied these three X rays.

registered. Since twins occur once in every 100 births, the institute estimates that there will be 1,300 cases in the state of North Rhine–Westphalia, where it is located. It is an indication of the prevalence of phocomelia that the state's Ministry of Health has set up a registry for all children with defective hands and arms who will need orthopedic help. As of January, 800 had been registered, 80 per cent suffering from phocomelia, and reports were in from only half the state. By now the total may have reached 2,000. Applying this experience to the population of West Germany as a whole, the country anticipates a minimum of 4,000 cases. I should not be surprised by a total of 6,000. There is every reason to believe that two-thirds of the infants will live for many years; indeed, the children appear to have a normal life expectancy.

In England, alas, the incidence is also high. Reports of phocomelia associated with Distaval appear regularly in *The Lancet,* the British weekly medical journal. Clifford G. Parsons of Birmingham has advised me that almost every physician at a medical meeting in England last spring had seen at least one case. The total for the country will probably be in the hundreds, however, not in the thousands.

Reports are still coming in from all over the world showing that phocomelia has occurred wherever thalidomide has

been used. Sweden has had 25 cases, from Contergan purchased in Germany. Switzerland has had four cases. The Portuguese preparation, Softenon, has caused seven cases in Lebanon. Distaval has produced a case in Israel. In Peru, Contergan obtained by the father in Germany caused a case. Lenz has written me of an outbreak of phocomelia in Brazil. As yet I have received no figures for Portugal.

In September, 1960, when the Merrell Company applied to the Food and Drug Administration for permission to distribute the thalidomide compound, none of these untoward developments could have been anticipated. Clearance was delayed because the initial submission of papers was found to be "incomplete." Over the next few months, while the manufacturer gathered and filed additional material in support of the application, the first indications of the drug's neuropathic side effects were reported in the German medical press. Frances Oldham Kelsey, a physician and pharmacologist at the agency, took note of these reports. She also noted that the proposed label for the drug recommended its use against the nausea of pregnancy. From her work with quinine in connection with the malaria project during World War II, Mrs. Kelsey had become "particularly conscious of the fact that the fetus or newborn may be, pharmacologically, an

entirely different organism from the adult." She therefore requested more data from the manufacturer to show that the drug was safe in pregnancy. Before her questions were answered the outbreak of phocomelia in Germany had brought withdrawal of the drug from the market in that country.

If thalidomide had been developed in this country, the story would have been quite different. Almost everyone agrees that with no knowledge of the delayed neuropathic effects of the drug and no appreciation of its dangers in pregnancy, the thought would not have occurred to anyone that it might injure the unborn child. Therefore permission for sale of the drug as a sedative would have been granted; it was an excellent sedative and appeared to be safe.

In the U.S. there have been only a few cases of the syndrome—two of them the twin offspring of a German woman who had married an American and brought Contergan with her to the U.S. Even the families of U.S. personnel stationed abroad have escaped—with one exception. At the U.S. Army headquarters in Heidelberg, in March, Thomas W. Immon was able to assure me that not one of the 16,000 babies born in U.S. hospitals in Germany during 1961 had phocomelia. More recently, however, he has had to report the birth in a U.S.

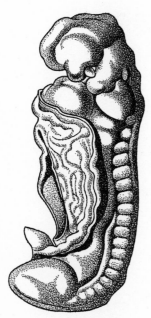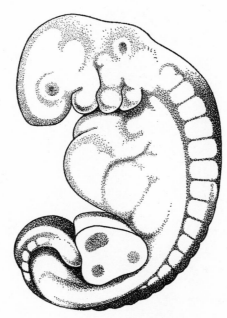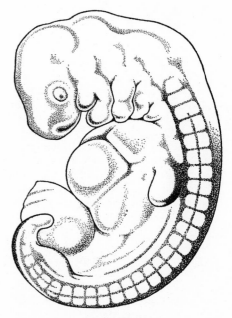

THIRD WEEK        FOURTH WEEK        FIFTH WEEK

**DEVELOPMENT OF HUMAN EMBRYO from third week after conception** (*far left*) **through eighth week** (*far right*) **is crucial.**    The embryo grows from about a quarter of an inch in length at end of third week to one and a quarter inches at end of eighth. Thalid-

Army hospital of one infant with phocomelia. The mother, a German, reported that she had taken Contergan in the early weeks of her pregnancy.

Unfortunately the people of Canada have had a different experience, even though the Dominion Government has a drug-regulating agency like that of the U.S. With two thalidomide preparations on the market in 1961, many pregnant women were exposed to the drug. At least 12 have delivered offspring afflicted with deformed arms and legs. The manufacturers issued a warning to physicians in December, advising them not to prescribe thalidomide for pregnant women. It was not until March, however, that governmental authorities asked the manufacturers to withdraw the drug entirely. Between now and the fall there will undoubtedly be additional casualties.

A generation ago new drugs, particularly those for relatively minor complaints such as insomnia, only gradually achieved widespread popularity. The rather small number of people using them in the first few years provided, albeit unwittingly, test cases not only for the efficacy but also for the long-term safety of the drug. Today "educational" representatives of drug houses visit each physician regularly. Pounds of lavish and expensive drug brochures assault the physician by mail. Most medical journals are crowded with handsome advertisements, many printed in full color on heavy cardboard or metallic paper, extolling the virtues of this year's model or modification of some recently invented tranquilizer, diuretic or antihypertensive compound. New drugs thus find huge markets within a few months.

In most countries, with the exception of Canada, governmental regulation of the pharmaceutical trade is less stringent than it is in the U.S. The Food and Drug Administration, however, is limited to considering only the safety and not the efficacy of a drug, and it exercises no control until the drug is ready for sale. During testing, conducted by and for the drug houses, a new compound may be distributed for clinical trial to many physicians. They are supposed to warn patients that the drug is experimental and to obtain a release signed by the patient. Not all physicians keep careful records of the cases in which they have distributed such test drugs. Clearance by the Food and Drug Administration, which rests on evidence of safety submitted by drug companies, must often be based in part on reports from observations made under clinical conditions that are, to say the least, not ideal. Certainly the procedure needs strengthening here.

Until recently no thought had been given to the need for the testing of drugs for potential harmfulness to the human embryo. In my laboratory at the Johns Hopkins School of Medicine I have not been able to obtain abnormalities in baby rabbits with thalidomide primarily because the massive doses I have used bring on so many abortions. This illustrates one of the problems of testing new drugs: what size dose in animals makes for a fair test? As thalidomide shows, animals may not react at all like humans.

Of course, no drug can ever be certified as completely safe. But all the hazards of a given drug should be established before it is marketed. In dealing with cancer and other serious diseases there is some justification for taking chances with new drugs. The less serious the illness is, the more certain it should be that the drug is harmless as well as effective. In the case of thalidomide, I wonder how long it would have taken to determine the cause of the malformations if the drug had produced some more common but less spectacular congenital defect. Any drug labeled safe should be relatively harmless for all people of all ages, including the unborn. Married women of childbearing age should avoid drugs as much as possible, particularly new ones.

For most people the story of thalidomide has ended. The tragedy will go on, however, for the infant victims of the "harmless" sedative and their families for the rest of their lives.

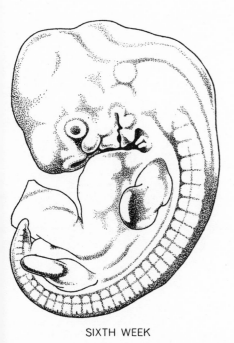

SIXTH WEEK

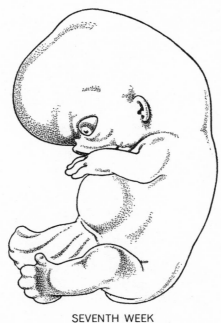

SEVENTH WEEK

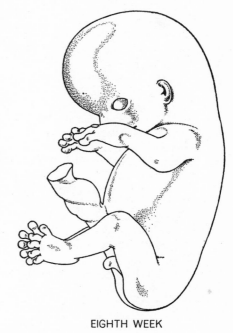

EIGHTH WEEK

omide seems to cause almost all its deformities when the mother takes the drug during the fourth, fifth or sixth week of pregnancy, as limb buds, ears, intestinal tract, heart and blood vessels are forming and going through first growth. These embryos are normal.

# 37 The Fighting Behavior of Animals

IRENÄUS EIBL-EIBESFELDT · December 1961

Fighting between members of the same species is almost universal among vertebrates, from fish to man. Casual observation suggests the reason: Animals of the same kind, occupying the same niche in nature, must compete for the same food, the same nesting sites and the same building materials. Fighting among animals of the same species therefore serves the important function of "spacing out" the individuals or groups in the area they occupy. It thereby secures for each the minimum territory required to support its existence, prevents overcrowding and promotes the distribution of the species. Fighting also arises from competition for mates, and thus serves to select the stronger and fitter individuals for propagation of the species. It is no wonder, then, that herbivores seem to fight each other as readily as do carnivores, and that nearly all groups of vertebrates, except perhaps some amphibians, display aggressive behavior.

A complete investigation of fighting behavior must take account, however, of another general observation: Fights between individuals of the same species almost never end in death and rarely result in serious injury to either combatant. Such fights, in fact, are often highly ritualized and more nearly resemble a tournament than a mortal struggle. If this were not the case—if the loser were killed or seriously injured—fighting would have grave disadvantages for the species. The animal that loses a fight is not necessarily less healthy or less viable; it may simply be an immature animal that cannot withstand the attack of a mature one.

In view of the disadvantages of serious injury to a member of the species, evolution might be expected to have exerted a strong selective pressure against aggressive behavior. But spacing out through combat was apparently too important to permit a weakening of aggressive tendencies; in fact, aggressiveness seems to have been favored by natural selection. It is in order to allow spacing out—rather than death or injury—to result from fighting that the ceremonial combat routines have evolved.

Investigators of aggressive behavior, often strongly motivated by concern about aggressive impulses in man, have usually been satisfied to find its origin in the life experience of the individual animal or of the social group. Aggressiveness is said to be learned and so to be preventable by teaching or conditioning. A growing body of evidence from observations in the field and experiments in the laboratory, however, points to the conclusion that this vital mode of behavior is not learned by the individual but is innate in the species, like the organs specially evolved for such combat in many animals. The ceremonial fighting routines that have developed in the course of evolution are highly characteristic for each species; they are faithfully followed in fights between members of the species and are almost never violated.

All-out fights between animals of the same species do occur, but usually in species having no weapons that can inflict mortal injury. Biting animals that can kill or seriously injure one another are usually also capable of quick flight. They may engage in damaging fights, but these end when the loser makes a fast getaway. They may also "surrender," by assuming a submissive posture that the winner respects. Konrad Z. Lorenz of the Max Planck Institute for the Physiology of Behavior in Germany has described such behavior in wolves and dogs. The fight begins with an exchange of bites; as soon as one contestant begins to lose, however, it exposes its vulnerable throat to its opponent by turning its head away. This act of submission immediately inhibits further attack by its rival. A young dog often submits by throwing itself on its back, exposing its belly: a pet dog may assume this posture if its master so much as raises his voice. Analogous behavior is common in birds: a young rail attacked by an adult turns the back of its head—the most sensitive part of its body—toward the aggressor, which immediately stops pecking. Lorenz has pointed out that acts of submission play a similar role in fights between men. When a victim throws himself defenseless at his enemy's feet, the normal human being is strongly inhibited from further aggression. This mechanism may now have lost its adaptive value in human affairs, because modern weapons can kill so quickly and from such long distances that the attacked individual has little opportunity to appeal to his opponent's feelings.

Most animals depend neither on flight nor on surrender to avoid damaging fights. Instead they engage in a ceremonial struggle, in the course of which the contestants measure their strength in bodily contact without harming each other seriously. Often these contests begin with a duel of threats—posturings,

CICHLID FISH (*Aequidens portalegrensis*) perform a ritual fight that begins with a threat and proceeds to bodily contact without damage to either. After a formal display (*a*) the fish fan their tails to propel currents of water at each other (*b*). Then the rivals grasp each other with their thick-lipped mouths and push and pull (*c*) until one gives up and swims away (*d*).

MALE MARINE IGUANA (*Amblyrhynchus cristatus*) of the Galápagos Islands defends his territory against intruding males. As the rival approaches (*a*), the territory owner struts and nods his head. Then the defender lunges at the intruder and they clash head on (*b*), each seeking to push the other back. When one iguana (*left at "c"*) realizes he cannot win, he drops to his belly in submission.

movements and noises—designed to cow the opponent without any physical contact at all. Sometimes this competition in bravado brings about a decision; usually it is preliminary to the remainder of the tournament.

On the lava cliffs of the Galápagos Islands a few years ago I observed such contests between marine iguanas (*Amblyrhynchus cristatus*), large algae-eating lizards that swarm by the hundreds over the rocks close to shore. During the breeding season each male establishes a small territory by defending a few square yards of rock on which he lives with several females. If another male approaches the territorial border, the local iguana responds with a "display." He opens his mouth and nods his head, presents his flank to his opponent and parades, stiff-legged, back and forth, his apparent size enlarged by the erection of his dorsal crest. If this performance does not drive the rival off, the resident of the territory attacks, rushing at the intruder with his head lowered. The interloper lowers his head in turn and the two clash, the tops of their heads striking together. Each tries to push the other backward. If neither gives way, they pause, back off, nod at each other and try again. (In an apparent adaptation to this mode of combat the head of the marine iguana is covered with horn-like scales.) The struggle ends when one of the iguanas assumes the posture of submission, crouching on its belly. The winner thereupon stops charging and waits in the threatening, stiff-legged stance until the loser retreats [*see illustration on opposite page*]. A damaging fight is triggered only when an invader does not perform the ceremonies that signal a tournament; when, for example, the animal is suddenly placed in occupied territory by a man, or crosses another animal's territory in precipitous flight from an earlier contest. On these occasions the territory owner attacks by biting the intruder in the nape of the neck. Female iguanas, on the other hand, regularly engage in damaging fights for the scarce egg-laying sites, biting and shaking each other vigorously.

The lava lizard (*Tropidurus albemarlensis*) of the larger Galápagos Islands engages in a similar ceremonial fight that begins with the rivals facing each other, nodding their heads. Suddenly one of them rushes forward, stands alongside his opponent and lashes him with his tail once or several times, so hard that the blows can be heard several yards away. The opponent may reply with a

**RATTLESNAKES** (*Crotalus ruber*) perform the combat dance shown in these drawings based on a study by Charles E. Shaw of the San Diego Zoo. The rivals move together (*a*) and then "Indian wrestle" head to head (*b*). Sometimes they face each other, weaving and rubbing their ventral scales (*c*). Finally one lashes out and throws (*d*) and pins (*e*) the other.

tail-beating of his own. Then the attacker turns and retreats to his original position. The entire procedure is repeated until one of the lizards gives up and flees.

According to Gertraud Kitzler of the University of Vienna, fights between lizards of the central European species *Lacerta agilis* may terminate in a curious manner. After an introductory display one lizard grasps the other's neck in his jaws. The attacked lizard waits quietly for the grip to loosen, then takes his turn at biting. The exchange continues until one lizard runs away. Often, however, it is the biter, not the bitten, that does the fleeing. The loser apparently recognizes the superiority of the

winner not only by the strength of the latter's bite but also by his unyielding resistance to being bitten.

Beatrice Oehlert-Lorenz of the Max Planck Institute for the Physiology of Behavior has described a highly ritualized contest between male cichlid fish (*Aequidens portalegrensis*). The rivals first perform a display, presenting themselves head on and side on, with dorsal fins erected. Then they beat at each other with their tails, making gusty currents of water strike the other's side. If this does not bring about a decision, the rivals grasp each other jaw to jaw and pull and push with great force until the loser folds his fins and

swims away [*see illustration on page 309*]. John Burchard of the same institution raised members of another cichlid species (*Cichlasoma biocellatum*) in isolation from the egg stage and found that they fought each other in the manner peculiar to their species.

The ritualization of fighting behavior assumes critical importance in contests between animals that are endowed with deadly weapons. Rattlesnakes, for example, can kill each other with a single bite. When male rattlesnakes fight, however, they never bite. Charles E. Shaw of the San Diego Zoo has described the mode of combat in one species (*Crotalus ruber*) in detail. The two snakes glide along, side by side, each with the forward third of its length raised in the air. In this posture they push head against head, each trying to force the other sideways and to the ground, in accordance with strict rules reminiscent of those that govern "Indian wrestling." The successful snake pins the loser for a moment with the weight of his body and then lets the loser escape [*see illustration on preceding page*]. Many other poisonous snakes fight in a similar fashion.

Among mammals, the fallow deer (*Dama dama*) engages in a particularly impressive ceremonial fight. The rival stags march along side by side, heads raised, watching each other out of the corners of their eyes. Suddenly they halt, turn face to face, lower their heads and charge. Their antlers clash and they wrestle for a while. If this does not lead to a decision, they resume their march. Fighting and marching thus alternate until one wins. What is notable about this struggle is that the stags attack only when they are facing each other. A motion picture made by Horst Siewert of the Research Station for German Wildlife records an occasion on which one deer turned by chance and momentarily exposed his posterior to his opponent. The latter did not take advantage of this opportunity but waited for the other to turn around before he attacked. Because of such careful observance of the rules, accidents are comparatively rare.

Mountain sheep, wild goats and antelopes fight similar duels with their horns and foreheads, the various species using their horns in highly specific ways. From observation of clashes between rapier-horned oryx antelope (*Oryx gazella beisa*) and other African antelope, Fritz Walther of the Opel Open-Air Zoo for Animal Research concludes that the function of the horns is to lock the heads of the animals together as they engage in a pushing match. In one instance a

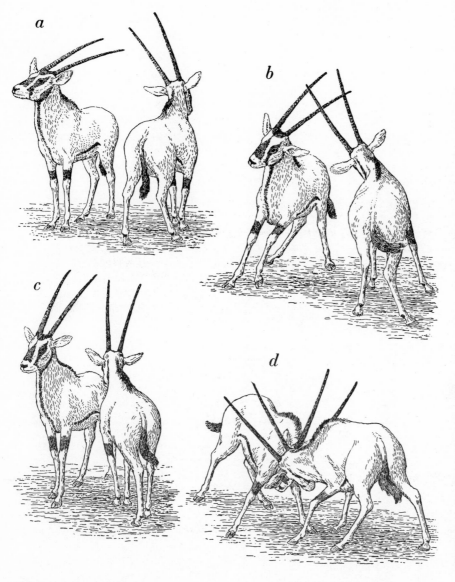

**ORYX ANTELOPE** (*Oryx gazella beisa*) has rapier-shaped horns but does not gore his rival. Two bulls begin combat with a display (*a*), then fence with the upper portion of their horns (*b*). After a pause (*c*) the rivals clash forehead to forehead (*d*) and push each other, using their horns to maintain contact. Drawings are based on observations by Fritz Walther.

duel between two oryx antelope in the wilderness was observed to begin with a display in which the two bulls stood flank to flank, heads held high. Then they came together in a first clash, only the upper third of their horns making contact. After a pause the animals charged again, this time forehead to forehead. They maintained contact by touching and beating their horns together [*see illustration on facing page*]. Oryx antelope never use their horns as daggers in intraspecies fights. One hornless bull observed by Walther carried out the full ritual of combat as if he still had horns. He struck at his opponents' horns and missed by the precise distance at which his nonexistent horns would have made contact. Equally remarkable, his opponents acted as though his horns were in place and responded to his im-

NORWAY RATS (*Rattus norvegicus*) fight in a species-specific manner whether they are raised in isolation or with a group of other rats. The aggressor approaches, displaying his flank and arching his back (*a*). Then, standing on their hind legs, the two rats wrestle. They push with their forelegs (*b*) and sometimes kick with their hind legs (*c*). If one rat is forced to his back as they tussle (*d*), he sometimes gives up; otherwise the tournament phase ends and the real fight begins with a serious exchange of bites (*e*).

aginary blows.

Until field observations of this kind had accumulated in support of the innateness of fighting behavior, laboratory experiments had made a strong case for the notion that such behavior is learned. Experiments by J. P. Scott of the Roscoe B. Jackson Memorial Laboratory in Bar Harbor, Me., had indicated, for example, that a rat or a mouse reacts aggressively toward another rat or mouse primarily because of pain inflicted by a nestmate early in life. Scott suggests that aggressiveness should therefore be controllable by a change in environment; in other words, rats that have had no early experience of pain inflicted by another rat should be completely unaggressive.

To test this conclusion I raised male Norway rats in isolation from their 17th day of life, an age at which they do not show any aggressive behavior. When each was between five and six months old, I put another male rat in the cage with him. At first the hitherto isolated rat approached the stranger, sniffed at him and sometimes made social overtures. But this never lasted long. The completely inexperienced rat soon performed the species-specific combat display—arching his back, gnashing his teeth, presenting his flank and uttering ultrasonic cries. Then the two rats pushed, kicked and wrestled, standing on their hind legs or falling together to the ground. Sometimes the fights ended at this point, the rat that landed on his back giving up and moving away. But usually the rats went on to exchange damaging bites. The patterns of display, tussling and biting were essentially the same in the case of the inexperienced rats as in the case of those who had

been brought up with other rats and were faced by an outsider [see illustration on page 313]. The steps in the ritual are apparently innate and fixed behavior patterns; many of the movements seem to be available to each rat like tools in a toolkit.

Raising rats in groups, where there was an opportunity for young rats to undergo early painful experiences, provided another check on the Scott theory. The members of a group displayed almost no aggressive behavior toward each other. The few fights that took place rarely included biting; for the most part the animals merely pushed each other with their paws. But when a stranger was introduced into the group, he was attacked viciously and was hurt. This agrees with observations of wild Norway rats; they live peacefully together in large packs but attack any rat not a member of their group. Because the attacked animal is able to escape, the species has not developed a tournament substitute for biting. In the laboratory a strange rat introduced into a colony from which it cannot escape is likely to be killed. In sum, the experiments demonstrate that aggressiveness is aroused in adult male rats whenever a stranger enters the territory, even when the defender has had no painful experience with members of its species. Similar experiments on polecats (Putorius putorius) have shown the same results.

The view that aggressiveness is a basic biological phenomenon is supported by physiological studies of the underlying neural and hormonal processes. Some investigators have actually elicited fighting behavior in birds and mammals by stimulating specific areas of the brain

with electrical currents. The mind of a newborn animal is not a blank slate to be written on by experience. Aggressive behavior is an adaptive mechanism by which species members are spaced out and the fittest selected for propagation. Learning is no prerequisite for such behavior, although it probably has an influence on the intensity and detailed expression of aggressiveness.

In the human species, it seems likely, aggressive behavior evolved in the service of the same functions as it did in the case of lower animals. Undoubtedly it was useful and adaptive thousands of years ago, when men lived in small groups. With the growth of supersocieties, however, such behavior has become maladaptive. It will have to be controlled—and the first step in the direction of control is the realization that aggressiveness is deeply rooted in the history of the species and in the physiology and behavioral organization of each individual.

In this connection, it should be emphasized that aggressiveness is not the only motive governing the interaction of members of the same species. In gregarious animals there are equally innate patterns of behavior leading to mutual help and support, and one may assert that altruism is no less deeply rooted than aggressiveness. Man can be as basically good as he can be bad, but he is good primarily toward his family and friends. He has had to learn in the course of history that his family has grown, coming to encompass first his clan, then his tribe and his nation. Perhaps man will eventually be wise enough to learn that his family now includes all mankind.

# 38 National Security and the Nuclear-Test Ban

JEROME B. WIESNER and HERBERT F. YORK · October 1964

The partial nuclear-test ban—the international treaty that prohibits nuclear explosions in the atmosphere, in the oceans and in outer space—has been in effect for a little more than a year. From July, 1945, when the first atomic bomb was set off in New Mexico, until August, 1963, when the U.S. completed its last series of atmospheric bomb tests in the Pacific, the accumulated tonnage of nuclear explosions had been doubling every three years [see top illustration on page 317]. Contamination of the atmosphere by fission products and by the secondary products of irradiation (notably the long-lived carbon 14) was approaching a level (nearly 10 percent of the natural background radiation) that alarmed many biologists. A chart plotting the accumulation of radioactive products can also be read as a chart of the acceleration in the arms race.

Now, for a year, the curve has flattened out. From the objective record it can be said that the improvement of both the physical and the political atmosphere of the world has fulfilled at least the short-range expectations of those who advocated and worked for the test ban. In and of itself the treaty does no more than moderate the continuing arms race. It is nonetheless, as President Kennedy said, "an important first step—a step toward peace, a step toward reason, a step away from war."

The passage of a year also makes it possible to place in perspective and evaluate certain misgivings that have been expressed about the effect on U.S. national security of the suspension of the testing of nuclear weapons in the atmosphere. These misgivings principally involve the technology of nuclear armament. National security, of course, involves moral questions and human values—political, social, economic and psychological questions as well as technological ones. Since no one is an expert in all the disciplines of knowledge concerned, it is necessary to consider one class of such questions at a time, always with the caution that such consideration is incomplete. As scientists who have been engaged for most of our professional lifetimes in consultation on this country's military policy and in the active development of the weapons themselves, we shall devote the present discussion primarily to the technological questions.

The discussion will necessarily rest on unclassified information. It is unfortunate that so many of the facts concerning this most important problem are classified, but that is the situation at this time. Since we have access to classified information, however, we can assure the reader that we would not have to modify any of the arguments we present here if we were able to cite such information. Nor do we know of any military considerations excluded from open discussion by military secrecy that would weaken any of our conclusions. We shall discuss the matter from the point of view of our country's national interest. We believe, however, that a Soviet military technologist, writing from the point of view of the U.S.S.R., could write an almost identical paper.

Today as never before national security involves technical questions. The past two decades have seen a historic revolution in the technology of war. From the blockbuster of World War II to the thermonuclear bomb the violence of military explosives has been scaled upward a million times. The time required for the interhemispheric transport of weapons of mass destruction has shrunk from 20 hours for the 300-mile-per-hour B-29 to the 30-minute flight time of the ballistic missile. Moreover, the installation of the computer in command and control systems has increased their information-processing capacity by as much as six orders of magnitude compared with organizations manned at corresponding points by human nervous systems.

It has been suggested by some that technological surprise presents the primary danger to national security. Yet recognition of the facts of the present state of military technology must lead to the opposite conclusion. Intercontinental delivery time cannot be reduced to secure any significant improvement in the effectiveness of the attack. Improvement by another order of magnitude in the information-processing capacity of the defending system will not make nearly as large a difference in its operational effectiveness.

The point is well illustrated by the 100-megaton nuclear bomb. Whether or not it is necessary, in the interests of national security, to test and deploy a bomb with a yield in the range of 100 megatons was much discussed during the test-ban debates. The bomb was frequently referred to as the "big" bomb, as if the bombs now in the U.S. arsenal were somehow not big. The absurdity of this notion is almost enough by itself to settle the argument. A one-megaton bomb is already about 50 times bigger than the bomb that produced 100,000 casualties at Hiroshima, and 10 megatons is of the same order of magnitude as the grand total of all high explosives used in all wars to date. Other technical considerations that surround this question are nonetheless illuminating and worth exploring.

There is, first of all, the "tactics" of the missile race. The purpose of a missile system is to be able to destroy or, perhaps more accurately, able to threaten to destroy enemy targets. No matter what the statesmen, military men and moralists on each side may think of the national characteristics, capabilities and morality of the other side, no matter what arguments may be made about who is aggressive and who is not or who is rational and who is not, the military planners on each side must reckon with the possibility that the other side will attack first. This means that above all else the planner must assure the survival of a sufficient proportion of his own force, following the heaviest surprise attack the other side might mount, to launch a retaliatory attack. Moreover, if the force is to be effective as a deterrent to a first strike, its capacity to survive and wreak revenge and even win, whatever that may mean, must be apparent to the other side.

Several approaches, in fact, can be taken to assure the survival of a sufficient missile force after a first attack on it. The most practical of these are: (1) "hardening," that is, direct protection against physical damage; (2) concealment, including subterfuge and, as in the case of the Polaris submarine missiles, mobility, and (3) numbers, that is,

presenting more targets than the attacker can possibly cope with. The most straightforward and certain of these is the last: numbers. For the wealthier adversary it is also the easiest, because he can attain absolute superiority in numbers. A large number of weapons is also a good tactic for the poorer adversary, because numbers even in the absence of absolute superiority can hopelessly frustrate efforts to locate all targets.

There is an unavoidable trade-off, however, between the number and the size of weapons. The cost of a missile depends on many factors, one of the most important being gross size or weight. Unless one stretches "the state of the art" too far in the direction of sophistication and miniaturization, the cost of a missile turns out to be roughly proportional to its weight, if otherwise identical design criteria are used. The protective structures needed for hardening or the capacity of submarines needed to carry the missile also have a cost roughly proportional to the volume of the missile. Some of the ancillary equipment has a cost proportional to the size of the missile and some does not; some operational expenditures vary directly with size or weight and some do not. The cost of the warhead generally does not, although the more powerful warhead requires the larger missile. It is not possible to put all these factors together in precise bookkeeping form, but it is correct to say that the cost of a missile, complete and ready for firing, increases somewhat more slowly than linearly with its size.

On the other hand—considering "hard" targets only—the effectiveness of a missile increases more slowly than cost as the size of the missile goes up. The reason is that the radius of blast damage, which is the primary effect employed against a hard target, increases only as the cube root of the yield and because yield has a more or less direct relation to weight. Against "soft" targets, meaning population centers and conventional military bases, even "small" bombs are completely effective, and nothing is gained by increasing yield. Given finite resources, even in the wealthiest economy, it would seem prudent to accept smaller size in order to get larger numbers. On any scale of investment, in fact, the combination of larger numbers and smaller size results in greater effectiveness for the missile system as a whole, as contrasted to the effectiveness of a single missile.

This line of reasoning has, for some years, formed the basis of U.S. mis-

sile policy. The administration of President Eisenhower, when faced with the choice of bigger missiles (the liquid-fueled Atlas and Titan rockets) as against smaller missiles (the solid-fueled Minuteman and Polaris rockets), decided to produce many more of the smaller missiles. The administration of President Kennedy independently confirmed this decision and increased the ratio of smaller to larger missiles in the nation's armament. During the test-ban hearings it was revealed that the U.S. nuclear armament included bombs of 23-megaton yield and higher, carried by bombers. Recently Cyrus R. Vance, Under Secretary of Defense, indicated that the Air Force has been retiring these large bombs in favor of smaller ones. There are presumably no targets that call for the use of such enormous explosions.

The argument that says it is now critical for U.S. national security to build very big bombs and missiles fails completely when it is examined in terms of the strictly technical factors that determine the effectiveness of a missile attack. In addition to explosive yield the principal factors are the number of missiles, the overall reliability of each missile and the accuracy with which it can be delivered to its target. The effectiveness of the attack—the likelihood that a given target will be destroyed—can be described by a number called the "kill probability" ($P_k$). This number depends on the number of missiles ($N$) launched at the target, the reliability ($r$) of each missile and the ratio of the radius of damage ($R_k$) effected by each missile to the accuracy with which the missiles are delivered to the target (CEP). The term "CEP," which stands for "circular error probable," implies that the distribution of a large number of hits around a given target will follow a standard error curve; actually, for a variety of reasons (which include the presence of systematic errors, coupling between certain causes of error and the sporadic nature of the larger error factors) the distribution does not really follow a standard error curve. The term "CEP" is still useful, however, and can be defined simply as the circle within which half of a large number of identical missiles would fall.

Now, in the case of a soft target, $R_k$ is very large for the present range of warhead yields in the U.S. arsenal. The reason is that soft targets are so highly vulnerable to all the "prompt" effects (particularly the incendiary effects) of thermonuclear weapons. The range of these effects, modified by various attenuation factors, increases approximately as the square root or the cube root of the yield at large distances. Under these circumstances, given the accuracy of existing fire-control systems, the ratio $R_k/\text{CEP}$ is large and the likelihood that the target will be destroyed becomes practically independent of this ratio. Instead $P_k$ depends primarily on $r$, the reliability of the missile. If $r$ is near unity, then a single missile ($N = 1$) will do the job; if $r$ is not near unity, then success in the attack calls for an offsetting increase in the number of missiles [$P_k = 1 - (1 - r)^N$]. In either case changes in $R_k$ make little difference. That is to say, a "big" bomb cannot destroy a soft target any more surely than a "small" one can.

When it comes to hard targets, the ratio $R_k/\text{CEP}$ becomes much smaller even for bombs of high yield. The blast effects—including the ground rupture, deformation and shock surrounding the crater of a surface burst—have comparatively small radii at intensities sufficient to overcome hardening. Moreover, as mentioned above, the radii of these effects increase only as the cube root of the yield. This rule of thumb is modified somewhat in both directions by the duration of the blast pulse, local variations in geology and other factors, but it is sustained by a voluminous record from weapons tests. Since the radius of blast damage is of the same order of size as the circular error probable, or smaller, the ratio $R_k/\text{CEP}$ must be reckoned with in an attack on a hard target. Yet even in this situation the cube root of a given increase in yield would contribute much less to success than a comparable investment in numbers, reliability or accuracy.

Yield is of course a product of the yield-to-weight ratio of the nuclear explosive employed in the warhead multiplied by the weight of the warhead. In order to gain significant increases in the first of these two quantities further nuclear tests would be necessary. Increase in the weight of the warhead, on the other hand, calls for bigger and more efficient missiles. In the present state of the art, efforts to improve CEP and reliability as well as weight-carrying capacity hold out more promise than efforts to improve the yield-to-weight ratio. The reason is that missile design and control involve less mature and less fully exploited technologies than the technology of nuclear warheads. Finally, an increase in the number of missiles, although not necessarily cheap, promises more straightforward and assured

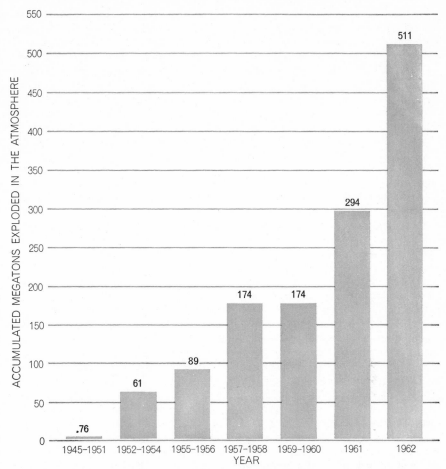

NUCLEAR EXPLOSIONS IN THE ATMOSPHERE from 1945 to 1962, the last full year in which the U.S. and the U.S.S.R. set off such explosions, are presented on the basis of accumulated megatons. The bars of equal height for the periods 1957–1958 and 1959–1960 reflect the informal moratorium on testing. The overall increase in megatons has doubled every three years. The data for this chart are from *Federal Radiation Council Report No. 4.*

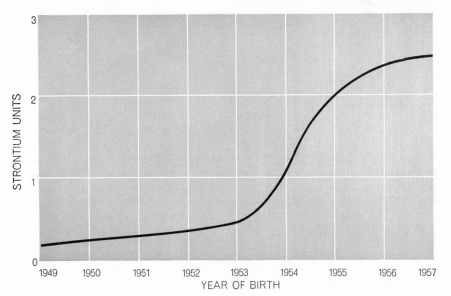

STRONTIUM 90 IN THE TEETH OF INFANTS between 1949 and 1957 was measured in a cooperative project of the Committee for Nuclear Information and the Washington University and St. Louis University schools of dentistry. This curve shows the strontium-90 activity in the deciduous teeth of bottle-fed infants. Because such teeth can be collected only some six years after the birth of the child, the curve does not come up to the present. The sharp rise in strontium-90 activity coincides with the period of extensive nuclear testing beginning in 1953. In the course of the project 110,000 teeth were collected.

results than a fractional increase in yield-to-weight ratio. Of all the various possible technical approaches to improving the military effectiveness of an offensive missile force, therefore, the only one that calls for testing (whether underground or in the atmosphere) is the one that offers the smallest prospect of return.

Suppose, however, a new analysis, based on information not previously considered, should show that it is in fact necessary to incorporate the 100-megaton bomb in the U.S. arsenal. Can this be done without further weapons tests? The answer is yes. Because the U.S.S.R. has pushed development in this yield range and the U.S. has not, the U.S. 100-megaton bomb might not be as elegant as the Soviet model. It would perhaps weigh somewhat more or at the same weight would produce a somewhat lower yield. It could be made, however, and the basic techniques for making it have been known since the late 1950's. The warhead for such a bomb would require a big missile, but not so big as some being developed by the National Aeronautics and Space Administration for the U.S. space-exploration program. Such a weapon would be expensive, particularly on a per-unit basis; under any imaginable circumstances it would be of limited use and not many of its kind would be built.

The extensive series of weapons tests carried out by the U.S.—involving the detonation of several hundred nuclear bombs and devices—have yielded two important bodies of information. They have shown how to bring the country's nuclear striking force to its present state of high effectiveness. And they have demonstrated the effects of nuclear weapons over a wide range of yields. Among the many questions that call for soundly based knowledge of weapons effects perhaps none is more important in a discussion of the technical aspects of national security than: What would be the result of a surprise attack by missiles on the country's own missile forces? Obviously if the huge U.S. investment in its nuclear armament is to succeed in deterring an attacker, that armament must be capable of surviving a first strike.

A reliable knowledge of weapons effects is crucial to the making of rational decisions about the number of missiles needed, the hardening of missile emplacements, the degree of dispersal, the proportion that should be made mobile and so on. The military planner must

bear in mind, however, that such decisions take time—years—to carry out and require large investments of finite physical and human resources. The inertia of the systems is such that the design engineer at work today must be concerned not with the surprise attack that might be launched today but rather with the kind and size of forces that might be launched against them years in the future. In addition to blast, shock and other physical effects, therefore, the planner must contend with a vast range of other considerations. These include the yields of the various bombs the attacker would use against each target; the reliability and accuracy of his missiles; the number and kind of weapons systems he would have available for attack; the tactics of the attacker, meaning the number of missiles he would commit to a first strike, the fractions he would allocate to military as against civilian targets and the relative importance he would assign to various kinds of military targets, the effects of chaos on the defender's capacity to respond, and so on. In all cases the planner must project his thinking forward to some hypothetical future time, making what he can of the available intelligence about the prospective attacker's present capabilities and intentions. Plainly all these "other considerations" involve inherently greater uncertainties than the knowledge of weapons effects.

The extensive classified and unclassified literature accumulated in two decades of weapons tests and available to U.S. military planners contains at least some observations on all important effects for weapons with a large range of yields. These observations are more or less well understood in terms of physical theories; they can be expressed in numerical or algebraic form, and they can be extrapolated into areas not fully explored in the weapons tests conducted by the U.S., for example into the 100-megaton range. As one departs from the precise circumstances of past experiments, of course, extrapolation becomes less and less reliable. Nonetheless, some sort of estimate can be made about what the prompt and direct effects will be under any conceivable set of circumstances.

Consider, in contrast, the degree of uncertainty implicit in predicting the number and kind of weapons systems that might be available to the prospective attacker. Such an uncertainty manifested itself in the famous "missile gap" controversy. The remarkable difference between the dire predictions made in the late 1950's—based as they were on

the best available intelligence—and the actual situation that developed in the early 1960's can be taken as indicating the magnitude of the uncertainties that surround the variables other than weapons effects with which the military planner must contend. Moreover, these factors, as they concern a future attack, are uncertain not only to the defender; they are almost as uncertain to the attacker.

Uncertainties of this order and kind defy reduction to mathematical expression. A human activity as complex as modern war cannot be computed with the precision possible in manipulation of the data that concern weapons effects. What is more, the uncertainties about this single aspect of the total problem are not, as is sometimes assumed, multiplicative in estimation of the overall uncertainty. Most, but not all, of the uncertainties are independent of one another. The total uncertainty is therefore, crudely speaking, the square root of the sum of the squares of the individual uncertainties.

In our view further refinement of the remaining uncertainties in the data concerning prompt direct physical effects can contribute virtually nothing more to management of the real military and political problems, even though it would produce neater graphs. Furthermore, if new effects should be discovered either experimentally or theoretically in the future, or if, in certain peculiar environments, some of the now known effects should be excessively uncertain, it will be almost certainly possible to "overdesign" the protection against them. Thus, although renewed atmospheric testing would contribute some refinement to the data on weapons effects, the information would be, at best, of marginal value.

Such refinements continue to be sought in the underground tests that are countenanced under the partial test ban. From this work may also come some reductions in the cost of weapons, modest improvements in yield-to-weight ratios, devices to fill in the spectrum of tactical nuclear weapons and so on. There is little else to justify the effort and expenditure. The program is said by some to be necessary, for example, to the development of a pure fusion bomb, sometimes referred to as the "neutron bomb." It is fortunate that this theoretically possible (stars are pure fusion systems) device has turned out to be so highly difficult to create; if it were relatively simple, its development might open the way to thermonuclear armament for the smallest and poorest powers in the world. The U.S., with its heavy investment in fission-to-fusion technology, would be the last nation to welcome this development and ought to be the last to encourage it. Underground testing is also justified for its contribution to the potential peaceful uses of nuclear explosives. Promising as these may be, the world could forgo them for a time in exchange for cessation of the arms race. Perhaps the best rationale for the underground-test program is that it helps to keep the scientific laboratories of the military establishment intact and in readiness—in

readiness, however, for a full-scale resumption of the arms race.

Paradoxically one of the potential destabilizing elements in the present nuclear standoff is the possibility that one of the rival powers might develop a successful antimissile defense. Such a system, truly airtight and in the exclusive possession of one of the powers, would effectively nullify the deterrent force of the other, exposing the latter to a first attack against which it could not retaliate. The possibilities in this quarter have often been cited in rationalization of the need for resuming nuclear tests in the atmosphere. Here two

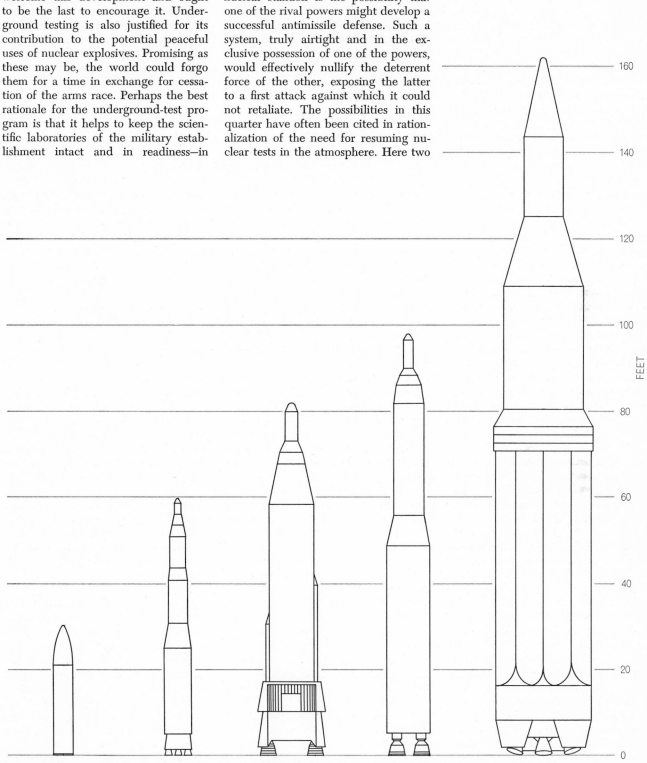

**PAYLOAD OF EXISTING ROCKETS** sets a limit on the size of nuclear weapons that can be used in a rocket attack. The five U.S. rockets shown here are drawn to scale. At left is the Polaris Type A-3, designed for launching from submarines; it weighs 30,000 pounds, has a range of 2,500 nautical miles and can carry a nuclear warhead of about one megaton. Second from left is Minuteman II; it weighs 65,000 pounds, has a range of 6,300 nautical miles and

can carry a warhead of about one megaton. Third is Atlas; it weighs 269,000 pounds, has a range of 9,000 nautical miles and can carry a warhead of about five megatons. Fourth is Titan II; it weighs 303,000 pounds, has a range of 6,300 nautical miles and can carry a warhead of about 20 megatons. To lift a larger warhead would require a rocket such as Saturn I (*right*), which weighs 1,138,000 pounds. Data are from the journal *Missiles and Rockets.*

questions must be examined. One must first ask if it is possible to develop a successful antimissile defense system. It then becomes appropriate to consider whether or not nuclear weapons tests can make a significant contribution to such a development.

Any nation that commits itself to large-scale defense of its civilian population in the thermonuclear age must necessarily reckon with passive modes of defense (shelters) as well as active ones (antimissile missiles). It is in the active mode, however, that the hazard of technological surprise most often lurks. The hazard invites consideration if only for the deeper insight it provides into the contemporary revolution in the technology of war.

The primary strategic result of that revolution has been to overbalance the scales in favor of the attacker rather than the defender. During World War II interception of no more than 10 percent of the attacking force gave victory to the defending force in the Battle of Britain. Attrition of this magnitude was enough to halt the German attack because it meant that a given weapons-delivery system (bomber and crew) could deliver on the average only 10 payloads of high explosive; such a delivery rate was not sufficient to produce backbreaking damage. In warfare by thermonuclear missiles the situation is quantitatively and qualitatively different. It is easily possible for the offense to have in its possession and ready to launch a number of missiles that exceeds the number of important industrial targets to be attacked by, let us say, a factor of 10. Yet the successful delivery of only one warhead against each such target would result in what most people would consider an effective attack. Thus where an attrition rate of only 10 percent formerly crowned the defense with success, a penetration rate of only 10 percent (corresponding to an attrition rate of 90 percent) would give complete success to the offense. The ratio of these two ratios is 100 to one; in this sense the task of defense can be said to have become two orders of magnitude more difficult.

Beyond this summary statement of the situation there are many general reasons for believing that defense against thermonuclear attack is impossible. On the eve of attack the offense can take time to get ready and to "point up" its forces; the defense, meanwhile, must stay on the alert over periods of years, perpetually ready and able to fire within the very few minutes available after the first early warning. The attacker can pick its targets and can choose to concentrate its forces on some and ignore others; the defense must be prepared to defend all possible important targets. The offense may attack the defense itself; then, as soon as one weapon gets through, the rest have a free ride.

The hopelessness of the task of defense is apparent even now in the stalemate of the arms race. A considerable inertia drags against the movement of modern, large-scale, unitary weapons systems from the stage of research and development to operational deployment. The duration and magnitude of these enterprises, whether defensive or offensive, practically assure that no system can reach full deployment under the mantle of secrecy. The designer of the defensive system, however, cannot begin until he has learned something about the properties and capabilities of the offensive system. Inevitably the defense must start the race a lap behind. In recent years, it seems, the offense has even gained somewhat in the speed with which it can put into operation stratagems and devices that nullify the most extraordinary achievements in the technology of defense. These general observations are expensively illustrated in the development and obsolescence of two major U.S. defense systems.

Early in the 1950's the U.S. set out to erect an impenetrable defense against a thermonuclear attack by bombers. The North American continent was to be ringed with a system of detectors that would flash information back through the communications network to a number of computers. The computers were to figure out from this data what was going on and what ought to be done about it and then flash a series of commands to the various interceptor systems. In addition to piloted aircraft, these included the Bomarc (a guided airborne missile) and the Nike-Hercules (a ballistic rocket). By the early 1960's this "Sage" system was to be ready to detect, intercept and destroy the heaviest attack that could be launched against it.

The early 1960's have come and yet nothing like the capability planned in the 1950's has been attained. Why not? Time scales stretched out, subsystems failed to attain their planned capabilities and costs increased. Most important, the offense against which the system was designed is not the offense that actually exists in the early 1960's. Today the offensive system on both sides is a mixture of missiles and bombers.

The Sage system has a relatively small number of soft but vital organs completely vulnerable to missiles—a successful missile attack on them would give a free ride to the bombers. As early as 1958 the Department of Defense came to realize that this would be the situation, and the original grand plan was steadily cut back. In other words, the Sage system that could have been available, say, in 1963 and that should have remained useful at least through the 1960's would in principle have worked quite well against the offense that existed in the 1950's.

To answer the intercontinental ballistic missile, the Department of Defense launched the development of the Nike-Zeus system. Nike-Zeus was intended to provide not a defense of the continent at its perimeter but a point defense of specific targets. To be sure, the "points" were fairly large—the regions of population concentration around 50 to 70 of the country's biggest cities. The system was to detect incoming warheads, feeding the radar returns directly into its computers, and launch and guide an interceptor missile carrying a nuclear warhead into intersection with the trajectory of each of the incoming warheads.

Nike-Zeus was not designed to defend the 1,000 or so smaller centers outside the metropolitan areas simply because there are too many of these to be covered by the resources available for a system so huge and complicated. Nor was the system designed to defend the retaliatory missiles, the security of these forces being entrusted to the more reliable protection of dispersal, concealment, mobility and number. In principle, the defense of a hardened missile silo would have presented by far the simplest case for proof of the effectiveness of Nike-Zeus as advanced by those who contend that such a system can be made to "work." There would be no ambiguity about the location of the target of the incoming warhead. By the same token Nike-Zeus might have been considered for the defense of a few special defense posts, such as the headquarters of the Air Defense Command of the Strategic Air Command. These special cases are so few in number, however, that it had to be concluded that the attacker would either blast his way through to them by a concentration of firepower or ignore them altogether.

At the time of the conception of the Nike-Zeus system its designers were confronted with a comparatively simple problem, namely that of shooting down

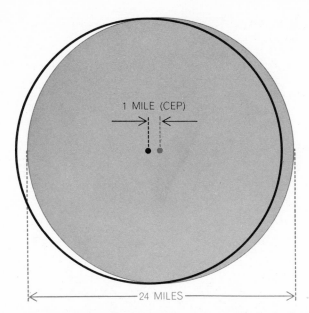

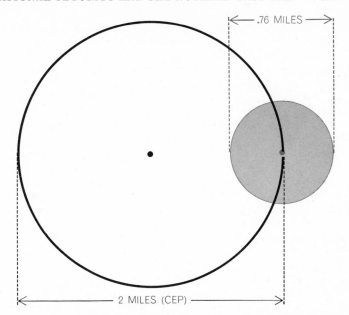

ACCURACY OF MISSILES has far more relevance for hard targets than for soft. It has been estimated that at maximum range both U.S. and Soviet rockets have a "circular error probable" of about a mile, that is, there is a probability of 50 percent that a rocket will hit within a mile of the target. The radius of fire damage for a one-megaton bomb will not be greatly affected by a near miss (*cir-* *cles at left*). The radius of kill for a one-megaton bomb aimed at a target hardened to 300 pounds per square inch, however, is so much smaller than the circular error probable (*circles at right*) that a number of weapons would have to be used to assure a hit. The illustrations in this article and the figures on which they are based are not the responsibility of the authors but of the editors.

the warheads one by one as they presented themselves to the detectors. Even this simple problem had to be regarded as essentially unsolvable, in view of the fact that a 90 per-cent success in interception constitutes failure in the inverted terms of thermonuclear warfare. At first, therefore, the designers of the offensive system did not take the prospect of an antimissile system seriously. Then the possibility that the problem of missile interception might be solved in principle gave them pause. Thereupon the designers of the offense began to invent a family of "penetration aids," that is, decoys and confusion techniques. The details of these and the plans for their use are classified, but the underlying principles are obvious. They include light decoys that can be provided in large numbers but that soon betray their character as "atmospheric sorting" separates them from the heavier decoys (and actual warheads) that can be provided in smaller numbers to confuse the defending detectors down to the last minute. Single rockets can also eject multiple warheads. Both the decoys and the warheads can be made to present ambiguous cross sections to the radar systems. These devices and stratagems overwhelmed the designed capability of the Nike-Zeus system and compelled its recent abandonment.

If the installation of the system had proceeded according to plan, the first Nike-Zeus units would have been operational within the next year or two. This could have been celebrated as a technical milestone. As a means of defense of a substantial percentage of the population, however, the system would not have reached full operational deployment until the end of the decade. In view of its huge cost the system should then have looked forward to a decade of useful life until, say, the late 1970's. Thus, in inexorable accordance with the phase-lag of the defense, the U.S. population was to be defended a decade too late by a system that might have been effective in principle (although most probably not in practice) against the missiles of the early 1960's.

The race of the tortoise and the hare has now entered the next lap with the development of the Nike-X system as successor to Nike-Zeus. The Advanced Research Projects Agency of the Department of Defense has been spending something on the order of $200 million a year on its so-called Defender Program, exploring on the broadest front the principles and techniques that might prove useful in the attempt to solve the antimissile problem. Although nothing on the horizon suggests that there is a solution, this kind of work must go forward. It not only serves the forlorn hope of developing an active antimissile defense but also promotes the continued development of offensive weapons. The practical fact is that work on defensive systems turns out to be the best way to promote invention of the penetration aids that nullify them.

As the foregoing discussion makes clear, the problems of antimissile development are problems in radar, computer technology, missile propulsion, guidance and control. The nuclear warheads for the antimissile missile have been ready for a long time for delivery to the right place at the right time. Although it is argued that certain refinements in the existing data about weapons effects are needed, the other uncertainties all loom much larger than the marginal uncertainties in these physical effects. The antimissile defense problem, then, is one in which nuclear testing can play no really significant part.

The pursuit of an active defense system demands parallel effort on the passive defense, or shelter, front because the nature of the defense system strongly conditions the tactics of the offense that is likely to be mounted against it. To take a perhaps farfetched example, a Nike-Zeus system that provided protection for the major population centers might invite the attacker to concentrate the weight of his assault in ground bursts on remote military installations and unprotected areas adjacent to cities, relying on massive fallout to imperil the population centers. This example serves also to suggest how heavily the effectiveness of any program for sheltering the civilian population depends on the tactics of the attacker. Fallout shelters by themselves are of no avail if the attacker chooses to assault the population centers directly.

In any speculation about the kind of attack to which this country might be exposed it is useful to note where the military targets are located. Most of the missile bases are, in fact, far from the largest cities. Other key military installations, however, are not so located. Boston, New York, Philadelphia, Seattle, San Francisco, Los Angeles (Long Beach) and San Diego all have important naval bases. Essential command and control centers are located in and near Denver, Omaha and Washington, D.C. The roll call could be extended to include other major cities containing military installations that would almost certainly have to be attacked in any major assault on this country. The list does not stop with these; it is only prudent to suppose still other cities would come under attack, because there is no way to know in advance what the strategy may be.

The only kind of shelter that is being seriously considered these days, for other than certain key military installations, is the fallout shelter. By definition fallout shelters offer protection against nothing but fallout and provide virtually no protection against blast, fire storms and other direct effects. Some people have tried to calculate the percentage of the population that would be saved by fallout shelters in the event of massive attack. Such calculations always involve predictions about the form of the attack, but since the form is unknowable the calculations are nonsensical. Even for the people protected by fallout shelters the big problem is not a problem in the physical theory of gamma-ray attenuation, which can be neatly computed, but rather the sociological problem of the sudden initiation of general chaos, which is not subject to numerical analysis.

Suppose, in spite of all this, the country were to take fallout shelters seriously and build them in every city and town. The people living in metropolitan areas that qualify as targets because they contain essential military installations and the people living in metropolitan areas that might be targeted as a matter of deliberate policy would soon recognize that fallout shelters are inadequate. That conclusion would be reinforced by the inevitable reaction from the other side, whose military planners would be compelled to consider a massive civilian-shelter program as portending a first strike against them. Certainly the military planners of the U.S.

would be remiss if they did not take similar note of a civilian-shelter program in the U.S.S.R. As a step in the escalation of the arms race toward the ultimate outbreak of war, the fallout shelter would lead inevitably to the blast shelter. Even with large numbers of blast shelters built and evenly distributed throughout the metropolitan community, people would soon realize that shelters alone are not enough. Accidental alarms, even in tautly disciplined military installations, have shown that people do not always take early warnings seriously. Even if they did, a 15-minute "early" warning provides less than enough time to seal the population into shelters. Accordingly, the logical next step is the live-in and work-in blast shelter leading to still further disruption and distortion of civilization. There is no logical termination of the line of reasoning that starts with belief in the usefulness of fallout shelters; the logic of this attempt to solve the problem of national security leads to a diverging series of ever more grotesque measures. This is to say, in so many words, that if the arms race continues and resumes its former accelerating tempo, 1984 is more than just a date on the calendar 20 years hence.

Ever since shortly after World War II the military power of the U.S. has been steadily increasing. Throughout this same period the national security of the U.S. has been rapidly and inexorably diminishing. In the early 1950's the U.S.S.R., on the basis of its own unilateral decision and determination to accept the inevitable retaliation, could have launched an attack against the U.S. with bombers carrying fission bombs. Some of these bombers would have penetrated our defenses and the American casualties would have numbered in the millions. In the later 1950's, again on its own sole decision and determination to accept the inevitable massive retaliation, the U.S.S.R. could have launched an attack against the U.S. using more and better bombers, this time carrying thermonuclear bombs. Some of these bombers would have penetrated our defenses and the American casualties could have numbered in the tens of millions.

Today the U.S.S.R., again on the basis of its own decision and determination to accept the inevitable retaliation, could launch an attack on the U.S. using intercontinental missiles and bombers carrying thermonuclear weapons. This

time the number of American casualties could very well be on the order of 100 million.

The steady decrease in national security did not result from any inaction on the part of responsible U.S. military and civilian authorities. It resulted from the systematic exploitation of the products of modern science and technology by the U.S.S.R. The air defenses deployed by the U.S. during the 1950's would have reduced the number of casualties the country might have otherwise sustained, but their existence did not substantively modify this picture. Nor could it have been altered by any other defense measures that might have been taken but that for one reason or another were not taken.

From the Soviet point of view the picture is similar but much worse. The military power of the U.S.S.R. has been steadily increasing since it became an atomic power in 1949. Soviet national security, however, has been steadily decreasing. Hypothetically the U.S. could unilaterally decide to destroy the U.S.S.R. and the U.S.S.R. would be absolutely powerless to prevent it. That country could only, at best, seek to wreak revenge through whatever retaliatory capability it might then have left.

Both sides in the arms race are thus confronted by the dilemma of steadily increasing military power and steadily decreasing national security. *It is our considered professional judgment that this dilemma has no technical solution.* If the great powers continue to look for solutions in the area of science and technology only, the result will be to worsen the situation. The clearly predictable course of the arms race is a steady open spiral downward into oblivion.

We are optimistic, on the other hand, that there is a solution to this dilemma. The partial nuclear-test ban, we hope and believe, is truly an important first step toward finding a solution in an area where a solution may exist. A next logical step would be the conclusion of a comprehensive test ban such as that on which the great powers came close to agreement more than once during 10 long years of negotiation at Geneva. The policing and inspection procedures so nearly agreed on in those parleys would set significant precedents and lay the foundations of mutual confidence for proceeding thereafter to actual disarmament.

# 39 The Shelter-Centered Society

ARTHUR I. WASKOW · May 1962

Civil defense has been a topic of increasing public concern since July 25 of last year, when President Kennedy, in an address to the nation on the Berlin crisis, called for the preparation of shelters against the local fallout that results from a nuclear explosion on the ground. Most public discussion—for example, the hearings and debates on civil defense legislation in Congress—has focused on whether fallout shelters would be useful during and after a nuclear attack. There has been little examination of the possible effects that the creation and operation of a shelter-centered civil defense system might have on U.S. society during peacetime. It is apparent, however, that these effects must be reckoned with, whether or not the usefulness of the system is ever tested.

In January the Peace Research Institute, a nonprofit organization headed by James J. Wadsworth, former Permanent U.S. Representative to the United Nations, brought together a group of social scientists to consider this aspect of the proposed civil defense system. The conference is one of a number of projects recently undertaken by the Peace Research Institute to stimulate scientific research concerning ways to further the cause of peace, in the same fashion that research has been effectively used in recent years in support of the arms race. The conferees [see Editor's Note at bottom of opposite page] prepared themselves by studying a number of background papers and documents; they were briefed, in the course of their deliberations, by officials of the National Security Council and the Office of Civil Defense and by experts from the Institute for Defense Analyses. In addition to their basic knowledge of social theory and of experimental findings in their fields of learning, the conferees brought to their study such special data as recent observations of overseas reactions to the U.S. civil defense program, scientific surveys of U.S. public opinion and locally observed reactions among students, patients and the general public.

On one conclusion the conferees felt they could confidently agree: The existence of a shelter-centered civil defense would be a wholly new departure in U.S. history. Because the prospect is without precedent they did not attempt to produce ironclad predictions of what would happen. They sought rather to define the problems that are likely to develop. As the product of their work together, the conferees issued not conclusions but a series of questions. They shared unanimously the sentiment that the questions are urgent and that action taken without careful consideration of these questions might lead to irreversible and disastrous consequences.

The civil defense program, the conferees agreed, portends an unprecedented departure in U.S. life because it implies major effects on our society as a whole. In official statements the program is described as "minimal insurance" against the "unlikely" event of a nuclear war. Because of its uniquely potent psychological and social appeal to survival instincts, however, it would be extremely difficult to limit the program to any predetermined minimum. A drive for continuous expansion of the program—a drive far more powerful than the usual pressures to expand, for example, Social Security—threatens to press constantly on the decision makers. Once having promised survival to some, they would soon have to meet all objections of inadequacy or noncoverage by broadening the program geographically and by improving its quality. To inspire any hope of effectiveness in war, civil defense must be able to call forth virtually universal teamwork. Since failure in any of a number of crucial tasks could gravely impair the operation of the system, the program must instill in all Americans a wholehearted willingness to carry out difficult orders on short notice. It would require the training of a large cadre of men and women to a fine pitch of elaborate knowledge and total dedication, and the training of the rest of the population for unquestioning obedience in a crisis.

All the evidence from the experience of the armed forces indicates that such "training" comes not from reading textbooks or instruction posters but from actually rehearsing crisis behavior. Civil defense would require whole detachments of civil defense workers to go into and stay in shelters, whole populations to practice responding to emergency signals, whole cities to drill on a winter night. The demand for disciplined obedience to authority extended to the entire population would be entirely new in U.S. life. Indeed, in virtually no society is there any precedent for maintaining a large portion of a civilian population over a long time in trained readiness for a threatening event with a low probability of occurrence.

Proponents of civil defense have made a virtue of the need for such co-ordination of sentiment and action and have argued that by making the danger to survival obvious to all, the shelter program would enhance a national sense of community. But the conferees, on the basis of sociological evidence from the past, were unanimous in the doubt that feelings of community would be thereby reinforced. People working together to face danger perceived as equally threatening to all, in a civil defense program perceived as equally protective of all, might well have their community solidarity strengthened. But the danger of attack weighs differently on different Americans, the prospective usefulness of shelters is vastly different in different situations, and the work of building and operating shelters would actually be done by different agencies working along different lines at different levels of expense and with different chances of success or failure. In these conditions the evidence suggests that existing stresses and strains in the community would be amplified.

Already the civil defense effort has strained the web of community. Some people have concluded that shelters (private or public) would be useless to them unless they were prepared to limit the number of occupants to those whom the shelter could physiologically support. They have therefore announced their intention of excluding neighbors, or people from the next block, or strangers from the next county, or casual visitors to town, from the family or community shelter. Suburbia has been pitted against city, one state against another. These strains cannot be expected to disappear. It is indeed likely that they would worsen as cities realize how vulnerable they are to attack, as racial and ethnic groups compete for space in and access to community shelters, as farmers realize that refugees from the cities will deplete their food stocks.

From the point of view of the individual, the conferees agreed, the announcement of the civil defense program represented simultaneously a high-

ly authoritative threat of personal death and social destruction and a promise that there is a way to meet this threat. Even a program announced as "minimal insurance" against an "unlikely war" signals to people that the danger is high ("Otherwise, why the program?") and that safety is possible ("Maybe not for other people, but for me").

It might seem that the threat is actually posed by the existence of nuclear weapons rather than by a shelter program. In people's minds, however, it is the civil defense program that spells out the danger. The call for civil defense is seen as a warning that war is highly possible and imminent; the physical trappings of civil defense make a visible and immediate impact on local and family affairs. In comparison the distant and half-realized military arsenal is a much less potent symbol of danger. At a still more distant remove is the outside military threat, which can be ignored, denied or suppressed in one's mind. Civil defense, however, is immediately visible, tangible and unavoidable.

The probable effect of this powerful threat and promise is to bring about three distinct reactions in the population. First, the threat generates anxiety in almost the entire population. Second, the promise of some protection provides a considerable amount of relief from the anxiety. It goes without saying, however, that the relief cannot fully or permanently offset the anxiety. The relief depends on sustained conviction that the shelter program is adequate, whereas the anxiety can disappear only if the threat disappears. Contradictory as they are, these two reactions are likely to be con-

founded by a third reaction. Among some people—an unknown proportion of the population—the civil defense program is bound to stir a dark attraction to the world of which civil defense is a warning: a world wiped clean of complications, ambiguities and dissension. The coexistence in the population of deep anxiety, precarious hope and an obsessive concern with violence and death would constitute a new situation for U.S. society.

This analysis of the impending impact of civil defense on American life suggests a number of urgent questions. First among them is the question of whether or not a commitment to the proposed program will tend to restrict the U.S. Government's freedom to negotiate with Communist governments. In the long run such a development would make it more likely that conflicts between the U.S.S.R. and the U.S. would lead to the use of force.

It is conceivable that public opinion might come under the sway of intense and uncontrolled hostility to the idea of negotiation with Communist states. Such hostility could result from the public's interpreting civil defense to mean that an enemy threatens imminent death to home, neighborhood and nation. Against this prospect it is sometimes argued that the shock and immediacy of a civil defense program might bring home to Americans the possibility and the peril of a nuclear war and thereby increase interest in and devotion to negotiations toward such goals as mutual disarmament. It was the unanimous judgment of the conferees, however, that a reaction in favor of disarmament is extremely

EDITOR'S NOTE

This article is a condensed version of the report of a conference on the potential implications of a national civil defense program, held by the Peace Research Institute in Washington, D.C., on January 13 and 14, 1962. Partial support for the conference was given by the National Institute of Mental Health and the American Psychological Association. The full report can be obtained from the Peace Research Institute.

The conferees were Raymond A. Bauer of the Harvard University Graduate School of Business Administration, Urie Bronfenbrenner of the Department of Psychology at Cornell University; Morton Deutsch of the Bell Telephone Laboratories; Herbert H. Hyman of the Department of Sociology at Columbia University; Erich Lindemann, professor of psychiatry at the Harvard Medical School and Psychiatrist-in-Chief of the Massachusetts General Hospital; David Riesman of the Department of Social Relations at Harvard University; Stephen B. Withey, director of Public Affairs Studies at the Survey Research Center of the University of Michigan; and Donald N. Michael, director of Planning and Programs for the Peace Research Institute, who was chairman of the conference. All the conferees are in essential agreement on the substance of the report.

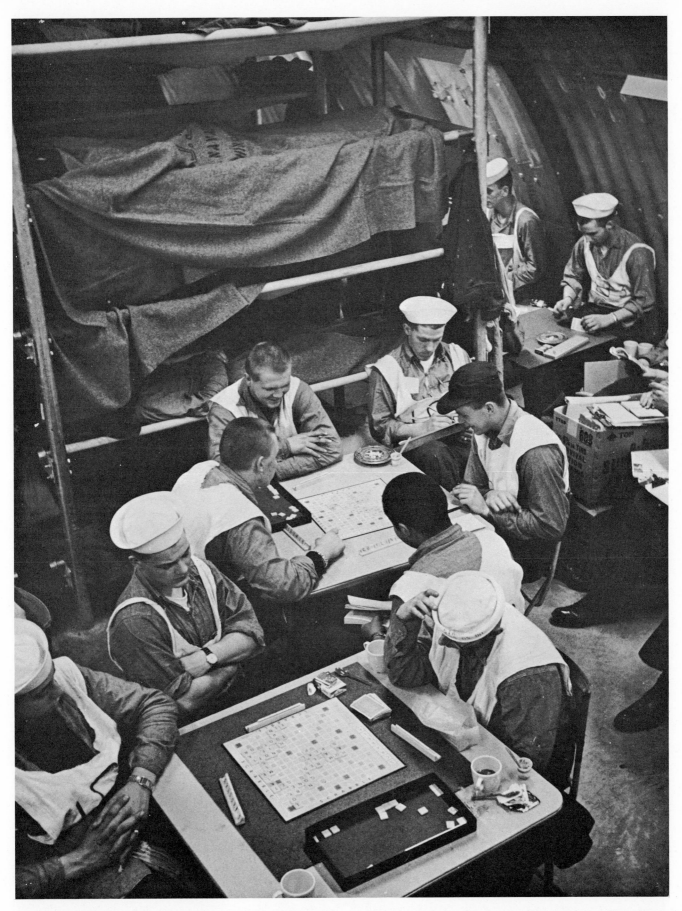

**FALLOUT-SHELTER TEST** run by the Navy last winter involved 100 men, who stayed in an underground steel and concrete shelter for two weeks. Ventilating fans supplied filtered air. The sailors ate emergency rations and spent the time sleeping, reading, playing cards and Scrabble. The test was designed to study the physical effects of long confinement underground in cramped quarters.

unlikely. They agreed that those people who were committed to supporting disarmament before the call for civil defense might take the call as a signal for desperately intensifying their previous efforts. For almost everyone else civil defense and disarmament are what is known in social psychology as "dissonant"; that is, civil defense fits into a view of the world in which negotiation has failed and war is looming, whereas disarmament fits into a view of the world in which negotiation seems possible and war seems avoidable. Confronted by the physical reality of shelters such popular support as there is for disarmament might weaken and wane. In other words, the shelters themselves might be symbolically even more threatening to hopes of disarmament than the call for civil defense.

Meanwhile there is some evidence to suggest that the civil defense program might have the unintended effect of restricting the area open to the U.S. Government for negotiation. Public opinion surveys, conducted by the Survey Research Center of the University of Michigan, have already shown that the President's call for civil defense, regardless of what he intended, was widely accepted as a warning of intense and immediate danger of war ("Why else should he want us to do this?"), a warning that negotiations with the U.S.S.R. were not working. Might not the popular anxiety aroused by this "signal" lead to popular belief that negotiations cannot succeed? Since a real civil defense program is not just paper but underground buildings and training programs that persist over long periods, might the hostility to negotiation also persist into periods when the Government would see a possibility of resolving previous crises? If so, the ability of the Government to negotiate might be severely impaired by anxiety among the people.

Urie Bronfenbrenner of Cornell University was able to report, on the basis of his recent trip to the U.S.S.R., that many Russians, plain citizens as well as officials, see in the U.S. civil defense program a threat of war. Thus, regardless of the carefully qualified remarks of the President in his call for civil defense, the call was seen in both the U.S. and the U.S.S.R. as a signal that war was near, that negotiations were failing, and in each country as evidence that the other was threatening aggression. The dangers of such an atmosphere are obvious.

The creation of civil defense will bring to life in every nook and cranny of the nation special institutions economically dependent on and deriving their power and prestige from a civil defense program: Government agencies, private builders and suppliers, a cadre of trained shelter managers, and so on. Even if not a single individual in these groups directly or deliberately attacked the notion of negotiating with an adversary, might not the mere existence of these groups immensely complicate the task of working out a plan for general disarmament that would not disrupt U.S. society?

Investigators in social psychology suggest that the existence of an omnipresent, persistent and highly visible symbol of one line of action might distract attention from other, parallel and alternative lines of action that lack such a symbol. Thus fallout shelters on a national scale might constantly call attention to nuclear war as the technique for conducting international conflict. Both proponents and opponents of civil defense might tend to concentrate on nuclear dangers and their mitigation instead of trying to discover alternatives to the use of nuclear weapons, such alternatives as "conventional war," political and economic pressure, tension-reducing initiatives or the invention of international institutions for conflict control.

The proposed civil defense program raises corresponding questions about this country's relations with its allies and neutral nations. Through civil defense the American people would in effect be searching for a way of survival for themselves and would tacitly be abandoning non-Americans to die if nuclear war should come. Among U.S. citizens the civil defense program might produce feelings of isolation from and lack of interest in the rest of the world. Among even the most friendly peoples the program might be taken to mean that the U.S. had withdrawn from its undertaking to promote the interests and the defense of its allies. From a recent visit to Japan, David Riesman of Harvard University was able to report that many people in that country feel considerable uneasiness over the U.S. shelter program and fear that it may indeed symbolize a turning inward of U.S. interests and policy. If this response should become more widespread, it might be seized on by some Americans as evidence of the unreliability of allies who could be so easily annoyed by American attempts at self-protection. Therefore the possibility exists that feelings of isolation in the U.S. could feed on feelings of isolation from the U.S., the two processes being constantly reinforced by progress in the civil defense program and culminating in substantial alienation of the U.S. from its friends and allies.

Just as civil defense might affect the course of American foreign policy, so it might change the ways in which the country's traditional democratic processes work at home. If mobilization of total support and participation should become a goal of the program, would not the civil defense organization be impelled to invade the privacy and liberty of individuals? There is the great danger that teachers, clergymen, editors, civil servants and other leaders of opinion would be required to become enforcers of official policy on civil defense—in the assumed best interests of those coerced. What if some teachers, clergymen, editors and civil servants should disagree with the policy? Would they be punished for encouraging "shelter dodgers" as they would be if they incited draft dodgers? Although no such official pressures have yet been exerted, it is disquieting to hear reliable reports from New York City that some high school students who refused to participate in shelter drills have been refused recommendations for admission to college.

It is possible that the "confusion" that has marked the civil defense effort so far is in reality a kind of unconscious civilian resistance to the half-understood possibilities of enforced conformity. Civilian doubts, hesitancies and ambivalences may be having a "last fling" in anxious anticipation of the absolute unanimity and centralization that might

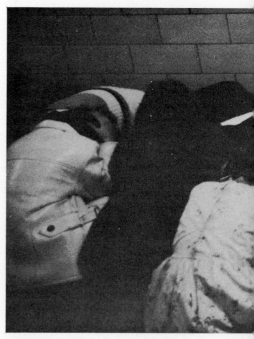

SHELTER DRILL is conducted from time to time in the Norwalk, Conn., elementary

be required if civil defense became a paramilitary organization of the entire population. Since the doubts and confusions themselves interfere with civil defense, they may themselves bring about more effort to eliminate the doubts and to control their expression more tightly. Thus the fears of centralized control could help to bring such control into force. To prevent this kind of repressive process from beginning or continuing— if it can be prevented at all—would take an understanding of the problem on the part of citizens and Government officials and a careful re-examination of the whole situation to locate the points at which the process could most effectively be halted.

These problems might be compounded if the peculiar imagery and symbolism involved in civil defense attracts particular personality types into leadership of civil defense organizations. Such special groups of people might be benign; for example, they might well include protective individuals, committed to saving, helping and nursing their fellow human beings in time of disaster. But the image of a world of death and destruction might act as a kind of "pornography of violence" to attract people to civil defense work who "want to get it over with"—who see nuclear war as a relief of intolerable tensions and as a way of "ending" international conflict— or who see themselves as survivors and rulers in a world where affluence and internal bickering had given way to pioneer exertions and tightly controlled or-

der. In fact, civil defense publications in certain localities suggest that people with these kinds of personality structure have already begun to dominate some local civil defense organizations.

The combined promise of life and warning of death put forward by civil defense involves such strains in individual hopes and fears that any failure, mistake, corruption or delay in the program might have far more basic consequences than even total collapse of an ordinary political proposal. There is a disturbing prospect that widespread disillusionment with the political leader, the scientist and the expert and even democratic government itself could grow out of a civil defense program.

Since there is a considerable "cultural lag" in translating new knowledge of weapons effects into new civil defense procedures, in transmitting the new procedures to local civil defense officials, and in putting the new procedures to work, there might exist at any time a publicly known gap between the need and the program. Such a gap might well provoke anger and disenchantment in citizens who knew that it might mean their death. The anger and disenchantment might be deep enough and broad enough to exceed the normal amount of disapproval felt by free peoples toward democratic governments.

For example, a leading businessman could be asked by his local civil defense director to make expensive alterations in his building at the very moment when the same businessman hears from his

Washington sources that these alterations are out of date and that specifications may soon be changed. Should he go ahead with the alterations or not? In either case, what would he and the local civil defense director think of the Federal Government? Since Federal officials will have recognized this difficulty, would they hesitate to keep the civil defense program up to date for fear of destroying morale? If they should decide to maintain an out-of-date program, what would happen to their own morale and self-respect?

Finally, it should be pointed out that in civil defense, as in every program in any society with any form of government, sooner or later there are sure to be mistakes, instances of corruption and so on. In most public programs people take such occasions in their stride (although in the U.S. they have sometimes led to dangerous contempt for politics and politicians). In a program that would be as deeply tied to national and personal life or death as civil defense, any fall from grace might provoke a much more serious revulsion against political leaders and possibly even against democratic politics. Similarly, the image of the scientist and the expert might suffer badly if the presumed experts disagree profoundly on what nuclear war could mean or urge a program of civil defense that is later shown to be ineffective. Since the scientist is perceived as the ranking "expert," disenchantment with him might generalize to disbelief in Government experts of all kinds. And cynicism

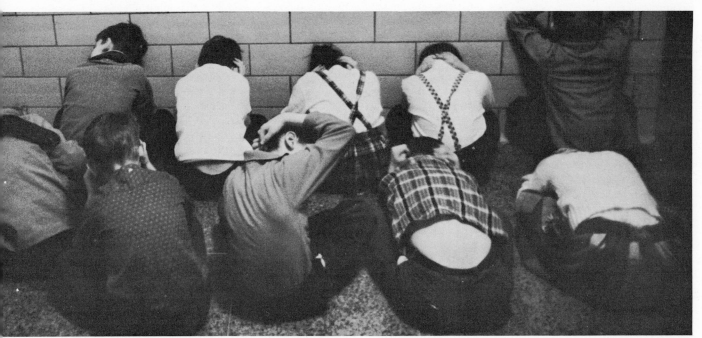

schools. These pupils are first-graders at the Tracey School. The children march out of their classrooms and line up along the walls of an interior corridor. They sit on the floor, head down and hands clasped behind neck for protection against a nuclear explosion.

among Government officials, if they privately see mistakes, failures, inadequacies and delays in so crucial a program, might still further sap belief in democracy and might make corruption or apathy more likely.

Of all the questions raised by civil defense, the conferees agreed, the most troublesome and dangerous is the question of how the commitment, once made, could ever be limited or reversed. A shelter-oriented civil defense system will of necessity create a large, highly organized institution with crucial connections in every area of American life. The civil defense hierarchy—Federal, state and local—will be carrying the heavy burden of training a large cadre of shelter managers and survival specialists. The trained cadres in turn will have the task of training large groups of people to follow orders in a hurry at a time of catastrophe and crisis, in spite of their anxieties, fears and lack of information. The civil defense organization will have to insist on the economic adjustments and controls necessary to implement and operate a shelter program without unsettling either long-range business investments or day-to-day business where shelters are being dug or buildings modified. If the civil defense organization should attempt to supply only shelter structures and other physical necessities, fearful of involvement in educational, psychological or economic problems, it is likely that local demands for drills, training and controls will quickly arise as the shelters themselves appear. The very existence of the civil defense system will make it a social force of great importance, powerful even if it abjures power.

As the shelter program grows, proponents and administrators of civil defense might become more preoccupied with imagined attack situations. They might feel that in the overwhelming emergency of attack it will be necessary to have fully co-ordinated action in order to use the shelters efficiently. Individuals who have not learned their places and tasks—who in panic block shelter entrances, who forget to take along essential personal medicines or who bring along too much luggage for the available space—will be endangering not only their own lives but also the lives of others. For this reason the civil defense organization will find itself more and more pressed to demand virtually universal acceptance of civil defense and preparation for it.

The social, psychological and political momentum generated by an operating civil defense system would therefore make it increasingly impossible for the nation to change its mind once the program was under way. The program would be much harder to reverse than most political decisions. One well-established social and psychological mechanism that might make civil defense irreversible is the common transformation of conflict and confusion into rigid and overwhelming commitment. The puzzlement and disagreement that will have preceded adoption of a civil defense program might bring about such a commitment to the program as it goes into effect. Having cast its doubts away and invested huge amounts of labor, capital, energy and imagination in civil defense, the nation might find it difficult to surrender the hope of survival through the new program. Once it acts for civil defense, the nation would find itself seeking constantly for new reasons to be so acting. This phenomenon—the bringing of ideas and wishes into line with action already being taken—is well known to behavioral scientists and politicians.

With the continued escalation of the destructiveness and accuracy of nuclear weapons and their delivery vehicles, it would be difficult to resist demands for constant expansion and intensification of civil defense. At any extreme—even underground cities—civil defense would be inadequate against many conceivable weapons (some already in existence) that could be brought against it. Thus at any existing level of civil defense various groups (for instance, the political opposition) might be able to demand a larger and more effective program. A system of escalating political blackmail could well develop. Such pressure would be difficult to resist if the Government had already implied that it could protect at least some people. With the pressure always in one direction, the civil defense program might be always expanding, never contracting.

The difficulty of reversing policy on civil defense can be made clearer by examination of the conditions in the past under which some major political decisions have actually been reversed by the U.S. political system. The abandonment of the National Industrial Recovery Act in the early days of the Roosevelt administration seems to have been one such reversal. But two crucial conditions accompanied that episode: it was legitimized by an institution specially assigned to make such reversals, the Supreme Court; and it was made palatable by the adoption of a series of alternative New Deal programs.

The fulfillment of these two conditions in the case of civil defense would be difficult. In matters of defense policy it is hard to see how any outside institutionalized body, such as the courts, could reverse the decisions made by the President and Congress. In fact, the decisions of the President in the field of defense have since 1940 been given such weight that it is difficult to tell whether a real option for reversal would exist even in the hands of Congress. As to alternatives, it has already been suggested that disarmament, for example, could probably not mobilize as much support within a shelter-centered society as it could before shelters were begun. Alternatives may therefore be hard to promote even should it seem wise at some later date to dismantle the civil defense program.

In thus detailing the questions raised by civil defense, the conferees did not suggest that a policy of no civil defense would be without problems. The anxiety aroused by the cold war and its crises, by nuclear weapons and the images of the destruction they would deliver already exists in the U.S. To do nothing would not reduce the anxiety, and to do nothing might well lead to problems other than those herein described as possible results of implementing civil defense.

Whether the appropriate action should be a search for alternatives to civil defense or a search for ways of so managing civil defense as to lessen or eliminate its difficulties is for the nation to decide. What is essential is that the problems that might very well grow out of civil defense be examined carefully and that policy be re-evaluated so that the nation need not be confronted by a world in which the possible difficulties have become real disasters.

The conferees therefore put to the American people and its leadership these questions:

Are we prepared to accept the possibility that unhappy social and political consequences will occur if the proposed civil defense program is implemented?

If we reject the possibility that adverse consequences will develop, on what grounds do we do so and with what assurance that we are right?

If we are not prepared to accept unhappy consequences, are we prepared to recognize the difficulties consciously and apply the arduous study that would be necessary to discover if ways exist of avoiding those consequences?

If, after study, there seems to be no way of avoiding the unhappy results, do we have alternative policies in mind?

# Biographical Notes
# and Bibliographies

## General References

Bronowski, J. SCIENCE AND HUMAN VALUES. New York: Messner, 1956.

Darwin, Charles. THE AUTOBIOGRAPHY OF CHARLES DARWIN, edited by Nora Barlow. London: Collins, 1958.

Hardin, Garrett. BIOLOGY: ITS PRINCIPLES AND IMPLICATIONS, 2nd ed. San Francisco: W. H. Freeman and Company, 1966.

Kubie, Lawrence B. NEUROTIC DISTORTION IN THE CREATIVE PROCESS. Lawrence: University of Kansas Press, 1958.

Kuhn, Thomas S. THE STRUCTURE OF SCIENTIFIC REVOLUTIONS. Chicago: University of Chicago Press, 1962.

Platt, John Rader. THE EXCITEMENT OF SCIENCE. Boston: Houghton Mifflin, 1962.

Polanyi, Michael. PERSONAL KNOWLEDGE. London: Routledge & Kegan Paul, 1958.

Whitehead, A. N. SCIENCE AND THE MODERN WORLD. New York: Mentor Books, 1948.

## PART I: ADAPTATION: "FEARFULLY AND WONDERFULLY MADE"

### 1.  Innovation in Biology

#### The Author

GEORGE WALD is Harvard University's well-known authority on the chemistry of vision. Born in New York, he graduated from New York University in 1927, then did graduate work in zoology at Columbia University under Selig Hecht. After receiving his Ph.D. in 1932, he traveled to Germany on a National Research Council fellowship. While studying in Otto Warburg's laboratory at the Kaiser Wilhelm Institute in Berlin, Wald made his first notable contribution to knowledge of the eye—his discovery of vitamin A in the retina. After another year of postdoctoral study at the University of Chicago, he went to Harvard, where he is now professor of biology. In 1967 he was awarded the Nobel Prize in physiology and medicine, sharing it with H. K. Hartline and Ragnar Granit.

#### Bibliography

DISCUSSION WITH EINSTEIN ON EPISTEMOLOGICAL PROBLEMS IN ATOMIC PHYSICS. Niels Bohr in *The Library of Living Philosophers*, Vol. 7, pages 199–241; 1949.

HERR EUGEN DÜHRING'S REVOLUTION IN SCIENCE (ANTI-DÜHRING). Frederick Engels. International Publishers, 1935.

THE ORIGIN OF SPECIES BY MEANS OF NATURAL SELECTION. Charles Darwin. D. Appleton and Company, 1895.

### 2.  Fleas

#### The Author

MIRIAM ROTHSCHILD is a naturalist who was educated at home, took no public examinations and holds no university degrees. Her chief interest is parasitology, but—in the tradition of the amateur—she has also investigated and published papers on such subjects as gigantism in winkles, the behavior of sea gulls, the defensive poisons of moths and butterflies, mimicry in insect smells, the life cycle of intestinal worms and the conservation of natural resources. Her recent work has been mainly on fleas; she explains that she has "found a study of these insects is relatively easy to combine with rearing a family of six children." She and G. H. E. Hopkins in collaboration have produced so far about half a million words on fleas, describing the collection made by her father, Charles Rothschild. Working with another amateur, Bob Ford, she has discovered a phenomenon described in her article: the only known example of a parasitic insect with a reproductive cycle controlled by the hormones of its vertebrate host.

#### Bibliography

FLEAS, FLUKES & CUCKOOS: A STUDY OF BIRD PARASITES. Miriam Rothschild and Theresa Clay. Collins, London, 1952.

PLAGUE. R. Pollitzer. World Health Organization, 1954.

THE RABBIT FLEA AND HORMONES. Miriam Rothschild in *Endeavour*, Vol. 24, No. 93, pages 162–168; September, 1965.

## 3. Butterflies and Plants

### The Authors

PAUL R. EHRLICH and PETER H. RAVEN are respectively professor and associate professor of biological sciences at Stanford University. Ehrlich, who was graduated from the University of Pennsylvania in 1953 and received a doctorate in entomology from the University of Kansas in 1957, has been at Stanford since 1959. His primary interest is in the structure, dynamics and genetics of natural populations of animals. Raven, who was graduated from the University of California at Berkeley in 1957 and obtained a Ph.D. in botany from the University of California at Los Angeles in 1960, went to Stanford in 1962. His principal concerns are the biosystematics and evolution of the higher plants and their pollination systems.

### Bibliography

BIRDS, BUTTERFLIES, AND PLANT POISONS: A STUDY IN ECOLOGICAL CHEMISTRY. Lincoln Pierson Brower and Jane Van Zandt Brower in *Zoologica*, Vol. 49, No. 3, pages 137–159; 1964.

BUTTERFLIES AND PLANTS: A STUDY IN COEVOLUTION. Paul R. Ehrlich and Peter H. Raven in *Evolution*, Vol. 18, No. 4, pages 586–608; January 28, 1965.

COEVOLUTION OF MUTUALISM BETWEEN ANTS AND ACACIAS IN CENTRAL AMERICA. Daniel H. Janzen in *Evolution*, Vol. 20, No. 3, pages 249–275; 1966.

## 4. Predatory Fungi

### The Author

JOSEPH J. MAIO originally intended to become a composer and still plays the piano and violin as a hobby. His interest in predatory plants stems from his high-school years, when he maintained a collection of Venus's-flytraps, sundews and pitcher plants. A three-year stay in a tuberculosis sanatorium made him especially aware of the activities of microorganisms, and in 1955 he received his B.S. in microbiology from the University of Washington and his M.A. two years later. As a research assistant at the University of Washington School of Medicine he is at present working on bacterial viruses. In addition to his musical diversions he enjoys oil painting.

### Bibliography

THE FRIENDLY FUNGI: A NEW APPROACH TO THE EELWORM PROBLEM. C. L. Duddington. Faber and Faber, 1957.

PREDACEOUS FUNGI. Charles Drechsler in *Biological Reviews*, Vol. 16, No. 4, pages 265–290; October, 1941.

THE PREDACIOUS FUNGI AND THEIR PLACE IN MICROBIAL ECOLOGY. C. L. Duddington in *Microbial Ecology*, pages 218–237; 1957.

THE PREDACIOUS FUNGI: ZOOPAGALES AND MONILIALES. C. L. Duddington in *Biological Reviews*, Vol. 31, No. 2, pages 152–193; May, 1956.

SOME HYPHOMYCETES THAT PREY ON FREE-LIVING TERRICOLOUS NEMATODES. Charles Drechsler in *Mycologia*, Vol. 29, No. 4, pages 447–552; July–August, 1937.

STIMULATED ACTIVITY OF NATURAL ENEMIES OF NEMATODES. M. B. Linford in *Science*, Vol. 85, No. 2,196, pages 123–124; January 29, 1937.

## 5. Nocturnal Animals

### The Author

H. N. SOUTHERN is senior research officer in the Bureau of Animal Population at the Botanic Garden at Oxford, England. He writes that he cannot remember the time when he was not fascinated by birds, mammals and flowers. He studied classics at Oxford University and spent some time in a London publishing house. But the pull of natural history was so strong that he returned to Oxford, graduated a second time in zoology and joined the staff of the Bureau of Animal Population. During World War II he worked on the control of rabbits, rats and mice. Since then he has turned to examining the role of birds of prey in controlling populations of voles and mice.

### Bibliography

THE SENSE ORGANS OF BIRDS. R. J. Pumphrey in *The Annual Report of the Smithsonian Institution for 1948*, pages 305–330; 1949.

TAWNY OWLS AND THEIR PREY. H. N. Southern in *The Ibis*, Vol. 96, No. 3, pages 384–410; July 1, 1954.

THE VERTEBRATE EYE AND ITS ADAPTIVE RADIATION. Gordon Lynn Walls. Cranbrook Institute of Science, 1942.

## 6. Moths and Ultrasound

### The Author

KENNETH D. ROEDER is professor of physiology at Tufts University, where he has served since 1931. He was born in England, was graduated from the University of Cambridge and did graduate work there and at the University of Toronto. "My lifelong interest in insects," he writes, "probably stems from a childhood enthusiasm for butterfly collecting." Roeder's research deals mainly with the biological aspects of insect behavior. In addition he is "an incurable tinkerer with mechanical and electronic gadgets," an activity that "led at one time to the construction of an electromechanical analogue of certain phases of cockroach behavior and has played a part in the work on moth hearing." He says he has "always felt that if one can make a subject clear and interesting to a nonspecialist, it becomes clearer and more interesting to oneself."

### Bibliography

THE DETECTION AND EVASION OF BATS BY MOTHS. Kenneth D. Roeder and Asher E. Treat in *American Scientist*, Vol. 49, No. 2, pages 135–148; June, 1961.

MOTH SOUNDS AND THE INSECT-CATCHING BEHAVIOR OF BATS. Dorothy C. Dunning and Kenneth D. Roeder in *Science*, Vol. 147, No. 3654, pages 173–174; January 8, 1965.

NERVE CELLS AND INSECT BEHAVIOR. Kenneth D. Roeder. Harvard University Press, 1963.

## 7. Electric Location by Fishes

### The Author

H. W. LISSMANN is lecturer in the department of zoology at the University of Cambridge. Lissmann, who was born in Russia, studied in Germany, where he obtained a Ph.D. at the University of Hamburg. He received an M.A. from Cambridge in 1947 and became assistant director of research there the same year. Lissmann was elected a Fellow of the Royal Society in 1954. He was made lecturer in zoology at the University of Cambridge the following year and was also elected a Fellow and Lecturer of Trinity College, Cambridge. Lissmann is interested mainly in the behavior of animals, their movements, sense organs and nervous systems. His studies of electric fishes, begun in 1950, are described in his article. Lissmann has found it "useful and illuminating" to collect his own fish in Africa and South America. His work is still frequently hampered by a shortage of experimental subjects, and Lissmann writes that he would be grateful to anyone who could suggest to him a possible source of supply.

### Bibliography

ECOLOGICAL STUDIES ON GYMNOTIDS. H. W. Lissmann in *Bioelectrogenesis: A Comparative Survey of its Mechanisms with Particular Emphasis on Electric Fishes*. American Elsevier Publishing Co., Inc., 1961.

ON THE FUNCTION AND EVOLUTION OF ELECTRIC ORGANS IN FISH. H. W. Lissmann in *Journal of Experimental Biology*, Vol. 35, No. 1, pages 156–191; March, 1958.

THE MECHANISM OF OBJECT LOCATION IN GYMNARCHUS NILOTICUS AND SIMILAR FISH. H. W. Lissmann and K. E. Machin in *Journal of Experimental Biology*, Vol. 35, No. 2, pages 451–486; June, 1958.

THE MODE OF OPERATION OF THE ELECTRIC RECEPTORS IN GYMNARCHUS NILOTICUS. K. E. Machin and H. W. Lissmann in *Journal of Experimental Biology*, Vol. 37, No. 4, pages 801–811; December, 1960.

## 8.   The Master Switch of Life

### The Author

P. F. SCHOLANDER is professor of physiology and director of the newly established Physiological Research Laboratory at the Scripps Institution of Oceanography. Scholander was born in Örebro, Sweden, in 1905 and received an M.D. from the University of Oslo in 1932. After two years as instructor in anatomy at Oslo he acquired a Ph.D. in botany there in 1934. He did research in botany and physiology in Norway until 1939, when he came to this country to join the department of zoology at Swarthmore College. During World War II Scholander served as an aviation physiologist in the U.S. Army Air Force, returning to Swarthmore in 1946 to continue his studies on the comparative physiology of diving. He investigated climatic adaptations of arctic and tropical animals and plants at the Arctic Research Laboratory in Point Barrow, Alaska, and in Panama from 1947 until 1949, when he became a research fellow in the department of biological chemistry at the Harvard Medical School. In 1952 he joined the staff of the Woods Hole Oceanographic Institution, and in 1955 he was appointed professor of physiology and director of the Institute of Zoophysiology at the University of Oslo. He joined the Scripps Institution in 1958.

### Bibliography

CIRCULATORY ADJUSTMENT IN PEARL DIVERS. P. F. Scholander, H. T. Hammel, H. LeMessurier, E. Hemmingsen and W. Garey in *Journal of Applied Physiology*, Vol. 17, No. 2, pages 184–190; March, 1962.

MESENTERIC VASCULAR INSUFFICIENCY: INTESTINAL ISCHEMIA INDUCED BY REMOTE CIRCULATORY DISTURBANCES. Eliot Corday, David W. Irving, Herbert Gold, Harold Bernstein and Robert B. T. Skelton in *The American Journal of Medicine*, Vol. 33, No. 3, pages 365–376; September, 1962.

RESPIRATION IN DIVING MAMMALS. Laurence Irving in *Physiological Reviews*, Vol. 19, No. 1, pages 112–134; January, 1939.

SELECTIVE ISCHEMIA IN DIVING MAN. R. W. Elsner, W. F. Garey and P. F. Scholander in *American Heart Journal*, Vol. 65, No. 4, pages 571–572; April, 1963.

## 9.   The Physiology of the Camel

### The Author

KNUT SCHMIDT-NIELSEN is professor of physiology in the department of zoology at Duke University. He studied the camel when he led an expedition of four scientists to the Sahara Desert in 1953 and 1954, while on a Guggenheim fellowship. He has long been interested in the water metabolism of animals, as indicated by two previous articles in SCIENTIFIC AMERICAN: one ("The Desert Rat") in collaboration with his wife in July, 1953, and the second ("Salt Glands") in January of this year. He was born in Norway and holds degrees from the University of Copenhagen. In addition to his work in physiology, he has done research in biochemistry and analytical chemistry. He studied for four years in Copenhagen under August Krogh, Nobel laureate in physiology, and married Krogh's daughter. The Schmidt-Nielsens came to this country in 1946. They worked at Swarthmore College, Stanford University and the University of Cincinnati before they went to Duke in 1952.

### Bibliography

BODY TEMPERATURE OF THE CAMEL AND ITS RELATION TO WATER ECONOMY. Knut Schmidt-Nielsen, Bodil Schmidt-Nielsen, S. A. Jarnum and T. R. Houpt. Department of Zoology, Duke University, 1959.

THE CAMEL, ITS USES AND MANAGEMENT. Major Arthur Glyn Leonard. Longmans, Green and Co., 1894.

PHYSIOLOGY OF MAN IN THE DESERT. E. F. Adolph and associates. Interscience Publishers, 1947.

## 10.   Adaptations to Cold

### The Author

LAURENCE IRVING is director of the Institute of Arctic Biology and professor of zoophysiology at the University of Alaska. A graduate of Bowdoin College, he received a master's degree at Harvard University in 1917 and a Ph.D. at Stanford University in 1924. He has worked in Alaska since 1947, going there after more than 20 years of teaching, mostly at Swarthmore College, "I have long been inclined to study the physiological adaptations that enable men and animals to succeed in extreme natural conditions," he writes. "It turned out that the natural physiological reactions of arctic animals to cold were of dimensions large enough to demonstrate general principles of adaptation to various temperatures that we had been unable to ascertain in mild climates and by the use of domesticated animals."

## Bibliography

BODY INSULATION OF SOME ARCTIC AND TROPICAL MAMMALS AND BIRDS. P. F. Scholander, Vladimir Walters, Raymond Hock and Laurence Irving in *The Biological Bulletin*, Vol. 99, No. 2, pages 225–236; October, 1950.

BODY TEMPERATURES OF ARCTIC AND SUBARCTIC BIRDS AND MAMMALS. Laurence Irving and John Krog in *Journal of Applied Physiology*, Vol. 6, No. 11, pages 667–680; May, 1954.

EFFECT OF TEMPERATURE ON SENSITIVITY OF THE FINGER. Laurence Irving in *Journal of Applied Physiology*, Vol. 18, No. 6, pages 1201–1205; November, 1963.

METABOLISM AND INSULATION OF SWINE AS BARE-SKINNED MAMMALS. Laurence Irving, Leonard J. Peyton and Mildred Monson in *Journal of Applied Physiology*, Vol. 9, No. 3, pages 421–426; November, 1956.

PHYSIOLOGICAL INSULATION OF SWINE AS BARE-SKINNED MAMMALS. Laurence Irving in *Journal of Applied Physiology*, Vol. 9, No. 3, pages 414–420; November, 1956.

TERRESTRIAL ANIMALS IN COLD: INTRODUCTION. Laurence Irving in *Handbook of Physiology, Section 4; Adaptation to the Environment*. American Physiological Society, 1964.

## 11. Habitat Selection

### The Author

STANLEY C. WECKER is an instructor in the department of biology at the City College of the City University of New York. After receiving a B.S. from City College in 1955, he studied at the University of Michigan, obtaining an M.S. in 1957 and a Ph.D. in 1962. His primary interest is vertebrate ecology, with some overlap into the field of animal behavior.

### Bibliography

THE DISTRIBUTION AND ABUNDANCE OF ANIMALS. H. G. Andrewartha and L. C. Birch. The University of Chicago Press, 1954.

THE ROLE OF EARLY EXPERIENCE IN HABITAT SELECTION BY THE PRAIRIE DEER MOUSE, PEROMYSCUS MANICULATUS BAIRDI. Stanley C. Wecker in *Ecological Monographs*. Vol. 33, No. 4, pages 307–325; Autumn, 1963.

THE STRATEGY OF THE GENES. C. H. Waddington. The Macmillan Company, 1957.

## 12. Crises in the History of Life

### The Author

NORMAN D. NEWELL has since 1945 been curator of the Department of Fossil Invertebrates at the American Museum of Natural History in New York and professor of invertebrate paleontology at Columbia University. Newell acquired his B.S. and M.A. from the University of Kansas and in 1933 received a Ph.D. in geology from Yale University. After a year as a Sterling Fellow at Yale, Newell taught at the University of Kansas until 1937, when he left to serve as a U.S. delegate to the 17th International Geological Congress held in Moscow. He returned to the U.S. and became associate professor of geology at the University of Wisconsin, remaining there until he joined the museum and Columbia. Since 1950 Newell has been involved in extensive research on the paleontology and ecology of the coral reefs of the Bahama Islands in the West Indies. This work has included expeditions to Andros Island and to Raroia (the Pacific atoll reached by the *Kon-Tiki*). He made a fossil-collecting tour of Mexico and Guatemala in 1956 and did field work in Greece and Turkey in 1960. The present article was originally given as the Ermine Cowles Case Memorial Lecture at the University of Michigan in 1962.

### Bibliography

BIOTIC ASSOCIATIONS AND EXTINCTION. David Nicol in *Systematic Zoology*, Vol. 10, No. 1, pages 35–41; March, 1961.

EVOLUTION OF LATE PALEOZOIC INVERTEBRATES IN RESPONSE TO MAJOR OSCILLATIONS OF SHALLOW SEAS. Raymond C. Moore in *Bulletin of the Museum of Comparative Zoology at Harvard College*, Vol. 112, No. 3, pages 259–286; October, 1954.

PALEONTOLOGICAL GAPS AND GEOCHRONOLOGY. Norman D. Newell in *Journal of Paleontology*, Vol. 36, No. 3, pages 592–610; May, 1962.

TETRAPOD EXTINCTIONS AT THE END OF THE TRIASSIC PERIOD. Edwin H. Colbert in *Proceedings of the National Academy of Sciences of the U.S.A.*, Vol. 44, No. 9, pages 973–977; September, 1958.

## Further Readings for Part I

Clausen, Jens. STAGES IN THE EVOLUTION OF PLANT SPECIES. Ithaca, New York: Cornell University Press, 1951.

Cott, Hugh B. ADAPTIVE COLORATION IN ANIMALS. London: Methuen, 1940.

Cowles, R. B. Some Ecological Factors Bearing on the Origin and Evolution of Pigment in the Human Skin. *American Naturalist*, Vol. 93, No. 872 (1959), pages 283–293.

Grant, Verne. THE ORIGIN OF ADAPTATIONS. New York: Columbia University Press, 1963.

Griffin, Donald R. ECHOES OF BATS AND MEN. New York: Doubleday Anchor Books, 1959.

Huxley, Julian, A. C. Hardy, and E. B. Ford, eds. EVOLUTION AS A PROCESS. London: Allen & Unwin, 1954.

Mayr, Ernst. ANIMAL SPECIES AND EVOLUTION. Cambridge, Mass.: Harvard University Press, 1963.

Rensch, Bernard. EVOLUTION ABOVE THE SPECIES LEVEL. New York: Wiley, 1966.

Schmidt-Nielsen, Knut. DESERT ANIMALS. Oxford: Clarendon Press, 1964.

Stebbins, G. Ledyard. PROCESSES OF ORGANIC EVOLUTION. Englewood Cliffs, N.J.: Prentice-Hall, 1966.

## PART II: NATURE'S CHALLENGES TO EVOLUTIONARY THEORY

### 13. The Spider and the Wasp

#### The Author

ALEXANDER PETRUNKEVITCH was emeritus professor of zoology at Yale before his death in 1964. A native of Russia, Petrunkevitch received his Ph.D. from the University of Freiburg in 1900. He came to the United States in 1903. He taught at Harvard and the University of Indiana and was honorary curator of Arachnida at the American Museum of Natural History before joining the Yale faculty in 1917.

#### Bibliography

TARANTULA VERSUS TARANTULA-HAWK: A STUDY IN INSTINCT. Alexander Petrunkevitch in *The Journal of Experimental Zoology*, Vol. 45, No. 2, pages 367–397; July 5, 1926.

### 14. The Evolution of Bowerbirds

#### The Author

E. THOMAS GILLIARD is curator of the Department of Birds at the American Museum of Natural History. Since he began his association with the American Museum in 1932 he has led numerous ornithological expeditions into remote regions of North and South America, Central Asia and the East and West Indies. He has had a part in the discovery and collection of many new species and subspecies of birds, mammals, fishes and reptiles. In 1956 Gilliard made his fifth trip into the interior of New Guinea, where he has been studying the behavior of bowerbirds and birds of paradise.

#### Bibliography

BIRD DISPLAY AND BEHAVIOR: AN INTRODUCTION TO THE STUDY OF BIRD PSYCHOLOGY. Edward A. Armstrong. Lindsay Drummond Ltd., 1942.

BIRDS OF CENTRAL NEW GUINEA. Ernst Mayr and E. Thomas Gilliard in *Bulletin of the American Museum of Natural History*, Vol. 103, Article 4, pages 315–374; April, 1954.

BOWER ORNAMENTATION VERSUS PLUMAGE CHARACTERS IN BOWER-BIRDS. E. Thomas Gilliard in *The Auk*, Vol. 73, No. 3, pages 450–451; July, 1956.

COURTSHIP AND DISPLAY AMONG BIRDS. C. R. Stonor. Country Life Limited. 1940.

ON THE BREEDING BEHAVIOR OF THE COCK-OF-THE-ROCK (AVES, RUPICOLA RUPICOLA). E. Thomas Gilliard in *Bulletin of the American Museum of Natural History*, Vol. 124, Article 2, pages 37–68; July, 1962.

### 15. Cleaning Symbiosis

#### The Author

CONRAD LIMBAUGH was an underwater naturalist and chief diving officer at the Scripps Institution of Oceanography, where he directed the Institution's diving program. He was killed in a skin-diving accident in the Mediterranean on March 20, 1960. Before his death Limbaugh had written a preliminary draft of the present article, which was later completed by his brother-in-law, Howard M. Feder of Hartnell College in California. Limbaugh was graduated from Whittier College in 1948 and did graduate work at the University of California at Los Angeles before going to the Scripps Institution in 1950. He was largely responsible for developing the diver-training program at Scripps, as well as many of the techniques now used by skin divers. Feder, a marine biologist on the faculty of Hartnell College since 1955, holds a Ph.D. from Stanford University. He is currently engaged in assembling and publishing the results of Limbaugh's numerous and diverse research projects.

#### Bibliography

ECOLOGICAL ANIMAL GEOGRAPHY. Richard Hesse, W. C. Allee and Karl P. Schmidt, John Wiley & Sons, Inc., 1951. Page 84.

EXAMPLES OF MIMICRY AND PROTECTIVE RESEMBLANCE IN TROPICAL MARINE FISHES. John E. Randall and Helen A. Randall in *Bulletin of Marine Science of the Gulf and Caribbean*, Vol. 10, No. 4, pages 444–480; December, 1960.

FISH LIFE IN THE KELP BEDS AND THE EFFECTS OF KELP HARVESTING ON FISH. Conrad Limbaugh. University of California Institute of Marine Resources, Report 55–9, pages 1–158; September, 1955.

GALÁPAGOS: WORLD'S END. William Beebe. G. P. Putnam's Sons, 1924. Pages 121–122.

A REVIEW OF THE LABRID FISH GENUS LABROIDES, WITH DESCRIPTIONS OF TWO NEW SPECIES AND NOTES ON ECOLOGY. John E. Randall in *Pacific Science*, Vol. 12, No. 4, pages 327–347; October, 1958.

SYSTEMATIC CATALOGUE OF THE FISHES OF TORTUGAS, FLORIDA. William H. Longley and Samuel E. Hildebrand. Carnegie Institute of Washington, Publication 535; 1941.

### 16. Biological Luminescence

#### The Authors

WILLIAM D. McELROY and HOWARD H. SELIGER are respectively director of the McCollum-Pratt Institute at Johns Hopkins University and research associate at the Institute. McElroy, also chairman of the department of biology at Johns Hopkins, acquired a Ph.D. in biochemistry from Princeton University in 1943 and from 1942 to 1945 was engaged in research on various war projects for the Office of Scientific Research and Development. Following a year of postdoctoral work with George W. Beadle at Stanford University, McElroy went to Johns Hopkins in 1945. At the McCollum-Pratt Institute, which he has directed since 1949, McElroy has been concerned primarily with the mechanism of light emission from chemical reactions, particularly those of biological origin. In addition to this work McElroy serves in an editorial capacity with several journals and as executive editor of *Archives of Biochemistry and Biophysics*. He is the author of some half-dozen books and was coauthor (with C. P. Swanson) of "Trace Elements" in the January 1953 issue of SCIENTIFIC AMERICAN. Seliger, whose chief research interests are energy transfer in bioluminescent processes and the physics of light-producing chemical processes, was originally trained as a nuclear physicist and received his Ph.D. from the University of Maryland in 1954. Before taking his present job in 1958 he had been supervisory physicist of the Radioactivity Section of the National Bureau of Standards.

### Bibliography

BIOLUMINESCENCE. E. Newton Harvey. Academic Press, Inc., 1952.

A SYMPOSIUM ON LIGHT AND LIFE. Edited by William D. McElroy and Bentley Glass. Johns Hopkins Press, 1961.

## 17. The Navigation of the Green Turtle

### The Author

ARCHIE CARR is professor of biology at the University of Florida. He was graduated from that university in 1933 and also received master's and doctor's degrees there. His investigations of marine animals, particularly sea turtles, have taken him to many parts of the world. He is currently writing a book on sea turtles. In addition to his work with marine animals, Carr has studied the wildlife of Africa, and two of his six published books deal with that subject. Another of his interests is the Caribbean Conservation Corporation, of which he is technical director.

### Bibliography

ANIMAL NAVIGATION: HOW ANIMALS FIND THEIR WAY ABOUT. J. D. Carthy. Charles Scribner's Sons, 1957.

THE GREEN TURTLE AND MAN. James J. Parsons. University of Florida Press, 1962.

HANDBOOK OF TURTLES: THE TURTLES OF THE UNITED STATES, CANADA AND BAJA CALIFORNIA. Cornell University Press, 1952.

TURTLES OF THE UNITED STATES AND CANADA. Clifford Pope. Alfred A. Knopf, Inc., 1939.

THE WINDWARD ROAD. Archie Carr. Alfred A. Knopf, Inc., 1956.

## Further Readings for Part II

Fisher, R. A. THE GENETICAL THEORY OF NATURAL SELECTION. New York: Dover, 1958.

Griffin, Donald R. BIRD MIGRATION. Garden City, N.Y.: Natural History Press, 1964.

Hutchinson, G. E. THE ENCHANTED VOYAGE. New Haven, Conn.: Yale University Press, 1962.

Klopfer, Peter H. BEHAVIORAL ASPECTS OF ECOLOGY. Englewood Cliffs, N.J.: Prentice-Hall, 1962.

McGill, Thomas E., ed. READINGS IN ANIMAL BEHAVIOR. New York: Holt, Rinehart, and Winston, 1965.

Marler, Peter, and William J. Hamilton, III. MECHANISMS OF ANIMAL BEHAVIOR. New York: Wiley, 1966.

Tinbergen, N. THE STUDY OF INSTINCT. Oxford: Clarendon Press, 1951.

Williams, George C. ADAPTATION AND NATURAL SELECTION. Princeton, N.J.: Princeton University Press, 1966.

## PART III: ELEMENTS OF SOCIALITY

## 18. Differentiation in Social Amoebae

### The Author

JOHN TYLER BONNER is professor of biology at Princeton University. He was born in New York City in 1920 and took his degrees at Harvard University. During World War II he did research in the Aero Medical Laboratory at Wright Field, and afterward was a junior fellow at Harvard. Bonner joined the faculty at Princeton in 1947. He started his research on social amoebae as an undergraduate under William H. Weston, and has been studying these life forms ever since. This is his fifth article for SCIENTIFIC AMERICAN.

### Bibliography

THE CELLULAR SLIME MOLDS. John Tyler Bonner. Princeton University Press, 1959.

EVIDENCE FOR THE SORTING OUT OF CELLS IN THE DEVELOPMENT OF THE CELLULAR SLIME MOLDS. John Tyler Bonner in Proceedings of the National Academy of Sciences, Vol. 45, No. 3, pages 379–384; March, 1959.

## 19. Pheromones

### The Author

EDWARD O. WILSON is associate professor of zoology at Har-

vard University. As a native of Alabama, Wilson fairly early in life became acquainted with the Southern agricultural pest known as the fire ant, which he discussed in an article for SCIENTIFIC AMERICAN ("The Fire Ant," March, 1958). Wilson received B.S. and M.S. degrees from the University of Alabama in 1949 and 1950. He took a Ph.D. in biology at Harvard, where he held a National Science Foundation fellowship and a junior fellowship in the Society of Fellows. He joined the Harvard faculty in 1956.

### Bibliography

OLFACTORY STIMULI IN MAMMALIAN REPRODUCTION. A. S. Parkes and H. M. Bruce in Science, Vol. 134, No. 3485, pages 1049–1054; October, 1961.

PHEROMONES (ECTOHORMONES) IN INSECTS. Peter Karlson and Adolf Butenandt in Annual Review of Entomology, Vol. 4, pages 39–58; 1959.

THE SOCIAL BIOLOGY OF ANTS. Edward O. Wilson in Annual Review of Entomology, Vol. 8, pages 345–368; 1963.

## 20. Sound Communication in Honeybees

### The Author

ADRIAN M. WENNER is associate professor of biology at the University of California at Santa Barbara. A native of Minnesota, Wenner received a B.S. in mathematics from Gustavus Adolphus College in 1951. He also acquired an M.S. in biology from Chico State College in California in 1955 and a Ph.D. in zoology from the University of Michigan in 1961. He joined the Santa Barbara faculty in 1960.

*Bibliography*

COMMUNICATION AMONG SOCIAL BEES. Martin Lindauer. Harvard University Press, 1961.

COMMUNICATION WITH QUEEN HONEY BEES BY SUBSTRATE SOUND. Adrian M. Wenner in *Science,* Vol. 138, No. 3538, pages 446–447; October, 1962.

SOUND PRODUCTION DURING THE WAGGLE DANCE OF THE HONEY BEE. A. M. Wenner in *Animal Behaviour,* Vol. 10, No. 1/2, pages 79–95; 1962.

ÜBER DIE SCHALLERZEUGUNG BEIM WERBETANZ DER HONIGBIENE. Harald Esch in *Zeitschrift für Vergleichende Physiologie,* Vol. 45, No. 1, pages 1–11; October, 1961.

## 21. The Curious Behavior of the Stickleback

### The Author

N. TINBERGEN is lecturer in animal behavior at the University of Oxford. He has been a naturalist ever since his boyhood days in Holland, and has studied everything from birds to flowers. Since 1937 he has worked closely with the noted naturalist Konrad Lorenz. Tinbergen's lectures at the University of Leiden had long been famous, and he was invited at the end of World War II to conduct the same sort of program at Oxford, where he now has many pupils. In his recent book, *The Herring Gull's World,* he wrote: "I know people often wonder whether it is worth while to spend so much time and energy in watching the ways of wild birds while there are so many urgent problems of human sociology to be solved. I am convinced it is. The utilitarian might be convinced when we remind him of the practical value this kind of work will have for human psychology and sociology. . . . But even if . . . I myself could not see any use in watching gulls, I am afraid I would not leave them alone."

*Bibliography*

THE STUDY OF INSTINCT. N. Tinbergen. Oxford University Press, 1951.

## 22. The Behavior of Lovebirds

### The Author

WILLIAM C. DILGER is assistant director of the Laboratory of Ornithology at Cornell University and head of the laboratory's research program. Dilger began his undergraduate studies at Cornell following the end of World War II, in which he had served as a combat and reconnaissance photographer with the Second Air Command Group in the Southeast Asia theater. He received his B.S. from Cornell in 1949, became curator of birds the same year and acquired his Ph.D. in 1955. Though trained primarily in evolutionary biology and vertebrate zoology, Dilger notes that he has "always been interested in living, whole animals." Dilger taught comparative anatomy and general zoology at St. Lawrence University for a year and then returned to Cornell in 1956.

*Bibliography*

THE COMPARATIVE ETHOLOGY OF THE AFRICAN PARROT GENUS AGAPORNIS. William C. Dilger in *Zeitschrift für Tierpsychologie,* Vol. 17, No. 6, pages 649–685; 1960.

THE EVOLUTION OF BEHAVIOR IN GULLS. N. Tinbergen in *Scientific American,* Vol. 203, No. 6, pages 118–130; December, 1960.

SOME RECENT TRENDS IN ETHOLOGY. R. A. Hinde in *Psychology: A Study of a Science,* Vol. 2, edited by Sigmund Koch, pages 561–610. McGraw-Hill Book Company, Inc., 1959.

THE STUDY OF INSTINCT. N. Tinbergen. Oxford University Press, 1951.

## 23. "Imprinting" in Animals

### The Author

ECKHARD H. HESS is professor of psychology and chairman of the department of psychology at the University of Chicago. A native of Germany, he came to the U.S. to study at Blue Ridge College and did graduate work in physiological psychology at Johns Hopkins University before going to Chicago in 1948. In addition to his work at Chicago, which is primarily in perception, Hess spends much time at an experimental station in Maryland, where he studies the "imprinting" of ducks and geese and also seeks to devise ways of fending off raccoons that prey on the birds.

*Bibliography*

EFFECTS OF MEPROBAMATE ON IMPRINTING IN WATERFOWL. Eckhard H. Hess in *Annals of The New York Academy of Sciences,* Vol. 67, Article 10, pages 724–733; May 9, 1957.

KING SOLOMON'S RING: NEW LIGHT ON ANIMAL WAYS. Konrad Z. Lorenz. Thomas Y. Crowell, 1952.

LEARNING AND INSTINCT IN ANIMALS. William Homan Thorpe. Harvard University Press, 1956.

## 24. Love in Infant Monkeys

### The Author

HARRY F. HARLOW is George Cary Comstock Professor of Psychology and head of the Primate Laboratory at the University of Wisconsin. He received his A.B. from Stanford University in 1927 and his Ph.D. from the same institution in 1930, the year in which he joined the Wisconsin faculty. Harlow is currently president of the American Psychological Association.

*Bibliography*

THE DEVELOPMENT OF AFFECTIONAL RESPONSES IN INFANT MONKEYS. Harry F. Harlow and Robert R. Zimmermann in *Proceedings of the American Philosophical Society,* Vol. 102, pages 501–509; 1958.

THE NATURE OF LOVE. Harry F. Harlow in *American Psychologist,* Vol. 12, No. 13, pages 673–685; 1958.

## 25. Attitude and Pupil Size

### The Author

For further information on ECKHARD H. HESS, see the biographical note under Article 23, " 'Imprinting' in Animals."

### Bibliography

PUPIL SIZE AS RELATED TO INTEREST VALUE OF VISUAL STIMULI. Eckhard H. Hess and James M. Polt in *Science*, Vol. 132, No. 3423, pages 349–350; August 5, 1960.

PUPIL SIZE IN RELATION TO MENTAL ACTIVITY DURING SIMPLE PROBLEM-SOLVING. Eckhard H. Hess and James M. Polt in *Science*, Vol. 143, No. 3611, pages 1190–1192; March 13, 1964.

## 26. Ulcers in "Executive" Monkeys

### The Author

JOSEPH V. BRADY is head of the department of experimental psychology in the Neuropsychiatry Division of the Walter Reed Army Institute of Research, Washington, D.C. Born in Brooklyn in 1922, he received his B.S. from Fordham University in 1943. While still an undergraduate, Brady had joined the R.O.T.C.; in 1945 he was sent overseas and commanded an infantry platoon in Europe. He remained in the Army after the war, and spent two years in Germany as Chief Clinical Psychologist in the European Command. The Army then sent him to the University of Chicago, where his interest soon shifted from clinical to experimental psychology. He received his Ph.D. in 1951; his thesis concerned emotional behavior in rats. Now a major in the Army's Medical Department, Brady presently works on the experimental analysis of behavior, with special reference to its physical concomitants.

### Bibliography

EVIDENCE ON THE GENESIS OF PEPTIC ULCER IN MAN. Stewart Wolf and Harold Wolff in *The Journal of the American Medical Association*, Vol. 120, No. 9, pages 670–675; October 31, 1942.

AN EXPERIMENTAL METHOD OF PRODUCING GASTRIC ULCERS. William L. Sawrey and John D. Weisz in *Journal of Comparative and Physiological Psychology*, Vol. 49, No. 3, pages 269–270; June, 1956.

## Further Readings for Part III

DeVore, Irven, ed. PRIMATE BEHAVIOR. New York: Holt, Rinehart, & Winston, 1965.

Fletcher, Joseph. SITUATION ETHICS. Philadelphia: Westminster Press, 1966.

Gray, Alexander. THE SOCIALIST TRADITION. London: Longmans, Green and Co., 1946.

Hutchinson, Sir Joseph, ed. ESSAYS ON CROP PLANT EVOLUTION. Cambridge, England: Cambridge University Press, 1965.

Lorenz, Konrad. ON AGGRESSION. New York: Harcourt, Brace & World, 1963.

Mayer, William, and Richard Van Gelder, eds. PHYSIOLOGICAL MAMMALOGY, Vol. I. New York: Academic Press, 1963.

Schrier, Allan M., Harry F. Harlow, and Fred Stollnitz, eds. BEHAVIOR OF NONHUMAN PRIMATES. New York: Academic Press, 1965.

Washburn, Sherwood L., ed. SOCIAL LIFE OF EARLY MAN. Chicago: Aldine, 1961.

Wiener, Norbert. THE HUMAN USE OF HUMAN BEINGS. Garden City, N.Y.: Doubleday Anchor Books, 1954.

Zeuner, F. E. A HISTORY OF DOMESTICATED ANIMALS. London: Hutchinson, 1963.

# PART IV: ECOLOGICAL APPROACHES TO POPULATION PROBLEMS

## 27. The Ecosphere

### The Author

LAMONT C. COLE is professor of zoology at Cornell University. Despite a boyhood passion for snakes, he graduated from the University of Chicago as a physicist. His return to the animal kingdom resulted from a trip down the Colorado River with A. M. Woodbury of the University of Utah, who inspired him to study ecology. Cole's chief interest is now in natural populations. He has taught at Cornell since 1948. Before that he occupied the late Alfred Kinsey's post in entomology at Indiana University, which he had taken over when Kinsey "turned to the study of bigger and better things."

### Bibliography

THE ECOLOGY OF ANIMALS. Charles Elton. John Wiley & Sons, Inc., 1950.

ENERGY IN THE FUTURE. Palmer Cosslett Putnam. D. Van Nostrand Company, Inc., 1953.

ELEMENTS OF PHYSICAL BIOLOGY. Alfred J. Lotka. Williams & Wilkins Company, 1925.

FUNDAMENTALS OF ECOLOGY. Eugene P. Odum. W. B. Saunders Company, 1953.

GEOCHEMISTRY. Kalervo Rankama and Th. G. Sahama. The University of Chicago Press, 1950.

THE WEB OF LIFE: A FIRST BOOK OF ECOLOGY. John H. Storer. The Devin-Adair Company, 1953.

## 28. The Human Population

### The Author

EDWARD S. DEEVEY, JR., is professor of biology and director of the Geochronometric Laboratory at Yale University. Though his researches have centered on paleoecology, he notes that "I seem to be a general ecologist for teaching purposes." A National Science Foundation award for research in the dating of lake sediments enabled him to spend several months recently boring into lake bottoms in the Auvergne and the Jura Mountains. Born in Albany, N.Y., in 1914, he developed an early interest in nature studies which won him 41 Boy Scout merit badges and the Boy Scout Nature Prize in 1928. His major relaxation is scientific field trips; when forced to stay home he enjoys reading and pre-Beethoven chamber music.

### Bibliography

THE NEXT HUNDRED YEARS: MAN'S NATURAL AND TECHNICAL RESOURCES. Harrison Brown, James Bonner and John Weir. Viking Press, Inc., 1957.

POPULATION AHEAD. Roy Gustaf Francis. University of Minnesota Press, 1958.

SCIENCE AND ECONOMIC DEVELOPMENT: NEW PATTERNS OF LIVING. Richard L. Meier. John Wiley & Sons, Inc., 1956.

WORLD POPULATION AND PRODUCTION: TRENDS AND OUTLOOK. W. S. Woytinsky and E. S. Woytinsky. Twentieth Century Fund, 1953.

## 29. The Last of the Great Whales

### The Author

SCOTT MCVAY is assistant to the president of Princeton University. Following his graduation from Princeton in 1955 he worked for three years in Berlin as a civilian with Army Intelligence. Then he spent nearly five years as recording secretary of Princeton University and two years as assistant to the director of the Communication Research Institute in Miami. McVay was an English major in college and became interested in whales as a result of reading *Moby Dick*. He has spent much time in reading, correspondence and research on the subject; he writes that what troubles him most is "the prospect that the whales, possessing the largest brains on earth and gloriously unique in the scheme of living things, will be gone from the earth before man may be able to understand them."

### Bibliography

CETACEA. William E. Schevill in *The Encyclopedia of the Biological Sciences*, edited by Peter Gray. Reinhold Publishing Corporation, 1961.

MOBY DICK OR THE WHALE. Herman Melville. Garden City Publishing Company, Inc., 1937.

MODERN WHALES, DOLPHINS, AND PORPOISES AS CHALLENGES TO OUR INTELLIGENCE. John C. Lilly in *The Dolphin in History*. The University of California Press, 1963.

WHALES. E. J. Slijper, Basic Books, Inc., Publishers, 1962.

WHALES, DOLPHINS AND PORPOISES. Edited by Kenneth S. Norris. The University of California Press, 1966.

## 30. The Ecology of Fire

### The Author

CHARLES F. COOPER works for the U.S. Agricultural Service in Boise, Idaho. He acquired a B.S. in forestry at the University of Minnesota in 1950, and M.S. at the University of Arizona and a Ph.D. in plant ecology at Duke University in 1958. "In the course of a rather short career," he writes, "I have been variously occupied as an aircraft mechanic, forester, pulpwood logger, manufacturer of creosoted fence posts, range conservationist and college teacher."

### Bibliography

CHANGES IN VEGETATION, STRUCTURE AND GROWTH OF SOUTHWESTERN PINE FORESTS SINCE WHITE SETTLEMENT. Charles F. Cooper in *Ecological Monographs*, Vol. 30, No. 2, pages 129–164; April, 1960.

THE DESERT GRASSLAND: A HISTORY OF VEGETATIONAL CHANGE AND AN ANALYSIS OF CAUSES. Robert R. Humphrey in *The Botanical Review*, Vol. 24, No. 4, pages 193–252; April, 1958.

FIRE AS THE FIRST GREAT FORCE EMPLOYED BY MAN. Omer C. Stewart in *Man's Role in Changing the Face of the Earth*, edited by William L. Thomas, Jr., pages 115–133. University of Chicago Press, 1956.

## 31. The Black Death

### The Author

WILLIAM L. LANGER is Archibald Cary Coolidge Professor of History at Harvard University. Langer was born in Boston in 1896 and took his degress at Harvard. He also studied at the University of Vienna in 1921 and 1922. He has been a member of the history department at Harvard since 1926. A veteran of the Saint-Mihiel and Argonne engagements of World War I, Langer served as chief of the Research and Analysis Branch of the Office of Strategic Services during World War II. In 1946 he reorganized the foreign intelligence services of the State Department as Special Assistant to the Secretary of State. From 1950 to 1952 he served as assistant director of the Central Intelligence Agency. He is at present a member of the President's Foreign Intelligence Advisory Board. Langer was director of the Russian Research Center and the Center for Middle Eastern Studies at Harvard from 1954 to 1959. In 1957 he was elected president of the American Historical Association. He spent the academic year 1959–1960 at the Center for Advanced Study in the Behavioral Sciences in Palo Alto, Calif. Langer has written extensively in the fields of European and American diplomatic history; he is also the editor of *An Encyclopedia of World History*, published in 1940, and of the series "The Rise of Modern Europe," of which 13 volumes have appeared to date.

### Bibliography

THE BLACK DEATH. G. G. Coulton. Ernest Benn Limited, 1929.

THE BLACK DEATH: A CHRONICLE OF THE PLAGUE. Compiled by Johannes Nohl. George Allen & Unwin Ltd., 1926.

THE BLIGHT OF PESTILENCE ON EARLY MODERN CIVILIZATION. Lynn Thorndike in *The American Historical Review*, Vol. 32, No. 3, pages 455–474; April, 1927.

THE BUBONIC PLAGUE AND ENGLAND. Charles F. Mullett. University of Kentucky Press, 1956.

PLAGUE AND PESTILENCE IN LITERATURE AND ART. Raymond Crawfurd. Oxford University Press, 1914.

## 32. Population Control in Animals

### The Author

V. C. WYNNE-EDWARDS is Regius Professor of Natural History at Marischal College of the University of Aberdeen. A graduate of Rugby School and the University of Oxford, he did research at the Marine Biological Laboratory in Plymouth from 1927 to 1929. After obtaining an M.A. from Oxford he taught zoology for a year at the University of Bristol before joining the faculty of McGill University in 1930. While in Canada he participated in the MacMillan Baffin Island expedition in 1937 and organized the Canadian Fisheries Research Board expeditions to the Mackenzie River in 1944 and to the Yukon Territory in 1945; he was also a member of the Baird expedition to Central Baffin Island in 1950. He was appointed to his present post in 1946.

*Bibliography*

ANIMAL DISPERSION IN RELATION TO SOCIAL BEHAVIOUR. V. C. Wynne-Edwards. Hafner Publishing Company, 1962.

THE LIFE OF VERTEBRATES. John Z. Young. Oxford University Press, 1950.

THE NATURAL REGULATION OF ANIMAL NUMBERS. David Lack. Oxford University Press, 1954.

## 33. Population Density and Social Pathology

### The Author

JOHN B. CALHOUN is research psychologist in the Laboratory of Psychology at the National Institute of Mental Health. Calhoun obtained his B.S. at the University of Virginia in 1939 and his M.S. and Ph.D. at Northwestern University in 1942 and 1943 respectively. After teaching at Emory and Ohio State universities Calhoun in 1946 joined a group at Johns Hopkins University that was studying the behavior of Norway rats. In 1949 he went to the Roscoe B. Jackson Memorial Laboratory in Bar Harbor, Me., to continue his research. From 1951 to 1955 he did research in the neuropsychiatry department of the Walter Reed Army Institute of Medical Research and spent 1962 at the Center for Advanced Study in Behavioral Sciences in Palo Alto, Calif. He has held his present position since 1954.

### Bibliography

THE HUMAN POPULATION. Edward S. Deevey, Jr., in *Scientific American*, Vol. 203, No. 3, pages 194–204; September, 1960.

A METHOD FOR SELF-CONTROL OF POPULATION GROWTH AMONG MAMMALS LIVING IN THE WILD. John B. Calhoun in *Science*, Vol. 109, No. 2831, pages 333–335; April 1, 1949.

POPULATIONS OF HOUSE MICE. Robert L. Strecker in *Scientific American*, Vol. 193, No. 6, pages 92–100; December, 1955.

THE SOCIAL ASPECTS OF POPULATION DYNAMICS. John B. Calhoun in *Journal of Mammalogy*, Vol. 33, No. 2, pages 139–159; May, 1952.

SOCIAL WELFARE AS A VARIABLE IN POPULATION DYNAMICS. John B. Calhoun in *Cold Spring Harbor Symposia on Quantitative Biology*, Vol. 22, pages 339–356; 1957.

## Further Readings for Part IV

Ardrey, Robert. THE TERRITORIAL IMPERATIVE. New York: Atheneum, 1967.

Burton, Ian, and Robert W. Kates, eds. READINGS IN RESOURCE MANAGEMENT AND ECOLOGY. Chicago: University of Chicago Press, 1960.

Hardin, Garrett, ed. POPULATION, EVOLUTION, & BIRTH CONTROL. San Francisco: W. H. Freeman and Company, 1964.

Hazen, William E., ed. READINGS IN POPULATION AND COMMUNITY ECOLOGY. Philadelphia: Saunders, 1964.

Le Cren, E. D., and M. W. Holdgate, eds. THE EXPLOITATION OF NATURAL ANIMAL POPULATIONS. Oxford: Blackwell, 1962.

Paddock, William, and Paddock, Paul. FAMINE 1975! Boston: Little, Brown & Co., 1967.

Thirring, Hans. ENERGY FOR MAN. Bloomington, Ind.: Indiana University Press, 1958.

Thomas, William L., ed. MAN'S ROLE IN CHANGING THE FACE OF THE EARTH. Chicago: University of Chicago Press, 1956.

Watt, Kenneth E. F. ECOLOGY AND RESOURCE MANAGEMENT. New York: McGraw-Hill, 1968.

Wynne-Edwards, V. C. ANIMAL DISPERSION IN RELATION TO SOCIAL BEHAVIOR. Edinburgh: Oliver & Boyd, 1962.

Zinsser, Hans. RATS, LICE AND HISTORY. Boston: Little, Brown & Co., 1935.

# PART V: MAN-CREATED PROBLEMS

## 34. The Control of Air Pollution

### The Author

A. J. HAAGEN-SMIT is professor of bio-organic chemistry at the California Institute of Technology. He was born in the Netherlands in 1900 and obtained an A.B. and a Ph.D. from The University of Utrecht in 1922 and 1929 respectively. After seven years of teaching organic chemistry at Utrecht he joined the faculty of Harvard University in 1936; the following year he went to Cal Tech. In 1950 he received the Fritzsche Award of the American Chemical Society for his work on essential oils and in 1958 he won the Chambers Award of the Air Pollution Control Association. He is a consultant to the Los Angeles Air Pollution District, California's State Motor Vehicle Pollution Control Board and various other state and county agencies dealing with atmospheric sanitation.

### Bibliography

AIR POLLUTION: VOLS. I AND II, edited by Arthur C. Stern. Academic Press, 1962.

AIR POLLUTION CONTROL. William L. Faith. John Wiley & Sons, Inc., 1959.

PHOTOCHEMISTRY OF AIR POLLUTION. Philip A. Leighton. Academic Press, 1961.

WEATHER MODIFICATION AND SMOG. M. Neiburger in *Science*, Vol. 126, No. 3275, pages 637–645; October, 1957.

## 35. The Effects of Smoking

### The Author

E. CUYLER HAMMOND has since 1946 been director of the Statistical Research Section of the American Cancer Society. Hammond received a B.S. from Yale University in 1935 and an Sc.D. from Johns Hopkins University in 1938. He was associate statistician in the division of industrial hygiene of the National Institutes of Health until 1942; as a major in the Army Air Force from 1942 to 1946 he served first as chief of the statistics department of the School of Aviation Medicine at Randolph Field in Texas and later as assistant chief of the statistics division of the Office of the Air Surgeon in Washington. Hammond, who has been studying the effects of smoking for more than a decade, was professor of biometry and director of statistical studies in the graduate school of Yale University from 1953 to 1958.

### Bibliography

CHANGES IN BRONCHIAL EPITHELIUM IN RELATION TO SEX, AGE, RESIDENCE, SMOKING AND PNEUMONIA. Oscar Auerbach, A. P. Stout, E. Cuyler Hammond and Lawrence Garfinkel in *The New England Journal of Medicine*, Vol. 267, No. 3; July 19, 1962.

LUNG CANCER AND OTHER CAUSES OF DEATH IN RELATION TO SMOKING. Richard Doll and A. Bradford Hill in *British Medical Journal*, Vol. 2, No. 5001, pages 1071–1081; November 10, 1956.

SMOKING AND DEATH RATES — REPORT ON FORTY-FOUR MONTHS OF FOLLOW-UP OF 187,783 MEN. I: TOTAL MORTALITY. E. Cuyler Hammond and Daniel Horn in *The Journal of the American Medical Association*, Vol. 166, No. 10, pages 1159–1172; March 8, 1958. II: DEATH RATES BY CAUSE. E. Cuyler Hammond and Daniel Horn in *The Journal of the American Medical Association*, Vol. 166, No. 11, pages 1294–1308; March 15, 1958.

SMOKING AND HEALTH: SUMMARY AND REPORT OF THE ROYAL COLLEGE OF PHYSICIANS OF LONDON ON SMOKING IN RELATION TO CANCER OF THE LUNG AND OTHER DISEASES. Pitman Publishing Corporation, 1962.

SMOKING: ITS INFLUENCE ON THE INDIVIDUAL AND ITS ROLE IN SOCIAL MEDICINE. C. van Proosdij. Elsevier Publishing Company, 1960.

TOBACCO CONSUMPTION AND MORTALITY FROM CANCER AND OTHER DISEASES. Harold F. Dorn in *Acta Unio Internationalis contra Cancrum*, Vol. 16, No. 7, pages 1653–1665; 1960.

## 36. The Thalidomide Syndrome

### The Author

HELEN B. TAUSSIG is professor of pediatrics at the Johns Hopkins School of Medicine, where she received her M.D. in 1927. With Alfred Blalock, a surgeon at Johns Hopkins, she conceived the famous "blue baby" operation, first performed on a human patient in 1945. The operation alleviates an interrelated group of congenital heart defects that lead to inadequate oxygenation of the blood, producing a characteristic blueness of the skin. Miss Taussig has received honorary degrees from more than a dozen institutions, including Columbia University, Harvard University and the University of Athens. Her other honors include the Lasker Award and the Feltrinelli prize. She has also been decorated by the French as Chevalier of the Legion of Honor.

### Bibliography

KINDLICHE MISSBILDUNGEN NACH MEDIKAMENT-EINNAHME WÄHREND DER GRAVIDITÄT? W. Lenz in *Deutsche Medizinische Wochenschrift*, Vol. 86, No. 52, pages 2555–2556; December 29, 1961.

THALIDOMIDE AND CONGENITAL ABNORMALITIES. A. L. Spiers in *The Lancet*, Vol. 1, No. 7224, pages 303–305; February 10, 1962.

THALIDOMIDE AND CONGENITAL ABNORMALITIES. G. F. Somers in *The Lancet*, Vol. 1, No. 7235, pages 912–913; April 28, 1962.

ZUR FRAGE EINER EXOGENEN VERURSACHUNG VON SCHWEREN EXTREMITÄTENMISSBILDUNGEN. R. A. Pfeiffer and W. Kosenow in *Münchener Medizinische Wochenschrift*, Vol. 104, No. 2, pages 68–74; January 12, 1962.

## 37. The Fighting Behavior of Animals

### The Author

IRENÄUS EIBL-EIBESFELDT is research associate in ethology at the Max Planck Institute for the Physiology of Behavior in Germany. He was born in Vienna in 1928 and studied zoology at the University of Vienna, acquiring his doctorate there in 1949. Later that year he joined the Institute for Comparative Behavior, where he worked with the noted student of animal behavior Konrad Z. Lorenz. When the institute was moved to West Germany in 1951 (becoming the Max Planck Institute in the process), Eibl-Eibesfeldt moved with it. Since then his study of symbiotic relationships among fishes has taken him all over the world. In 1953 he accompanied the Xarifa Expedition of the International Institute for Submarine Research to the Caribbean and the Galápagos Islands. His memorandum on the rapid destruction of flora and fauna in the Galápagos led to his being sent by UNESCO in 1957 to make a survey of the conditions there. The results of his recommendations were the creation of the Darwin Foundation in Brussels and the establishment of a biological station in the Galápagos. The following year Eibl-Eibesfeldt accompanied another Xarifa Expedition, this time to the Indian Ocean. In 1961 he was a visiting lecturer in ethology at the University of Chicago. He is also the author of the book *Galápagos* (published in 1961).

### Bibliography

AGGRESSION. J. P. Scott. University of Chicago Press, 1958.

KAMPF UND PAARBILDUNG EINIGER CICHLIDEN. Beatrice Oehlert in *Zeitschrift für Tierpsychologie*, Vol. 15, No. 2, pages 141–174; August, 1958.

STUDIES ON THE BASIC FACTORS IN ANIMAL FIGHTING. PARTS I–IV. Zing Yang Kuo in *The Journal of Genetic Psychology*, Vol. 96, Second Half, pages 201–239; June, 1960.

STUDIES ON THE BASIC FACTORS IN ANIMAL FIGHTING. PARTS V–VII. Zing Yang Kuo in *The Journal of Genetic Psychology*, Vol. 97, Second Half, pages 181–225; December, 1960.

ZUM KAMPF-UND PAARUNGSVERHALTEN EINIGER ANTILOPEN. Fritz Walther in *Zeitschrift für Tierpsychologie*, Vol. 15, No. 3, pages 340–380; October, 1958.

## 38. National Security and the Nuclear–Test Ban

### The Authors

JEROME B. WIESNER and HERBERT F. YORK have been engaged for most of their professional lifetimes in consultation on this country's military policy and in active development of the weapons. Wiesner, now dean of science at the Massachusetts Institute of Technology, was chairman of the President's Science Advisory Committee and special assistant to the President for science and technology during the Kennedy Administration. York, now chancellor of the University of California at San Diego, was the first director of the Livermore Laboratory, organized in 1952 when the Truman Administration decided to proceed with the development of thermonuclear weapons. Wiesner received a B.S. in 1937 from the University of Michigan and was proceeding with his graduate education there when the outbreak of war called him into service at the Radiation Laboratory of the Massachusetts Institute of Technology. In 1945 he joined the staff of the Los Alamos Scientific Laboratory. Returning to M.I.T. in 1946 as a member of the department of electrical engineering, he completed his doctoral work, the degree being conferred by the University of Michigan in 1950, and was promoted to professorial rank that year. At M.I.T. he also served as director of the Research Laboratory of Electronics and continued his work in military technology as a member of the Army Science Advisory Committee. York's graduate education was similarly interrupted by war service. A graduate of the University of Rochester in 1942, he went to work under the late Ernest O. Lawrence at the Radiation Laboratory of the University of California at Berkeley. He received a Ph.D. there in 1949 and continued as a member of the staff until he assumed responsibility for the new Livermore Laboratory. In 1958, under the Eisenhower Administration, he was called to Washington as chief scientist of the Advanced Research Projects Agency of the Department of Defense and director of defense research and engineering in the office of the Secretary of Defense. Wiesner and York continue their Government service as members of the President's Science Advisory Committee.

### Bibliography

THE EFFECTS OF NUCLEAR WEAPONS. Edited by Samuel Glasstone. United States Atomic Energy Commission, April, 1962.

STEPS TOWARD DISARMAMENT. P. M. S. Blackett in *Scientific American*, Vol. 206, No. 4, pages 45–53; April, 1962.

WORLD PEACE THROUGH WORLD LAW. Louis B. Sohn and Grenville Clark. Harvard University Press, 1960.

A WORLD WITHOUT WAR. Walter Millis, Reinhold Niebuhr. Harrison Brown, James Real and William O. Douglas. Washington Square Press, Inc., 1961.

## 39. The Shelter–Centered Society

### The Author

ARTHUR I. WASKOW is a member of the staff of the Peace Research Institute in Washington. Waskow was graduated from Johns Hopkins University in 1954 and has studied and taught American history at the University of Wisconsin, where he took his M.A. in 1956; he expects to receive his Ph.D. from that institution sometime this year. Before joining the Peace Research Institute early last year, Waskow had been legislative assistant to Congressman Robert W. Kastenmeier of Wisconsin since October, 1959. Waskow is the author of *The*

*Limits of Defense* (published in 1962), an analysis of disarmament and U.S. defense policy.

### Bibliography

THE LIMITS OF DEFENSE. Arthur I. Waskow. Doubleday & Company, Inc., 1962.

## Further Readings for Part V

Advisory Committee to the Surgeon General. SMOKING AND HEALTH. Washington, D.C.: U. S. Government Printing Office, 1964.

Air Conservation Commission. AIR CONSERVATION. Washington, D.C.: American Association for the Advancement of Science, 1965.

Boulding, Kenneth E. CONFLICT AND DEFENSE. New York: Harper, 1962.

Carr, Donald E. THE BREATH OF LIFE. New York: Norton, 1965.

———. DEATH OF THE SWEET WATERS. New York: Norton, 1966.

Carson, Rachel. SILENT SPRING. Boston: Houghton Mifflin, 1962.

Committee on Pollution. WASTE MANAGEMENT AND CONTROL. Washington, D.C.: National Academy of Sciences, 1966.

Cooley, Richard A. POLITICS AND CONSERVATION. New York: Harper & Row, 1963.

Dasmann, Raymond F. THE LAST HORIZON. New York: Macmillan, 1963.

Eyring, Henry, ed. CIVIL DEFENSE. Washington, D.C.: American Association for the Advancement of Science, 1966.

Goodman, Gordon T., R. W. Edwards, and J. M. Lambert, eds. ECOLOGY AND THE INDUSTRIAL SOCIETY. Oxford: Blackwell, 1965.

Hachiya, Michihiko. HIROSHIMA DIARY. Chapel Hill: University of North Carolina Press, 1955.

Kahn, Herman. ON ESCALATION. New York: Praeger, 1965.

Lapp, Ralph E. KILL AND OVERKILL. New York: Basic Books, 1962.

President's Science Advisory Committee. RESTORING THE QUALITY OF OUR ENVIRONMENT. Washington, D.C.: U.S. Government Printing Office, 1965.

Proosdij, C. van. SMOKING, ITS INFLUENCE ON THE INDIVIDUAL AND ITS ROLE IN SOCIAL MEDICINE. New York: Elsevier, 1960.

Ridker, Ronald G. ECONOMIC COSTS OF AIR POLLUTION. New York: Praeger, 1967.

Rothschild, Jacquard Hirshorn. TOMORROW'S WEAPONS, CHEMICAL AND BIOLOGICAL. New York: McGraw-Hill, 1964.

Rudd, Robert L. PESTICIDES AND THE LIVING LANDSCAPE. Madison: University of Wisconsin Press, 1964.

Schubert, Jack, and Ralph E. Lapp. RADIATION: WHAT IT IS AND HOW IT AFFECTS YOU. New York: Viking, 1957.

United Nations Scientific Committee. REPORT OF THE UNITED NATIONS SCIENTIFIC COMMITTEE ON THE EFFECTS OF ATOMIC RADIATION. New York: United Nations, 1962.

# Index